THE COMPARATIVE ANATOMY OF THE NERVOUS SYSTEM OF VERTEBRATES, INCLUDING MAN

THE COMPARATIVE ANATOMY
OF THE NERVOUS SYSTEM
OF VERTEBRATES,
INCLUDING MAN

BY

C. U. ARIËNS KAPPERS, M.D., Sc.D., LL.D.

DIRECTOR OF THE CENTRAL INSTITUTE OF BRAIN RESEARCH,
AMSTERDAM, AND PROFESSOR OF COMPARATIVE NEUROLOGY
IN THE UNIVERSITY OF AMSTERDAM

G. CARL HUBER, M.D., Sc.D.

LATE DEAN OF THE GRADUATE SCHOOL, DIRECTOR OF THE
ANATOMICAL LABORATORIES, AND PROFESSOR OF ANATOMY
IN THE UNIVERSITY OF MICHIGAN

AND

ELIZABETH CAROLINE CROSBY, Ph.D.

ASSOCIATE PROFESSOR OF ANATOMY IN THE
UNIVERSITY OF MICHIGAN

VOLUME TWO

HAFNER PUBLISHING COMPANY
NEW YORK
1960

Originally published
in 2 volumes
in 1936

Published by
Hafner Publishing Co., Inc.
31 East 10th Street
New York 3, N. Y.

Library of Congress Catalog Card Number 60-6766

Printed in the U.S.A.

NOBLE OFFSET PRINTERS, INC.
NEW YORK 3, N. Y.

CONTENTS

CHAPTER VII

CHAPTER VIII

CONTENTS

CONTENTS

CONTENTS

CHAPTER VII
THE CEREBELLUM

CHAPTER VII

THE CEREBELLUM

The dorsolateral area or alar plate of the medulla oblongata is not only a primary center for the reception of various incoming stimuli but also a region in which develop centers for important sensory correlations. The discussion in previous chapters has indicated the presence of several correlation centers within this area, such as those concerned with the interrelation of tactile and gustatory impulses or with equilibrium and general sensibility. However, the most outstanding of these correlation centers is situated at the cephalic end of the medulla oblongata. This is the cerebellum, which embryological and comparative neurological work has shown to be an outgrowth of the dorsal lip of the fourth ventricle, arising thus from the somatic sensory — but not the visceral sensory — portion of the alar plate. It is a region of correlation of various somatic impulses predominantly, if not exclusively, proprioceptive in character, that is, impulses concerned with equilibrium and orientation of the body in space.

The types of connection within the cerebellum show a high degree of specialization. It appears desirable, then, before entering upon an account of the comparative anatomy of this organ, to describe the histologic structure as found in higher forms. On the whole, this structure is similar in type in all classes of vertebrates with the exception of the most primitive, namely, the cyclostomes. The following account is based on mammals, where the details have been studied most thoroughly and are best known. Such differences as appear in other forms will be discussed in the appropriate sections.

The present knowledge of the finer structure of the cerebellum is the result of years of untiring effort on the part of many observers. Among these, particular mention may be made of *Purkinje* ('37), *Henle* ('79), *Golgi* ('86, '98), *Obersteiner* ('88), *von Kölliker* ('90, '00), *van Gehuchten* ('91), *Retzius* ('92), *Falcone* ('93), *Dogiel* ('96), *Bielschowsky* and *Wolff* ('04), *Oudendal* ('12), *Ramón y Cajal* and *Illera* ('07), *Addison* ('11), *Stefanelli* ('31), and especially *Ramón y Cajal* ('88, '89, '90, '90a, '96, '00, '11).

The fully developed cerebellar cortex is divided into a superficial or molecular layer, a layer of Purkinje cells, a granular layer, and an inner white layer or stratum album. The first three layers comprise the cortex of the cerebellum (fig. 348). Sometimes the molecular and Purkinje cell layers are termed the plexiform layer (*Ramón y Cajal*, '11). The so-called nuclei of the cerebellum are deep within the mass, separated from the cortex by the myelinated fiber tracts.

The histologic structure is the same for all parts of the cerebellar cortex of mammals. Different cytoarchitectonic regions, such as are demonstrable in the

various areas of the cerebral cortex, are not present in the cortical portions of the
cerebellum.   This is significant of the differences in type of function of the two
brain centers, as will be seen.   Indications of localization of function are found
principally in the phylogenetic and ontogenetic history of the cerebellum, for
certain portions of the organ appear at particular times and under special conditions, while the size of various parts varies with the general body structure and
habits of the animal type under consideration.   The uniformity in histologic
pattern has been a great hindrance to any concept of cerebellar localization; yet

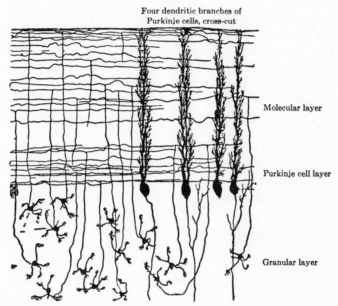

Four dendritic branches of
Purkinje cells, cross-cut

Molecular layer

Purkinje cell layer

Granular layer

Fig. 348.   A schematic section through the cerebellum of a mammal,
parallel to the cerebellar lamellae (also transverse to the axis of the
body).   The ascending neuraxes of granular cells dichotomize and
form parallel fibers running transversely across the field.   The dendrites of the Purkinje cells have been cut at right angles to their
greatest spread.   *von Kölliker*.

that such localization does exist is far more than probable.   This question will be
discussed toward the end of the present chapter.

The Purkinje cell (*Purkinje*, 1837), through its dendrites and neuraxis, is
associated with all the layers of the cerebellar cortex; hence it will be considered
first.   Its cell body is flask shaped and from about 35 to 65μ in diameter in man,
although its size varies in different mammals.   It has a relatively large nucleus
and the cytoplasm contains the Nissl substance, the neurofibrillar elements, and
the Golgi-Holmgren canalicular system already described as characteristic of
neurons in general.   A Purkinje cell may be bipolar or multipolar, consequently
the dendrites may pass out as a single or as double or triple branches.   Such
branches soon divide and redivide to distribute throughout the molecular layer.
There are certain peculiarities of this branching which need emphasis.   In the
first place, as *Ramón y Cajal* ('11) and others have noted, the branching is arci-

form and not angular.   In the second place, it occurs in a single plane (*Henle*, '79; *Obersteiner*, '88; *Dogiel*, '96; *Ramón y Cajal*, '96, and many others), a plane at right angles to the convolutions and to the horizontally running fibers of the molecular layer.   Thus sections parallel to the cerebellar lamellae show few if any branches of the Purkinje cell dendrites while long sweeps of parallel fibers come to view (fig. 48A); on the contrary, transverse sections of the lamellae, in proper preparations, show the parallel fibers as a series of dots, but exhibit a great richness of dendritic branches of the Purkinje cells (fig. 48B).   The Purkinje cells (*Addison*, '11) develop with the increasing development of the growing rat. They increase in size particularly during the first week after birth.   After ten days, their dendrites, which originally spread in all directions, are arranged perpendicular to the course of the parallel fibers.   The major dendrites of the Purkinje cells are relatively large, but the twigs passing out from the secondary and tertiary branches are finer.   They are usually short and thorny, but frequently divide and redivide.   Such dendritic branches supply all parts of the layer extending to the periphery where they may even turn back again toward the deeper regions (*Ramón y Cajal*, '11), but they give off no descending branches to the granular layer.   The neuraxis of the Purkinje cell arises on the side opposite the place of origin of the dendrite from an axon hillock, which, however, is not so clearly marked as in most neurons (*Ramón y Cajal*, '11).   For some distance this neuraxis is unmyelinated (*Koschewnikoff*, '69, and others).   Just above the place of appearance of the myelin sheath there is a reduction in the size of the neuraxis, a point to which *Ramón y Cajal* ('89, '11) called attention.   It attains the usual size with the appearance of the myelin.   To *Deiters* ('65) belongs the credit of having first demonstrated the neuraxes of Purkinje cells.   It was *Golgi* ('86), however, who first definitely traced these processes and who demonstrated that they give off collaterals during their course.   Such collaterals *Golgi* believed distribute to both granular and molecular layers.   However, the observations of *Ramón y Cajal* ('88, '89, '90, '11), *Retzius* ('92), and others indicated that these collaterals distribute in the main to the outer regions of the cerebellum and not to the inner or granular zone.   *Golgi's* work was based largely on a study of human material; *Ramón y Cajal* studied the cerebellum of various mammals; *Retzius* presented particularly well the relations in the cat.   Such collaterals are myelinated and turn back toward the molecular layer, where they branch near the cell bodies of the Purkinje cells; branches arise from other fibers which course for long distances and so form the fiber plexus found in the deeper parts of the molecular layer.   Such fibers terminate along the major dendritic branches of the Purkinje cells (mainly of other than the cell from which the neuraxis took origin). For the greater part of their extent the collaterals of the Purkinje neuraxes and their branches are myelinated (see figs. 348 and 350).

In the molecular layer are the cell bodies of stellate or basket cells (fig. 350). These cell bodies are about a third the size of those of the Purkinje cells, the diameter (10–20μ) varying from the superficial to the deep layers.   Such cells are not rich in Nissl substance.   The basket cells have three or four dendrites, which branch and rebranch.   On the basis of their direction they have been classified by *Ramón y Cajal* ('11) into ascending, descending, and horizontal dendrites. Of these, the first mentioned are most numerous and are thick and spiny; they divide many times, thus forming a richly branching system which runs toward the surface of the cerebellum where marginal and descending branches may be given off. The horizontal dendrites are also long and thick and may ultimately become ascending; the more delicate descending dendrites are found much less frequently and are often lacking, particularly in the more deeply situated cells. In '89, *Ramón y Cajal* pointed out that basket-cell dendrites are oriented in the same general plane as are those of the Purkinje cells and alternate with them, although the orientation is not quite so precise for the former as for the latter cells. The neuraxes of the basket cells have been demonstrated by many observers, beginning with *Golgi* ('86) and *Golgi* and *Fusari* ('86). Early observers were inclined to regard their direction as horizontal, but later work indicates that it may also be transverse. The neuraxes run for very considerable distances, giving off in their course, thin ascending and thicker, more numerous descending branches. These latter form pericellular baskets around the cell bodies of the Purkinje cells— "like the wickerwork around a demijohn." Below such a basket the fibers extend down as a terminal brush around the first, unmedullated portion of the neuraxis of the Purkinje cell in question. These pericellular baskets have been studied by many observers in attempts to determine the finer structure of the synapse, and to decide whether the relation was one of contiguity or of actual fibrillar continuity. The question of synaptic structure has been discussed in Chapter I (pp. 23 to 26) and will not be considered further here. It may be stated in passing that certain observers (*Bielschowsky* and *Wolff*, '04; *Oudendal*, '12; *Tiegs*, '30, see p. 131) believed that fibrillae of these pericellular fibers become directly continuous with the intracellular network of the Purkinje cell, while *Ramón y Cajal* ('88, a and b, '11, and elsewhere) and others thought that the fibers end only in contact with the cell membrane. The neuraxes of the most peripherally situated stellate cells of the molecular zone do not form pericellular baskets around Purkinje cells. Between such cells and the typical basket cell just described, there are various gradations.

Within the granular zone there are, in addition to neuroglia cells, granule cells and various types of stellate cells, the latter subdivided by *Ramón y Cajal* ('11) into the ordinary stellate cell or corpuscle of *Golgi*, the fusiform horizontal cell, the stellate cell with long axis cylinder, and the displaced stellate cell. The cells of the granular layer have been studied by *Denisenko* ('77), *Henle* ('79), *Golgi* ('86), *Ramón y Cajal* ('88, '90, '96), *van Gehuchten* ('90), *von Kölliker* ('90), *Retzius* ('92, '92a), *Lugaro* ('94), *Dogiel* ('96), *Stefanelli* ('31), and many others (see figs. 348 and 350).

The granule cells, first recognized as nerve cells by *Golgi* ('86), were later described in detail by *Ramón y Cajal* in a series of contributions ('88, '90, '11) and by *Dogiel* ('96). Such cells have from three to six dendrites which, after a short course end in claw-like terminations which are in synaptic relations with mossy fibers. The terminations have been called cerebellar glomeruli (glomérules cérébelleux) by *Held* ('97) and protoplasmic islands by *Ramón y Cajal* ('11).

This latter worker gave a description of them as early as 1888.   The delicate neuraxes of the granule cells (fig. 350) run toward the periphery, where each forms a T- or Y-shaped division within the molecular layer.   The figures of *Ramón y Cajal* ('88, '11) show that such a neuraxis may arise in many cases from a dendrite rather than from the cell body of the neuron.   To a large extent, at least, these neuraxes are unmedullated.   The branches resulting from the T-shaped division run parallel to the surface and at right angles to the plane of branching of the Purkinje cells.   This orientation of the dendrites of the Purkinje cells and of the basket cells also, at right angles to the parallel fibers, is suggestive of a similar arrangement described previously in the cord of cyclostomes.   In this cord the dendrites of certain of the motor and intercalated cells are perpendicular to the course of the parallel fibers of the cord.   This is regarded as due to the lateral irradiation of the impulse (perpendicular to the course of the naked neuraxes) which makes a perpendicular position of the dendrites most favorable for conduction.[1]

Scattered among the granule cells are the cells of Golgi.   These are large stellate or polygonal neurons situated throughout the granular layer, although slightly more plentiful in regions near the Purkinje cells.   Their dendrites are long and richly branched, and extend in all directions.   Many of them pass toward the surface and are in relation probably with the parallel fibers from the neuraxes of granular cells.   The dendritic branches of the Golgi cells are differentiable within the molecular layer from those of the Purkinje cells because the former branch in more than one plane and have longer, less numerous, more spiny processes than the latter.   *Golgi* ('86), *Ramón y Cajal* ('88, '90, '11), *van Gehuchten* ('91), and *Retzius* ('92 and '92a) studied these cells with great care.   The neuraxis of a cell of Golgi after a short course breaks up into a great many small branches which form a rich plexus of fibers (fig. 350).   These terminal fibers are in synaptic relation with the mossy fibers.

Certain cells in the molecular layer resemble the Golgi cells except for differences in position and are regarded by *Ramón y Cajal* ('96b, '11) as displaced granule cells.   Much smaller neurons with fusiform- or triangular-shaped cell bodies and a smaller number of dendrites are likewise present in the granular layer.   In some cells of this type, the neuraxis runs horizontally, giving off ascending and descending collaterals but with its final destination unknown.   In other cells of this type (the so-called "cellule intermediare" of *Lugaro*, '94) the neuraxis, after a complicated course, enters the plexiform layer.   Certain of the stellate or fusiform cells send their neuraxes into the white matter of the cerebellum.   Such cells are

---

[1] *Tretjakoff* ('09 ; see bibliography for Chapter II) was of the opinion that such dendrites are perpendicular to the cord because they thus reach the periphery by the shortest possible course and there lie in close relation with the food material carried in the perimedullary lymph spaces. Such relations to the surface are regarded as the more necessary because of the lack of intramedullary blood vessels within the cord of cyclostomes.   The relation of the dendrites of the Purkinje cells to the parallel neuraxes of the granular cells does not favor such conclusions, for the molecular layer of the cerebellar cortex in gnathostome fishes and in all higher animals contains a large number of blood vessels and, if food supply were the operating factor, such orientation to the surface would be unnecessary.

few in number and found only near or within the white substance. These cells have been described in detail and figured by *Ramón y Cajal* ('11), and need receive but brief mention here. They consist, according to this author, of external cells, marginal cells, and deep or interstitial cells. The external cells are large, with cell bodies situated within the granular layer and dendrites supplying both the molecular and granular layers. The dendrites of the marginal cells likewise reach both layers, but their cell bodies lie at the edge of the white substance. As

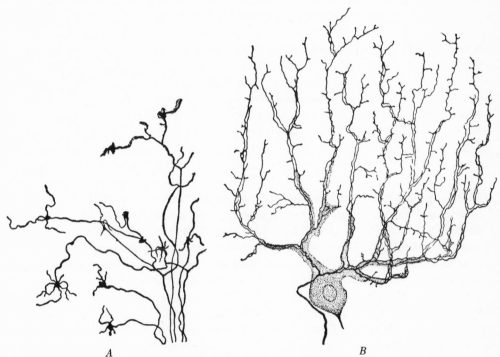

A   *B*

FIG. 349. *A*. Branching of the mossy fibers in the granular layer. *van Gehuchten.*
B. Branching of a climbing fiber (black) around the dendrites of a Purkinje cell. *Ramón y Cajal.*

the name implies, the cell bodies of the interstitial neurons lie between the bundles of fibers within the stratum album; their dendrites also distribute among the bundles. Certain of these cells appear to be very large (*Ramón y Cajal*, '11), in which case the dendrites distribute to the cerebellar cortex while the neuraxes course through white substance and bifurcate within the capsule of the roof nucleus.

Recently *Landau* ('33) has described "cellule synarmotiques" with stellate, round, or oval cell bodies situated in the gray substance, in the white substance, or at the line between the two layers in the carnivore and human cerebella. Such cells vary in size but have a considerable spread of processes and serve as associative elements between gray layers separated by white substance.

The incoming impulses reach the cerebellar cortex by the central white matter, the stratum album (arbor vitae). The recognized types are mossy fibers and climbing fibers.   The mossy fibers terminate in relation to neurons of the granular zone, the climbing fibers come into synaptic relation with the Purkinje cells (fig. 349).

The mossy fibers, so named because of their appearance in the region of their termination, are differentiable from the descending neuraxes of Purkinje cells. They divide in or near the stratum album and then enter the granular layer, where they divide and redivide many times, twenty or thirty or even more branches being given off according to certain observers.   A fiber, through its collaterals, may supply a whole cerebellar lamella or even two adjoining lamellae (*Ramón y Cajal*, '11).   It appears to be the consensus of opinion that mossy fibers lose their myelin sheaths before their final terminations, although *Dogiel* ('96) believed that he could demonstrate them on secondary and tertiary branches in birds.   The terminal branching occurs either along the course of the branches or the main trunk, at their places of division or at their terminations.   The synapses between the terminals of the mossy fibers and the dendrites of the granule cells are termed eosinophilous or protoplasmic islands or cerebellar glomeruli (*Held*, '97 ; *Berliner*, '05 ; *Ramón y Cajal*, '11).   In such a terminal branch of the mossy fiber, the relative amount of neuroplasm within the fiber apparently increases (hence the staining) and the branches themselves follow a circuitous, irregular course, with side branches, and so may form an elaborate ending.   For the details of this termination, the figures of *Bielschowsky* and *Wolff* ('04), *Held* ('93 and '97), *Ramón y Cajal* ('11), and *Craigie* ('26, see bibliography for birds) should be consulted.   The work of various observers, and in particular that of the last mentioned workers, indicates that there may be many of these differentiated terminations along a mossy fiber and its branches and that each termination may come into synaptic relation with the dendrites of several granule cells.   Thus impulses coming in over a mossy fiber may be distributed to a very considerable number of granule cells.   *Craigie* ('26) studied these endings in birds and mammals.   Among the birds studied he found the simplest endings in the blackbird. Since this bird is an excellent flier and its equilibratory activities are necessarily very highly developed, *Craigie* hesitated to draw any definite conclusions from his observations.   Among the mammals studied by him, *Craigie* found the least ramified and most slender endings in man.

The climbing fibers were pointed out by *Ramón y Cajal* ('90), who described them in birds and mammals (fig. 349).   His work has been verified by many later observers.   Such fibers come in through the white substance without dividing.   They pass through the granular zone, following a sinuous course, to the level of the Purkinje cells.   The fiber (sometimes after division) climbs up the major dendrites of the Purkinje cell and there breaks up into two or three divisions which are proportional in size to the size of the dendritic branches which they accompany.   These major divisions branch and rebranch, following a zigzag course along the processes of the Purkinje cells, and terminate in free endings. Some of the branches overlie the upper part of the cell body of the Purkinje neuron (*Retzius*, '92a).   *Lugaro* ('94) showed that climbing fibers reach all parts of the dendritic branches of the Purkinje cells.   *Ramón y Cajal* was able to demonstrate in adult human material, prepared by his silver impregnation methods, that the climbing fibers, on reaching the point where the terminal dendritic branches are given off by the cells, loop back to supply the deeper dendrites, but that at the loop very delicate, faintly staining fibers accompany the terminal dendrites. There appears to be some direct relation between the complexity of the dendritic branching of the Purkinje cells in an animal and the degree of development of the climbing fibers. They are very well developed in man.

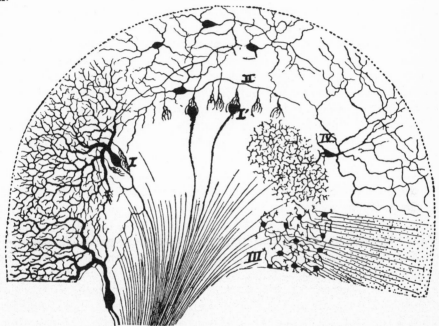

Fig. 350. A composite section through the cerebellum at right angles to a cerebellar lamella and in the longitudinal axis of the body. *I*, Purkinje cells with dendrites spread out toward the surface; *I'*, cell body of Purkinje cell surrounded by the processes of basket cells; *II*, neuraxis and collaterals of basket cell; *III*, groups of granule cells the neuraxes of which ascend into the parallel fiber layer; *IV*, Golgi cell. *van Gehuchten.*

Lack of space forbids a discussion here of the structural details of the supporting tissue of the cerebellum. A considerable number of observers (*Retzius*, '94; *Terrazas*, '97; *Ramón y Cajal*, '96a and '11, and others) have devoted much time to the study of this phase of cerebellar structure.

The question now arises as to the origin of the mossy and climbing fibers. Their thickness and number within the white substance of the cerebellum indicate that they are extracerebellar fibers. Are they endings of different fibers or different endings of the same fibers? The latter is not probable, since a bifurcation, one branch of which forms a mossy fiber and one branch a climbing fiber, has never been seen. However, this does not exclude the possibility that they may be different fibers of the same fiber system. It is generally assumed, then, that the fibers represent different systems of extracerebellar tracts, and that certain of such tracts run as mossy fibers and end in relation with the granular layer while the other tracts terminate as climbing fibers in synaptic relation with the dendrites of the Purkinje cells, but this cannot be regarded as proved beyond question.   It is not possible to state definitely the mode of termination of all the afferent systems to the cerebellum, for concerning the manner of termination of certain tracts there is grave doubt and, with regard to others, decided disagreement among competent workers.

Ramón y Cajal (summarized, '11) and *Sauer* ('14) considered that the ponto-cerebellar tracts terminate in climbing fibers.   This view appears to have met with rather general acceptance, although *Jelgersma* ('18) believed that degeneration of pontine nuclei is associated with a diminution of the granular layer, which might be regarded as indicating a connection of the pontine nuclei with this layer, presumably by mossy fibers.   *Brouwer* and *Coenen* ('21) regarded the ponto-cerebellar system as terminating in mossy fibers, while they described the olivo-cerebellar system as ending in climbing fibers.   In disagreement with this last statement are the results of *Schweiger* ('06), who, from his study of a case of cerebellar sclerosis in which the granular layer was practically the only part of the cerebellum disturbed, but in which the inferior olivary nucleus and the olivo-cerebellar fibers were destroyed, reached the conclusion that the olivo-cerebellar fibers terminate as mossy fibers.   *Barany* ('14) considered that the ponto-cerebellar, the olivo-cerebellar, and the spino-cerebellar fibers end as climbing fibers while the vestibular system finds termination as mossy fibers.   His interpretations were based on theoretical and clinical grounds.   *Ariëns Kappers* ('21) regarded the vestibular fibers as terminating within the molecular layer of the cerebellum, basing his conclusions on neuro-anatomical grounds.   According to this observer, the greater relative development of the molecular layer as compared to the granular layer and the extension of the crista cerebellaris over the lateral line centers of the medulla oblongata in such forms as Acanthias and Spinax, are associated, then, with the greater relative development of lateral line, vestibular, and tectal connections as compared with the development of the olivo-cerebellar and spino-cerebellar systems in these animals, while the great size of the granular layer in such higher forms as birds and mammals is associated with the increased development of the latter fiber systems and the disappearance of the lateral-line fibers.   These facts appear to favor the hypothesis that the climbing fibers are terminal fibers of vestibular, lateral line, tecto-cerebellar (and ponto-cerebellar) tracts,[2] while the mossy fibers represent the terminations of spino-cerebellar and olivo-cerebellar fiber bundles, but do not exclude the possibility that each system may contribute, although in varying amounts, to both the gran-

[2] It has been stated in an earlier chapter (Chapter III) that the crista cerebellaris of the medulla oblongata of fishes is a continuation of the molecular layer of the cerebellum in these forms and contains the dendrites of Purkinje-like neurons.   Into this crista, terminating in climbing fibers around the dendrites of these Purkinje-like cells, are the terminal fibers of the lateral-line and vestibular nerves (*Tello, Ariëns Kappers,* and others; see Chapter IV), a termination analogous to that described for the vestibular fibers within the cerebellum of higher forms by *Ramón y Cajal* ('11).   Furthermore, the development of the crista is coincident with the great development of the lateral-line system in fishes.   However, the incoming lateral line and vestibular fibers in fishes terminate not only in the crista cerebellaris but also in the granular layer beneath it.

ular and molecular layers.   The distribution of tecto-cerebellar (mesencephalo-cerebellar) fibers in ganoids (*Johnston*, '01) to the molecular layer of the cerebellum is believed to be reflected in the distribution of the tecto-cerebellar systems in frogs, reptiles, birds, and mammals, but a further documentation of such distribution would be desirable for higher vertebrates.   Most of the afferent paths of the inferior cerebellar peduncle (aside from the vestibular), and particularly the dorsal spino-cerebellar and olivo-cerebellar tracts, have been regarded by *Ariëns Kappers* ('21) as terminating in mossy fibers.   This assumption is based particularly on the fact that at the time that these tracts develop and enter the cerebellum, the granular layer contains a large number of branched fibers, which are certainly not as yet fully developed mossy fibers but appear analogous to them. Since the pontine tracts are not formed at this time and the ascending vestibular root is regarded as ending as climbing fibers, it is probable that the branched fibers just mentioned are the terminations of the spino-cerebellar and olivo-cerebellar tracts.   As to whether or not these fibers terminate only as mossy fibers within the granular layer, or whether they may terminate also as climbing fibers, is still a matter of doubt.   Thus *Schaper* ('94), *Franz* ('11), and *Shimazono* ('12) claimed that in teleosts and birds [3] all fiber systems entering the cerebellum terminate, in part at least, within the molecular layer of the cortex, since, in degeneration material, they were able to trace such tracts (including those from the spinal cord and medulla oblongata) to the base of the Purkinje cells, and so arrived at the conclusion that all afferent cerebellar tracts give off climbing fibers.

Other points of view with regard to vestibular terminations within the cerebellum are current.   Thus *Estable* ('23) believed that vestibular fibers terminate as mossy fibers, basing his conclusions on embryological and physiological data as well as on those afforded by comparative neurology.   *Winkler* ('27) carried olivo-cerebellar and ponto-cerebellar fibers (which he regarded as the phylogenetically newer system) to the cerebellum as climbing fibers, and the spino-cerebellar and vestibulo-cerebellar (the phylogenetically older system of fibers) to the cerebellum as mossy fibers.   *Jakob* ('28) in general favored the interpretation of *Winkler*, but agreed with the assumption of *Ariëns Kappers* that single systems of fibers may give rise both to mossy and climbing fibers, but that one type is predominant over the other for a given system.   Several of the later textbooks (for example, *Piersol's* Anatomy, '30 ; *Ranson's* Anatomy of the Nervous System, '31) regard afferent fibers of the inferior cerebellar peduncle as terminating as mossy fibers and those of the middle cerebellar peduncle as climbing fibers. The ventral spino-cerebellar tract, in so far as it terminates in the cerebellar cortex, ends probably as mossy fibers.

The termination of mossy fibers through one or more cerebellar lamellae by collaterals to the cells of the granular layer and the redistribution of the impulse for considerable distances over the cerebellum to dendrites of Purkinje and basket

---

[3] In plagiostomes, the incoming tracts from the medulla oblongata and the cord reach the region and even enter the layer of Purkinje cells, a relation suggestive of the presence of climbing fibers.   Moreover, the large number of such fibers in the corpus cerebelli of these animals suggests strongly that they are to some extent from centers of the medulla oblongata and of the spinal cord.

cells by way of the parallel-running branches of the neuraxis and further diffusion of the impulse through the neuraxes of basket cells militate against a precise localization of the impulses brought in by the spino-cerebellar and olivo-cerebellar paths. What is lost in precision of localization is compensated for, in some degree, by intensity of response. The cytologic pattern of the cerebellum is such that impulses brought in over relatively few mossy fibers, by way of neuraxes of granular cells, may discharge many Purkinje, basket, and Golgi cells. The basket cells in turn discharge to Purkinje cells and the neuraxes of Purkinje cells, by way of their collaterals, distribute the impulse to other cells of the same type. Thus the stored-up neuronic energy of many Purkinje cells may be released by the stimulation of relatively few proprioceptive terminations. This is typical of the avalanche type of conduction described for the cerebellum by *Ramón y Cajal* ('11). In so far as the climbing fibers represent terminations of ponto-cerebellar fibers, they appear to offer an efficient mechanism for the control of the cerebellar cortex by the cerebral cortex, since the ponto-cerebellar fibers are processes of the neurons of the second order in the cortico-ponto-cerebellar path.

The question of cerebellar localization will be considered later, but one phase of the subject may be mentioned here. The cytological structure of the cerebellar cortex is essentially the same for all regions. This has sometimes been used as an argument against cerebellar localization. However, the cerebellum is to be regarded as dominantly an efferent discharge center in the sense that one regards the motor cortex of the cerebral hemispheres and the tectum, at least of lower forms, as such efferent centers. However, within the cerebellar cortex, and within the tectum as well, there is no cytological differentiation sufficiently marked to give a basis for the recognition of areas. The localization within the cerebral cortex, as evident histologically, is based on the cytological differentiation evident between any two types of afferent centers and between afferent and efferent, and afferent and association areas. Thus, as compared with other brain regions, we should not expect a cytological picture clear-cut and sharp enough within the cerebellum to serve as a determinant for the localization within that organ, since the picture would show an efferent type of cortex. This localization will be rather in terms of outgoing fiber pathways, the functions of which must be determined by fiber connections of their cells of origin and the relation of these cells to the other centers of the nervous system.

THE CEREBELLUM OF CYCLOSTOMES

For the most part, observers have been inclined to question the presence of any cerebellar tissue in myxinoids. However, *von Kupffer* ('99) believed that a cerebellum is present at the cephalic end of the rhombencephalon in the embryos of Bdellostoma stouti. *Conel* ('29), working on the development of the brain of Bdellostoma, appears to have agreed with the conclusions of *von Kupffer*, although inclined to wait for further study of his material before arriving at positive conclusions. *Conel* stated that in these forms the cerebellar tissue is not visible from the external surface, but that it is situated at the anterior end of the rhombencephalon. Later studies appear to have convinced *Conel* ('31) that no cerebellum is present in this myxinoid. For Myxine glutinosa, *Jansen* ('30) concluded that "a cerebellum cannot be recognized with certainty in adults." The present account concerns itself with the petromyzonts.

Immediately behind the tectum opticum (fig. 4), the somewhat elevated lateral portions of the medulla oblongata of petromyzonts come into contact with each other, forming what is known as the cerebellar plate. This plate is actually nothing but the modified lateral portions of the medulla oblongata and was regarded by certain earlier observers as a commissure of fibers. *Falcone* ('93) and *Schaper* ('99), in particular, pointed out that the cells of the region characterize it as cerebellar in structure (see fig. 351).

Johnston ('02), in writing of Petromyzon, stated that the cerebellar character of the dorsal bridge between the acoustico-lateral areas of the two sides is indicated by the presence of a small fiber bundle from the inferior lobes which gives to the region the characteristics of a coördinating center. According to this observer, the cellular structure of the cerebellum of Petromyzon does not as yet clearly reflect the higher conducting character of the region, since the large cells, which are in all probability the forerunners of the Purkinje cells of higher mammals, are exactly similar to cells within the acoustico-lateral area of the medulla. *Jeleneff* ('79), *Schaper* ('99), and *Johnston* ('02) recognized an outer fibrous layer and an inner cell layer (granular layer, John-

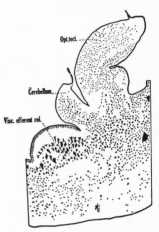

Fig. 351. A sagittal section through the cerebellum of Petromyzon marinus. *Huber* and *Crosby*.

ston), containing larger and smaller cells. The fibrous layer is continuous with the primordial cerebellar crest.

In Chapter IV the structure of the area statica or acoustico-lateralis in these animals has been reviewed. Three nuclei are present at the level of entrance of the facial nerve. The most dorsal of these nuclei is the lobus nervi lateralis anterioris or dorsal nucleus, which receives the more anterior lateral-line nerve. Farther frontalward this most dorsal nucleus disappears, leaving a dorsomedial or medial cell group, associated chiefly with the nervus lateralis posterior but receiving fine fibers from the nervus lateralis anterior as well, and a ventrolateral or ventral nucleus receiving mainly vestibular fibers. The cephalic ends of these two medial nuclei fuse, and this fusion leads to the formation of the cerebellum (*Pearson*,'33). Thus the cerebellar plate, in the primitive form in which it appears in petromyzonts, represents the direct continuation and bilateral amalgamation of the nuclei associated with the lateral-line nerves, particularly the posterior lateral-line nerve, and the vestibular fibers. The direct relation between these nuclei and the cerebellum is the more evident because of the continuity of the fine fibrous neuropil with its terminal lateral-line fibers which covers the area statica of the medulla oblongata (the crista cerebellaris) and the molecular layer of the cerebellum. It is remarkable to what an extent the medial nucleus of the static area (the nucleus of the posterior lateral-line nerve) contributes to the formation of the cerebellum in petromyzonts.[4] These relations are particularly well marked in higher fishes. *Hausman* ('29) spoke of it as "essentially a lateralis-vestibular organ, only slightly differentiated from its segmental foundation; *i.e.* the octavo-lateral area."

In harmony with the gross relations noted for the medial nucleus of the lateral-line area and cerebellum is a correspondence in the cytologic structure of the regions (fig. 352). The granular cells of the cerebellum are not materially different from those of the static area, except that their neuraxes are longer and may cross as commissural fibers in the molecular layer — the possible forerunners of the parallel fibers found in this area in higher forms.   True Purkinje cells, according to *Johnston* ('02) and to *Tretjakoff* ('09), are present neither in the larval nor adult forms of Petromyzon.   The latter observer found less resemblance in Ammocoetes to the Purkinje cells of higher forms than did *Johnston* in the adult animal. These results are in accord with the fact that even in higher vertebrates these cells attain their characteristic form relatively late in development. *Johnston* ('02) pointed out that the larger cells in the cerebellum of Petromyzon are to be regarded as the forerunners of Purkinje cells,

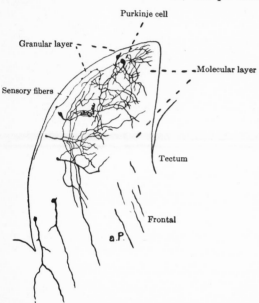

FIG. 352.   The cerebellum of Petromyzon.   *Johnston.*

although they are not as yet arranged as a definite layer but are scattered among the granule cells in much the same way that similar cells are scattered among smaller elements in the area statica.   Aside from their size, the most marked resemblance of these cerebellar cells to the Purkinje cells of higher forms is to be found in the distribution of their dendritic branches to regions homologous to the molecular layer of higher forms, in such arrangement as to be most clearly visible in a sagittal plane (fig. 352, after *Johnston*).

Afferent impulses reach the cerebellum of petromyzonts by way of both anterior and posterior lateral-line nerves.   The fibers are crossed in part, and those from the posterior lateral-line nerve are formed by particularly large neuraxes. The vestibular nerve sends fibers to the cerebellum, also.   Bulbo-cerebellar con-

---

[4] A further evidence that it is with the lateral-line nuclei that the cerebellum is particularly closely related genetically is to be found in the fact that the crista cerebellaris is continued primarily over the nuclei of termination of the lateral-line nerves rather than of the vestibular nerves. Moreover, this relation explains the absence of a crista cerebellaris over the medulla oblongata of the higher vertebrates in which lateral-line nerves are lacking.

nections from the acoustico-lateral area to the cerebellum have been described by *Clark* ('06), *Tretjakoff* ('09), and *Ariëns Kappers* ('21). Bulbo-spino-cerebellar fibers have been demonstrated by *Pearson* ('33), but as yet fibers have not been traced to the cerebellum from the center which *Johnston* ('02) regarded as the inferior olivary nucleus. It appears more than probable that trigeminal root fibers accompany secondary trigemino-cerebellar fascicles to the cerebellum.

Afferent fibers reach the cerebellum from the lobi inferiores of the hypothalamus over the tractus lobo-cerebellaris. According to *Johnston* ('02), who worked with silver preparations, these end in the granular layer; according to *Tretjakoff* ('09), who studied methylene-blue material, their termination is in the molecular layer. The tractus lobo-cerebellaris is regarded by certain authors as a cerebello-fugal system, but there is considerable evidence to suggest that it is in large part cerebello-petal. It is uncrossed and clearly belongs to the most primitive coördinating system of the cerebellum. Its exact function is not clearly understood as yet since the functions of the lobi inferiores have not been definitely defined. Tecto-cerebellar (*Clark*, '06; *Tretjakoff*, '09; crossed and uncrossed, *Pearson*,' 33), cerebello-tectal (*Ariëns Kappers*, '21), cerebello-toral (*Pearson*, '33), and cerebello-tegmental (*Clark*, '06; *Ariëns Kappers*, '21) connections have been described. A résumé of the incoming paths indicates that the cerebellar plate in petromyzonts is more than a mere continuation of the acoustico-lateral area; it is a place of correlation of various stimuli and is favorably situated for carrying out such correlations, since it lies at the place of transition from the medulla oblongata into the mesencephalon.

The cerebellar commissure, divided by *Johnston* ('02) into dorsal and ventral commissures, carries decussating fibers of the trochlear nerve (*Tretjakoff*, '09; *Addens*, '28), of the acoustic and anterior lateral-line nerves (*Tretjakoff*, '09), and crossing posterior lateral line, bulbo- and spino-cerebellar fibers and tecto-cerebellar tracts (*Pearson*, '33, Dissertation).

Efferent fibers, arising from the large primordial Purkinje cells of the cerebellum and from the large neurons of the acoustico-lateral area, together with the neuraxes of similar cells of the area statica, form the tractus cerebello- et octavo-motorius, or the fibrae arcuatae dorsales. This primitive efferent system ends in the motor regions of the medulla oblongata and midbrain, partly on the same side and partly on the opposite side.

At the line where the cerebellum passes over into the medulla oblongata lies the nucleus octavo-motorius anterior (*Ariëns Kappers*, '20). This nucleus is subcerebellar, corresponding in position to the nuclei of the vestibular and lateral-line nerves, and has been considered with these cell masses (Chapter IV). According to *Ariëns Kappers* a study of the cerebellar nuclei in higher animals suggests that a migration of neuronic elements has occurred from this nucleus, or at least from its immediate neighborhood, into the cerebellum. This suggests that the cerebellar nuclei originate in relation to this nuclear area. At all events, in Petromyzon, nucleus octavo-motorius anterior [5] is entirely under the influence of

---

[5] So named by *Ariëns Kappers* in contrast to nucleus octavo-motorius posterior situated at the level of entrance of the acoustic nerve.

fibers of the vestibular and lateral-line systems, which terminate around its cells. In this it shows great resemblance to the cerebellum itself.   The neuraxes of the neurons comprising the nucleus octavo-motorius anterior are coarser than those forming the fibrae arcuatae dorsales and run in a more frontoventral direction. They form a bundle which decussates completely at the base of the midbrain at the level of exit of the oculomotor roots.   The fibers terminate in the midbrain region in an area adjoining the nuclei of the oculomotor nerves.   It is evident from the foregoing account that just as the afferent side of the cerebellum has its forerunner in the nuclei of termination of the lateral line and vestibular nerves, so the efferent side of this brain region finds its forerunner in nucleus octavo-motorius anterior, whether or not it is considered the direct source of cerebellar nuclei.

The root fibers of the trochlear nerve cross in the anterior part of the cerebellum and the cells of the trochlear nucleus lie dorsal to the ventricle and actually within the cerebellum itself, a condition found in the cerebellum of no other animal (compare fig. 227B).

THE CEREBELLUM OF PLAGIOSTOMES

The cerebellum of the plagiostomes is more complex in its structure than that of the cyclostomes.   It is most easily understood in the smaller representatives of the class because, in accordance with the law of Baillarger and Dareste, the cerebellar cortex increases with an increase in the size of the animal.   With the

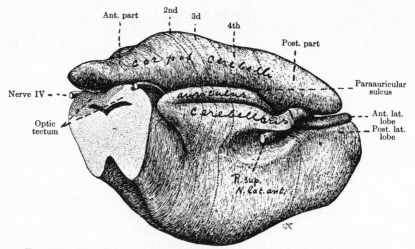

FIG. 353.   Wax reconstruction of the cerebellum of Spinax niger.   *Voorhoeve.*

great increase in its cortex, and consequently in the number of its folds, it is very difficult to understand the fundamental pattern of its structure in the larger forms. *Voorhoeve* ('17), who worked particularly in this field, made a wax reconstruction of the cerebellum of selachians, using for this purpose a young specimen of Spinax niger (see also figs. 353–358 and 232).   This reconstruction verifies the presence of a central, unpaired portion, the corpus cerebelli, and two lateral portions, the

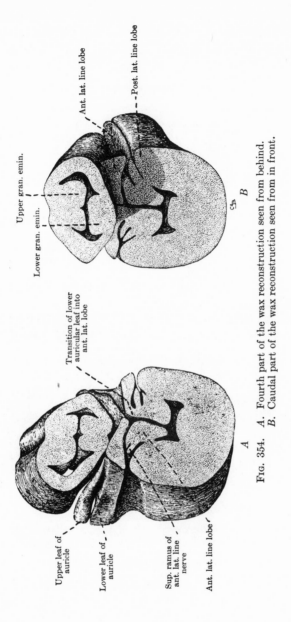

Ant. lat. line lobe

Post. lat. line lobe

Upper gran. emin.

Lower gran. emin.

B

Transition of lower
auricular leaf into
ant. lat. lobe

Upper leaf of
auricle

Lower leaf of
auricle

Sup. ramus of
ant. lat. line
nerve

Ant. lat. line lobe

A

FIG. 354.   *A.* Fourth part of the wax reconstruction seen from behind.
           B. Caudal part of the wax reconstruction seen from in front.

711

auricles; regions which had been identified by earlier workers (*Edinger*, '08, and others). Each auricle consists of two layers which unite with each other orally and so inclose between them a space, the recessus lateralis auriculi. This recess is covered over by the choroid plexus, which is not visible in the reconstruction, but which may be seen in the other figures. The upper leaf of the auricle on its medial side is continuous through the so-called lower lip (fig. 365) into the body of the

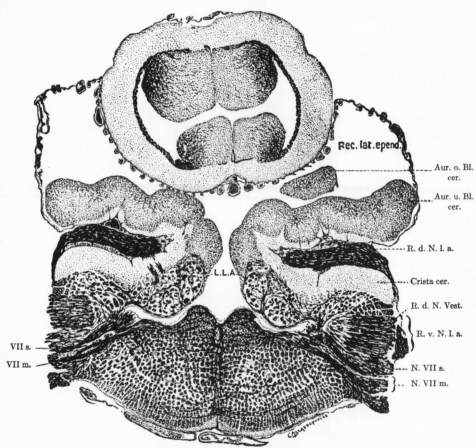

FIG. 355. Cross section through the caudal part of the cerebellum of Scyllium canicula. The upper leaf of the auricle (*Aur.o.Bl.*) is not present on the left side of the section, but a small part of it is visible still on the right. The under leaf of the auricle (*Aur.u.Bl.*) passes over into the lobus nervi lateralis anterioris (*L.L.A.*). *N.VIIs.*, nervus facialis sensibilis; *N.VIIm.*, nervus facialis motorius; *R.d.N.l.a.*, ramus dorsalis nervi lateralis anterioris; *R.d.N.Vest.*, ramus dorsalis nervi vestibularis (or nervi octavi); *R.v.N.l.a.*, ramus ventralis nervi lateralis anterioris. *Schepman.*

cerebellum (fig. 360A), and, furthermore, extends a short distance (Aur. o. Bl. cer.; fig. 355) below the caudal part of the body in order to connect with the upper layer of the other side and then passes caudally into the membranous roof of the fourth ventricle. The lower leaf of the auricle, which extends much farther caudalward than does the upper layer, becomes continuous with the anterior lateral-line lobe and the medulla oblongata (fig. 355), as is to be seen in the wax reconstruction (fig. 354A and B). It has only a relatively narrow connection with the lobus nervi lateralis anterioris. This connection occurs where the ramus superior of the anterior lateral-line nerve enters the lobe (see fig. 355). Behind this place of attachment the under leaf of the auricle extends for a distance caudalward over this lobe but free from it. In front of its attachment with this lobe the lower layer thickens considerably and has a broad connection (figs. 356 and 365) with the dorsal part of the medulla oblongata, which has fibers of the anterior lateral-line nerve and, particularly, bundles of the vestibular and the posterior lateral-line nerves (fig. 365, right side). This connection with the medulla oblongata is comparable with the relations found in cyclostomes, where the cerebellum is connected more particularly with the nuclear area associated with the posterior lateral-line nerves than with the nucleus dorsalis of the anterior lateral-line nerve.

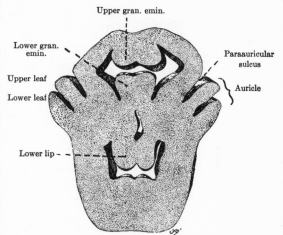

FIG. 356. Third part of the wax reconstruction seen from in front.

The corpus cerebelli has no direct connection caudalward with the medulla oblongata. However, at about the point where the lower leaf of the auricle becomes attached to the margin of the medulla oblongata (see fig. 366) the two auricular layers in part become united with each other. The upper layer is also connected with the corpus cerebelli in this region (fig. 356). In this way a connection of the corpus cerebelli is established through the auricle with the medulla oblongata so that fibers entering from the dorsolateral angle of the medulla oblongata may penetrate through the layers of the auricle into the corpus cerebelli (fig. 366). In front of this region the body of the cerebellum is connected with the medulla oblongata and the auricular layers form a sort of appendix lateral to the body of the cerebellum, and at about the place where the trochlear nerve becomes visible (fig. 357) the auricles become continuous with each other, forming a blind sack, the diverticulum anterior auriculi.

The corpus cerebelli, although an unpaired structure in the full-grown animal, especially in the smaller plagiostomes, shows indications of its paired origin through the presence on the dorsal surface of a slight longitudinal depression in the midline (fig. 359), which corresponds to a narrow longitudinal zone in which the granular eminence is lacking. Lateralward the corpus is separated from either auricle by a deep groove, the sulcus paraauricularis (figs. 353–357). This sulcus becomes connected under the corpus cerebelli with the corresponding sulcus of the other side. The medial connecting groove may be termed the sulcus postremus. This fissure marks the boundary between the under lip of the cerebellum (formed by the medial confluence of the upper auricular layers or leaves) and the true corpus cerebelli, into the granular eminence of which the lower lip passes.   In the region of transition between the lower lip and the body there are two small paired lobi postici or posteriores, separated from the remainder of the corpus cerebelli by a paired transverse fissure, the sulcus posticus (fig. 365).   Two portions of the corpus cerebelli can be distinguished; a pars anterior and a pars posterior.   The pars anterior is continuous laterally with the medulla oblongata and passes cephalically into the velum medullare anterius, which connects it with the roof of the midbrain.   The granular enlargements or eminences previously mentioned, which lie on either side of the midline, continue forward below the velum for a short distance, but the nervus trochlearis decussates anterior to them.   The pars posterior is continuous with the upper leaf

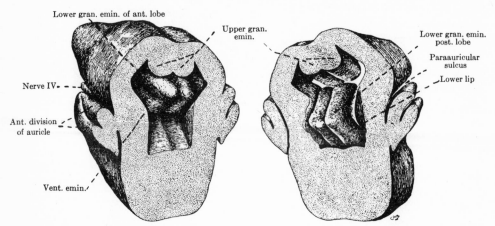

FIG. 357.   Second part of the wax reconstruction   FIG. 358.   Anterior part of the wax reconstruction
seen from in front.   seen from behind.

of the auricle through the under lip in the way just described.   The pars anterior and pars posterior are separated in most forms by a transverse fissure.   This is absent only in the most primitive plagiostomes (Heptanchus, Hexanchus, Scymnus lichia) and the smallest representatives of the neoselachians (Spinax, Scyllium; fig. 359).   In all other sharks and in all the Rajidae this fissure is present.   It is very deep in the larger animals, the deepest and most constant of all the cerebellar fissures of plagiostomes, with the exception of the sulcus paraauricularis.   Since it is the first transverse fissure to make its appearance in the corpus cerebelli, *Voorhoeve* ('17) termed it the sulcus primus transversus cerebelli (fig. 360, *a*) without intending to imply any sort of homology with the fissura prima found in the cerebellum of higher vertebrates.   It corresponds nearly always to the place where the ventricle of the cerebellum communicates with the rhomboidal ventricle (fig. 360) and where thus a place of lessened resistance occurs. In larger plagiostomes, transverse fissures are formed on the body of the cerebellum, frontalward and lateralward to the sulcus primus.   This increase in the number of transverse fissures is usually paralleled by an increase in the size of the animals (fig. 359), due to the operation of the law of Baillarger and Dareste.   The median sagittal fissure, on the contrary, usually disappears with the increase of nervous tissue.

The complicated transverse fissures follow a more or less regular, fixed pattern in their development. The sulcus primus transversus of *Voorhoeve* ('17) assumes a complex form (fig. 360), having two or more projections into the cerebellar substance. The anterior lobe, situated cephalad to this fissure, is divided further by a deep but usually a relatively simple fissure (sulcus anterior, *b*) into a smaller lobulus primus and a larger lobulus secundus (fig. 360, Mustelus, Carcharias, Lamna). The posterior lobe of the cerebellum is divided by a transverse fissure (sulcus posterior, *c*) into a lobulus primus and a lobulus secundus, although the fissure separating the two is frequently less deep than is the case in the anterior lobe. These lobuli of the anterior and posterior lobes are divided into sublobuli in the largest plagiostomes.

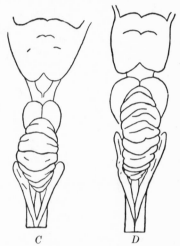

The fact observed by *Voorhoeve*, that an enlargement of the corpus cerebelli is not necessarily correlated with an enlargement of the auricles, is of interest. The corpus cerebelli increases with an increase in the size of the body, thereby indicating the predominantly general somatic character of the stimuli reaching it. The enlargement of the auricles in no way parallels this. These latter regions are supplied by tracts origi-

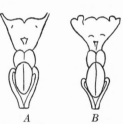

Fig. 359. Increase in the cerebellar fissures in the larger sharks. *A*, Spinax nig.; *B*, Scyllium can.; *C*, Galeus can.; *D*, Lamna corn.

nating principally from the roots of the lateral line and vestibular nerves or from their nuclei of termination within the medulla oblongata. The independence in the development of the auricles and corpus cerebelli is very clearly demonstrated by the relations found in the Rhinidae (Squatina angelus and Squatina fimbriata) and in Lamnidae. In the former the corpus cerebelli is relatively small and the auricles relatively large. In the latter the reverse relations are found.

The cerebellum (figs. 361A and C) of the electric ray (Batoidei) differs from that of the sharks in its compact structure. A second peculiarity is in the occurrence of relatively shallow lateral depressions on the dorsal surface, as a result of which the more central portion appears to bulge somewhat more. When this condition is rendered more complex by an increase in the transverse fissures, a very peculiar pattern is the result. In such cases a number of button-shaped swellings occur in the midline of the corpus cerebelli.

The sulcus primus transversus is present in all the rays, even in the smallest (torpedo). It is very probably the result of the compression which modifies the form relations in these animals in other ways as well. The sulcus is present at the level where the ventricle of the cerebellum communicates with the ventriculus rhomboidalis, which is to be regarded as the locus minoris resistentiae. In the Rajidae the cerebellum is divided by the sulcus primus (of *Voorhoeve*, '17) into a

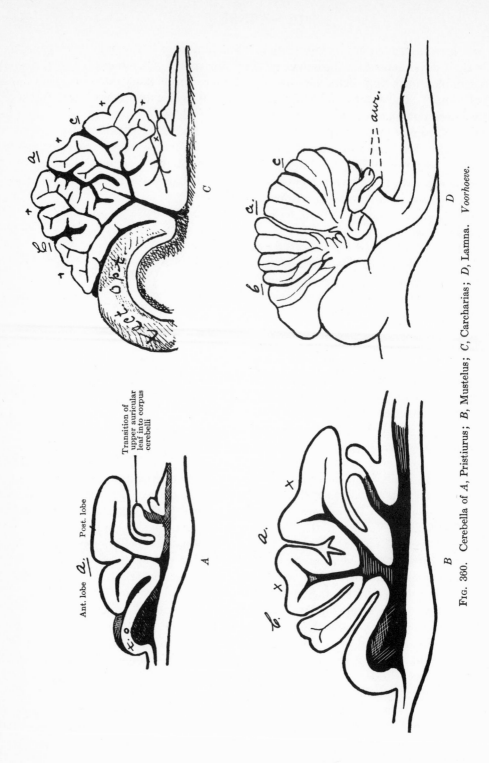

Ant. lobe

Post. lobe

Transition of
upper auricular
leaf into corpus
cerebelli

FIG. 360. Cerebella of *A*, Pristiurus; *B*, Mustelus; *C*, Carcharias; *D*, Lamna. *Voorhoeve*.

smaller anterior and a larger posterior lobe ; in Torpedinidae, the two lobes are of about equal size ; in Trygonidae and Myliobatidae the anterior lobe is the larger, particularly lobulus primus which is especially well developed in these forms.

A

B

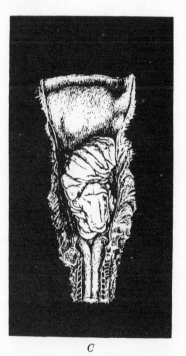

C

FIG. 361. The cerebella in different Rajidae. *A*, Raja clavata; *B*, Myliobatis aquila; *C*, Myliobatis taurus. *Voorhoeve.* Attention is directed particularly to the size of the auricle in Raja clavata, and to the asymmetry of the corpus cerebelli in Myliobatis aquila and Myliobatis taurus.

The greatest depth of fissures occurs in those Rajidae, Trygonidae, and Myliobatidae, which have the largest cerebella.   This agrees with the conditions in sharks. However, in the Rajidae, due to this enlargement associated with the compact structure of the organ, there is a tendency for the cerebellum to show asymmetry so that often the central lobe is rotated entirely to one side (fig. 361B and C).

In Rajidae, as in sharks, the development of the auricles and the corpus cerebelli is not parallel. In Raja clavata (fig. 361), for example, the auricles are relatively much larger than in the Myliobatidae, which illustrates again the relative independence of these two portions.

Relatively little attention has been devoted as yet to the finer structure of the plagiostome cerebellum. Certain tracts have been studied by degeneration methods (*Wallenberg*, '07) and observations based on Golgi preparations have

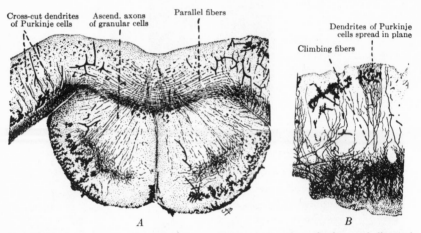

FIG. 362.   *A*, a cross section, and *B*, a sagittal section through the cerebellum of Acanthias.   (Preparation by *Droogleever Fortuyn*.)

been recorded by *Sauerbeck* ('96), *Schaper* ('98), *Houser* ('01), and *Catois* ('01), and similar preparations have been placed at the disposal of *Ariëns Kappers* ('21) by Droogleever Fortuyn. The observations indicate that the plagiostome cerebellum presents a much more perfected cerebellar structure than does that of cyclostomes, and that its neuron pattern resembles much more nearly that of higher vertebrates than that of petromyzonts.

The three layers — the molecular, the Purkinje, and the granular layers — are clearly differentiable and are strongly and regularly developed. As compared with the cyclostomes, there is a considerable increase in the granular layer which as yet does not cover the entire molecular and Purkinje layers on the inner side but accumulates (see figs. 355, 362A, 365 to 367) in two longitudinal swellings along either side of the midsagittal line of the cerebellum but separated in the midline by a narrow prolongation of the cerebellar ventricle (pressed together and scarcely visible in fig. 362A). These relations are evident in the wax reconstruction. The indication is that the tissue has its beginning in relation to the medial place of attachment of the primitive tela. In the region of the under lip of the cerebellum, the granular eminence passes over into the upper leaf of the auricle. The granular layer is lacking in the lateral part of the corpus cerebelli, the layer over the ventricular lining being only the molecular layer, the layer of Purkinje cells, and a fiber layer internal to the latter (figs. 355 and 365 to 367). These conditions may be summarized by the statement that the outer layers have a wider extent than has the granular layer.

The Purkinje cell layer is very regularly arranged. It is only a single cell in thickness and extends over the whole of the cerebellar cortex with the exception of the region immediately adjacent to the midline. The dendrites of such a cell (accompanied by climbing fibers) extend only into the molecular layer and are oriented in a sagittal plane. The molecular layer of plagiostomes, as compared with that of petromyzonts, has increased considerably in thickness. This is to be

expected, since the increase in granule cells implies the increase of neuraxes of these cells, which, as parallel fibers, comprise a large part of the molecular layer (fig. 362A). The entrance of neuraxes of the granule cells into the molecular layer occurs primarily in those regions in which Purkinje cells are absent (*Schaper*, '98), that is, near the midsagittal line (fig. 362A). Measurements show that whereas the Purkinje cell layer remains unicellular and consequently is of equal thickness in all selachians, the molecular layer is larger in the larger sharks than it is in the smaller. This increase in thickness in the larger selachians is not inconsiderable (since in Hexanchus the area may be twice the size of that in Spinax).

Many small stellate cells are present in the molecular layer of selachians. The

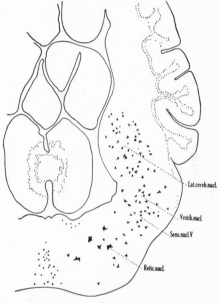

FIG. 363. Nerve cells of the eminentia ventralis cerebelli of Selache maxima. *van Hoevell.*

dendrites of these cells lie in a sagittal plane, although their orientation is not as perfect as that of the Purkinje cells. Typical basket cells have not been identified as yet in selachians. However, it is not unlikely that certain of the more deeply situated stellate cells are forerunners of this basket cell type, inasmuch as the neuraxes of certain of the smaller stellate cells have a horizontal course suggestive of that of basket cells of higher forms.

Fibers bringing impulses into the cerebellum all appear to terminate within the molecular layer. They thus represent a primitive type of climbing fiber (fig. 362B). Analogous intramolecular terminations are present in the crista cerebellaris of the medulla oblongata. The details of relation of these intramolecular fibers to the dendrites of the Purkinje cells are not known. Certainly such intimate intertwining of the incoming fibers with the dendrites of the Purkinje cells as occurs in mammals has never been pointed out for selachians; similarly, in the selachian crista cerebellaris no such intimate synapses have been demonstrated, and they appear to be lacking in teleosts also. True mossy fibers have not been identified

in the selachian cerebellum.   Quite a number of medullated fibers disappear from
view in the lateral part of the granular layer.   These fibers may be the primitive
mossy fibers which have not as yet acquired their characteristic "mossy" appearance (*Ariëns Kappers*, '21).

The plagiostome cerebellum differs very considerably from that of higher
vertebrates, such as birds and mammals.   This difference is to be noted in the
enormous width of the ventricles (compare figs. 367 and 415), in the absence of a
central core of myelinated fibers (an arbor vitae), and in the lack of such central

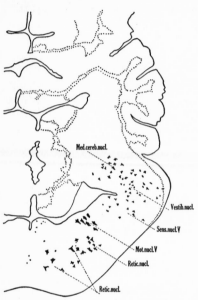

nuclei of the cerebellum as nucleus fastigius
and nucleus dentatus.   Whereas in higher
vertebrates a large number of myelinated
fibers is found below the granular layer in the
center of the cerebellum, in the selachians, in
reality, only that layer of fibers has developed
which is situated immediately below the layer
of Purkinje cells and which may be termed the
superficial myelinated layer (*Ariëns Kappers*,
'21), in contrast to the central myelinated
layer of mammals.   This superficial layer
(fig. 366) consists of various cerebello-petal
and cerebello-fugal fibers.   It can be traced
to the lateral part of the granular layer of the
corpus cerebelli where a part of the afferent
fibers end, possibly as mossy fibers.   A considerable contingent of the fibers of this superficial myelinated layer is formed by neuraxes
of Purkinje cells, which soon after their origin

Fig. 364.   Nerve cells from Selache
maxima, but taken from a more frontal
level than that of fig. 363.   *van Hoevell.*
turn lateralward into this layer and course in
it without giving off collaterals, as is the case
in higher vertebrates.   Such fibers run directly from the beginning of the auricle
of the cerebellum to the nucleus lateralis cerebelli and into the medulla oblongata,
where in part they cross in the raphé as fibrae arcuatae dorsales or cerebello-
tegmentales et motoriae and in part run caudalward either in or beside the
homolateral medial longitudinal fasciculus.

True nuclei of the cerebellum are not present in plagiostomes.   However, in
the region in front of the level of the trigeminal root and behind the velum there is
found a projection, the eminentia ventralis cerebelli, in which is situated a large
nucleus, the nucleus lateralis cerebelli.   In part this is said to be a nucleus of
termination for ascending fibers of the vestibular and lateral-line nerves (*Ariëns
Kappers*, '06, '21) and to be a possible homologue of the nucleus octavo-motorius
anterior of cyclostomes.   Such homology finds support not only from its relation
with the root fibers of the vestibular and lateral-line nerves, but also from its
topographic position at the level of entrance of the trigeminal.   In sharks (figs.
363 and 364) this nucleus lateralis cerebelli is thought to represent more than the
nucleus octavo-motorius anterior; according to *van Hoevell* ('16), it is also a

primitive anlage of the cerebellar nuclei, particularly the nucleus tecti, but this
interpretation is not beyond question.   This explains the relation of a large part
of the superficial myelinated fiber layer of the cerebellum to the eminentia ventralis, for this is a connection analogous with the distribution of the neuraxes of
the Purkinje cells of birds and mammals to nuclei of the cerebellum, and the origin
from these nuclei of many of the fiber bundles of the brachium conjunctivum.

   First to be mentioned among the cerebello-petal paths in plagiostomes are the
root fibers of the lateral-line nerves (figs. 365 and 366).   A large number of such

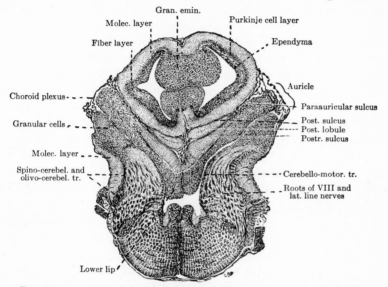

FIG. 365.   A cross section through the caudal part of the cerebellum of
Spinax niger at the level of entrance of the nervus acusticus or octavus and the
nervus lateralis anterior.   *Voorhoeve.*

fibers enter the cerebellum from the posterior as well as from the anterior lateral-
line nerves.   They reach particularly — possibly even exclusively — the lower
leaf of the auricle (compare fig. 355, p. 712).   A considerable number of vestibular
fibers also reach the lateral part of the auricle.   In Spinax such fibers consist of
two bundles which run medial to the fascicles of the nervus lateralis posterior and
which can be traced with ease from the entrance of the root to the base of the
auricle.

   The fact that so many root fibers of the lateral line and vestibular nerves run
to the base of the auricle suggests that the auricle is chiefly a further development
of the area acustico-lateralis of the medulla oblongata and that its considerable
size here is associated with the marked development of the lateral line and vestibular systems (see pp. 447, 448).   A similar connection of the vestibular and
lateral-line nerves with the auricles is to be found in teleosts and amphibians.
Root fibers of the lateral-line nerves, and probably also secondary fibers, reach the
plagiostome nucleus lateralis cerebelli (*Ariëns Kappers*, '06, '21).

   A second cerebellar fiber tract, associated particularly with the auricle, is the
interauricular commissure of *Wallenberg* ('07).   This is a horseshoe-shaped com-

missure, the fibers of which cross frontocaudalward with the opening of the horse-shoe at the back.   The decussation occurs immediately behind and below that of the cerebellar peduncle.   Its course corresponds directly with the interauricular commissure of teleosts (figs. 374–375) and the interfloccular commissure of mammals, a fact which offers substantiation for the homologizing of the auricle of the selachians with the flocculus of higher forms.

It is uncertain as to whether or not direct root fibers of the trigeminal reach the body of the cerebellum or the auricles in selachians.   The evidence for such a connection is insufficient at present.   Other branchial nerves do not contribute root fibers to the cerebellum, except as mentioned above.

A spino-cerebellar tract is present in selachians.   This is a partly crossed but mostly uncrossed tract which, as it approaches the cerebellum, consists of two portions, a small anterior or cephalic portion and a larger posterior or caudal portion.   The cephalic part ascends in front of the auricle to the anterior medullary velum, through which it enters the cerebellum.   Possibly this path corresponds with the tractus spino-cerebellaris ventralis of mammals.

The larger caudal part, probably the homologue of the dorsal spino-cerebellar tract, has a position along the dorsolateral margin of the medulla oblongata.   It enters the posterior part of the corpus cerebelli by way of the auricle.   Some of the fibers of the dorsal spino-cerebellar tract, as well as those of the ventral spino-cerebellar tract, decussate to the other side.   The decussation of the spino-cerebellar tracts does not take place in a special commissure; crossing fibers are present directly under the molecular layer over the entire extent of the body of the cerebellum.

The dorsal spino-cerebellar tract is accompanied by olivo-cerebellar fibers (fig. 366).   Such fibers originate in what has been regarded as the contralateral inferior olive.   At first they occupy a position along the ventral surface of the medulla oblongata, then ascend between the trigeminal (in front of the attachment of the auricle) and the vestibular roots, passing to the corpus cerebelli behind the eminentia ventralis cerebelli (*Ariëns Kappers*, '20).   Not only the course of this olivo-cerebellar path through the peripheral region of the medulla oblongata and its turn medialward through the auricle into the body of the cerebellum, but also the thickness of its fibers and their dark color in Weigert preparations are characteristic of the system (figs. 365 and 366).   The fibers reach all parts of the body of the cerebellum (fig. 366).   Neither the dorsal spino-cerebellar bundle nor the olivo-cerebellar path end to any appreciable extent within the auricle.   The fiber distribution, then, indicates a pronounced difference between the auricles and the body of the cerebellum.

Tractus mesencephalo-cerebellaris superior is one of the major cerebello-petal tracts.   It is a large bundle of fibers which collects in the anterior dorsal part of the tegmentum mesencephali and (at a considerable distance from the surface) extends backward through the tegmentum to the medulla oblongata.   In front of the eminentia ventralis it runs lateralward into the cortex of the corpus cerebelli. The fibers may cross in part after their entrance into the cerebellum; they certainly do not cross previous to that time.   Thus far, the origin of the bundle has not been determined satisfactorily and it is impossible to say whether it is comparable to the tractus mesencephalo-cerebellaris anterior of teleosts, which is related to optic tectal areas of the mesencephalon, or to the tractus mesencephalo-cerebellaris posterior of these animals, which is related to static centers. Possibly the plagiostome tractus mesencephalo-cerebellaris superior is the homologue of both of these teleostean tracts. There is indication, certainly, that it carries fibers which originate in the frontal part of the tectum opticum (see Chapter VI).

There is some possibility of a lobo-cerebellar tract (from the lobi inferiores in plagiostomes). A tecto-cerebellar tract (from the posterior part of the optic

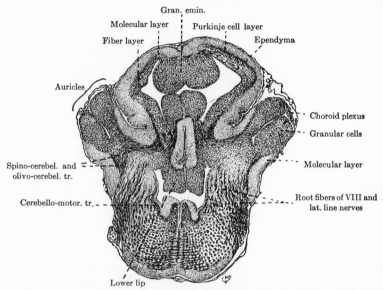

Gran. emin.

Molecular layer Purkinje cell layer

Fiber layer Ependyma

Auricles

Choroid plexus

Granular cells

Spino-cerebel. and olivo-cerebel. tr.

Molecular layer

Cerebello-motor. tr.

Root fibers of VIII and lat. line nerves

Lower lip

Fig. 366. A cross section through the cerebellum of Spinax niger in front of the plane of fig. 365. At the left, note the passage of spino- and olivo-cerebellar fibers into the corpus cerebelli. *Voorhoeve.*

tectum through the anterior medullary velum to the cerebellum) has not been clearly demonstrated in selachians.

The efferent cerebellar tracts show considerably greater development in plagiostomes than in cyclostomes. Three cerebello-fugal systems have been described. The first of these is the tractus cerebello-motorius cruciatus et rectus, which was first described in 1906 by *Ariëns Kappers*, whose observations were later confirmed by several observers (*Wallenberg*, '07; *Sterzi*, '12; figs. 365 and 366). This tract arises from the corpus cerebelli and the auricles, and (since no true cerebellar nucleus is present) probably also from the Purkinje-like cells. The fibers form the most medial part of the white substance of the cerebellum and border directly upon the ependyme of the ventricle. They retain this position in their course toward the midline. The greater part of the fibers, crossed and uncrossed, run caudalward in or near the medial longitudinal fasciculus. They are accompanied caudalward by octavo-motorius fibers. In consequence of these bundles, from this level caudalward the longitudinal bundle is very greatly enlarged (see Chapter IV, page 449). The cerebello-motorius fibers ultimately terminate around motor and reticular centers of the medulla oblongata and spinal cord. A small part of the cerebello-motorius system runs forward to the region of the eye muscle nuclei.

A second efferent system is highly developed in sharks — the brachium conjunctivum anterius, which (fig. 367, Sup. cerebel. ped.) leaves the cerebellum in the region of the nucleus lateralis cerebelli, that is, from the eminentia ventralis cerebelli. Whether it arises from this nucleus wholly or in part, or from neuraxes of the Purkinje cells, at present is unknown. The brachium conjunctivum anterius runs medialward and forward near the ventricular floor, crosses the fibers of the

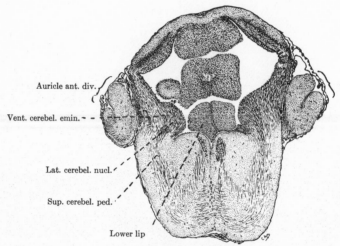

Auricle ant. div.

Vent. cerebel. emin.

Lat. cerebel. nucl.

Sup. cerebel. ped.

Lower lip

Fig. 367. A cross section through the cerebellum of Spinax niger in front of the plane of fig. 366. Eminentia ventralis cerebelli and the brachium conjunctivum are to be noted. *Voorhoeve.*

mesencephalic root of the trigeminal nerve, and then runs cephalward to the raphé, where it decussates completely (fig. 429) directly below the medial longitudinal fasciculus. After contributing a few fibers to the reticular gray of the medulla oblongata, it sends some scattered bundles dorsalward to the oculomotor and perhaps to the trochlear nuclei. The majority of its fibers terminate in the primitive nucleus ruber [6] and in the hypothalamus (*Wallenberg,* '07). It probably is strengthened by fibers from a cell group which lies at the lateral angle of the anterior medullary velum.

Tractus cerebello-vestibularis et cerebello-bulbaris rectus (*Wallenberg,* '07) is the third major cerebello-petal tract of plagiostomes. The fascicles of this tract leave the cerebellum at the level of the eminentia ventralis cerebelli. They run into the dorsolateral part of the medulla oblongata and are probably to be regarded as paths for correlating impulses from the cerebellum with those from bulbar static regions. They are present in higher animals such as birds and mammals.

[6] The homologue in sharks of the red nucleus of higher forms is a group of large reticular elements found near the base of the midbrain.

In a comparison of the structure of the plagiostome cerebellum with that of cyclostomes[7] the most striking differences are: (1) the more typical differentiation of the cytologic elements, and (2) the greater differentiation between auricles and corpus cerebelli in the plagiostomes.   This differentiation is discernible both in the morphologic relations and the fiber connections.   The auricles are concerned primarily with the lateral line and vestibular sense organs.   The corpus cerebelli develops with the development of the body and particularly with the increase of its proprioceptive sensibility (as carried in spino-cerebellar and olivo-cerebellar tracts).   The difference between the auricles and the body of the cerebellum is a fundamental one which is evident in terrestrial animals also, such as birds and mammals.   With the disappearance of the lateral-line system in these latter forms the auricles decrease, while the increase in somatic afferents from the body is accompanied by a great increase in the body of the cerebellum.

THE CEREBELLUM OF GANOIDS AND TELEOSTS
(With brief mention of the relations in Dipnoi)

Before considering the cerebellum of teleosts, on which, to a large extent, the following descriptions are based, a brief account will be given of the cerebellar relations in certain ganoids, since the relations in these forms are in many ways transitional between those found in plagiostomes and those found in teleosts.   *Van der Horst* ('19; see '25, '25a) discovered that, during its development in the Chondrostei, the flat plate which forms the early cerebellum becomes so large that it bends down into the ventricle and forms a massive central portion, while in Crossopterygii, although a thickening occurs, a space between two thickened portions remains in the midline (these two halves become connected only by an ependymal membrane), an indication of the early development. Certainly in the adult Polyodon (which belongs to the Chondrostei) *Hocke Hoogenboom* ('29) found no indication of a bilateral origin of the cerebellum from its external appearance.

In ganoids a well-developed auricle is present which, as it extends forward, becomes separated from the main mass of the cerebellum and terminates, as in plagiostomes, in a blind sac.   In Polyodon (*Hocke Hoogenboom*), where this structure is particularly well developed (being even larger than the homologous lateral lobes of Acipenser, as described by *Johnston*, '01), many of the relations correspond in essentials with those described for plagiostomes, for the ventral leaf or part of the auricle passes over into particularly close relation with the medial and ventral lateral-line and probably with the nucleus.   Not all of the auricle of a form such as Polyodon is comparable to the auricle of other forms.   *Hocke Hoogenboom* has pointed out that the medial side is constituted by the eminentia granularis.

The eminentia granularis is a mass of granule cells found in the lateral part of the corpus cerebelli.   Presumably it is homologous to the similarly formed

---

[7] Functionally the cerebellum of cyclostomes suggests two developing auricles, although it is similar morphologically to the body of the cerebellum of the frog.   (See German edition of this text, page 658.)

structure in the teleosts but, unlike this cell mass, in Polyodon is visible from the surface only at about the level of decussation of the trochlear nerve.   As was stated in the preceding paragraph, it also forms the upper medial portion of the auricle in this fish.

The corpus cerebelli forms the main mass of the cerebellum between the auricles and is continued forward as a folded portion of cerebellar tissue which lies within the optic ventricle and is known as the valvula.   Molecular substance constitutes a large part of the central portion of the body, but granule cells are found occasionally.   At the lateral border are granule cells which, in Polyodon, come together to form a broad medial band of granular substance, at the transition of the corpus cerebelli into the valvula (*Hocke Hoogenboom*), with the molecular layer above and below it.   In the valvula the granular substance decreases in amount and the front end of the valvula consists of molecular substance only. Purkinje cells are present in Acipenser (*Johnston*, '01) and Polyodon (*Hocke Hoogenboom*), and probably in all ganoids, although for the most part they are in groups, which groups may show in certain regions a tendency to arrange in rows. However, scattered Purkinje cells occur in the molecular layer.

A most interesting nuclear mass extending along the lateral periphery of the medulla oblongata at the level of the cephalic trigeminal root has been described in Polyodon by *Hocke Hoogenboom*.   This observer considered this nuclear mass, which dorsally is continuous with the granule cells of the ventral leaf of the auricle (in the region of transition of these granule cells to the cells of the static area), as comparable to the ponto-bulbar body described for man by *Essick* ('12; see bibliography for mammals).

The connections described for ganoids correspond in most respects to those given for plagiostomes, consisting of root fibers and secondary connections of vestibular and lateral-line systems, spino-cerebellar fibers, an anterior tecto-(mesencephalo-) cerebellar tract, a posterior mesencephalo-cerebellar tract of *Johnston* ('01), and a lobo-cerebellar tract.   Detailed accounts of these connections are to be found in the contributions quoted, particularly in those of *Johnston* ('01) and *Hocke Hoogenboom* ('29).

The major subdivisions are not so easily recognizable in the fully developed cerebellum of most teleosts as in that of most plagiostomes or ganoids.   Therefore, it is essential for a better understanding of this region to be familiar with its development.   The following description is based on the data furnished by *Schaper* ('94; see also figs. 368 and 369A and B).

The teleostean cerebellum appears embryologically as two bilaterally symmetrical thickenings of the rhomboidal lip of the lateral ventricle, near the region of transition from the future rhombencephalon into the future midbrain.   Its lateral portion is the more primitive part, as is to be expected in view of its intimate relation with the area statica.   When the ependymal roof of the IVth ventricle is removed, bilateral enlargements project from the medulla oblongata into the ventricle and are connected with each other by a narrow bridge.   It is of interest that at the beginning of its development (fig. 368) the cerebellum has a bend in a frontal direction, similar to that found in the primitive cerebellum of cyclostomes, in the cerebellum of Rana (fig. 379) and, even more markedly, in that of certain lizards (fig. 381). The lateral parts, which include the anlagen for the auricles, increase rapidly during the later development and, in fact, play the leading part in forming the cerebellum proper, while the center portion lags behind for some time, although a slight growth forward into the midbrain ventricle indicates the beginning of a valvula cerebelli (figs. 368B and 369). Soon there is an increase caudally of the lateral and central parts of the cerebellum followed by a great growth toward the ventricle, in consequence of which the lateral eminences (L. w., fig. 368) fuse in the midline, leaving a narrow slit in front, behind and above this union, which is the remains of the ventriculus

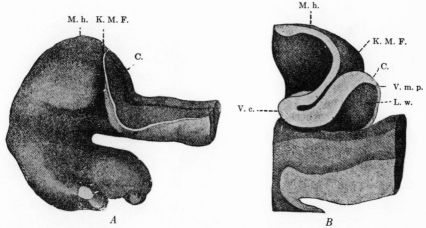

FIG. 368. A. The brain of a trout larva 46 days old. B. The brain of a trout larva 79 days old. *Schaper.* C., cerebellum; K.M.F., cerebello-midbrain fold; L.w., inner lateral eminence; M.h., midbrain roof; V.c., valvula cerebelli; V.m.p., velum medullare posticum.

cerebelli (cavum cerebelli, fig. 369B, C.e.). In addition to these lateral enlargements, two median enlargements occur during the development, a dorsal swelling, which is concerned in forming the median corpus cerebelli, and a frontoventral enlargement which grows forward into the optic ventricle to form the valvula cerebelli. Further increase of the cerebellum proper is due to the progressive augmentation of the lateral walls; however, the valvula cerebelli is due primarily, at least, to this excessive growth of the medial part of the cerebellar anlage.

The cerebellum thus formed is very compact in appearance. Auricles containing the lateral recesses of the fourth ventricle, such as form a conspicuous picture of the cerebellum in lower fishes, are said to be absent in some teleosts. Their position is said to be occupied in certain teleosts (for example, in Ameiurus and Silurus, *Herrick*, '24), by the eminentia granularis, which substitutes functionally for the auricles and in these forms produces a swelling on the surface of the cerebellum. It will be remembered that the medial part and upper leaf of the auricle was formed in Chondrostei (*Hocke Hoogenboom*, '29) by the eminentia granularis. In the teleosts the eminentia granularis has increased to so marked an extent that the lateral recess has become greatly reduced or even obliterated. A trace of the under leaf of the auricle of ganoids is said to be found in a small clump of granular cells which lie at the periphery of the region and which are continuous frontally with granular cells of the eminentia granularis. This clump of cells has been termed the auricle by *Holmgren* and *van der Horst* ('25). *Palmgren* ('21) found an auricle in Salmo salvelinus; *Pearson* ('33, Dissertation) described an auricle in the sunfish and trout. At the anterior end of the cerebellum is an auricular-shaped mass formed of the stratum moleculare of the cerebellum (*Ariëns Kappers*, '21). According to this observer, its identity with the auricle of selachians receives confirmation through its relations with the commissura interauricularis

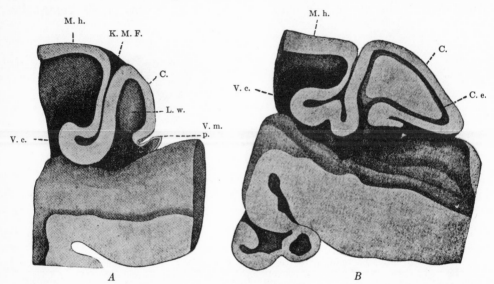

FIG. 369. *A.* The brain of a trout embryo 100 days old. *B.* The brain of a trout 6 months old. *Schaper.* *C.*, cerebellum; *C.e.*, the remains of the cerebellar ventricle; *K.M.F.*, cerebello-mid-brain fold; *L.w.*, the inner lateral eminence; *M.h.*, midbrain roof; *V.c.*, valvula cerebelli; *V.m.p.*, velum medullare posticum.

and the choroid plexus, the lateral part of which is attached to its caudal border and forms the covering for the recessus ependymalis. In the sense in which *Franz* ('11) used the term in teleosts, the eminentia granularis appears to include not only the auricle, but also the very short teleostean anterior lateral-line lobe (see also *Holmgren* and *van der Horst*, '25, page 123). The eminentia granularis extends forward to become continuous with the valvula cerebelli and is connected with its fellow of the opposite side through the pars postrema, a granular mass along the ventral and caudal border of the corpus cerebelli. Extending from the eminentia granularis over the surface of the lateral line (and vestibular) region of the medulla oblongata is the cerebellar crest. This cerebellar crest with its under-lying area and the eminentia granularis (including the true auricular anlagen and the pars postrema) constitute very important terminal regions and correlating centers for vestibular and lateral-line impulses.

It is evident that certain very important differences exist between the cere-bella of full-grown teleosts and of plagiostomes. The greater massiveness of the teleostean cerebellum is indicated in the almost complete disappearance of the ventricle in the adult cerebellum, in the entire or almost entire lack of sulci on the corpus cerebelli, in the increase in size of the auricles associated with an almost total loss of their diverticular appearance, and in the development of the anterior medial part to form the valvula cerebelli. This valvula is present in nearly all teleosts and may be enormously hypertrophied (Megalops, fig. 370;

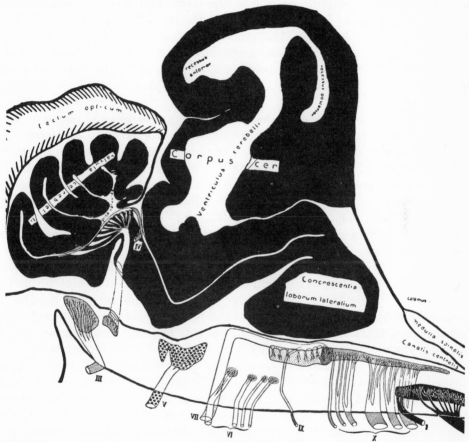

FIG. 370. A sagittal section near the midline through the cerebellum (black) of a bony fish (Megalops cyprinoides). *van der Horst*. Note the marked development and folding of the valvula cerebelli.

Siluroids; Mormyrus). The ganoid cerebellum possesses a valvula cerebelli, which, on the whole, is less massive than that of teleosts, and presents a larger auricle containing a well-developed lateral recess.

According to *Franz* ('11), the causes of these specific characteristics of the cerebellum are traceable to a very great extent to the spatial relations within the skull. *Franz* studied both embryonic and adult forms and pointed out that the embryo, unlike the full-grown animal, has a brain which entirely fills the skull and is affected by its pressure.[8] His conclusions are very plausible and harmonize

---

[8] The considerable increase in space within the skull probably is due to the appearance of muscles, which function only after larval life. At their insertion these muscles exert a traction

directly with personal observations and conclusions (*Ariëns Kappers* and *Carpenter*, '11; see also Chapter IX) regarding the factors influencing the development of the teleostean forebrain. The general massiveness of the brain is an indication of this attempt at economizing space. Evidences of the effort to economize space are numerous in the teleostean cerebellum. In the first place, there is an absence in teleosts, except occasionally in the valvula, of the ependymal layer characteristic of the midline portion of the cerebellum in many sharks. The molecular and granular layers are present in the region in teleosts but the Purkinje cells may be lacking. Also, through the development of the valvula cerebelli within the optic ventricle, a considerable saving of space is effected. Other factors which influence the position of the valvula will be discussed under the description of the fiber tracts (tractus mesencephalo-cerebellaris posterior, page 737).

The degree of development of the valvula differs with different teleosts. The largest valvula is found in Mormyridae, in which it exceeds to a considerable extent, the size of the corpus cerebelli. In these forms it arches forward under the greatly reduced roof of the midbrain to a position far beyond the forebrain, while its lateral parts, greatly folded, extend in a caudal direction along the corpus cerebelli. Unlike all the other cerebellar convolutions, those occurring in the valvulae are longitudinal (fig. 195, Chapter IV). Its cortex is less massive, the granular layer being much less developed than elsewhere in the cerebellum, while the molecular layer is the predominant layer.

Next to the Mormyridae, the siluroids show the most specialized development of the valvula. The corpus cerebelli is also highly developed in siluroids and is peculiar in that it is directed forward over the optic tectum instead of bent backward in the usual manner. The cause of this forward bend is as yet unexplained. Perhaps an explanation of this forward bend is to be found in the embryological history of the cerebellum, as given by *Schaper* ('94), since at an early stage in its development this structure is directed somewhat frontalward. The frontally directed cerebellum of an adult Thynnus or Megalops would represent an exaggeration of this early condition. In Thynnus and Megalops (fig. 370), *van der Horst* has described a high degree of development and a rich folding of the valvula, which is not there limited to a medial lobe. In cyprinoids and Gadidae the valvula is smaller, although still well developed, while it is least well developed in Lophius piscatorius and Lophius bridegassa.

The development of the valvula influences greatly the position of all fiber tracts in the region of the velum. The fibers of the trochlear nerve are particularly affected (see Chapter V), since the bundle may be pushed forward as in Mormyrus and Silurus (*Berkelbach van der Sprenkel*, '15) or may be separated into several divisions as indicated by the work of *Huet* ('11) and *Franz* ('11), and especially by that of *van der Horst* ('19).

The histogenesis of the cerebellum begins near the ventricular surface. From

on the skull which results in an enlargement of the bones and of the intracranial space. As is well known, this space is sufficiently large to surpass, in many full-grown teleosts, the volume of the brain (*Ariëns Kappers*, '21).

a region of proliferation near the ventricle of the embryonic neural tube, indifferent cells wander out toward the mantle zone and give rise to both neuroglia cells and nerve cells. Later, when the primitive sources of food supply are increased by the appearance of intracerebellar capillaries, a second zone of proliferation makes its appearance, the transitory superficial granular layer (*Schaper*, '94). This layer consists not only of granule cells, but of indifferent cells as well, which are able to produce both nerve cells and neuroglia cells. Since this zone is a derivative of the primitive epithelial layer of the medullary tube, it is found only in those regions in which the roof membrane borders on the massive cerebellar anlage; *i.e.* at the line of attachment of the epithelial membrane, which later constitutes the choroid plexus (*Schaper*). These places of attachment are in the median line, at the posterior end of the cerebellum, where the midline epithelial portion is preserved for some time, and along the lateral recesses. From these regions the superficial granular layer extends out in all directions over the cerebellum and gradually disappears in such a manner that the cell bodies of the nervous elements become associated with the granular layer, leaving only their dichotomously branching neuraxes as parallel fibers in the molecular layer, while the neuroglia elements remain, in part, within the molecular layer. This shifting of the cell bodies of the neurons into relation with the granular layer is undoubtedly due to the neurobiotactic influence of the mossy fibers upon these neurons.

In the adult teleostean cerebellum the usual layers are found, in the same arrangement as described in selachians. The present knowledge of the finer structure of the cerebellum of adult teleosts is the result in particular of the researches of *Fusari* ('87), *Schaper* ('93), *Ramón y Cajal* ('94 and '11), and *Franz* ('11).

In contrast to the arrangement in most vertebrates, in many parts of the teleostean cerebellum the Purkinje cells are arranged in several layers and, according to the personal observations of *Ariëns Kappers* ('06, '21), are placed less regularly between the molecular and granular layers than in plagiostomes. Not infrequently these neurons extend somewhat deeper into the granular layer and show some tendency toward group arrangement, although such groups are not sharply circumscribed (Gadus, Lophius). The enormously rich dendritic branches which are oriented in a sagittal plane usually appear early (fig. 371). Situated somewhat more deeply than the Purkinje cells, among the upper cells of the granular layer, are large, pear-shaped or irregular cells. Such cells have a dendritic net which, although extending into the molecular layer, is less in extent than that of the Purkinje cell and does not branch in so regular a manner. The structure of the dendrites varies also. The neuraxes of these cells (fig. 372A), which belong to the Golgi type, soon disappear among the granular cells and have not been followed to their termination. These neurons are suggestive of the large Golgi cells described for mammals at the beginning of this chapter (p. 700). The most numerous constituents of the granular layer are small granule cells, distinguished in teleosts by the short, claw-like appearance of their dendrites. The neuraxes of these cells enter the molecular layer, divide dichotomously, and form transversely running, parallel fibers which constitute the chief substance of the molecular layer.   Another type of nerve cell is present in the molecular layer, characterized by having exceedingly long dendrites which extend forward and backward for so great a distance that the spread of their dendrites frequently reaches two-thirds of the length of the cerebellum.   These dendrites are much less numerous than those of the Purkinje cells (fig. 371), but extend in the same plane (fig. 372C).   The neuraxes of these cells of the molecular layer run in a sagittal direction and give collaterals to the Purkinje cell layer. Their relations suggest that they may be the forerunners of the basket cells of mammals.   The appearance of these cells is a step in advance of the conditions

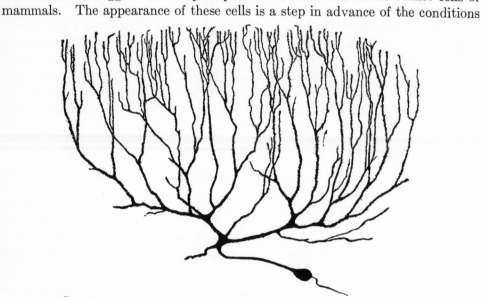

FIG. 371.   Purkinje cell from the cerebellum of a 10.5 cm. perch.   *Schaper.*

in plagiostomes, where as yet no such primitive basket cells have been found with certainty.   However, in teleosts it has not been possible to demonstrate true baskets at the end of the collaterals of these neuraxes.   The majority of the cells of the molecular layer are similar to the stellate cells of higher forms, and their connections have not been ascertained in a satisfactory way.

The afferent fibers constitute much the larger number of the cerebellar fiber paths, and they terminate in both the molecular and granular layers.   Two types of endings are said to be distinguishable in the molecular layer : one type terminates in freely-branching terminal endbrushes in the middle and upper parts of the molecular layer ; the other type forms climbing fibers around the body and main dendritic branches of the Purkinje cells.   According to *Ramón y Cajal* ('11), the termination around the cell body corresponds to that of a stage in the embryonic development of higher forms while, according to *Bielschowsky*, it corresponds to an adult condition in higher animals.   These facts indicate that in teleosts the molecular layer is the chief receptive layer of the cerebellum.   However, some cerebello-petal fibers terminate in the granular layer, constituting the teleostean mossy fibers (*Catois*, '01).

In certain regions the cells of the granular layer are grouped in such a way as to suggest a type of cerebellar nuclei. Such a group is to be found in the posterior part of the body of the cerebellum in relation to the branching fibers of tractus mesencephalo-cerebellaris. Such cell groups are probably in no sense homologous with the cerebellar nuclei of higher forms. The primitive homologue

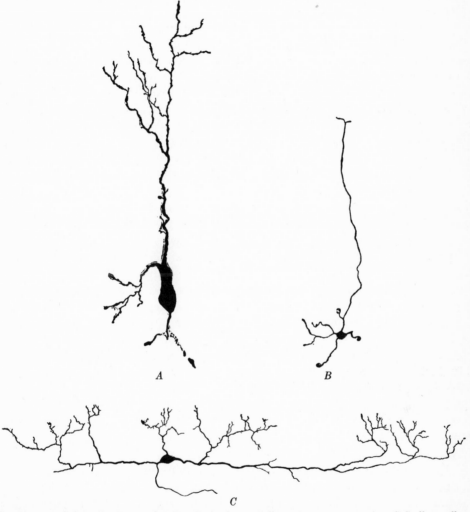

A   B

C

FIG. 372. *A*, Golgi cell; *B*, granule cell. From the cerebellum of a 10.5 cm. perch. *C*, Stellate cells or primitive basket cells of the molecular layer of the cerebellum of a 3-months-old salmon. *Schaper*.

of the mammalian cerebellar nuclei is to be sought in cells situated at the border between medulla oblongata and the cerebellum, and giving rise to outgoing tracts. According to *Franz* ('11), the pear-shaped cells which lie at the angle between the cerebellum and the medulla oblongata are probably the forerunners of such nuclei. This group may correspond with the nucleus subcerebellosus of *Ramón y Cajal's* account ('94), a nuclear group referred to by him in 1911 as comparable, possibly, to the nucleus lateralis cerebelli of *Edinger*.   If these neurons, as *Catois* ('01) believed, are cells of origin of the efferent cerebellar fibers through the brachium conjunctivum, it appears very probable that they may represent the forerunner of efferent cerebellar nuclei (according to certain observers, for example, the roof nuclei, *Ariëns Kappers*, '21), and that they are homologous to the nucleus eminentia ventralis cerebelli described as the nucleus lateralis cerebelli in plagiostomes.

On the whole, the tracts associated with the cerebellum are similar to those already described for plagiostomes.   Certain connections are present in teleosts which thus far have not been identified in plagiostomes.   The connections in teleosts may be summarized briefly as follows : Ascending root fibers of both the posterior and anterior lateral-line nerves (fig. 373) reach the posterior lateral part of the cerebellum.   Such root fibers were present in cyclostomes and selachians ; phylogenetically considered, they are among the oldest tracts associated with the cerebellum.   Fibers of anterior and posterior (*Hocke Hoogenboom*, '29, Polyodon) and posterior (*Johnston*, '01, and *Ariëns Kappers*, '20, for Amia) lateral-line nerves occur in ganoids.   In teleosts the root fibers pass forward to the posterior lateral part of the cerebellum.   Besides distributing to the eminentia granularis, certain of these fibers decussate in the midline (*Tello*, '09) in the posterior ventral part of the corpus cerebelli (the pars postrema), apparently to reach the molecular layer.   In Gadus some fibers of the anterior lateral-line nerve continue forward through the eminentia granularis and then turn medially into the more cephalic part of the body of the cerebellum.   Here they soon cross the midline, some passing through the valvula and some through the more cephalic part of the corpus cerebelli to end in these regions (*Addison*, '23 ; *Burr*, '28, and others).   Secondary fibers pass from the lateral-line areas to the cerebellum.   Vestibular root fibers and secondary vestibulo-cerebellar or octavo-cerebellar fibers can be traced as far as the eminentia granularis (*Burr*, '28). The direct connection of the vestibular nerve with the cerebellum is not so evident as is that of the lateral-line nerves in teleosts, a further evidence of the significance of these latter nerves in the phylogenetic development of the cerebellum.   Vestibular root fibers pass to the cerebellum of Amia (*Ariëns Kappers*, '07).   The possible distribution of root fibers of the trigeminal nerve to the cerebellum in ganoids and teleosts needs further study.

An interauricular commissure is present in bony fishes as well as in sharks. It originates from the eminentia granularis and runs along the periphery of the medulla oblongata to the contralateral eminentia granularis, forming an arch in its course with the opening directed caudalward.   The commissure was identified first in Cyprinoides by *Wallenberg* ('07).   In Gadus, the commissura interauricularis, or commissura eminentiae granularis as it was termed by *van der Horst* ('19), is but slightly developed.   In Arius (a siluroid), the commissure is so highly developed (fig. 374) that it is one of the most prominent of the cerebellar tracts.   This is in conformity with the fact that there is a relatively marked development of the static functions of the cerebellum in these animals, where its great development is associated beyond doubt with the importance of the lateral

line apparatus.[9] The origin and termination of this commissure are illustrated
in figure 373, its decussation in figure 375, at about the level of crossing of
brachium conjunctivum.

Spino-cerebellar systems have been seen by *Herrick* ('07), *Wallenberg* ('07),
Franz ('11), *Ariëns Kappers* ('21), *Addison* ('23), *van der Horst* ('25a), and others.
Two spino-cerebellar systems have been pointed out for teleosts; these are the
tractus spino-cerebellaris dorsalis and the tractus spino-cerebellaris ventralis
(*Ariëns Kappers*, '21).   The tractus spino-cerebellaris ventralis (which from its

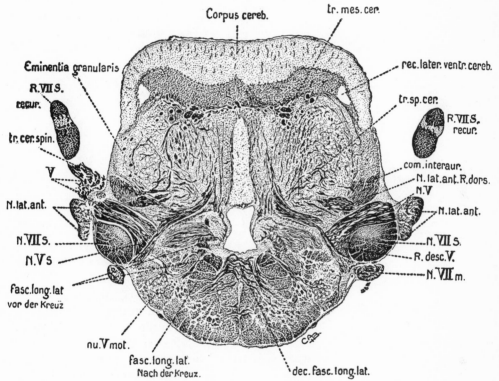

FIG. 373.   A cross section through the cerebellum and medulla oblongata of a siluroid (Arius) at the
level of the nervus lateralis anterior (*N.lat.ant.*).   For explanation, see the text.

position might be termed the tractus spino-cerebellaris lateralis) occupies a ventrolateral position within the cord.   In the medulla oblongata it retains a peripheral
position.   It runs upward between the roots of the trigeminal and facial nerves,
accompanied by olivo-cerebellar fibers, and ends in the corpus cerebelli of the
same and opposite side (*Ariëns Kappers*, '21).   The contralateral fibers cross
dorsal to the decussatio veli and the commissure of the "Rindenknoten."   The
decussation of the spino-cerebellar fibers in plagiostomes does not occur at any
set level but is scattered over the entire cerebellum.   In teleosts it is concentrated

---

[9] *Wallenberg* ('05, see bibliography for mammals) has shown its presence in rabbits as a commissura interfloccularis, a fact which indicates that it is related to the vestibular as well as to the
lateral-line apparatus.

in the more frontal region, in relation to the decussatio veli and the commissure of the "Rindenknoten." This spino-cerebellar tract of fishes is probably in a very general way the primitive homologue of the mammalian ventral spino-cerebellar tract, but the division here is arbitrary.

Whereas the ventral spino-cerebellar tract shows relatively uniform development among teleosts, the dorsal spino-cerebellar, described by *C. J. Herrick* ('07), is especially well developed in those animals in which the sensory fibers of the cervical nerves are especially numerous, as in Triglidae (see Chapter II, page

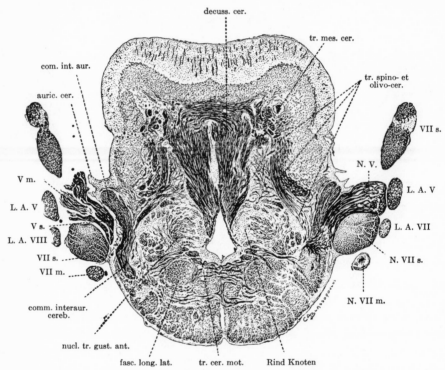

FIG. 374. A cross section through the cerebellum and the medulla oblongata of a siluroid (Arius), somewhat in front of the level of figure 356. See text for explanation.

177) and in Lophius. In the European Trigla hirundo the dorsal spino-cerebellar tract, a well-medullated bundle, can be traced forward from the dorsal enlargement in the cervical region. In its rostral course it has a fairly dorsal position close to the descending root of the trigeminal nerve but easily distinguishable from it. Having reached the cerebellar peduncle it ends chiefly in the homolateral corpus cerebelli above the "Rindenknoten." It is accompanied through the latter part of its course by secondary fibers from the anterior sensory nucleus of the trigeminus. Root fibers of the trigeminal nerve to the cerebellum have not been demonstrated with certainty in teleosts (see fig. 374).

The olivo-cerebellar tract is an entirely crossed system of fibers, the decussation taking place in the medulla oblongata. This cerebellar component is much smaller in teleosts than in plagiostomes, because of the less development of its nucleus of origin, the inferior olive, in the former animals. Sometimes the olivo-cerebellar tract is so small as to be recognized only with difficulty, but in most teleosts, Belone and Lophius for example, it is relatively easily demonstrated (*Kooy*, '17). This tract follows the course typical for it in most vertebrates. From their cells of origin the neuraxes forming the bundle cross mainly ventral to the olive and to some extent behind it, pass to the region of the ventral spino-cerebellar tract, but then swing dorsalward, slightly ahead of this latter tract, join the dorsal spino-cerebellar tract, and, in company with it, enter the cerebellum (fig. 374).

The tracts to the cerebellum from more cephalic regions of the brain are developed to a much greater degree in most teleosts than in plagiostomes. They enter the cerebellum in part through the valvula cerebelli. Among these may be mentioned the tractus mesencephalo-cerebellares, which originate in part from the midbrain, from the nucleus lateralis valvulae situated in the tegmental region, and in part from the torus longitudinalis in front of the posterior commissure, and particularly from the anterior margin of the tectum opticum. In Gadus, and in such teleosts in general as have highly-developed optic tracts, the more cephalic tract of the two — tractus mesencephalo-cerebellaris anterior (*Ariëns Kappers*, '21; *Addison*, '23; *Herrick*, '24, and others; tractus tecto-cerebellaris of *Goldstein*, '05, also *Ariëns Kappers*) — is the more highly developed; in such teleosts as Arius and Mormyrus the tractus mesencephalo-cerebellaris posterior, from the nucleus lateralis valvulae, is the larger. From the anterior margin of the optic tectum and probably in part from the pretectal nucleus, the tractus tecto-cerebellaris or mesencephalo-cerebellaris anterior (see fig 375) runs caudalward below the optic ventricle. Apparently this is the tractus pretecto-cerebellaris of *Burr* ('28), described as arising from the pretectal nucleus of Orthagoriscus. For a part of its course it is bordered on its medial side by the acoustico-lateral lemniscus (lateral longitudinal fasciculus) and joins the tractus mesencephalo-cerebellaris posterior from the tegmentum of the midbrain (nucleus lateralis valvulae). These two tracts in ganoids and in teleosts, such as Gadus, pass to the cerebellum by way of the valvula. Part of their fibers terminate in the valvula; others enter the corpus cerebelli, cross in the most caudal part of the cerebellum through the molecular layer, and terminate near the midline. The importance of the tractus mesencephalo-cerebellaris anterior as a system relaying impulses from the mesencephalic optic centers to the cerebellum is indicated by the facts that the tract is larger in Gadus than in Arius and that Gadus has the larger eyes (*Addison*, '23). In Arius, the tract from the nucleus lateralis valvulae (the tractus mesencephalo-cerebellaris posterior, *Ariëns Kappers*, '21; *Addison*, '23; *Herrick*, '24, and others, and, in Orthagoriscus, the tractus tegmento-cerebellaris of *Burr*, '28; see also figure 375), which is developed particularly well in this animal, does not join the bundle from the tectum opticum. This latter tract, which is quite minute, enters the corpus cerebelli relatively farther caudalward. The tract from the nucleus lateralis has been regarded sometimes as carrying gustatory impulses. There is more reason to suppose that this tract carries impulses to the cerebellum from the lateral line and vestibular than from gustatory centers (*Berkelbach van der Sprenkel*, '15).   Thus in Mormyridae, this tract is of tremendous size (*Stendell*, '14),[10] and the valvula cerebelli is likewise enormously increased.   In these same animals there is a remarkable increase of the primary lateral-line fibers, the secondary connections of which (through the acoustico-lateral lemniscus) end at the place of origin of the tractus mesencephalo-cerebellaris posterior.   It seems relatively certain that there is a direct relation between

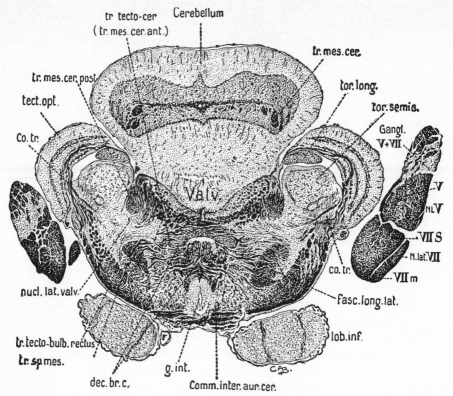

Fig. 375.   A cross section through the cerebellum and isthmus of a siluroid (Arius), rostral to figure 374.   Explanation in text.

the size of the lateral-line system and the development of this cerebellar tract, and that this latter carries static impulses to the cerebellum.   The facts just given for Mormyrus can be substantiated further in other fishes.   Thus in Arius the tract is larger and the lateral-line system more highly developed than in Gadus (cf., *Addison*, '23).   It has been pointed out already that the development of the valvula is to be attributed very largely to its relations with the lateral-line system on the one hand and to the cerebellum proper on the other hand.   The valvula is a subtectal structure which permits also the interrelation of impulses from the midbrain correlation centers for the vestibulo-lateral-line system and from the optic tectum with those from cerebellar centers.

[10] In Acipenser (*Johnston*, '01) this bundle follows a much shorter course, since the lower margin of the tectum abuts against the valvula and the fibers pass more directly to the cerebellum.

Tractus lobo-cerebellaris (*Ariëns Kappers*, '06 and '21; *Addison*, '23; *Herrick*, '24; *Burr*, '28; *Pearson*, '33, Dissertation) is more difficult to explain from the functional standpoint. It constitutes a fairly compact, medullated bundle which proceeds as an uncrossed fiber fasciculus from the posterior part of the inferior lobe through the basis mesencephali into the body of the cerebellum.[11] Its cerebello-petal character has been demonstrated by *Wallenberg* ('07) in degeneration preparations. Exactly the type of stimuli carried by this tract is at present unknown. That these stimuli differ from those conducted over the tractus mesencephalo-cerebellaris posterior is indicated by the fact that the size of the tractus lobo-cerebellaris does not reflect changes in the lateral-line system. The lobi inferiores increase in size not only through the enlargement of the olfactory apparatus, but also, apparently, through their relation to the optic tectum. They also possess a sense organ in the saccus vasculosus (*Boeke*, '01; *Dammerman*, '10; see Chapter VIII) which very probably serves for the perception of fluid pressure and, since such pressure increases with the increase in the distance from the surface of the water, with the perception of depth. It may be that these stimuli determine the kind of impulse carried to the cerebellum over the lobo-cerebellar tract. It is present even in cyclostomes.

Efferent tracts from the cerebellum are grouped as the tractus cerebello-tectalis (see p. 911), the tractus cerebello-motorius or cerebello-tegmentalis and the brachium conjunctivum anterius. In teleosts two subdivisions of the cerebello-motorius system may be distinguished — an anterior or mesencephalic portion and a posterior or bulbar portion. The exact place of origin of these tracts is unknown. Apparently special nuclei of origin have not been identified for them and it seems probable that they represent neuraxes of Purkinje cells.

The brachium conjunctivum anterius is to be regarded as a special derivative of the cerebello-motorius system. Its exact origin is not known. This tract, which leaves the cerebellum in front of the tractus cerebello-motorius (fig. 374), appears to take origin from the entire corpus cerebelli (perhaps from its Purkinje-like cells). It is very large in Arius, a fact which suggests that there may be some relation between the development of this frontal cerebello-fugal bundle and that of lateral line-vestibular components passing directly or indirectly to the cerebellum. Its fibers constitute a thick bundle which runs downward quite near the ventricle and medial to the nucleus of the secondary ascending gustatory tract. The decussation (fig. 375) occurs below the fasciculus longitudinalis medialis and in such fashion that the more posterior fibers cross more dorsally (above the commissura interauricularis) than do the more anterior ones, which latter extend almost to the commissura ansulata (*Mayser*, '81; *Goldstein*, '05), as is also the case in plagiostomes (see fig. 429 of the midbrain). The brachium conjunctivum anterius terminates in the tegmental regions of the midbrain, partly, perhaps, in the oculomotor nucleus, partly farther cephalad. According to *Brickner* ('29), this termination is chiefly under the posterior commissure but to some extent in the ventral thalamus.

[11] It is still an open question as to whether the crossed lobo-cerebellar of the hypothalamo-cerebellar tract of amphibians is directly comparable with the tract here under consideration.

The decussatio veli, the commissure of the anterior secondary gustatory nuclei, and the crossing fibers of the trochlear nerve are yet to be mentioned. These connections do not belong to the cerebellum. The decussatio veli appears to provide for the interconnection of the lateral parts of the midbrain. The commissure of the anterior secondary gustatory nuclei interconnects these gustatory centers. It is situated directly beneath the decussatio veli. The position of the trochlear decussation varies with the development of the valvula.

Tuge ('34) found that extirpation of the corpus cerebelli in Carassius affected regulatory power in this fish and tonus of body muscle. His results favored *Ingvar's* theories of cerebellar function (pp. 828 to 830). The cerebellum of Dipnoi has been studied by *Bing* and *Burckhardt* ('04) and by *Holmgren* and *van der Horst* ('25). In studying Ceratodus these latter observers found a relatively large cerebellum compared with that of the ganoid Protopterus, with which *van der Horst* ('25) has especial familiarity. It has a well-marked, although small and everted, auricle and a lateral recess, and the auricle is delimited rather sharply externally from the corpus cerebelli on the one hand and the anterior lateral-line lobe on the other hand. Only a slight sulcus in the midline, at the rostral end of the cerebellum, indicates the bilateral origin of the cerebellum, but two much deeper, longitudinally running ventricular sulci were found (*Holmgren* and *van der Horst*), which sulci include between them a mass of cerebellar tissue (composed of both molecular and granular layers) projecting far out into the ventricular space. A second projection occurs on the lateral side of each longitudinal sulcus. This projection contains a nuclear mass which is continuous farther caudalward with the cerebellar granular mass and was regarded by *Holmgren* and *van der Horst* as a nucleus lateralis cerebelli.

The Purkinje cells are arranged somewhat as in teleosts and are often found in the molecular and granular layers, as well as at the line between these two layers. They appear not to be present at all levels and many irregular types have been found among them.

The fiber connections of the cerebellum of Ceratodus, as elucidated by the work of *Holmgren* and *van der Horst* ('25), consist of root and secondary fibers of the lateral-line system, which may distribute to the small auricle but reach particularly the cerebellum in front of the auricle. Further fiber connections are through the spino-cerebellar tract, the trigemino-cerebellar tract entering the corpus cerebelli, the tecto-bulbar tract, and a brachium conjunctivum which could not be traced across the midline or to the red nucleus, but which distributes in part to the homolateral tegmentum of the midbrain.

THE CEREBELLUM OF AMPHIBIANS

The cerebellum of an amphibian resembles more nearly that of a cyclostome than that of a teleost. In certain respects it is comparable to that of selachians, at least in so far as the auricle is concerned. In the following account the cerebellum of the tailed Amphibia will be discussed first and its structure and connections compared with those noted in the tailless Amphibia. An account of the development of the cerebellum of Amblystoma has recently been published by *Larsell* ('34, see bibliography, p. 854).

Herrick ('14) and others have pointed out that the cerebellum of the lower amphibians shows a marked resemblance to the very early stages in the development of the mammalian cerebellum. In such lower amphibians the lateral recess is extremely large and the cerebellar tissue is represented only in its walls and in a dorsal commissural band uniting the two areas. In fact, the cerebellum is so greatly reduced in certain of these forms that its presence has been denied or only the commissural band recognized by various observers. However,

variations occur in the size of the lateral recess in the tailed Amphibia, as *Röthig* ('27) has pointed out. Thus in Siren lacertina this observer found a lateral recess so large that it extends far forward and has not only a membranous roof with a much folded choroid plexus but a membranous tip as well, while in Cryptobranchus japonicus the recess is more shallow, does not extend so far forward, and does not possess a membranous tip. Where the lateral recess is greatly developed, a part of its wall overhangs the lateral side of the midbrain, forming a blind pouch or an anterior diverticulum (Necturus, *Kingsbury*, '95; *Herrick*, '14). This

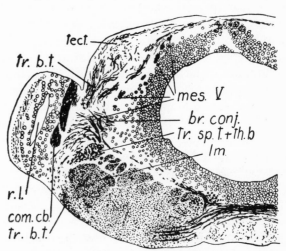

Fig. 376.   Cross section through the lateral recess, tectum and isthmus of Necturus.   *Herrick*.   *br.conj.*, brachium conjunctivum; *com.cb.*, commissura cerebelli (medullated component); *lm.*, lemniscus (tr. bulbo-tectalis, somatic sensory); *mes.V.*, radix mesencephalica trigemini; *r.l.* recessus lateralis rhombencephali; *tect.*, tectum mesencephali; *tr.b.t.*, tractus bulbo-tectalis (visceral sensory s.); *tr.sp. +th.b.*, tractus spino-tectalis plus tractus thalamo-bulbaris.

pouch is the homologue of the auricle which is so prominent a structure in plagiostomes and in certain ganoids. The wall of this diverticulum in amphibians consists of gray matter. *Herrick* has shown in Necturus that the medial wall of the diverticulum fuses with the gray matter of the midbrain in the region where the two areas lie beside each other, and that in this form, while the roof of the rest of the recess is plexiform, that of the anterior diverticulum is massive. Both *Kingsbury* and *Herrick* have emphasized the wide spread, forward and lateralward, beyond the limits of the underlying cerebellar tissue, of these evaginated choroid plexuses which form the roof of the recess. The posterior part of this diverticulum, which extends to the facial nerve, is comparable to the posterior part of the selachian auricle and has also a highly developed ependymal roof (see figs. 376 to 378).

The auricular lobe is essentially a direct continuation of the area acoustico-lateralis of the medulla oblongata, this area extending forward almost to the tip of the lobe.   The anterior lobe of the acoustico-lateral area forms the major part of the posterolateral wall of the lateral recess in Necturus and the entire massive lateral wall in Amphiuma.   Its anteromedial wall is formed by the corpus cerebelli.

In front of the eminentia trigemini, on the floor of the medulla oblongata, is a second elevation, the eminentia cerebellaris ventralis of *Herrick* (em. cb. v., fig. 378), which passes forward into the corpus cerebelli.   In Necturus and Amphiuma (*Herrick*, '14) and in Siren lacertina (*Röthig*, '27) the corpus cerebelli is really a bilateral structure represented on either side by a mass of gray forming an eminence, with the two eminences connected by a band of fibers beneath which, at least in Necturus, are a few scattered cells.   This commissure is comparable to the decussatio veli of other forms and has decussating trochlear and mesencephalic V fibers in it.   Indications of an approach to an unpaired cerebellum are to be found in the neurons scattered among the commissural fibers. In his study of the phylogeny of the cerebellum, *Palmgren* ('21) has emphasized the fact that in amphibians the cerebellum consists of a medial corpus cerebelli and two auricular portions, the latter connected by a cell band.   *Larsell* ('31) substantiated such an interconnection of the auricular portions in Triturus torosus, regarding the interconnecting cell band as the line along which a caudal vestibulo-lateral cerebellar lobe develops.

In Cryptobranchus alleghaniensis (*Herrick*, '24) and in Cryptobranchus japonicus (*Röthig*, '27) a somewhat more massive type of corpus cerebelli is found, with a narrow cell band as well as commissural fibers connecting the eminences of the two sides.   In higher urodeles, such as Amblystoma, this dorsal band becomes massive (*Herrick*).   A dense neuropil overlies the entire superficial surface of the cerebellum, constituting the stratum moleculare, and also is found along the medial border of the anterior diverticulum of the lateral recess as far down as its level of fusion with the midbrain (*Herrick*, '14).

Neurons in the cerebellum of Necturus consist of a reduced type of Purkinje cell.   The small granule cells present in cyclostomes have not been identified in Necturus.   The dendrites of the large cells of the eminentia ventralis cerebelli are in synaptic relation with the spino-cerebellar pathways (fig. 378, tr. sp. cer. d., tr. sp. cer. v.) and with ascending fibers from the area acustico-lateralis. Certain of the neurons are in relation with secondary fibers from the sensory trigeminal nucleus.   The neuraxes of these neurons form the tractus cerebello-tegmentalis and a kind of brachium conjunctivum.   The cells within the diverticulum anterius are relatively better developed.   Their dendrites run forward and downward to enter into synaptic relations with the spino-cerebellar, hypothalamo-cerebellar, and tecto-cerebellar fibers.   Their neuraxes enter the tractus cerebello-motorius and the brachium conjunctivum (br. conj., fig. 376).

The cerebellum of urodeles, like the cerebellum of cyclostomes, shows striking resemblance in fiber connections to the area acustico-lateralis.   However, in the lower tailed amphibians, such as Necturus, root fibers of the lateral line and vestibular nerves do not appear to have been traced to the cerebellum (*Herrick*, '14), although what appear to be secondary vestibulo-cerebellar fibers, accompanied by fibers from several sources, have been described (*Herrick*, '30). In Salamandrina (*Ariëns Kappers*, '21) medullated root fibers of the lateral line and vestibular nerves have not been traced into the cerebellum; the presence of nonmedullated fibers of this type is not excluded. In the land stage of Triturus torosus, *Larsell* ('31) was not able to trace myelinated lateral line fibers to the auricles. In certain higher urodeles (as Amblystoma, *Herrick*, '14a), direct root fibers of the lateral line and vestibular nerves reach the most frontal portions of the auricle, and vestibular root fibers can be traced dorsalward from this region into the lower part of the corpus cerebelli.

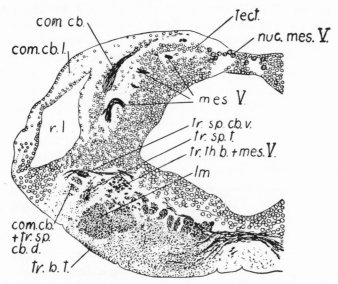

Fig. 377. Cross section through the cerebellum and midbrain of Necturus. *Herrick*.

com.cb., commissura cerebelli (medullated component); *com.cb.* + *tr.sp.cb.d.*, commissura cerebelli plus tractus spino-cerebellaris dorsalis; *com.cb.l.*, commissura cerebelli (lateral unmedullated component); *lm.*, lemniscus (tr. bulbo-tectalis, somatic sensory); *mes.V.*, radix mesencephalica trigemini; *nuc.mes.V.*, nucleus mesencephalicus trigemini; *tect.*, tectum mesencephali; *tr.b.t.*, tractus bulbo-tectalis (visceral sensory); *tr.sp.cb.v.*, tractus spino-cerebellaris ventralis; *tr.sp.t.* tractus spino-tectalis; *tr.th.b.* + *mes.V.*, tractus thalamo-bulbaris plus radix mesencephalica trigemini.

The urodele cerebellum receives certain other specific paths. Characteristic connections of the urodele cerebellum, as contrasted with the urodele acoustico-lateral area, are found in the spino-cerebellar and bulbo-cerebellar (or olivo-cerebellar) tracts which are related to the corpus cerebelli. The tractus spino-cerebellaris ventralis, together with the spino-tectal tract, ascends in the large lateral fasciculus of the spinal cord and medulla oblongata. At the upper levels of the medulla oblongata it lies lateral to the bulbar lemniscus, while at the level of emergence of the root fibers of the trigeminal it is between this lemniscus and the motor fibers of the trigeminal nerve. In front of the recessus lateralis, where the corpus cerebelli is continuous with the eminentia ventralis cerebelli, the mixed bundle divides into its two components, the tectal and the cerebellar bundles.   The latter, which is the tractus spino-cerebellaris ventralis, presumably the forerunner of the tract of Gowers, terminates in part in the cerebellum of the same side and crosses in part to the opposite side in the cerebellar commissure.

Herrick ('14; figs. 377, 378) described a small dorsal spino-cerebellar tract which in renewed study of his material (*Herrick*, '30) he was not able to verify. The existence of such a tract in certain tailed amphibians, therefore, is open to question at the present time, in spite of casual references to it in the literature. *Larsell* ('20) described a dorsal spino-cerebellar tract in Amblystoma, but renewed investigation led to the conclusion that this tract was in reality a part of the ascending trigeminal bundle, similar to that described by him in Triturus (*Larsell*, '31).   The spino-cerebellar systems are strengthened by fibers arising as the bifurcation of the sensory roots of the trigeminal nerve.   Such fibers pass to the auricles in certain tailed Amphibia but do not enter the corpus cerebelli (*Herrick*, '14; *Ariëns Kappers*, '21).   Secondary fibers arising from the anterior sensory nucleus of the trigeminal appear to enter the cerebellum proper.   Such secondary trigeminal connections are said to be small in Amblystoma (*Larsell*, '20).

The frontal cerebello-petal tracts are not so highly developed in amphibians as in fishes in general and in teleosts in particular, where they form the chief components of the cerebellar fiber system.   The lesser development of these tracts is associated with the smaller size of the corpus cerebelli in amphibians as compared with that of fishes.   The supposed connection between the hypothalamus and cerebellum, usually termed either a lobo-cerebellar or a mammillo-cerebellar tract, was thought, on later investigation, to constitute a connection between hypothalamic and gustatory centers.   It passes through the edge of the cerebellum in certain tailed Amphibia but has no functional cerebellar connection (*Herrick*, '14, '17; *Larsell*, '20).   Recently, however, *Larsell* ('31) believed that he could demonstrate a mammillo-cerebellar connection in Triturus torosus. Consequently the presence or absence of this fiber tract needs confirmation in the various tailed amphibians.   The tractus mesencephalo-cerebellaris posterior of teleosts has not as yet been identified in amphibians.   This is not surprising since the lateral-line nerves, with the central connections of which this branch is concerned, are much less developed in tailed Amphibia than in fishes, and are absent in adult tailless forms.   A tractus tecto-cerebellaris has been described by *Herrick* ('14) for Necturus and by *Röthig* ('27) for various amphibians, as for example Cryptobranchus japonicus.   *Larsell* ('20) believed it to be present in Amblystoma, but was unable to establish it beyond question.

The efferent systems of the cerebellum are similar in amphibians to those previously described for fishes.   The cerebello-motorius fibers descend from the octavo-lateralis region of the cerebellum, where they run medialward along the border of the periventricular granular layer and enter the medulla, and, after a partial decussation, take a position ventrolateral to the medial longitudinal fasciculus.   Two such strongly medullated bundles are the uncrossed tract *a* and tract *b* of *Kingsbury* ('95), which connect respectively the dorsal and the ventral parts of the acoustico-lateral area with the midline.   The majority of the fibers descend ; a small part ascends, probably to eye muscle nuclei. The system from the cerebellum is analogous with, and inseparable from, that from the acoustico-lateral area. Such cerebello-tegmental or cerebello-motorius fibers have been described by various students of urodele material such as *Herrick* ('14, '30), *Larsell* ('20), *Röthig* ('27), and others.

In addition to the above-mentioned efferent system, fibers arise from the caudodorsal part of the cerebellum. These fibers are partly homolateral and partly contralateral ; the crossing, where present, occurs below or within the fasciculus longitudinalis medialis. Associated with these fibers is the primitive

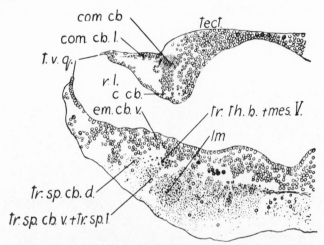

Fig. 378. Cross section through the cerebellum, tectum, and isthmus of Necturus. *Herrick.*

c.cb., corpus cerebelli ; com.cb., commissura cerebelli (medullated component) ; com.cb.l., commissura cerebelli (lateral unmedullated component) ; em.cb.v., eminentia ventralis cerebelli ; lm., lemniscus (tr. bulbo-tectalis, somatic sensory) ; r.l., recessus lateralis rhombencephali ; tect., tectum mesencephali ; tr.sp.cb.d., tractus spinocerebellaris dorsalis ; tr.sp.cb.v. + tr.sp.t., tractus spino-cerebellaris ventralis plus tractus spino-tectalis ; tr.th.b. + mes.V., tractus thalamo-bulbaris plus radix mesencephalica trigemini ; t.v.q., taenia ventriculi quarti.

homologue of the brachium conjunctivum anterius of mammals. Its fibers arise chiefly from the floor of the recessus lateralis (that is, the eminentia ventralis cerebelli) and they all cross. The decussation does not lie directly below the fasciculus longitudinalis medialis but is farther ventral, near the lower part of the midbrain. The fibers end in the tegmental regions at the base of the midbrain, where in higher animals the nucleus ruber makes its appearance. However, in amphibians the area is represented by large reticular cells. This fiber system is accompanied by fascicles from the acoustico-lateral area. The origin of this tract from the eminentia ventralis suggests that in this eminence is to be sought the urodele representative of the efferent cerebellar nuclei of higher forms.

In the region of the anterior medullary vellum occurs, as in other forms, the decussatio veli. A part of the crossing fibers in this region have no functional connection with the cerebellum. To such fibers belong the decussating fibers of the trochlear nerve and fibers of the mesencephalic root of the trigeminal (*Herrick*, '14, '30; *Larsell*, '20; *Röthig*, '27).   Other decussating fibers in the region, and those which wholly or in part exhibit cerebellar relations, are the intertrigeminal commissure of *Hirsch Tabor* ('08), *Bindewald* ('11), and *Röthig* ('27), or the myelinated commissura cerebelli of *Herrick* ('14, '30; figs. 377 and 378) and *Larsell* ('20).   This commissure has connections not only for the superior trigeminal nuclei but also for the bilateral portions of the corpus cerebelli (*Herrick*, '30). This observer has been unable to determine to what extent the fibers are commissural and to what extent decussating.   (Fibers intrinsic to the cerebellum are termed fibrae propriae cerebelli.)   A second nonmyelinated commissure in this

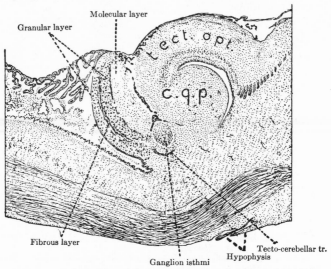

Fig. 379.   A sagittal section, not far from the midline, through the cerebellum and optic tectum of Rana temporaria.   *c.q.p.*, corpus quadrigeminum posterius.   *Ingvar.*

region, usually designated the commissura cerebellaris lateralis (figs. 377 and 378), is an interauricular commissure.   *Larsell* has been able to carry vestibular (octavus) root fibers into this commissure (the vestibulo-lateral commissure) in Triturus.   The ventral spino-cerebellar tract has a partial decussation in the decussatio veli.

Thus far the present account has been based on the conditions found in tailed amphibians.   The tailless type (frog, for example) will be discussed only briefly and with the idea of emphasizing the differences between the two amphibian types. The relation between the tailed and tailless amphibians is best understood through a knowledge of the development of the latter forms, for the conditions in adult urodeles, as these have been described by *Kingsbury* ('95), *Bindewald* ('11), *Herrick* ('14, '24, '30), *Larsell* ('20), *Röthig* ('27), and others, can be documented to a considerable degree in developmental stages of the tailless amphibians.   *Larsell* ('25, '29) studied the development of the cerebellum in the frog.   The following account is based on the work of this observer.   In young tadpoles the entire roof of the rhomboid fossa is membranous.   Embryos of 16–18 mm. length have an oblique membranous plate (the cerebellar plate) in the region later occupied by the cerebellum, which is continuous in front with the midbrain, behind with the choroid roof of the ventricle, and, at the sides, with the rhomboid lip of the medulla oblongata. At the 18 mm. stage, the anlagen of a corpus cerebelli and an eminentia ventralis are present as a mass of nervous tissue which bulges upward from the floor along the anterior lateral wall of the ventricle. The corpus cerebelli is separated from the eminentia ventralis by a sulcus cerebellaris ventralis. This latter area, which is small in the earlier stages, has become prominent by the time a 25 mm. stage is reached. Later, however (36 mm. stage), it is overshadowed on the lateral side by the greatly increased corpus cerebelli. The frontal and lateral boundaries of the anterior diverticulum are formed by a thin membranous layer, the caudal boundary by the lateral-line lobe and the acousticolateral area, and the frontomedial boundary by the eminentia ventralis and the anlage of the corpus cerebelli. The floor is a depressed area bounded by the corpus cerebelli and eminentia ventralis in front and the lateral-line lobe behind and laterally. Such are the boundaries of the anterior diverticulum at the 25 mm. stage. Later (36 mm.) it becomes relatively narrower. This area is important, for, as *Herrick* ('24) and others have indicated, it is along the walls of this diverticulum that the future cerebellum develops. The auricular lobe, which lies lateral to the anterior diverticulum, is connected with the corpus cerebelli by a thin strand of nervous tissue (25 mm. length), which later becomes greatly thickened and continuous with the tegmental area. The auricular lobe or auricle is reduced in the adult frog as a result of the loss of the lateral-line system, and the line of separation between this structure and the corpus cerebelli becomes very faint. The auricular lobe is continuous with the lateral-line lobe in the 25 mm. larva. In the 36 mm. larva a mass of cells merges on the one hand into the auricular lobe and on the other hand into the lateral-line lobe. This mass of cells *Larsell* regarded as homologous with the eminentia granularis of fishes. Nevertheless, as *Larsell* has pointed out, it is still possible to recognize, by study of the structural pattern, the primitive relations of these areas and of the eminentia cerebellaris as well.

The wall connecting the two anlagen of the body of the cerebellum is entirely membranous at an early stage ; later, with the greater development of these lateral anlagen, the membranous portion is reduced, and at the 36 mm. stage *Larsell* found the whole wall massive, although thinner in the midline than at the sides. The medial portion thickens gradually to reach the condition characteristic of the adult animal. Gradually, also, tegmental areas in the floor of the lateral recess increase in size so that the fossa between the acoustic areas and the eminentia ventralis very nearly disappears. This latter region fuses with the corpus cerebelli, forming thus a thick medial wall for the anterior diverticulum. The roof of this recess has become massive caudally at the 36 mm. stage, but the cephalic end of the diverticulum extends into a sort of pocket with thin, membranous walls. The acoustic area (which forms an eminence on the outer surface of the medulla) and the auricular lobe are continuous rostrally with the corpus cerebelli and medially with the eminentia ventralis. *Larsell's* study of the histologic development of the cerebellum indicates that the stratum album and stratum griseum of the medulla oblongata are the anlagen, respectively, of the molecular and granular layers of the cerebellum.   He also considered the cerebellar and vestibular nuclei to be related genetically.   In the adult frog a stratum moleculare, a stratum Purkinje, and a stratum granulosum are present (figs. 379 and 380).

The cerebellum of the frog differs from that of Necturus in having a much more highly developed corpus cerebelli and relatively less developed auricles. The study of the selachian cerebellum showed that the auricular portions are both directly and indirectly related to the area acustico-lateralis.   It is to be expected, then, that adult, tailless amphibians, which lack lateral-line nerves, will have reduced auricles as compared with those of the tailed form, in which such lateral-line nerves are present.   The increase in size of the corpus cerebelli is associated with the change in habits of the tailless amphibians, which have learned to live on land.   Birds and mammals, which are terrestrial in their habits, have, on the whole, highly developed extremities.   This progressive development of the extremities is associated with an increase in those proprioceptive spino-cerebellar tracts (fig. 380) which carry impulses from the body to the cerebellum.   Such tracts have been found in fishes to terminate within the corpus cerebelli ; this relation is even more evident in higher forms.   The above facts indicate that the enlargement of the corpus cerebelli and the reduction of the auricles in the frog are in logical relation with the development of the cerebellum in other forms.

This increase in size in the frog is associated with an increase in differentiation so that in this form the medial part of the cerebellum becomes an evident cellular layer which arches forward as in Petromyzon and in early embryonic stages of teleosts (fig. 368).   Moreover, there is an advance toward separation into layers and toward higher differentiation of the cellular elements.   Everywhere distinct granular and molecular layers are demonstrable.   The granular layer is separated into two parts by myelinated fibers, mainly of the spino-cerebellar system.   The Purkinje cells in amphibians, as those in plagiostomes, are absent only in the midline.   As in teleosts, they are not arranged invariably in a single row.   Their dendrites, which lie in a sagittal plane, extend into the molecular layer.   In this layer are stellate cells and the typical parallel fibers arising from cells of the granular layer.

It is not necessary nor desirable to consider in detail the cerebellar connections in the tailless amphibians, since in principle they are the same as those of the tailed forms.   The differences are rather those of emphasis than of kind, the most important being the increase in spino-cerebellar fibers, to which reference has already been made.

THE CEREBELLUM OF REPTILES

There is a great variation in form relations in the cerebella of different classes of reptiles.   In Sphenodon (*Hindenach*, '31) and in lizards the cerebellum is folded forward, so as to appear everted, for what is usually the under side of the cerebellum appears as its upper surface, while the surface usually dorsal

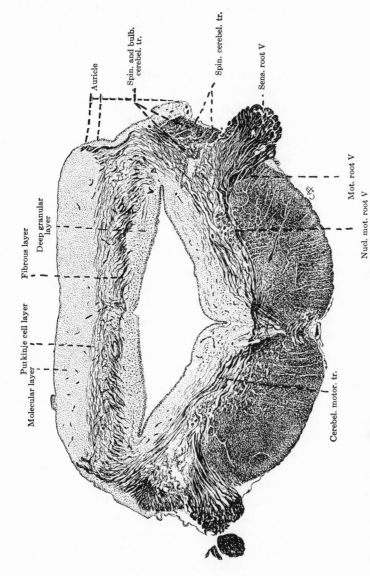

Molecular layer

Purkinje cell layer

Fibrous layer

Deep granular layer

Auricle

Spin. and bulb. cerebel. tr.

Spin. cerebel. tr.

Sens. root V

Mot. root V

Nucl. mot. root V

Cerebel. motor. tr.

Fig. 380. Cross section through the cerebellum of Rana mugiens at the level of entrance of the trigeminal nerve.

749

appears ventral (fig. 381). This is well illustrated in Varanus (*de Lange*, '17; see also figure 381, where a sulcus is present). The eversion of the cerebellum is evidenced in many figures of the brains of lizards found in the literature, among the more recent of which may be listed those found in the contributions of *Ariëns Kappers* ('29), *Hausman* ('29), *Shanklin* ('30, in Chameleon vulgaris), *Frederikse* ('31, in Lacerta vivipara), and *Huber* and *Crosby* ('33, in Anolis carolinensis). This dorsofrontal folding represents an exaggeration of a primitive condition met with in petromyzonts, in embryos of teleosts, and in the full-grown frog. It is seen temporarily during the development of the human cerebellum, as indicated in figure 401. What factors are concerned in producing this eversion of the cerebellum of certain reptiles it is not possible to state at present. It may be attributable to the greater increase in the granular layer which thus caused the folding, but this does not explain why this greater development of the granular layer should become a permanent characteristic of the cerebellum in these forms. A satisfactory explanation of the condition cannot be offered at present. In many reptiles the tip of the cerebellum is turned caudalward, projecting back over the fourth ventricle.

Most observers have described within the cerebellum a body and auricles, or flocculi (*Larsell*, '34), and it has been recognized that the differences in the size and in the development of various regions of the cerebellum are correlated with differences in body structure and particularly with the degree to which the limbs are used in locomotion. In snakes, where the body consists of a trunk without extremities, the cerebellum is smallest (fig. 382) since it consists merely of a flat, transverse lamella which arches over the fourth ventricle. In turtles (fig. 383) and crocodiles (see fig. 386, alligator) the body of the cerebellum is more highly developed, with a distinct cerebellar ventricle into which the choroid plexus grows in part.

Anterior (x) and posterior (y) cerebellar fissures, bounding anterior, medial, and posterior lobes, occur in crocodilian forms (fig. 405), according to *de Lange* ('17) and *Ingvar* ('19). On the basis of external caudal fissures the cerebellar lobes have been identified in chameleons and in the everted cerebellum of Iguana by *Hausman* ('29). *Larsell* ('26) found corresponding lobes and fissures in Gerrhonotus, although they were developed less than in the alligator, which he has studied in some detail recently (*Larsell*, '34). Fissura anterior cerebelli is situated about half way from the summit of the cerebellum to the velum medullare anterius, and is very deep, particularly in the midline. The posterior fissure also has its greatest depth in the midline. It grows much more shallow laterally, is discontinuous for a space, and then passes over into a very shallow furrow, the fissura parafloccularis,[12] which adjoins the auricular part of the cerebellum rostrally, separating it from the corpus cerebelli.

The anterior fissure is regarded as homologous with the fissura prima of mammals (*Ingvar*, '19; *Larsell*, '34). The posterior fissure was believed by *Ingvar* to

[12] At present it is not possible to homologize with finality these reptilian fissures with those present in the fish cerebellum. Probably the fissura parafloccularis is the homologue of the selachian sulcus paraauricularis.

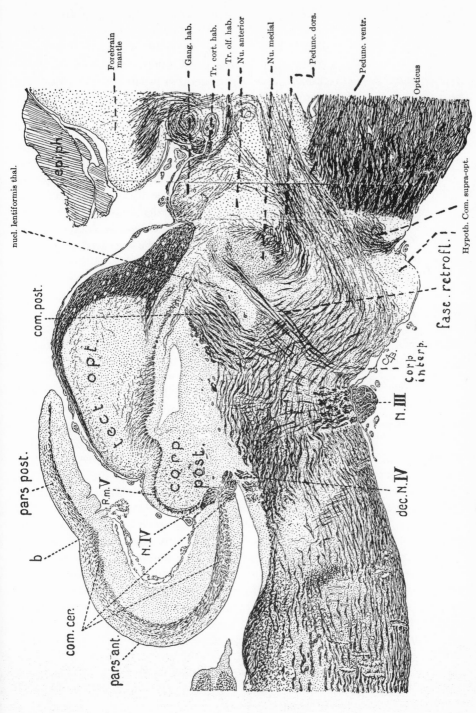

nucl. lentiformis thal.

Forebrain mantle

Gang. hab.

Tr. cort. hab.

Tr. olf. hab.

Nu. anterior

Nu. medial

Pedunc. dors.

Pedunc. ventr.

Opticus

ep. ph.

com. post.

tect. opt.

corp. post.

R. m. V

N. IV

pars post.

b

com. cer.

pars ant.

corp. interp.

N. III

dec. N. IV

fasc. retrofl.

Hypoth. Com. supra-opt.

Fig. 381. A sagittal section through the cerebellum, midbrain, and diencephalon of a lizard, Varanus salvator.

751

correspond to that between the tuber and pyramid of the mammalian cerebellum. It was compared to the mammalian postpyramidal fissure (fissura secunda, *Elliot Smith*, refer to p. 780) by *Larsell*. Moreover, *Larsell* ('34) separated off from the posterior lobe of *Ingvar* a portion which he considered the forerunner of the mammalian nodule and flocculus, and grouped them together as the parafloccular lobe.

The auricle or flocculus is only slightly developed in some reptiles; much less developed, for example, than in fishes. In snakes it is scarcely discernible. This state of affairs is not surprising since the lateral-line nerves which exert so great an influence upon the development of the auricle in fishes are lacking in reptiles, while other connections which lead to an enlargement of this area in higher vertebrates have not appeared as yet.

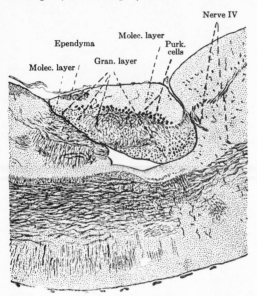

FIG. 382.   A sagittal section through the cerebellum of a snake (Eunectes murinus).   *de Lange.*

Another division of the reptilian cerebellum, based on what he believed to be a most fundamental and very primitive arrangement, was made by *Larsell* ('26). This worker called attention to the fact that the body of the cerebellum consists of bilateral masses of nervous tissue connected by the membranous roof of the ventricle in adult Necturus and embryonic Amblystoma and frog, that the membranous midline region is replaced in adult Amblystoma by a band of nervous tissue and in adult frog by a massive wall, and that these stages are repeated during the embryologic development of higher forms, including man. This medial portion of the cerebellum between the two primitive corpora cerebelli, *Larsell* termed pars interposita. It varies greatly in its degree of development in different reptiles, being relatively large in those forms in which the trunk muscles are the chief organs of locomotion. Between the auricular lobe and the corpus cerebelli, across the floor of the lateral recess, according to *Larsell*, another portion of the cerebellum develops, which he termed, together with the primitive corpus cerebelli, the pars lateralis. This new portion of pars lateralis is recognizable in lower amphibians and frogs and becomes sufficiently large in reptiles to overshadow the small auricular lobe. The pars lateralis appears to be concerned chiefly with movements of the limbs and it was suggested (*Larsell*) that it is the forerunner of the lobulus ansiformis of the cerebellar hemisphere described for mammals by *Bolk* ('06). If later work should substantiate *Larsell's* interpretation, these observations are of great importance, since they indicate a beginning of cerebellar hemispheres in forms well below mammals, but further corroboration and amplification is desirable.

As evidence for the importance and the variability in development of pars interposita and pars lateralis, *Larsell* presented a study of the cerebella of certain snakes and lizards. The following is a brief summary of certain of his results. In the legless lizard Anniella, which makes its home by burrowing in the sand, the cerebellum is relatively small, with no sign of an auricular lobe. It is massive across the midline, however, indicating the presence of a clearly developed pars interposita. In this lizard the cerebellum is not everted, the granular layer facing downward and caudalward, as in amphibians. In the swift (Sceloporus) and in the horned lizard (Phrynosoma) there is extreme

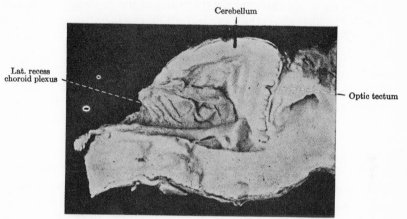

Cerebellum

Lat. recess
choroid plexus

Optic tectum

FIG. 383. A sagittal section through the cerebellum of a turtle, Chelone imbricata.
de Lange.

eversion of the cerebellum and a specialization of the pars lateralis, with relatively much less development of the pars interposita. The large size of the pars lateralis is associated with the habits of these forms, for these lizards are extremely active animals which make great use of their legs and little or no use of their tails in locomotion. Between Thamnophis and Anniella, which progress by means of trunk and tail musculature, and Sceloporus and Phrynosoma, which use their limbs as the chief organs of locomotion, is the lizard Gerrhonotus (also studied by *Larsell*) which uses trunk, tail, and limb musculature in moving over the ground. This last-mentioned animal has a well-developed pars interposita, comparable with that of snakes, and a pars lateralis which suggests that of the swift, although relatively not so highly developed. These facts necessarily give strong support to *Larsell's* statement that the pars interposita is concerned with trunk and tail musculature, the pars lateralis particularly with limb musculature. However, no reference to this particular interpretation was made in *Larsell's* recent review of the morphogenesis and evolution of the cerebellum (*Larsell*, '34).

The internal structure of the reptilian cerebellum need not be discussed fully, since the structure of the molecular layer and the relations of the Purkinje cell and granular layers (fig. 382) to it are in principle the same as those described at the beginning of this chapter. For details the original accounts should be consulted

(*Ramón y Cajal*, '11 ; *Larsell*, '32).   It is to be emphasized that in contrast to fishes and amphibians, true basket cells are present in reptiles in the molecular layer (*Ramón y Cajal*, '11) ; furthermore, that the dendritic branching of the Purkinje cells, although richer than in sharks, is less than in teleosts, birds, and mammals, and that the collaterals of neuraxes of Purkinje cells are very scarce ; as a rule only one is found in reptiles while in birds there are two and in mammals several.   The neuraxes of the Purkinje cells run as in fishes in a ventrolateral direction.   Some of them appear to enter the medulla oblongata itself ; others terminate in nuclei situated at the border line between cerebellum and medulla oblongata.

Reptiles offer valuable material for the study of the phylogenetic development of the cerebellar nuclei, since they present all stages from those found in sharks to those characteristic of birds.   *Edinger* ('08) pointed out the presence of nuclei in the reptilian cerebellum.   *Van Hoevell* ('16) found that the groups of cells that occur in the eminentia ventralis cerebelli of the shark (at about the level of the trigeminal nerve), and that quite evidently develop in relationship with the vestibular nerve, show a considerable increase in a mediodorsal direction in Chelonia and more particularly in saurians and hydrosaurians, and are incorporated into the area of the cerebellum itself.   The eminence of the tuberculum produced by the nuclear gray is slight in Chelonia and Ophidia, as in sharks, and the cerebellar ventricle is consequently very wide.   It has increased medially considerably in the crocodile, so that the right and left tubercula touch each other, forming a dorsal arch above the medulla oblongata.   In this way, the ventricle is contracted to a narrow slit which widens again dorsally and extends frontalward and caudalward within the corpus cerebelli, forming a recessus anterior and a recessus posterior ventriculi cerebelli.   In this enlargement (whether large or slight), which is incorporated in this manner within the main mass of the cerebellum, cell groups can be distinguished, although the mass is continuous caudally with the vestibular gray occupying the dorsal portion of the medulla oblongata, which suggests its intimate relationship to subcerebellar regions of the medulla oblongata.   In Sphenodon (*Hindenach*, '31) through fiber connections, but in most reptiles through cell characters, this gray can be separated at many levels into a medial and a lateral nucleus (fig. 384 ; *van Hoevell*, '11 ; *Larsell*, '26 ; *Shanklin*, '30, and others).   The characteristic neuron of the medial nucleus is large and oval to multangular, of the lateral is smaller oval or bipolar.   In Chameleon *Shanklin* has described opposite cellular characteristics, but his identification of the nuclei is uncertain.   The possible direct homologies of the reptilian cerebellar nuclei with those of the mammalian cerebellum must be left an open question until a detailed study of their specific fiber relations and possibly of their development shall throw more light on this subject.   There has been a rather general tendency to regard the medial nucleus as the forerunner of the mammalian nucleus tecti (nucleus fastigius) and to consider this nucleus as the most primitive cerebellar nucleus (*Ariëns Kappers*, '21).   It appears probable, at least, that the anlage for the cerebellar nuclei is originally subcerebellar and becomes incorporated secondarily within the cerebellum, under the neurobiotactic influence of impulses received from Purkinje cells.

While discussing these masses of gray associated with the cerebellum, brief reference must be made to a cell mass of unknown significance to which *van Hoevell* ('16) and *Ariëns Kappers* ('21) have given the name "nucleus of the brachium conjunctivum." This is a small mass of somewhat scattered cells situated ventral to the medial cerebellar nucleus and above the ventricle, and extending forward toward the mesencephalon in the anterior medullary velum. Its fiber connections are unknown as yet.

The reptilian cerebellum receives a number of afferent fiber systems and gives rise to certain clearly recognizable efferent paths. Some of the more important of these connections will be listed and briefly described. For details of their connections the original papers cited should be consulted. These major connections are (1) the spino-cerebellar tracts (*Edinger*, '08; *de Lange*, '17; *Ariëns Kappers*, '21; *Huber* and *Crosby*, '26; *Larsell*, '26; *Shanklin*, '30; *Hindenach*, '31, and *Weston*, '33, Dissertation, and others); (2) the olivo-cerebellar tract (*van Hoevell*, '16; *Larsell*, '26); (3) the vestibular root fibers and vestibulo-cerebellar and cerebello-vestibular tracts, including tractus cochleo-vestibulo-cerebellaris (*Edinger*, '08; *Beccari*, '12; *Ariëns Kappers*, '20; *Huber* and *Crosby*, '26; *Larsell*, '26; *Weston*, '33, Dissertation, and others); (4) an uncrossed trigemino-cerebellar tract (*Ariëns Kappers*, '21), and crossed and uncrossed trigemino-cerebellar connections (*Huber* and *Crosby*, '26; *Larsell*, '32, and *Weston*, '33, Dissertation), together with trigeminal root fibers such as have been described for Amphibia (*Weston*, '33, Dissertation); (5) tractus

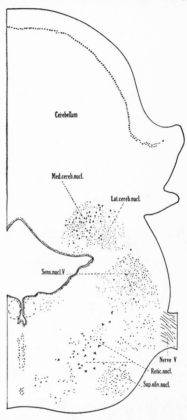

Fig. 384. The cerebellar nuclei of *Alligator mississippiensis*. *Huber* and *Crosby*.

tecto-cerebellaris (*Ariëns Kappers*, '21; *Huber* and *Crosby*, '26 and '32; *Larsell*, '26 and '32; *Shanklin*, '30; *Hindenach*, '31, *Weston*, '33, Dissertation); (6) the cerebello-tegmental or cerebello-motorius and cerebello-spinal systems (*Ariëns Kappers*, '21; *Huber* and *Crosby*, '26; *Weston*, '33, Dissertation); (7) brachium conjunctivum anterius or tractus cerebello-tegmentalis mesencephali (*de Lange*, '17; *Ariëns Kappers*, '21; *Huber* and *Crosby*, '26; *Larsell*, '26; *Shanklin*, '30; *Hindenach*, '31; *Weston*, '33, Dissertation).

The spino-cerebellar system in reptiles is described usually as consisting of a dorsal spino-cerebellar (bulbo-cerebellar) tract and a ventral spino-cerebellar tract (*Larsell*, '26, '32; *Shanklin*, '30; *Hindenach*, '31). In the medulla oblongata the dorsal spino-cerebellar tract lies at the lateral surface. It gradually swings dorsalward, lateral to the descending root of the trigeminal, and terminates in the cerebellum of the same and of the opposite side.   It is joined on its medial border by the olivo-cerebellar tract described by *van Hoevell*.

The dorsal spino-cerebellar tract (figs. 165 and 385) was described by *Huber* and *Crosby* ('26) under the name of the spino-cerebellar tract.   Its exact homology with the dorsal spino-cerebellar tract of higher mammals was then, and is

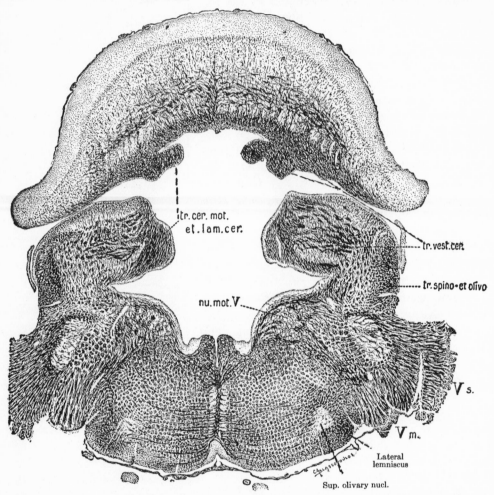

Fig. 385.   A cross section through the middle part of the cerebellum of a crocodile (Crocodilus porosus).

now, uncertain, unless ample qualifications are made (*Larsell*, '32, and *Weston*, '33, Dissertation).   The dorsal spino-cerebellar tract of mammals arises from the nucleus dorsalis of Clarke.   A portion of the so-called dorsal spino-cerebellar tract of reptiles has an homologous origin (*Banchi*, '03).   However, another and a relatively larger portion appears to arise from other regions, and particularly from the cervical cord.   These cervical components, owing to the mode of formation of the tract, occupy in general a more ventral position, and such components in the higher mammals presumably would course in the ventral spino-cerebellar tract. In our use of the term spino-cerebellar tract (*Huber* and *Crosby*, '26), cognizance was given to these considerations. There is no objection to the use of the term dorsal spino-cerebellar tract in reptiles, if pure topographic relations are implied therewith. It is here stated with emphasis that the spino-cerebellar tract of *Huber* and *Crosby* ('26) is not the ventral spino-cerebellar tract as described and labeled by *Hindenach* ('31) for Sphenodon, as this writer has supposed.

The ventral-spino-cerebellar tract (fig. 165) runs forward with the spino-mesencephalic or spino-tectal tract. In front of the sensory nucleus of the trigeminal the cerebellar component swings dorsalward and enters the cerebellum. In Alligator mississippiensis, the series available show a small ventral spino-cerebellar tract which appears to contribute to the roof nuclei of both sides and to the granular layer, the fibers crossing in the inferior cerebellar commissure. In certain snakes and lizards the tract is very large, according to *Larsell* ('26), and fibers from it reach the granular layer of both sides, decussating by way of the ventral or inferior cerebellar commissure, and in the swift by a dorsal (or superior) cerebellar commissure as well. It is interesting that *Larsell* found the tract smaller in the alligator lizard Gerrhonotus. *Hindenach* ('31) described a ventral spino-cerebellar tract in Sphenodon. Arcuate fibers from the posterior funicular nuclei to the cerebellum have been described by *Banchi* ('03).

Vestibular root fibers reach the auricular lobes in the alligator, and vestibulo-cerebellar and cerebello-vestibular tracts (fig. 165A) have been described for snakes, lizards, and crocodiles. The tractus cochleo-vestibulo-cerebellaris, arising from nucleus laminaris and Deiters' nucleus (the lateral or ventrolateral vestibular nucleus), swings dorsalward along the dorsolateral border of the medulla oblongata, over the vestibulo-cerebellar tract. The fibers of both systems reach the medial or roof nucleus and perhaps the granular layer as well.

The passage of direct trigeminal root fibers into the cerebellum was suggested in preparations of certain reptilian brains and has recently received confirmation by *Weston* ('33). *De Lange* ('17) and *Larsell* ('26) were unable to demonstrate unquestionably the presence of trigemino-cerebellar connections to the cerebellum. Both uncrossed and crossed trigemino-cerebellar tracts are present in the silver preparations of Alligator mississippiensis (fig. 165A; *Huber* and *Crosby*, '26) in relations similar, even in detail, to those described for birds by *Sanders* ('29). In his 1932 paper Larsell made reference to trigemino-cerebellar paths. The dorsal trigemino-cerebellar tract is an uncrossed bundle arising from the neurons of the chief sensory nucleus of the trigeminal and passing directly dorsalward to the cerebellum. The ventral trigemino-cerebellar tract arises from the nucleus of the descending root of the trigeminal of one side, crosses the ventral part of the bulbar field in company with other secondary trigeminal fibers, and forms a small, compact bundle of fibers ventral to the nucleus of the descending root of the other side, where it is joined by a small number of homolateral trigemino-cerebellar fibers. The tract then swings dorsalward around the outer surface of the nucleus to the cerebellum. With it run other nucleo-cerebellar fibers, including ventral superficial arcuates (*Banchi*, '03).

In silver preparations of Chrysemys marginata, a bundle of fibers passes ventralward from the more caudal part of the optic tectum, then turns caudalward ventral to the decussating fibers of the trochlear nerve and enters the cerebellum (*Huber* and *Crosby*, '26 and '33; *Shanklin*, '30). Other tectal fibers pass to the cerebellar commissure (*Larsell*, '26; *Shanklin*, '30; *Huber* and *Crosby*, '33, and *Weston*, '33), probably constituting a crossed cerebello-tectal system. The termination within the cerebellum is uncertain; the uncrossed tract has been traced as far as the granular layer (see fig. 479).

Within the cerebellum, immediately in front of the contracted portion of the ventricle, there is a very considerable commissure, the commissura inferior cerebelli, or sometimes merely the cerebellar commissure, that joins the decussatio veli rostrally. In the majority of reptiles, the more anterior bundles are the crossed ventral spino-cerebellar fibers, the number of fibers depending upon the size of the tract in the reptile under consideration, and upon whether or not certain bundles cross in the superior cerebellar commissure, as in the swift (*Larsell*, '26). Certain fibers of the dorsal spino-cerebellar tract cross to the opposite side in the commissure, although a relatively large part of the tract remains uncrossed. A group of fibers arising in part, at least, from the medial cerebellar nuclei, decussates in the commissure and, joined by homolateral fibers, passes to the efferent nuclei of the brain stem as cerebello-motorius fibers (*Ariëns Kappers*, '21; *Hindenach*, '31), or as cerebello-tegmental fibers (*Huber* and *Crosby*, '26; figs. 165A and 385). The bundles have been followed to the motor nuclei and reticular nuclei of the medulla and to the medial longitudinal fasciculi of both sides. They are accompanied through the commissure by fibers of similar origin, which, joined by homolateral fibers, constitute the reptilian homologue of the fasciculus of Russell and pass to the lateral or ventrolateral vestibular nucleus and possibly to other vestibular centers and even to the upper portion of the spinal cord. The most complete account current of the reptilian Russell's fasciculus is available in the dissertation of *Weston*, '33.

The most important efferent tract is the brachium conjunctivum anterius, or tractus cerebello-tegmentalis mesencephali, the primitive relations of which it is difficult to ascertain. This fiber bundle appears to arise not only from the lateral nucleus of the cerebellum (*Larsell*, '26; *Hindenach*, '31), but possibly also from the medial nucleus (*Ariëns Kappers*, '21). The number of these latter fibers is relatively small in reptiles; a mammalian cerebellum of approximately the same size will have a relatively much greater number of these fibers, but in the mammalian forms the cerebellar nuclei are developed much better, also. The tract passes forward and downward from its origin and distributes to the primitive red nucleus of reptiles (fig. 324), and probably to other tegmental cells of the midbrain. It leaves the cerebellum with fibers of the cerebello-motorius system to the motor nuclei of the trochlear and possibly of the oculomotor nuclei.

THE CEREBELLUM OF BIRDS

Mesdag ('09) identified the anlage of the cerebellum in 4½-day chicks. In the 5-day chick *Ingvar* ('19) found this organ represented by two bilateral swellings

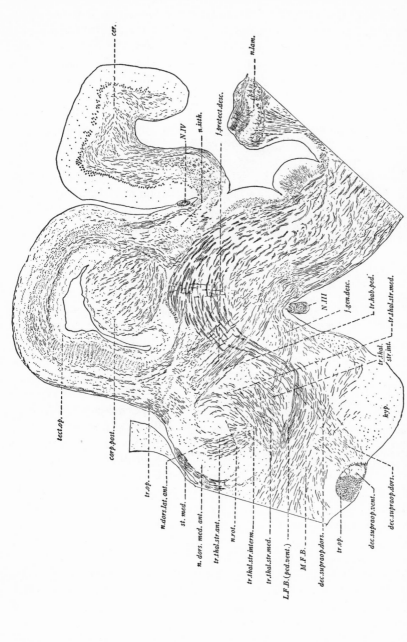

Fig. 386. A median sagittal section through the midbrain and cerebellum of Alligator mississippiensis. Weigert series. ×13. *Huber and Crosby.*
cer., cerebellum; *corp.post.*, corpus quadrigeminum posterius; *dec.supraop.dors.*, decussatio supraoptica dorsalis; *dec. supraop.vent.*, decussatio supraoptica ventralis; *f.gen.desc.*, fasciculus geniculatus descendens; *f.pretect.desc.*, fasciculus pretectalis descendens; *hyp.*, hypothalamus; *M.F.B.*, medial forebrain bundle; *L.F.B.(ped.vent.)*, lateral forebrain bundle (ventral peduncle); *n.dors.lat.ant.*, nucleus dorsolateralis anterior; *n.dors.med.ant.*, nucleus dorsomedialis anterior; *n.isth.*, nucleus isthmi; *n.lam.*, nucleus laminaris; *n.rot.*, nucleus rotundus; *N.III*, IIIrd nerve; *N.IV*, IVth nerve; *st.med.*, stria medullaris; *tect.op.*, tectum opticum; *tr.hab.ped.*, tractus habenulo-peduncularis; *tr.op.*, tractus opticus; *tr.thal.str.ant.*, tractus thalamo-striatalis anterior; *tr.thal.str.int.*, tractus thalamo-striatalis internus; *tr.thal.str.interm.*, tractus thalamo-striatalis intermedius; *tr.thal.str.med.*, tractus thalamo-striatalis medialis.

759

not as yet joined in the midline, but with the auricular or floccular portion separated from the corpus cerebelli on each side by a slight depression.   Up to the 8th or 9th day the bilateral eminences forming the body of the cerebellum are completely separated from each other except for the membranous roof of the ventricle, and the surface of the cerebellum is smooth, with no transverse fissures, although the fissura paraflocularis is present, as in earlier stages.   In the chick of 9 days and 12 hours, the next stage studied by *Ingvar*, the eminences have increased in size and fused in the midline.   A midline sagittal fissure remains for some time as an indication of the bilateral origin of the organ.   This is a permanent fissure in selachians.   In the chick embryo of 9 days and 12 hours, four transverse fissures were seen by *Ingvar* (fig. 387).   Following *Brouwer* ('13), he designated these as the fissures *x*, *y*, *w*, and *z*.   The fissure *x* separates the anterior from the median lobe; it is the homologue of the mammalian fissura prima.   This fissure is deepest in the midline, but gradually fades out toward the sides.   The fissure *y* is continuous laterally with the parafloccular fissure. *Brouwer's* fissures *x* and *y* were regarded by *Ingvar* ('19) as morphologically the principal fissures of the cerebellum of birds and mammals.

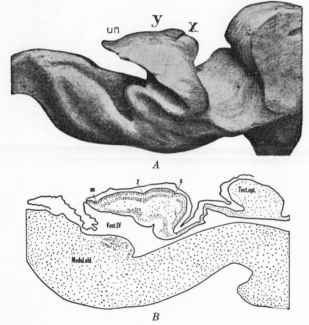

A

B

Fig. 387.   *A*, a wax reconstruction of the cerebellum and medulla oblongata of a chick embryo of 9 days and 10 hours. Note the laterally and forward extending auricle with its lateral recess terminating blindly.

B, a sagittal section through the same embryo.   The section is taken slightly lateral to the midline.   *Ingvar.*

By means of these the corpus cerebelli is divided into three parts; a lobus anterior, a lobus medius, and a lobus posterior (fig. 391).   It is probable that these three divisions are comparable to those in reptiles.   Ontogenetically the anterior and posterior lobes develop ahead of the middle lobe and are of approximately uniform development in all birds, while the middle lobe varies in its degree of development in the different species.   These conditions suggest that the anterior and posterior lobes are the more primitive parts of the cerebellum, and the middle lobe the more recent part, since the progressive development of the cerebellum is always associated with an increased number of lamellae in the middle lobe, which gradually surpasses the other lobes and particularly the posterior lobe.

The anterior lobe is the most constant in its structure.   In most full-grown birds it has four lamellae (*Brouwer*, '13; *Ingvar*, '19).   The lobus medius is the most variable.   The lobus posterior really consists of only three lamellae that, enumerated from before backward, probably correspond with the mammalian pyramis, uvula, and nodulus.   Laterally these three lamellae go over into the auricles, which form the lobuli flocculi.   Confirmation of their primitive character is to be found in the fact that the first myelinization occurs in the auricles synchronously with the myelinization of the acoustic area (*Shimazono*, '12). The degree of development of these divisions varies considerably in the different species.   In the most primitive birds, the Ratatores, the auricle of the new born animal is very well developed (fig. 388).   In the fully developed condition its size is considerably less in comparison to that of the corpus cerebelli (fig. 388, Rhea; fig. 390, Dromaeus nov. Holland).   In many animals the auricle remains relatively large even in the adult condition.   The auricle, then, in birds may be indicated only, as in the crocodile, by a lateral indentation along the caudal, ventrolateral border of the corpus cerebelli, may be similar to an auricle (Oligyps auricularis, Sula bassana, and others) or may be in the form of a pedunculated brain portion (Pavo and Eulabia ; see fig. 390, C).

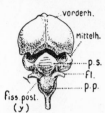

FIG. 388.   The brain of an ostrich embryo just before hatching.   Note the fissure *y* (designated here as the posterior sulcus) cutting off the part of the cerebellum caudal to it.   *Ingvar*.

There are great differences in the degree of development of the corpus cerebelli.   In the new born ostrich (fig. 389), just leaving the shell, two portions are visible macroscopically in the corpus cerebelli, and these are separated by a deep, branched fissure.   The fissure forms a boundary between the pyramidal portion of the posterior lobe and the remainder of the cerebellum, and is the avian homologue of the mammalian fissura secunda (*Elliot Smith*, see p. 780), or, in the terminology often used for man, the postpyramidal fissure (which has also been termed the prepyramidal fissure, *Ingvar*, '19; *Ariëns Kappers*, '21).   The remainder of the cerebellum in this young ostrich is the anlage for the lobus anterior and the lobus medius.   At this stage, the region shows many small depressions. An examination of the cerebellum in adult birds indicates that the greater growth during the development occurs in the regions in front of this fissure and that secondarily these regions partly or entirely overlap the lobus posterior.   The gradual overlapping of the posterior lobe by the anterior cerebellar regions is very evident if the cerebella of small birds are compared with those of larger birds. In the small birds (figs. 390 and 392 ; Ottocampsa leucotis and Nucifraga and also in Regulus and Parus) the lobus posterior is prominent as a distinct, separate division, just as in the new born ostrich (*Ariëns Kappers*, '21).   It is characterized frequently by its more whitish appearance.   This portion is greatly overlapped in large birds (Struthio, Oligyps, and Sula bassana ; see fig. 388) so that the size of the trunk and extremities of an animal appears to play a considerable part in determining the size of that portion of the cerebellum lying in front of the posterior lobe.   In such cases the fissura postpyramidalis is no longer easily distinguishable, particularly since in the larger animals (in accordance with the law of Baillarger and Dareste) the number of fissures becomes extraordinarily large.

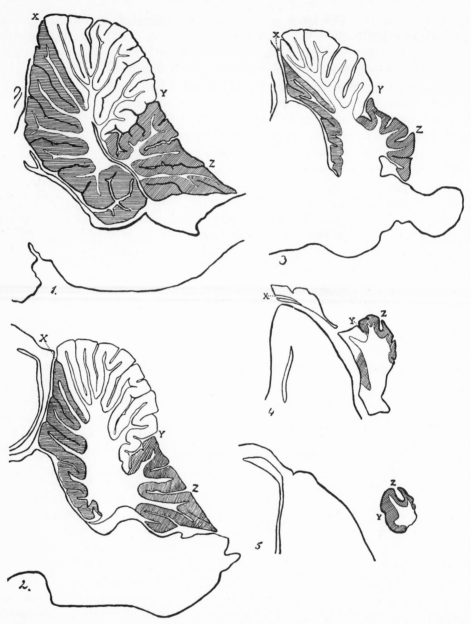

Fig. 389. Sagittal sections through the cerebellum of ostrich, just before hatching. *1*, midline section; *2, 3*, and *4*, sections taken in planes progressively farther lateralward; *5*, section through the auricle. *Ingvar*.

x, fissura primaria; *y*, fissura prepyramidalis of Ingvar, homologous to the mammalian post-pyramidalis of *Herrick* ('31), *Ranson* ('31), and *Piersol's* Anatomy ('30); *z*, fissura uvulonodularis. The very characteristic fissure *y* (compare fig. 388) can be seen clearly within the auricle. Horizontal cross hatching indicates the anterior lobe; transverse hatching, the posterior lobe; and the median lobe is clear.

762

Frequently only two fissures are distinguishable in the posterior lobe of the cerebellum in larger animals. These correspond to the fissura prepyramidalis and the fissura uvulonodularis of mammals. By means of these fissures, three divisions of the posterior lobe are formed, comparable, presumably, to the three most posterior lobules of the mammalian vermis — the pyramid, the uvula, and the nodule as was stated earlier.

The more variable lobus medius, which increases considerably in larger mammals, corresponds to that portion immediately behind the sulcus primarius (fissura prima) in mammals, while a lobus anterior corresponds with the lingula, the lobulus centralis, and the culmen of the latter animals.

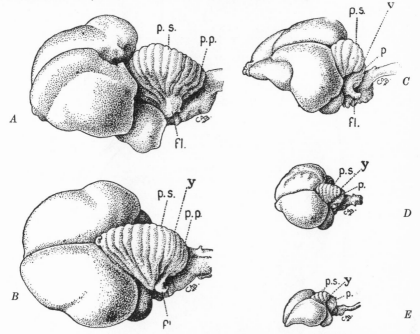

FIG. 390. The cerebellum of *A*, Dromaeus novae hollandiae; *B*, Sula bassana; *C*, Eulabia indica; *D*, Nucifraga; *E*, Ottocampsa leucotis. Note the sharpness of fissure *y* in the smaller animals. *Ingvar.* *p.p.*, posterior lobe; *p.s.*, lobus medius.

There is very considerable variation in the shape of the cerebellum as a whole in birds (*Brouwer*, '13). While in most birds it is somewhat rounded in outline, in some it is compressed from in front backward (Turdus); in others it protrudes forward (Haliaetus) or backward (Cygnus). These differences are due to differences in the skulls rather than to fundamental, internal differences. It is noteworthy that in the American eagle the cerebellum is always covered over by parasites (*Ariëns Kappers*, '21).

The internal structure of the cerebellum in birds is characterized by the very great prominence of the granular layer and by the appearance of very considerably developed nuclei of the cerebellum. The increase in the internal structure has reduced the ventricle very considerably as compared with that of reptiles. This contraction of the ventricle has occurred in a very typical manner, for the eminentiae ventrales cerebelli, which in the embryo lie far apart (see fig. 387), in the full-grown animals grow together so that only a small slit remains immediately above the center of the fourth ventricle — the aqueductus cerebelli — which widens out somewhat dorsally into a ventriculus cerebelli (fig. 391), with a recessus posterior and a recessus anterior, analogous to those in the alligator.

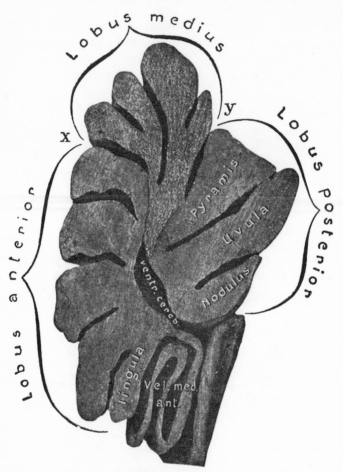

Fig. 391.   The cerebellum of a chick embryo 16 days old.   Median section.   *Ingvar*.

Lateral and dorsal to the aqueductus cerebelli lie the cerebellar nuclei (fig. 393). The form relations and differentiation of the several cerebellar nuclei vary in different birds.   A study of the histology of the avian cerebellar cortex reveals a pattern common to the cerebella of higher forms (see pp. 781 and 782) with all the major elements represented and the Purkinje cells showing an especially rich branching of the dendrites.   Reference is made here to the opening pages of this chapter (see particularly p. 702).

There are two modes of approach to the study of the deep cerebellar gray or cerebellar nuclei; brief reference will be made to each and then their inter-

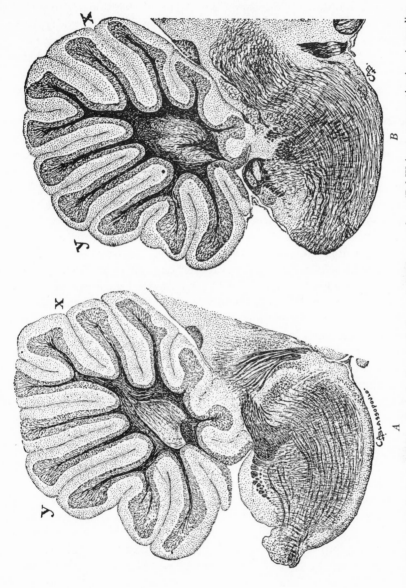

Fig. 392. Sagittal sections through the cerebellum of Parus coeruleus (Pal-Weigert preparations). A, median section; B, more laterally placed. *Ingvar.*

Note that in this cerebellum the y fissure is not coincident with the wide, open fissure coming to the surface in the posterior part.

765

relation discussed.   The older and more usual approach to the consideration of the interrelation of the different nuclei of the cerebellum will be discussed first, and in the account presented, use is made of the nomenclature employed by *Ramón y Cajal* ('08) and adopted by *Sanders* ('29).   The descriptions here given are based on relations as seen in the sparrow, a form particularly figured by *Ramón y Cajal* and *Sanders*, the latter basing her observations on material familiar to *Huber* and *Crosby*.   From accounts in the literature it is apparent that the degree of differentiation varies considerably in different birds.   Thus in birds such as Ciconia and Haliaetus it is difficult or even impossible to identify satisfactorily the usual nuclear masses described (*Ariëns Kappers*, '21).   According to the terminology of *Ramón y Cajal* as here employed, four major nuclear groups are recognizable within the deep cerebellar gray : *a*, nucleus tecti, or the internal cerebellar nucleus ; *b*, nucleus intercalatus ; *c*, nucleus intermedius ; *d*, nucleus lateralis (see fig. 393).

The internal nucleus, or nucleus tecti, or the nucleus fastigii of *Craigie* ('28), makes its appearance slightly in front of the other cerebellar nuclei, at least in such forms as the sparrow.   It varies in appearance from section to section.   Its most characteristic form is that of a U with medial and lateral limbs, and with the opening, filled with fiber bundles, on the dorsal side.   In wax reconstructions it presents more or less the form of a corrugated bag with the opening directed dorsally.   The nucleus lies near its fellow of the opposite side, although separated in birds, such as the sparrow, by a prolongation of the cerebellar ventricle, particularly at the caudal end.   Extending slightly caudal to the level of the internal cerebellar nucleus is a small intercalated nucleus which interconnects the former nucleus with the nucleus intermedius cerebelli.

The nucleus intermedius cerebelli is in no plane sharply separable from the internal cerebellar nucleus, and both sections and reconstructions indicate that at proper levels they are continuous through the nucleus intercalatus.   Although its form varies from section to section, it is divisible in general into a large-celled portion, comparable to the pars magnocellularis of the medial cerebellar nucleus of *van Hoevell*, and a small-celled portion, comparable to the pars parvocellularis of the same nuclear mass (*Ramón y Cajal*, '08 and '11 ; *van Hoevell*, '16 ; *Sanders*, '29).

The lateral cerebellar nucleus has been divided by *Ramón y Cajal* ('08) and *Sanders* ('29) into a superior and an inferior portion.   It is somewhat uncertain whether the inferior lateral cerebellar nucleus of *Craigie* ('28) corresponds to the inferior or superior group of the above observers.   At best the terms are relative, since in reconstructions the gray of the whole nuclear mass is actually continuous, although somewhat folded, and hence in sections presents the appearance of separate cell groups.   The name of nucleus lateralis superior is applied to the more dorsal portion of the mass, which in typical cross sections (*Ramón y Cajal*) has the form of the letter U.   The inferior lateral cerebellar nucleus is in reality interpolated between the nucleus intermedius cerebelli and the superior lateral nucleus.   As do the other cerebellar nuclei, this nucleus varies in appearance from section to section, sometimes presenting a U-shaped appearance and sometimes appearing as cell clusters (fig. 393). *Ramón y Cajal* believed that the portions of the lateral cerebellar nucleus could be distinguished from each other, at least to some extent, through the presence of smaller cells in the superior lateral portion than in the inferior lateral portion. *Sanders* found no marked difference in cell character, although the smaller cells seemed slightly more numerous in the superior portion. *Van Hoevell* ('16) identified the two subdivisions of the lateral cerebellar nuclear gray in parrots.

The homologies of the above four nuclear groups with those of lower forms are uncertain. There seems little question but that the nucleus tecti of *Ramón y Cajal* ('08), or the internal cerebellar nucleus, is contained in the medial nuclear group of reptiles, and that the lateral nucleus of this author falls within the lateral reptilian group, but there appears to be uncertainty as to whether the nucleus intermedius of *Ramón y Cajal* falls partly or completely within the medial group, since it forms a connecting link, at least in the sparrow, between the medial and the lateral nuclear masses. *Ramón y Cajal* has offered the following suggestions with regard to the homologies with mammalian forms, which are, perhaps, the best interpretations, although they require a much more complete knowledge of the fiber connections than is at present available for their final and complete acceptance. *Ramón y Cajal* regarded the nucleus internus or nucleus tecti as the homologue of the nucleus tecti or nucleus fastigii of mammals, an interpretation with which the majority of students of this region are in agreement;

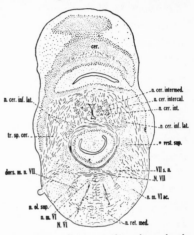

Fig. 393. Cross section through the cerebellar nuclei of the sparrow. Toluidin-blue preparation. × 8.5. *Sanders.*
dors.m.n.VII, dorsal motor nucleus of facial nerve; *n.cer.inf.lat.*, nucleus cerebellaris inferior lateralis; *n.cer.intercal.*, nucleus cerebellaris intercalatus; *n.cer. int.*, nucleus cerebellaris internus; *n.cer. intermed.*, nucleus cerebellaris intermedius; *n.m.VI ac.*, accessory motor nucleus of abducens nerve; *n.m.VI*, chief motor nucleus of abducens nerve; *n.ol.sup.*, nucleus olivarius superior; *n.ret.med.*, nucleus reticularis medius; *n.vest.sup.*, nucleus vestibularis superior; *N.VI*, abducens nerve; *N.VII*, facial nerve; *tr.sp.cer.*, tractus spino-cerebellaris; *VII s.n.*, visceral sensory nucleus of facial nerve.

nucleus intercalatus was regarded as the forerunner of nucleus globosus, nucleus intermedius as comparable to the mammalian nucleus emboliformis, and nucleus lateralis as the homologue of the dentate nucleus of mammals.

It was stated at the beginning of this account of the cerebellar nuclear gray that there are several modes of approach to the consideration of these structures, all of which deserve emphasis since they are mutually helpful in explaining differences in the accounts of form relations as given by different authors. *Edwin J. Doty*, working in the Laboratory of Comparative Neurology, University of Michigan, made a wax reconstruction of the deep cerebellar gray of the sparrow. This model, verified by *Huber* and *Crosby*, admits of the following fundamental interpretation. It is found, for the sparrow at least, that the whole of the cerebellar nuclear gray constitutes a continuous nuclear mass, presenting regional thickenings and definite undulations, which in separate sections and in different planes of section, give varied pictures of apparent nuclear forms and nuclear groupings. The repetition of U-shaped patterns, as seen in sections, represents, when interpreted through the model, merely cross sections of somewhat definite folds, the openings of which have fibers of passage to or from cerebellar gray. It is evident to *Huber* and *Crosby* that this folding of the cerebellar gray, which, in its beginning, may be noted in the reptile and reaches a much higher development in the bird, serves the purpose of increasing the surface area of the cerebellar gray and, by spreading it in a relatively thin layer, permits of more definite localization of afferent and efferent paths. Differences of cellular structure within the mass of gray evidence localization of functional differences. Furthermore, these differences in cell structure suggest that along this mass of nuclear gray there are differentiating both afferent and efferent centers with respect to the cerebellum, since centers which are predominantly efferent are not prone to show marked differences in cell types. The results of reconstruction are confirmatory of the presence of functional nuclear groups, even though these be structurally interconnected, and emphasize the importance of a study of cell types and fiber connections rather than of minute descriptions of nuclear form and arrangement as seen in sections, and serve to indicate the manner in which in phylogeny the cerebellar nuclei have differentiated.

These cerebellar nuclei are not wholly independent of the underlying brain stem gray. From the caudal part of the more medial cerebellar gray a strand of cells extends ventralward into the medulla oblongata, constituting the nucleus processus cerebelli. In Palaeornis (see also *van Hoevell*, '17) there is a similar connection between the lateral cerebellar nucleus and the underlying gray. These connections suggest a genetic relation between the cerebellum and the gray of the frontal vestibular area.

A survey of the fiber connections of the avian cerebellum indicates a particular increase in the caudally directed efferent systems as compared with those present in reptiles. Some of the more important afferent systems demonstrated by various workers on the avian brain are : 1, the dorsal and ventral spino-cerebellar systems (*Friedländer*, '98 ; *Ingvar*, '19 ; *Sanders*, '29) ; 2, the olivo-cerebellar tract ; 3, the cerebello-laminar tract (*Mesdag*, '09), cochleo-cerebellar (*Bok*, '15), or lamino-cerebellar tract (*Sanders*, '29) ; 4, the direct vestibular root fibers (*Ramón y Cajal*, '08 and '11, *Wallenberg*, '00 ; *Sanders*, '29) and vestibulo-cerebellars (*Ramón y Cajal*, '08 ; *Shimazono*, '12 ; *Groebbels*, '27, etc., *Sanders*, '29) ; 5, the direct trigeminal root fibers and contralateral and homolateral trigemino-cerebellar tracts (*Biondi*, '13 ; *Craigie*, '28 ; *Sanders*, '29, and others) ; 6, the tecto-cerebellar tract (*Münzer* and *Wiener*, '98 ; *Wallenberg*, '00 ; *Frenkel*, '09 ; *Shimazono*, '12, and others) ; 7, the tractus semilunaris cerebellaris (*Craigie*, '28 ; *Sanders*, '29) ; 8, the so-called striocerebellar tract (*Schroeder*, '11 ; *Huber* and *Crosby*, '29 ; *Sanders*, '29 ; *Muskens*, '30).

The main efferent cerebellar paths are : 1, the cerebello-spinal tract (*Ramón y Cajal*, '08 ; *Frenkel*, '09 ; *Shimazono*, '12) ; 2, the superior and the inferior cerebello-reticular tracts (*Sanders*, '29) ; 3, the cerebello-motorius system (*Wallenberg*,

'00; *Frenkel*, '09; *Sanders*, '29); 4, the cerebello-vestibular system (*Sanders*, '29, and others); 5, the brachium conjunctivum or the tractus cerebello-tegmentalis mesencephali (various observers); 6, the tractus cerebello-diencephalicus (*Frenkel*, '09; *Muskens*, '30).

The following account is based on literature cited above, on the very rich collection of avian material available at the Central Institute for Brain Research at Amsterdam, where the work of *Ingvar* was carried out, and on the very rich collection at the University of Michigan, where the contribution of *Sanders* was prepared.

The spino-cerebellar system (figs. 393 and 394), usually divided into a dorsal and a ventral spino-cerebellar tract (which are not necessarily strictly homologous with similar bundles in mammals), is highly developed. Experimental work gives evidence that its fibers take origin from the spinal cord as far caudally as the lumbar region (*Friedländer*, '98). Within the cord this system occupies practically all of the surface area of the lateral white funiculus. As the bundles reach the medulla oblongata, they occupy most of the lateral superficial surface. Gradually the more dorsal fascicles swing external to the nucleus of the descending root of the trigeminal

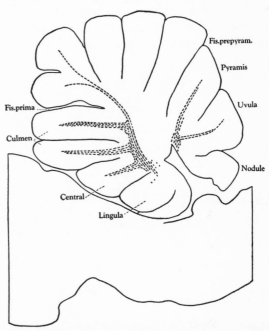

FIG. 394. The termination of the spino-cerebellar system in the dove, shown in a median section through the cerebellum (Marchi preparation). *Ingvar.*

and then run forward and dorsalward into the cerebellum. The more ventral part of the system swings far forward and then curves dorsalward and backward into the cerebellum. These systems carry both crossed and uncrossed fibers, the decussation occurring in the cerebellar commissure. To what extent they may decussate in the spinal cord is uncertain. They terminate to a large extent in the cerebellar cortex, but certain bundles reach the more medially placed cerebellar nuclei. The fibers to the cerebellar cortex end in the anterior and posterior lobes (*Ingvar,* '19, *Hausman*, '29).

The inferior olivary nucleus is interconnected with the cerebellum by olivo-cerebellar and possibly cerebello-olivary fibers. Such paths are heavily medullated and consequently particularly clear in Weigert material.

A cerebello-laminar (*Mesdag*, '09), cochleo-cerebellar (*Bok*, '15), or lamino-cerebellar (*Sanders*, '29) tract from nucleus laminaris has been described for various birds, although unquestioned evidence as to the direction of conduction over this fiber bundle is not at hand. *Bok* carried it to the lateral cerebellar nucleus.

There is marked difference of opinion among observers as to the presence of direct vestibular root fibers to the cerebellum. *Ramón y Cajal* ('08) and *Wallenberg* ('00) were of the opinion that such fibers are present, although the latter stated that his lesion did not exclude the restiform body or angular nucleus. More recently *Sanders* ('29) traced direct vestibular root fibers·to the inferior lateral cerebellar nucleus. However, there are a number of observers who have been unable to demonstrate such a connection, among whom may be mentioned *Frenkel* ('09). There is no doubt with regard to secondary vestibulo-cerebellar tracts and also cerebello-vestibular tracts. Such a bundle — tractus octavo-floccularis — was described by *Shimazono* ('12) from the "internal" vestibular nucleus to the cerebellum. *San-*

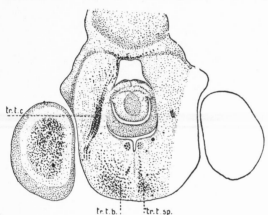

FIG. 395. The tecto-cerebellar tract (*tr.t.c.*) in the dove. *Frenkel.* tr.t.b., tractus tecto-bulbaris; *tr.t.sp.*, tractus tecto-spinalis.

ders ('29) found connections between the ventrolateral vestibular nucleus and the cerebellum, and traced fiber bundles from the superior vestibular nucleus to the inferior lateral cerebellar nucleus and possibly to other cerebellar nuclear groups. The neurons of the medial and intermediate divisions of the dorsolateral vestibular nuclear group (see page 478) were found to be so oriented that their dendrites came into relation with vestibulo-cerebellar, direct vestibular, and cerebello-motorius fibers. Their neuraxes entered the latter tracts. *Ramón y Cajal* ('08) traced vestibulo-cerebellar fibers to the roof nuclei. It appears that the vestibular tracts are related mainly with floccular portions, with the most posterior median part of the vermis (the interfloccular portion) and with the cerebellar nuclei. *Groebbels* ('27) carried fibers from his "Otolithenbahn" to the processus cerebelli, as well as secondary connections ('27, '28, etc.) from vestibular areas to the lateral cerebellar nucleus and the cerebellar cortex.

It is uncertain whether or not direct trigeminal fibers to the cerebellum are present in birds, although such relations have been suggested (*Sanders*, '29, and others) and certain of the series available strongly indicate the presence of root fibers which run in company with the bundles to the chief sensory nucleus but pass beyond that nucleus into the cerebellum. Secondary crossed and uncrossed trigemino-cerebellar paths, similar in detail to those noted for the alligator, have been identified in the sparrow and dove material, and, in addition, a bundle which passes dorsalward from the chief sensory nucleus decussates in the anterior medullary velum, and is believed then to enter the cerebellum (*Sanders*, '29). *Biondi* ('13) described the uncrossed trigemino-cerebellar tract in the chick and *Craigie* ('28) an homologous tract in the humming bird.

The tractus tecto-cerebellaris (fig. 395) was found in birds by *Münzer* and

Wiener ('98). Later it was observed by *Wallenberg* ('00), *Frenkel* ('09), *Shima-zono* ('12), *Sanders* ('29), and others. It arises from the medial gray along the ventricle and degenerates, according to *Frenkel*, after an injury of the inner wall of the optic tectum. It follows a medioventral course for a short distance caudally in order to enter the cerebellum behind the place of entrance of the spino-cerebellar tract. Part of the tecto-cerebellar fibers cross in the superior cerebellar commissure, the major portion of them end uncrossed in the cerebellar cortex, particularly in the caudal and medial portions of the corpus cerebelli (*Frenkel* and *Shimazono;* fig. 395). The avian tecto-cerebellar tract is most probably the homologue of the tractus mesencephalo-cerebellaris anterior of fishes.

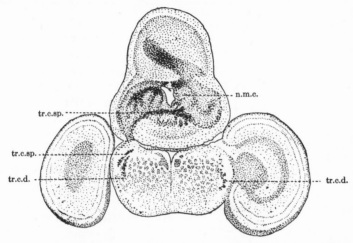

Fig. 396. The cerebellar paths of the dove. *Frenkel. n.m.c.,* nucleus internus cerebelli or nucleus tecti; *tr.c.d.,* tractus cerebello-diencephalicus; *tr.c.sp.,* tractus cerebello-spinalis.

Accompanying the tecto-cerebellar system in the sparrow (*Sanders*) is the tractus semilunaris cerebellaris, first identified by *Craigie* ('28) in the humming bird.

A strio-cerebellar tract has been described by *Schroeder* ('11), *Craigie* ('28), and *Huber* and *Crosby* ('29) as connecting the striatal region of the forebrain with the cerebellum. This tract accompanies the ventral peduncle of the lateral forebrain bundle in its course through diencephalon and mesencephalon and then swings dorsalward to enter the cerebellum. Recent work suggests the possibility that the path may be, at least in part, cerebello-striate (see fig. 493A and B).

Thus far, ponto-cerebellar fibers have not been identified in birds. This is in agreement with the lack of distinct cerebellar hemispheres in these forms. However, in many birds there are accumulations of gray along the base of the medulla oblongata at the level of the cerebellum which are suggestive of primitive pontine gray, but the function of which is not certainly known.

Comparisons of the afferent cerebellar tracts of birds and fishes offer points worthy of note. In birds the number of fibers running frontalward from the cerebellum is decreased rather than increased. Of such connections, the tecto-cerebellar alone may be regarded as larger than the homologous tracts of lower vertebrates.   The hypothalamo-cerebellar tracts, the function of which has not as yet been explained, have disappeared and also the tractus mesencephalo-cerebellaris posterior, the presence of which was questionable even in amphibians.   The latter tract is greatly hypertrophied in such animals as Mormyrus, where the lateral-line nerves are large.   Its absence in birds, where these nerves are lacking, is not surprising.   In the ascending and descending tracts connecting the avian cerebellum with more caudal areas, naturally the lateral-line components are lacking.   However, secondary and possibly primary tracts from vestibular and trigeminal areas end in the flocculus and the pars posterior of the cerebellum. The spino-cerebellar systems are highly developed in birds.   They reach the

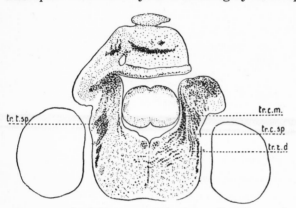

cerebellum from all levels of the cord down to the lower lumbar segments, bringing to it impulses concerned with static and kinetic functions. The differences in the paths in birds and fishes are due, then, to differences in their modes of life.   Orientation and the maintenance of equilibrium in aquatic animals such as fishes are made possible almost exclusively through stimuli entering over the vestibular and lateral-line nerves.   This explains the

FIG. 397.   Cerebellar tracts of the dove.   *Frenkel. tr.c.d.,* tractus cerebello-diencephalicus;   *tr.c.m.,* tractus cerebello-mesencephalicus;   *tr.c.sp.,* tractus cerebello-spinalis;   *tr.t.sp.,* tractus tecto-spinalis.

presence of a large tractus mesencephalo-cerebellaris posterior in fishes.   Specialized stimuli from joints and extremities are scarcely developed in fishes, but in birds, muscle tension and proprioceptive stimuli in general from the body and extremities determine orientation in space and the maintenance of equilibrium to a considerable extent.   This situation explains the great increase in spino-cerebellar fibers in avian forms.   (The differences between tailed and tailless amphibians have been discussed previously.)

On the efferent side, also, significant differences between lower forms and birds are seen.   Two main efferent paths from the cerebellum have been discussed for lower vertebrates.   These are the tractus cerebello-motorius and the brachium conjunctivum anterius (tractus cerebello-tegmentalis mesencephali).   To these must be added fibers from the cerebellum to the acoustico-lateral areas.   From such areas bundles join the tractus cerebello-motorius and perhaps the brachium conjunctivum in fishes.   In birds somewhat analogous conditions occur although with certain variations.   In the first place, in avian forms, the efferent tracts originate from clearly developed cerebellar nuclei, both medial and lateral cerebellar nuclear groups contributing to these tracts.

Among the efferent tracts of the cerebellum is the cerebello-spinal (and cerebello-bulbar) tract (fig. 397), which arises principally from the medial nucleus and which, after partial decussation in the inferior cerebellar commissure (*Ramón y Cajal*, '08, '11 ; *Frenkel*, '09 ; *Shimazono*, '12), passes caudalward, medial to the ventral spino-cerebellar tract of Gowers (*Frenkel*) and the olivo-cerebellar tract. At the level of the motor nucleus of the trigeminus, certain of its fibers turn medialward, then continue caudalward in a somewhat more ventral position, and finally course downward in the ventral part of the lateral funiculus as far as the lumbar cord. It is probable that in a general way this tract is comparable with the uncinate fasciculus (Russell's fasciculus) of the mammalian brain. The increased size of this tract is in harmony with the increased interrelation in general between cerebellum and cord. Probably with this group runs the inferior cerebello-reticular tract described by *Sanders* ('29) as connecting the cerebellum with the inferior reticular nuclei of the medulla oblongata.

A cerebello-motorius system has been described wholly or in part by numerous observers, among whom may be mentioned *Frenkel* ('09), *Wallenberg* ('00), *Ariëns Kappers* ('21), *Groebbels* ('27, '28, etc.), and *Sanders* ('29). Such bundles are said to arise from all of the cerebellar nuclei including the lateral superior, but it is probable that they receive particularly large contributions from the more medial gray. Certain of these bundles run medialward, internal to the spino-cerebellar path, turn directly medialward under the nucleus quadrangularis, and terminate in the contralateral and homolateral abducens nuclei. They correspond to the connection described by *Wallenberg* ('00). Other bundles from nucleus tecti (*Groebbels*) run ventralward and, joined by fibers from the inferior lateral cerebellar nuclei (*Sanders*), distribute to vestibular nuclei. These constitute a cerebello-vestibular tract. The motor trigeminal nucleus also receives cerebello-motorius fibers from the cerebellar nuclei, the fibers being partly crossed in the intertrigeminal decussation. *Groebbels* ('28, '28a, and elsewhere) carried fibers of this type from the lateral cerebellar nucleus to the medial longitudinal fasciculus of the same side and that of the opposite side. He ('28) traced the contralateral fibers to the motor centers of the spinal cord, regarding them as part of the reflex path for movements of the tail lateralward. His conclusions were based on experimental-anatomical work.

The tractus cerebello-tegmentalis mesencephali, or brachium conjunctivum anterius (according to *Ariëns Kappers*, '21, the tractus cerebello-diencephalicus, figs. 396 and 397, of *Frenkel*, whose contribution was not available to *Huber* and *Crosby*), originates chiefly or solely from the lateral nucleus (nucleus dentatus) of the cerebellum. The fibers can be traced, after crossing, as far as the red nucleus, which is quite well developed in birds. This nucleus provides a means of discharge for the cerebellum to lower centers through its rubro-bulbar paths, and the brachium conjunctivum, therefore, is merely a specialized cerebello-motorius system or cerebello-tegmental system. The mammalian nucleus ruber has a connection with the cortex and the striatum (cortico-rubral tract and ansa lenticularis) and with the thalamus (dento-rubro-thalamic tract) and is a way station on the path to these centers.[13] With this new function is associated

[13] It is probable that in birds there is present a small strio-rubral path (see Chapter VIII, page 1019).

an increase in the small cells of the nuclear mass, and the red nucleus in certain mammals projects forward into the diencephalon.   Fibers accompany the brachium conjunctivum anterius for the cells of the superior reticular group.   These constitute the tractus cerebello-reticularis superior of *Sanders* ('29).   Cerebello-tegmental fibers pass to other reticular gray.

Proprius fibers interconnect various regions of the cerebellum.   Prominent among such fibers are those arising as neuraxes of the Purkinje cells.   In fishes such neuraxes run lateralward soon after their origin and then course to the lateral side of the cerebellum and disappear within the white matter of the bulb (*Ramón y Cajal*, '11).   In birds these fibers, after giving off one or two recurrent collaterals, break through the granular layer of the cerebellum and terminate in the medial and lateral cerebellar nuclei.   These nuclei, from a topographic position in relation with the acoustico-lateral centers in the lower vertebrates, have secondarily become intracerebellar in position, due to a migration of subcerebellar cells, such as are present in shark, into the cerebellum.   With this migration, the neuraxes of the Purkinje cells, which were originally an efferent cerebellar system, become secondarily proprius fibers.   The question arises as to whether all of the neuraxes of the Purkinje cells terminate within the cerebellum, or whether certain neuraxes representative of the more primitive efferent fibers to the bulbar centers from the cerebellum may still be present in birds.   This latter relation appears to have been established by the work of *Shimazono* ('12), who found that penciling the cerebellar cortex with a 10 per cent solution of formol led to the degeneration of fibers and that such fibers could be traced not only to the cerebellar nuclei, but also as far as the region of Deiters' nucleus.[14]

As regards other intrinsic cerebellar fibers, mention need be made here only of the neuraxes of such intrinsic cells as the basket and horizontal cells of the cerebellar cortex.   The presence of processes of such cells below the cortex is improbable.   *Shimazono* ('12), who studied this subject exhaustively, reached the conclusion that interlobular association fibers do not exist.

The interauricular commissure of fishes is present in birds as an interfloccular commissure.   Commissural fibers interconnect the cerebellar nuclei (*Shimazono*, '12).   Such internuclear connections of the lateral cerebellar nuclei are particularly clear in silver preparations.

To review the great mass of experimental work, except as mention has been made of it in the preceding pages and in connection with the study of the avian vestibular centers (pp. 478 to 480), is beyond the scope of the present text. Obviously the cerebellum of birds, as that of other forms, is a great proprioceptive center.   Its close interrelation with the vestibular apparatus and centers has been emphasized by various observers, notably by *Groebbels*, who has made much of this interrelationship in his very interesting series of studies, by anatomical-experimental methods on the labyrinth, and the vestibular and cere-

---

[14] These neuraxes of Purkinje cells which extend to Deiters' nucleus must not be confused with the neuraxes of cells of the cerebellar nuclei which also run to the Deiters' nucleus.   The presence of both groups of fibers suggests the close relationship existing between the centers in question.

bellar centers of birds. These studies have been reviewed in the present text under the account of the avian vestibular centers (see pp. 479 and 480) and that review need not be repeated here.

The Cerebellum of Mammals

ONTOGENETIC AND PHYLOGENETIC DEVELOPMENT OF LOBES AND FISSURES AND THEIR ADULT RELATIONS

The cerebellum of mammals, as compared with that of lower vertebrates, is characterized by the greater development of its transverse diameter. In most mammals this increase is to be noted not only in lobus medius, from which the hemispheres are chiefly formed, but also in the floccular portion of the posterior lobe. To the above statement the monotremes are an exception. Thus in Echidna — as may be seen from the accompanying illustrations by de Lange ('18) — the floccular parts have increased considerably in size but that portion of the cerebellum lying in front of them presents scarcely any increase in transverse diameter.

Studies of *Elliot Smith* ('02, '03, '03a) and *de Lange* (figs. 398, 399) have indicated that the lateral parts of the cerebellum are relatively poorly developed in monotremes. The monotreme cerebellum forms a transition type between the cerebellum of lower and that of higher forms. When compared with the avian cerebellum, the cerebellum of monotremes is characterized by the great wealth of convolutions in the auricular region, where a floccular and parafloccular portion may be recognized. Anterior, middle, and posterior lobes are present in Echidna, the former separated by the fissura prima, the latter by the fissura post-pyramidalis, while a fissura prepyramidalis, a fissura uvulo-nodularis and other secondary fissures are recognizable.

In all higher mammals the lateral parts of the cerebellum, including the region in front of the flocculus, are considerably developed. Frequently they are more or less distinctly separated from the central portions by a shallow groove. For many decades the central part has been termed the vermis, the lateral portions the hemispheres. A sharp line between these areas cannot be drawn at all points or in all animals. Moreover, for the lingula (lobulus I lobi anterioris of *Bolk*) there is no hemispheric representative. However, this is the only region which does not have a definite hemispheric extension. Laterally along the remainder of the lobus anterior, a simple enlargement occurs, particularly in man. In the lobus medius of *Ingvar* ('19), between the sulcus primarius and the sulcus post-pyramidalis, occurs the major development of each hemisphere, especially in the lobulus ansiformis and lobulus paramedianus of *Bolk*. Lobulus ansiformis and lobulus paramedianus are structures characteristic of the mammalian cerebellum. In the lobus posterior, the vermis region (fig. 409) is separated from the para-flocculus and flocculus (which still adjoin them in birds) by the extensive growth caudalward of the paramedian lobule; the primitive connection is represented by the thin posterior medullary velum, a paired lateral part (*Johnston*, '34, J. Anat., vol. 68, p. 471) of the cerebellum, rudimentary, without gray.

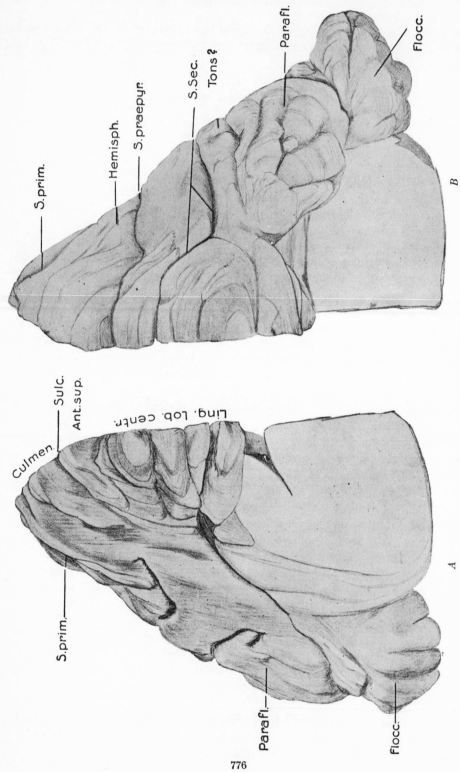

S. prim.

Hemisph.

S. praepyr.

S. Sec.

Tons?

Parafl.

Flocc.

B

Culmen.

Sulc.
Ant. sup.

Ling. Lob. centr.

S. prim.

Parafl.

Flocc.

A

Fig. 398. *A* and *B*. Anterior and posterior views of the cerebellum of Echidna. Wax reconstruction. Compare with figure 409. *de Lange.*

Phylogenetic and ontogenetic studies of the anatomy of the cerebellum and pathologic-anatomic researches indicate that the vermis and flocculus are the most primitive portions of this brain center, while the hemispheres are to be regarded as of later formation. Studies in comparative neurology (*Edinger*, '08; *Comolli*, '10) confirm this, and work on the ontogenetic development (*van Valkenburg*, '13) shows that the histologic development of the organ begins with the vermis and flocculus. *H. Vogt* and *Astwazaturow* ('11) and *Brouwer* ('13) have pointed out that in the atrophy of certain cerebellar connections (connections with the forebrain) only the hemispheres suffer, while the vermis and flocculus remain unchanged. In accordance with these facts, the above mentioned group of authors has separated the cerebellum into a neocerebellar portion and a paleocerebellar

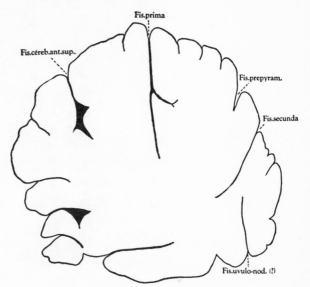

portion, and this nomenclature has received general acceptance. The two parts are not to be regarded as working antagonistically but as being complementary and supplementary to each other. The very continuance of the fissures of the vermis out through the hemispheres emphasizes the intimate relation between the two portions. With regard to these matters, the work of *Bolk* ('02, '02a, '02b, '05, '06, '07) should be consulted.

Before turning to a consideration of the adult structure of the cerebellum there are certain points with regard to its development which need emphasis, since they aid in an understanding of the adult structure and the comparison of the mammalian cerebellum with that of lower forms. Figures 400 and 401 indicate that in mammals, as in lower vertebrates, the cerebellum arises as bilateral outgrowths of the upper lip of the rhombencephalon. In a 13 mm. embryo the dorsolateral portion of the rhombencephalon is only slightly thickened in the region immediately behind the mesencephalon, but it projects farther dorsalward than does the remainder of the region. Medialward it extends only slightly into the ventricular space. Immediately behind the plica mesencephalo-cerebellaris are the eminences on the two sides, connected at first only by a narrow seam, to the free upper and lateral margins of which the tela attaches. During the second month (27 mm. length) the two lateral parts have increased in thickness and are more nearly horizontal, with lateral margins extending outward and forward. In this way an eversion is formed temporarily, which is suggestive of the permanent

Fig. 399. The cerebellum of Echidna. A section of a wax reconstruction by *de Lange*.

eversion of the cerebellum in the lizard, except that the protrusion is more nearly laterofrontalward in human embryos and more nearly dorsofrontalward in reptiles.   At this period the bilateral origin of the cerebellum is very apparent in the mammalian embryo.   In the shark evidence of the bilateral origin is found throughout the life of the animal (see page 713).

Near the midline the dorsal plate increases considerably in thickness.   This thickening marks the beginning of the vermis (*Streeter,* '12).   Below the cerebellar eminence there is an elevation of the lateral part of the cerebellum.   This passes over partially into the dorsolateral portion of the cerebellum and possibly may be

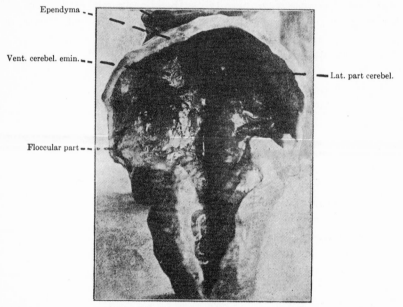

FIG. 400.   A wax reconstruction of the cerebellum of a human foetus of 13 mm. length.   (Preparation by *de Vries.*)

homologous to the eminentia ventralis cerebelli.   This eminence on the ventricular floor is particularly distinct in rat embryos, as is apparent in figure 402, which shows a reconstruction in wax of a 10 mm. rat embryo.

During the third month marked changes occur in the cerebellar region of the human embryo and this brain portion takes on the shape characteristic of higher forms.   This constitutes a very evident transformation of which not all the details are known as yet.   Previous to the third month (fig. 401) the place of attachment of the tela is moved frontalward and lateralward by the peculiar eversion of the primitive cerebellar plate and the tela itself lies at some distance beyond the everted inner side of the cerebellum.   An examination of an embryo at the end of the third month shows that the picture is entirely changed, for the line of attachment of the tela is no longer at the upper margin but at the posterior end of the cerebellum.   These differences in relations between the 2 and 3 months-old human foetuses are reminders of differences in cerebellar relations seen in lizards (fig. 381) and in certain other reptiles (figs. 383 and 386).   These changes are explained, from observations of *Bolk* ('05) and *His* ('91), as due to the secondary fusion of the tela with the dorsally turned ventricular wall so that the later line of attachment is secondarily acquired. To a small degree such a

Exverted cerebellum

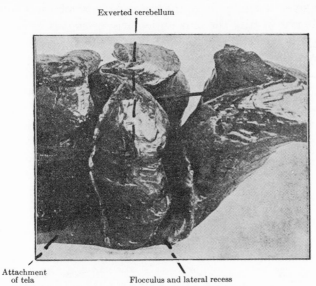

Attachment
of tela   Flocculus and lateral recess

FIG. 401. A wax reconstruction of the cerebellum of a human foetus of 27 mm. length. (Preparation by *de Vries*.) Note the eversion of the cerebellum.

concrescence of the two layers does occur by a new growth of cells from both the tela and the body of the cerebellum (*Langelaan*, '08), so that the space between the two is gradually filled in. This produces a condition relatively favorable for the development of cerebellar cysts (*Henschen*, '07). This line of attachment, where the thicker nervous tissue passes over into the thin tela (the so-called taenia), is an important proliferation zone for nervous tissue (an observation made earlier by *Schaper*, '94; see bibliography, p. 844). *Ingvar* ('19) questioned whether such a deformation and closing of the tela occurs, and *Ariëns Kappers* ('21) was of the opinion that these factors do not explain sufficiently the great differences between the everted embryonic type and the later developed inverted type of

Vent. cerebel. emin.   Cerebellum

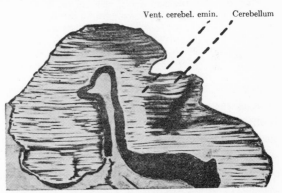

FIG. 402. The ventricular side of the brain of a rat embryo of 10 mm. length. (Preparation from the Anatomical Institute in Amsterdam.)

cerebellum. This latter observer is inclined to regard the great growth of the lobus anterior, which presses the more posterior portions of the area downward and backward, as the principal cause for the difference in the relations of the tela.

As soon as such growth has taken place, and at a very early stage of development, a sulcus is formed which cuts off the posterolateral margin from the remainder of the region.   This posterolateral portion is a delicate appendix-like structure which passes over caudally into the recessus lateralis and into the medulla oblongata.   It is evidently the pars auricularis, or as it is known in these forms, the pars or gyrus floccularis of the cerebellum.   The sulcus (*p*) which accompanied this part forward is the sulcus parafloccularis of *Bolk* ('02b, '06, etc.), the primitive homologue of which has been encountered in lower animals.

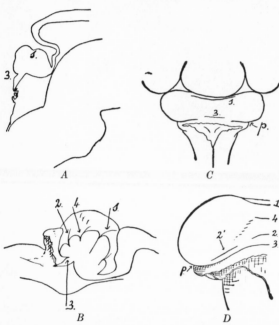

After the cerebellum has acquired its typical vaulted outline, horizontal fissures begin to develop in the central portion.   In an 8 cm. human embryo two fissures make their appearance practically simultaneously.   One of these lies immediately in front of the highest part of the cerebellum and is the fissura prima or sulcus primarius of *Kuithan* ('95; fig. 403, I; fig. 404).   The other lies in the posterior part of the cerebellum and is the sulcus or fissura uvulo-nodularis of *Bolk* ('02b, '06, etc.; fig. 403, 3; also fig. 404).   It separates off the lobulus floccularis of *Larsell* ('34).   According to *Elliot Smith* ('02), in certain lower mammals (as for example, in

Fig. 403.   Sagittal and dorsal views of the human cerebellum.   *A* and *C* show embryos 9 cm. in length; *B* and *D*, embryos 11 cm. in length.   *Bolk*.   *1*, fissura prima; *2*, fissura secunda; *3*, fissura uvulo-nodularis; *4*, fissura prepyramidalis (*Ingvar*), postpyramidalis (human anatomy); *p*., fissura paraflocculularis.

Dasyurus) the sulcus uvulo-nodularis appears somewhat earlier than does the sulcus primarius.   At its first appearance in man, the former sulcus is independent, apparently, of the sulcus or fissura paraflocculularis (fig. 403, *Bolk*), then for a time becomes connected with it, and later is again independent.   *Ingvar* doubted even this temporary connection.

In front of the uvula, in the 8 cm. human embryo, is the fissura secunda (prepyramidal fissure of *Piersol's* Anatomy, '30, of *Symington*, as in *Herrick*, '31, and of *Ranson*, '31) of *Elliot Smith* and then the fissura postpyramidalis (prepyramidalis of *Ingvar*), which latter is of particular importance because it is the boundary line between the middle and posterior lobes according to *Ingvar*. *Elliot Smith* ('02), however, regarded his fissura secunda as forming such a boundary and therefore included the pyramis with the middle lobe.   By means of the fissures thus described the main divisions of the mammalian cerebellum are

bounded.   *Larsell* and *Dow* ('35, J. Comp. Neurol., vol. 62, p. 443) have described
the development of the cerebellum in certain lower mammals.

From the preceding account it is evident that the mammalian sulcus or
fissura parafloccularis separates the auricular part of the cerebellum from the
corpus cerebelli.   This sulcus is, in all probability, the homologue of the fissura
paraauricularis of submammalian forms.   The fissura x of the bird cerebellum
appears to be the primitive homologue of the mammalian sulcus primarius

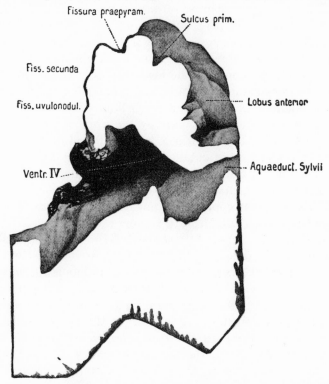

FIG. 404.   Median section of the cerebellum of a human embryo
of 11 cm. total length.   Note that the fissures bounding the anterior
and posterior lobes and the chief fissures subdividing them are present, while the lobus medius, between the fissura prima and the fissura prepyramidalis of *Ingvar*, has no fissures.   The taenia choroidea
is dark.   *Ingvar.*

or fissura prima, the anterior lobe in each case being bounded posteriorly
by it.   The anterior lobes in both birds (*Brouwer* — 64 per cent of cases) and
mammals are usually separable into four distinct lobuli.   The homologizing of
sulcus primarius with the sulcus anterior of reptiles is suggested by a comparison
of the conditions in the crocodile (fig. 405) with those occurring during the development of the mammalian cerebellum (*Bolk*, '02, '03, '05, and '07; also fig.
403).   The results of *Ingvar* with regard to the distribution of the spino-cerebellar system in reptiles and birds support such a homology (fig. 405).   *Ingvar*
('19) suggested that the avian fissure y is the homologue of the mammalian
sulcus prepyramidalis often termed the sulcus postpyramidalis in human

anatomy.   The region behind this sulcus in mammals is the lobus posterior, comparable to that lobe of birds.   He believed that the fiber connections warrant such a homology, but particularly emphasized the fact that in each animal type the region consists of three lobuli — pyramis, uvula, and nodulus — and that in each case it has similar relations with the floccular region.   The most posterior of the major fissures of birds (z) is the probable homologue of the fissura uvulo-nodularis.   The main points emphasized by *Ingvar* were that it is possible in both birds and mammals to separate off a pars posterior by means of a fissure which primarily is connected with the flocculus.   This fissure forms the posterior boundary of a middle lobe which is present in birds in varying size, depending upon the degree of development of the body.   In mammals this lobe becomes the main region of development of the hemispheres.   The middle lobe is separated from an anterior lobe in both birds and mammals by means of the sulcus primarius.   The manner in which the cerebellum is formed phylogenetically and ontogenetically has been made clear by the work of *Bolk* ('02, '02a, '02b, '05, '06, '07), *Elliot Smith* ('02, '03, '03a), *Bradley* ('03), *Ingvar* ('19), and others.

A consideration of the more detailed structure of the anterior, the middle, and the posterior lobes of the cerebellum shows that they are broken up into a number of subdivisions, which are termed either lobes (*Ariëns Kappers*, '21, see table on pages 788 and 789, copied with few changes from the 1920–21 edition of this text, and various figures from the same source; consult also *Marburg*, '24) or lobules (*Bolk*, '06; *Ingvar*, '19; *Larsell*, '34).   The choice of terms here is a matter of personal preference, of course, but in view of the fact that the main divisions are termed lobes, the use of the term lobule for smaller subdivisions contributes to the ease with which relations may be explained and has been employed freely in the following paragraphs (*Huber* and *Crosby*).

The lobus anterior cerebelli, lying in front of the fissura prima (sulcus primarius, fissura precliva), remains relatively narrow in mammals.   It may be subdivided into three lobuli: 1, the lingula (lobulus I of *Bolk*), which has no representative in the hemispheres; 2, the central (lobulus II of *Bolk*), continued out into the hemispheres as alae lobuli centralis; 3, the culmen (lobulus III and lobulus IV of *Bolk*), the lateral extension of which forms on either side the anterior quadrangular or anterior lunate lobe or lobule.   The lamellae of the lobus anterior are in a transverse direction but show a slight frontal concavity (see figures 405 to 408).

According to *Ingvar*, that part of the cerebellum lying behind the fissura prima (sulcus primarius) and in front of the fissura prepyramidalis of *Ingvar*, or postpyramidalis of some anatomists, is the lobus medius.   Its anterior portion is the lobulus simplex of *Bolk*, the vermis portion of which is the clivus of many anatomists, while the hemispheric portion is the lobulus (or lobus) quadrangularis or lunatus posterior.   The division between the vermis and hemispheric portions, however, is relatively indistinct.   Behind the clivus is a small vermis fold usually designated as folia vermis or folia cacuminis, with lateral extensions often termed lobulus (or lobus) posterior superior.   Sometimes folia vermis is counted with the tuber which lies behind it.   The lateral extensions of the tuber into the hemispheres are the posterior inferior lobules (or lobes). The tuber (probably together with the folia vermis) constitutes the lobulus medius medianus of *Ingvar*, which is the caudal portion of the vermis region of the middle lobe as described by this observer. *Elliot Smith* ('07) included the pyramis, which lies behind the tuber, within the middle lobe, making the caudal boundary of this lobe, the fissura postpyramidalis of *Ingvar* or the fissura prepyramidalis of various other observers. *Ingvar*

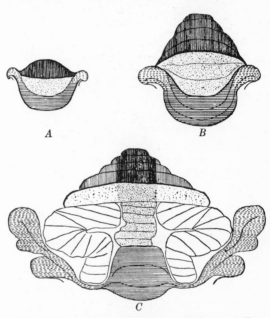

and others have regarded, as hemispheric portions of the middle lobe behind the lobulus simplex, all of the territory back to the paraflocculus and the flocculus. This region consists of (1) a lobulus ansiformis, which includes not only the lateral extensions of the folia vermis and the tuber — according to the older terminology, the superior posterior and the inferior posterior lobules respectively — but also the lateral extensions of the pyramid — the biventer or biventral lobules — and (2) a lobulus paramedianus, which is formed by the tonsil, earlier regarded as a lateral extension of the uvula (see figures 407 and 408.) *Bolk* called the area behind the lobulus simplex, lobulus complicatus. Thus lobulus (or lobus) complicatus includes the tuber and pyramis in the vermis region and the associated

FIG. 405. A schematic diagram of the cerebellum: A, crocodile; B, bird; C, mammal. *Ingvar*.

The lobus anterior is indicated by vertical lines; the lobus posterior by horizontal lines; the auricular portion by broken lines. The lobus ansoparamedianus is left white; the dotted portion represents the lobulus simplex and the vermis part of the lobus medius behind it.

hemispheric portions or lobi laterales, the two being separated by a sulcus paramedianus. The tuber and the pyramis are sublobules C_2 and C_1 of *Bolk*. The hemispheric portions corresponding to these two sublobules, according to *Bolk*, are the crus primum C_1 and the crus secundum C_2 of the ansiform lobule together with the paramedian lobule. The paramedian lobule corresponds to the tonsilla, one crus of the ansiform lobule is the biventer and the other crus the posterior inferior and posterior superior lobules of the older terminology. The two crura are separated by the intercrural fissure (the hemispheric portion of the postpyramidal fissure of human anatomy, or prepyramidal fissure of *Ingvar*). In physiologic literature the term lobulus or lobus ansoparamedianus is often used; it includes the crura of the lobulus ansiformis and the lobulus paramedianus. *Bolk's* terminology is distinctly confusing in that he uses crus secundum with lobulus C_1 and crus primum with lobulus C_2. Perhaps *Testut* ('11) changed the terminology of C_1 and C_2 in his text in order to avoid such confusion. The vermis portion of the posterior lobe, according to *Ingvar* ('19), includes the pyramis, the uvula, and the nodule — the so-called lobulus medianus posterior — while the hemispheric portions consist of the flocculus and the paraflocculus. *Elliot Smith* ('07) included the pyramis (fig. 406) in the middle lobe. *Larsell* ('34) separated off the nodulus and the flocculus from the rest of the cerebellum and termed

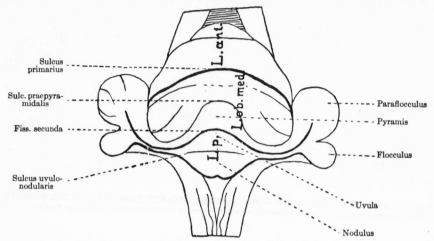

FIG. 406.   The subdivisions of the cerebellum.   *Elliot Smith.*

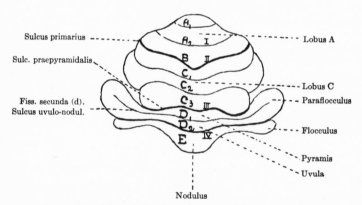

FIG. 407.   The subdivisions of the cerebellum.   *Bradley.*

them a floccular lobe. Behind the pyramis of the vermis, *Bolk* recognized a lobulus *B*, the uvula of the current human anatomy, and a lobulus *A*, the nodulus of human anatomy. The majority of anatomists have counted the flocculus and the paraflocculus, separated from the paramedian lobule by a parafloccular fissure, as portions of the cerebellar hemispheres, but *Bolk* and *Gratiolet* have termed these regions the formatio vermicularis. A chief difference between the divisions of *Bolk* and *Ingvar* is to be found in the fact that *Bolk* placed the crus secundum of the ansiform lobule (biventer lobule) and the paramedian lobule (tonsilla) with the pyramis, while *Ingvar* regarded the hemispheric portions above mentioned, together with the crus primum and the lobulus

simplex, as parts of the lobus medius and the pyramid as part of the lobus posterior. *Ingvar* emphasized that the lateral portion of the lobus medius is not
simply a lateral expansion of the vermis lamellae. The transitions to the
lateral systems in the lobulus paramedianus are too incomplete and irregular
for this to be the case in all animals. That the fissura prepyramidalis of *Ingvar*
(postpyramidalis of human anatomy) is a fissure of morphologic significance is
evinced in certain mammals, such as the horse and the sheep, by the fact that the
lamellae of the pyramid are conspicuously thicker and broader than those of the

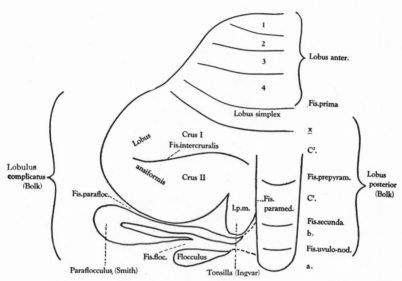

Fig. 408. Divisions of the cerebellum according to *Bolk*. *l.p.m.*, lobulus paramedianus (tonsilla of *Ingvar*); *p.t.*, pars tonsillaris formationis vermicularis (paraflocculus
of *Elliot Smith*, *Bradley*, and *Ingvar*); *F*, flocculus.

vermis area in front of it, while they resemble rather closely those of the uvula
and nodule.

Another great difficulty in homologizing parts is met with in a study of the
development of the tonsilla. According to *Bolk* and *Langelaan* ('19), pars
tonsillaris is formed by a lateral outgrowth of the pars posterior between the
fissura secunda and the fissura uvulo-nodularis, in conjunction with the uvula.
Its genetic and topographic connections with the vermis present certain difficulties. According to *Elliot Smith* ('02; see also '03 and '03a) and *Bradley*
('03) the pars tonsillaris must be regarded as a lateral outgrowth of the pyramis
which is connected with it by means of a fine lamella, the copula pyramidis.
Ingvar did not regard the pars tonsillaris as an enlarged copula pyramidis but
as the lobulus paramedianus of his lobus medius, because, particularly in lower
mammals such as Macropus, it is seen not in connection with the pyramis, but
with those portions of the vermis in front of it. That the tonsilla happens to be
situated lateral to the pyramis and uvula depends upon the caudal shifting of
the lateral portions of the cerebellum with reference to the medial portions, as
Bolk had already pointed out. Topographically the tonsilla frequently lies in

close approximation to the flocculus, and this probably led *Bolk* to speak of it as a pars tonsillaris of the formatio vermicularis and to regard it as representative of the pars parafloccularis of other authors. With this statement neither *Elliot Smith* nor *Ingvar* was in agreement. The latter observer, working

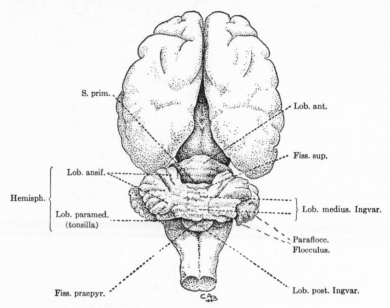

FIG. 409. Cerebellum of Phascolomys latifrons.

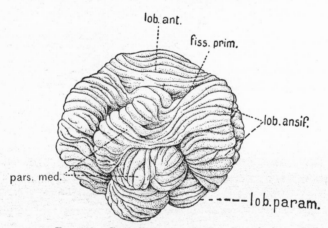

FIG. 410. Cerebellum of a giraffe. Dorsal view. *Bolk*.

in the Institute at Amsterdam, found that a rudiment of the paraflocculus exists behind the tonsilla. Thus, if the tonsillae were to be counted with the flocculi they would have to be regarded as new formations and not as arising from the primitive pars auricularis of the cerebellum. Their relation to other than primitive auricular portions is supported by the fact that they almost disappear in cases of neocerebellar atrophy. Also, they have fiber connections which are characteristic of cerebellar regions other than the flocculus. The old division of the formatio vermicularis into two parts, a pars parafloccularis and a pars tonsillaris, apparently will be superseded by a division of this formation into a pars floccularis and a pars paraflocccularis (*Elliot Smith*, '02; *Bradley*, '03; *Ingvar*, '19). These last-mentioned observers connected the paraflocculus with the uvula and pyramis, and the flocculus with the nodulus. *Larsell* ('34) grouped the flocculus and nodulus into a lobus floccularis.

In conclusion it may be said that superficial observation makes possible the identification of the anterior, middle, and posterior lobes in the more primitive mammals (Macropus and Phascolomys, fig. 409). In higher animals,

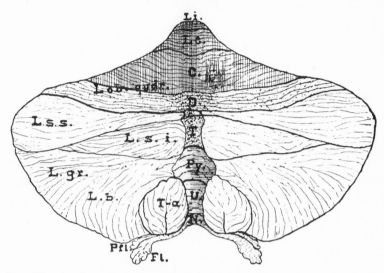

FIG. 411. A schematic diagram of the human cerebellum. *Ingvar*. Upper view (see also figures 413 and 414).

the separate parts are less easily distinguished, particularly in adult forms. Study of the development, however, indicates that a common pattern exists for all mammals, including man. The table on pages 788 and 789 illustrates the old and new terminology as applied to cerebellar regions. The old names are inclosed in brackets. Certain of them have been taken over into the new terminology. It is gratifying that the older cabalistic nomenclature is gradually being replaced by the newer and more logical terminology. Recently *Riley* ('29) discussed the difficulties arising from the various terminologies for cerebellar regions and suggested an even more simplified system of nomenclature. It cannot be predicted now which of the various systems of nomenclature will be adopted.

In so far as the development and the general morphology of the cerebellum of mammals are concerned, the main features are demonstrated excellently in the marsupial, Phascolomys latifrons (fig. 409). In respect to its special morphology the various classes exhibit great differences, which are undoubtedly dependent upon different factors most of which are as yet unknown to us. *Bolk* ('03) has pointed out that the anterior lobe (fig. 410) is a median, unpaired structure and

SUMMARY OF THE CEREBELLAR SUBDIVISIONS WITH NOTATION OF THE VARIOUS NOMENCLATURES USED.

Lobus Anterior (Bolk, Ingvar)

Lobulus I (Lingula)

Sulcus postlingualis

Lobulus II (Lobulus centralis)

Ala lobuli centralis

Ala lobuli centralis

Sulcus postcentralis

Lobus quadrilaterus anterior or
quadrangularis anterior or
Lobus lunatus anterior or
Anterior crescentic lobule

{ Lobulus III
  Lobulus IV } Culmen

Lobus quadrilaterus anterior or
quadrangularis anterior or
Lobus lunatus anterior or
Anterior crescentic lobule

Sulcus primarius or
Fissura prima or
Sulcus superior anterior or
preclival sulcus

Lobus Medius (Ingvar)

Lobulus simplex (Bolk)

Lobus quadrilaterus posterior or
quadrangularis posterior or
Lobus lunatus posterior or
Posterior crescentic lobule

Lobus quadrilaterus posterior or
quadrangularis posterior or
Lobus lunatus posterior or
Posterior crescentic lobule

Sulcus superior posterior or
Fissura postlunata or
postclival sulcus

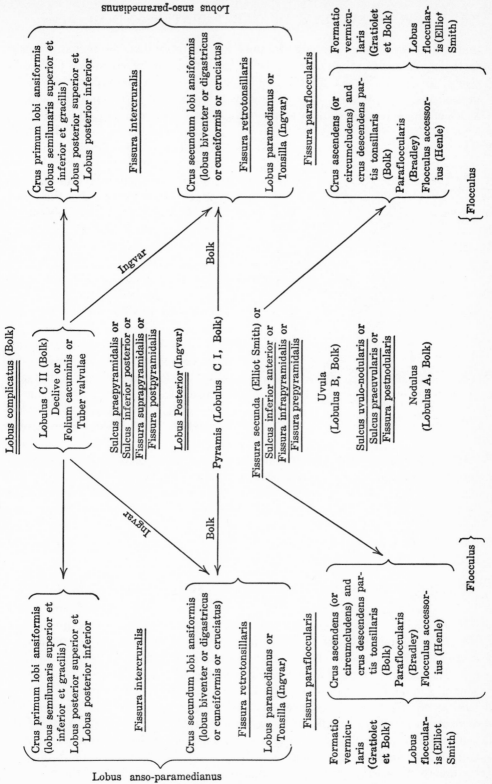

Lobus anso-paramedianus

Lobus complicatus (Bolk)

Lobulus C II (Bolk)
Declive or
Folium cacuminis or
Tuber valvulae

Crus primum lobi ansiformis
(lobus semilunaris superior et
inferior et gracilis)
Lobus posterior superior et
Lobus posterior inferior

Fissura intercruralis

Crus secundum lobi ansiformis
(lobus biventer or digastricus
or cuneiformis or cruciatus)

Fissura retrotonsillaris

Lobus paramedianus or
Tonsilla (Ingvar)

Fissura parafloccularis

Crus ascendens (or
circumcludens) and
crus descendens par-
tis tonsillaris
(Bolk)
Parafloccularis
(Bradley)
Flocculus accessor-
ius (Henle)

Formatio
vermicu-
laris
(Gratiolet
et Bolk)

Lobus
floccular-
is (Elliot
Smith)

Flocculus

Ingvar

Bolk

Sulcus praepyramidalis or
Sulcus inferior posterior or
Fissura suprapyramidalis or
Fissura postpyramidalis

Lobus Posterior (Ingvar)

Pyramis (Lobulus C I, Bolk)

Fissura secunda (Elliot Smith) or
Sulcus inferior anterior or
Fissura infrapyramidalis or
Fissura prepyramidalis

Uvula
(Lobulus B, Bolk)

Sulcus uvulo-nodularis or
Sulcus praeuvularis or
Fissura postnodularis

Nodulus
(Lobulus A, Bolk)

Ingvar

Bolk

Crus primum lobi ansiformis
(lobus semilunaris superior et
inferior et gracilis)
Lobus posterior superior et
Lobus posterior inferior

Fissura intercruralis

Crus secundum lobi ansiformis
(lobus biventer or digastricus
or cuneiformis or cruciatus)

Fissura retrotonsillaris

Lobus paramedianus or
Tonsilla (Ingvar)

Fissura parafloccularis

Formatio
vermicu-
laris
(Gratiolet
et Bolk)

Lobus
floccular-
is (Elliot
Smith)

Crus ascendens (or
circumcludens) and
crus descendens par-
tis tonsillaris
(Bolk)
Parafloccularis
(Bradley)
Flocculus accessor-
ius (Henle)

Flocculus

Lobus   anso-paramedianus

that it and the lobulus simplex are much less variable than the region posterior to them. The variations appear to be restricted chiefly, although not exclusively, to the region behind the lobulus simplex. Foci of variation are found in the tuber and pyramis. Sometimes, as in Talpa, the vermis may be smooth; at other times it may show a series of cauliflower-like convolutions formed by groups of lamellae as in the giraffe

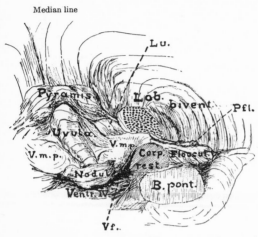

Median line

FIG. 412. The human cerebellum from below and behind, showing nidus avis (space between velum medullare posterius and nodulus and uvula). *Ingvar.* *B.pont.*, brachium pontis; *corp.rest.*, corpus restiforme; *Lu.*, ala uvulae; *Pfl.*, paraflocculus, which is obviously smaller than the flocculus; *V.m.p.*, velum medullare posterius.

(fig. 410). That the differences are not due simply to the working out of the law of Baillarger and Dareste is proved by the fact that the vermis in the elephant is relatively simply constructed (*Bolk*, '02b). Another center of variation is found in each lateral part of the lobus medius. In some animals the ansiform lobules (lobes) are in the form of simple bands or small groups of regularly arranged lamellae (rodents); in other animals the area may become so complicated (anthropoids, man) that it is scarcely possible to recognize the fundamental scheme of cerebellar structure. The paramedian lobule (lobe) is relatively constant throughout mammals.

The paraflocculus and flocculus (the formatio vermicularis of *Bolk*) are the most variable portions of the lobus posterior. In elephants and in man (figs. 411, 412, and 413) this general region is developed relatively poorly in contrast with the rest of the hemisphere, but in Cetacea (fig. 414) and in Pinnipedia it is almost as large as the hemispheres, and between these two extremes all degrees of variation are found. This portion of the cerebellum does not develop in direct proportion to the size of the body.

THE HISTOLOGIC STRUCTURE AND THE NUCLEI OF THE CEREBELLUM

The histologic structure of the cerebellar cortex was considered fully at the beginning of the present chapter and need not receive further description here. However, a brief account of the cerebellar nuclei in mammals is demanded. In the lowest mammals, the monotremes and marsupials, the cerebellar nuclei are divisible into a medial roof nucleus and a lateral nucleus, a condition in general similar to that in many reptiles. In Echidna the roof nucleus (nucleus tecti or nucleus fastigii) is already clearly circumscribed. In most mammals it appears to receive, in addition to vestibular connections and collaterals of the ventral spino-cerebellar tract, neuraxes of Purkinje cells of the lobus anterior and lobulus simplex (*van Valkenburg*, '13). Its relative uniformity throughout the mammals is associated with the relatively uniform structure of these cortical

areas of the cerebellum. In lower mammals the nucleus tecti is associated laterally with the lateral cerebellar nucleus. Nucleus lateralis shows much greater
variation throughout the mammalian line than does the roof nucleus.

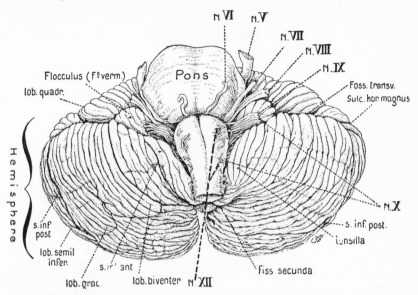

FIG. 413. Human cerebellum. View from the under side. (See figures 411 and 412.)

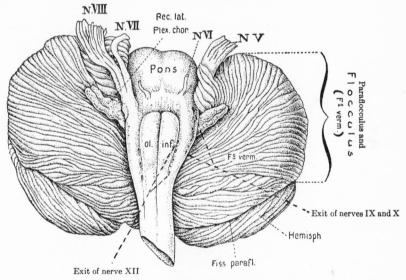

FIG. 414. Cerebellum of a whale, seen from below. *Bolk*. Note the enormous extent
of the floccular portion (F° vermicularis, *Bolk*) in this animal.

In Macropus (fig. 415) and in Hypsiprymnus the roof nucleus and the lateral
nucleus are clearly differentiated from each other. In various other mammals
below primates, including representative rodents, edentates, chiropteres, insectivores, ungulates, and carnivores, a third nuclear group, the nucleus inter-

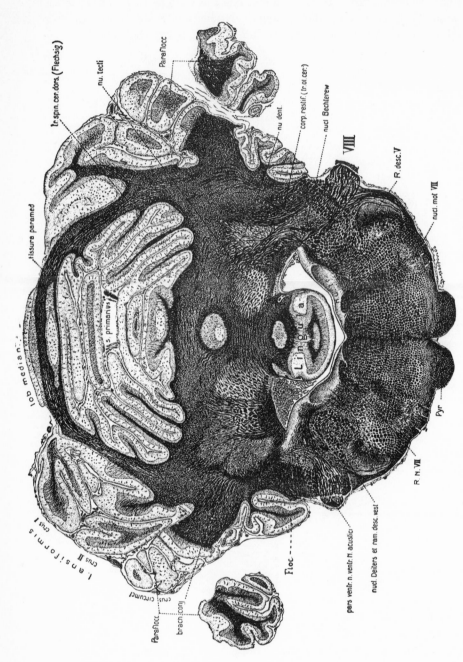

FIG. 415. A cross section through the cerebellum of Macropus robustus.

792

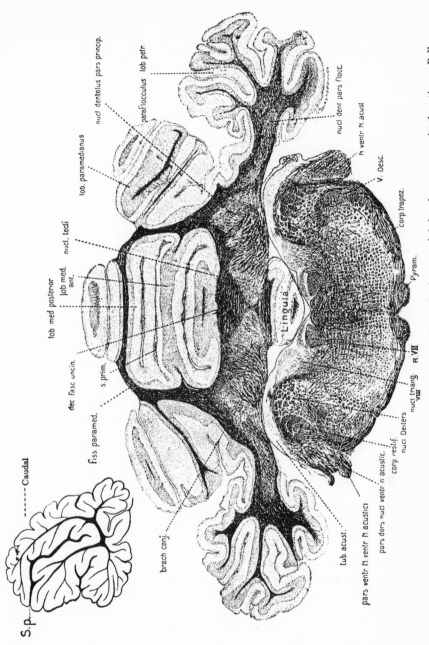

S.p.

Caudal

nucl dentatus pars princp.

paraflocculus lob petr

lob. paramedianus

nucl dent pars flocc

n ventr N acust

V. Desc.

corp trapez.

Lingula

Pyram.

lob med posterior

nucl. tecti

lob med. ant.

s prim.

dec fasc uncin.

fiss paramed.

nucl trang.
VIII   R VII

nucl Deiters

corp restif.

pars dors nucl ventr n acustic.

pars ventr N ventr N acustici

tub acust.

brach conj.

Fig. 416. A cross section through the cerebellum of a rabbit. In the upper left-hand corner, a sagittal section. *Bolk.*

793

positus or nucleus intermedius (*Weidenreich*, '99; *Brunner*, '19; *Allen*, '24; *Dowd*, '29; *Larsell*, '34) has been described, which, according to *Brunner*, reaches its highest differentiation in quadrupeds. In cetaceans there is some further specialization, but the type is essentially a modification of that seen in carnivores. In primates (above Simia, *Brunner*, '19) the nucleus intercalatus or interpositus is differentiated into a nucleus emboliformis and a nucleus globosus. In rodents there is some evidence of lamination within the dentate nucleus (fig. 416).

In cetaceans, carnivores, and primates, the lamellation is much greater than in rodents. A study of the dentate nucleus in these higher animals indicates that with the progressive development of the lamellation of the nucleus there is a corresponding thinning of the lamellar walls. Thus the lamellation is greater and the walls of the gray mass are thinner in man and higher apes than in lower apes. This increase in surface of the nucleus is probably associated with the further development of the cerebellar hemispheres, since it is from these areas that the nucleus receives many of its stimuli. In its progressive development this nucleus shows a marked resemblance to the inferior olivary nucleus. In each case the nucleus takes on a sac-like shape, the walls being formed by a thin, folded layer of gray which receives the incoming impulses. The efferent discharge in each case is largely through the center of the mass, the bundles of fibers passing out at the hilus of the nucleus.

Weidenreich ('99) and *Brunner* ('19) believed that the cross-sectional area of the cerebellar nuclei as compared to that of the medullated fibers is greater in lower animals than in man. *Weidenreich* found that in the mouse the area of the nuclei to that of the fiber bundles is as $1:2$, in the German marmot and guinea pig as $1:2\frac{1}{2}$, in the mole, rabbit, and cat, as $1:3$, in the sheep and dog, as $1:4$, and in man as $1:15$. *Brunner* ('19) stated, "Aus dem Umstand, dass bei gewissen Tieren (Maus, Hamster, Meerschweinchen) die Kleinhirnkerne fast die Hälfte des ganzen Innenraums im Kleinhirn einnehmem, ergiebt sich dass sie jedenfalls sehr viel Reize aus der Rinde aufzunehmen berufen sind. Da wir aber sehen, dass denoch bei den Kleinhirnkernen dieser Tiere die Volumzunahme bedeutend das Oberflächenwachstum übertrift, so ergeibt sich daraus, dass die Theorie von *Kappers* auf die Kleinhirnkerne überhaupt nicht oder nur mit sehr weit hergeholten Deutungsversuchen angewendet werden kann." To the above statement *Ariëns Kappers* ('21, p. 722) replied as follows: 1, That the relations of the cerebellar nuclei to the white matter of the cerebellum, favoring the nuclei more in small animals than in large animals, represents only a special case of the general law that the relations between gray and white substance in higher animals is in favor of the white substance (*Danilewsky, de Vries, Hovy*, see Chapter II; for underlying causes see footnote on page 212 and the text figure 639). 2, That the cerebellar nuclei, like many other nuclei, are larger in smaller animals (and in this case in lower animals) than in man does not signify that in smaller animals these nuclei receive more impulses. On the contrary, the fibers passing to them are naturally less in number than in higher animals such as monkeys and man. In these larger animals, and particularly in the higher animals with a greater body size, such as anthropoid apes and man, the number of Purkinje cell neuraxes passing to the cerebellar nuclei is much increased because of the large increase of cerebellar cortex in these forms.

FIG. 417. Wax reconstruction of the nucleus dentatus in adult man. Above, the medial surface with hilus toward the front. Below, the lateral surface, completely closed.

In figure 417, two views of the human nucleus dentatus as seen in a wax reconstruction, with relations to the nucleus emboliformis and the nucleus globosus, are given. The human nucleus dentatus is a sac-like structure, the opening of which is directed medialward and frontalward.   The lamellation of the mass is such that the furrows between folds lie in the longitudinal axis of the nervous system.   The nucleus emboliformis is a longitudinally running mass of gray at the medial margin of the nucleus dentatus and is partly connected with it. Medial to the more frontal portion of the nucleus emboliformis lies the nucleus globosus.   This is not completely reproduced in the reconstruction since its anterior end consists of diffusely scattered cells.   The names used by *Weidenreich* ('99), namely, nucleus lateralis anterior for the nucleus emboliformis and nucleus lateralis posterior for the nucleus globosus, do not appear to describe their positions in mammals and therefore have not received general acceptance.

On the basis of their fiber connections and possible functions, several divisions of the cerebellar nuclei have been made.   Thus *Allen* ('24) divided the deep cerebellar gray into a medial group represented by the nucleus fastigii, and a lateral group, made up of the remaining cerebellar nuclei.   He considered the medial group to be concerned with vestibular connections and the lateral group to be the source of fibers of the brachium conjunctivum.   *Mussen* ('27), *Tilney* ('27), and *Sachs* and *Fincher* ('27) placed the nucleus globosus with the nucleus fastigii in the medial group of cerebellar nuclei, leaving the nucleus emboliformis with the nucleus dentatus in the lateral group.   *Tilney* regarded the medial group as constant for mammals and as subserving archikinetic functions (of balance) ; the lateral group as concerned with neokinetic functions.   *Brun* ('25) classified as neocerebellar nuclei, the caudal half of the nucleus dentatus and the ventrolateral part of its frontal half ; as paleocerebellar nuclei, the dorsomedial part of the frontal half of the nucleus dentatus and the remaining cerebellar nuclei.   In view of the conflicting accounts of fiber connections given by the above quoted workers and other observers, as based on both normal and experimental material, it is not possible to pass any final judgment on which of the foregoing subdivisions is the most correct although *Huber* and *Crosby* are inclined to favor the interpretation of *Brun* ('25).

Incoming impulses reach the dentate nucleus, as *Ramón y Cajal* ('11) and others have pointed out, largely through the neuraxes of Purkinje cells.   These come from the hemispheres, according to *Allen* ('24) and many others, and also, according to *Brun* ('25) and others, from the vermis and, in part, from the flocculus.   They surround the outside of the whole complex with a "Fliesz" or "Amiculum."   That portion of the nucleus dentatus (its dorsomedial frontal portion) which receives fibers from the vermis (and possibly the flocculus) is probably the primitive nucleus lateralis cerebelli of reptiles and birds.   It might be termed the paleocerebellar portion of the nucleus (see *Brun*, '25). There is indication that both in form relations and in staining reactions with differential staining, the nucleus dentatus of human adults consists of two portions (*Demole*, '27), a dorsomedial (frontal) portion and a ventrolateral (frontal and caudal) portion.   Of these two portions the dorsomedial frontal portion has short, shallow convolutions (*Gans*, '24; *Winkler*, '27) with larger and less closely packed cells which stain less deeply, resembling in their reaction that of the cells of cerebellar nuclei medial to this portion (*Gans*, '24; *Jakob*, '28).

Large multipolar cells with richly branched dendrites (*Saccozzi*, '87 ; *von Kölliker*, '90 ; *Lugaro*, '95 ; *Ramón y Cajal*, '00) make up the characteristic cells of the nucleus dentatus. From such cells the neuraxes run toward the white core, giving off collaterals in their course, and out of the hilum of the nucleus dentatus into the brachium conjunctivum, of which they constitute the larger part (*Ramón y Cajal*, '00, and others). These large cells are arranged in characteristic rows, while between them are small, scattered, spindle-shaped cells (*Saccozzi*, '87 ; *Lugaro*, '95 ; *Ramón y Cajal*, '00 and '11 ; *Jakob*, '28, and others).

The nucleus emboliformis, which is connected at several levels with the nucleus dentatus, lies on the medial side of that nucleus at the place where the brachium conjunctivum leaves the cerebellum. Its close interrelation with the dentate nucleus is indicated by its similar fiber connections (*Ramón y Cajal*, '11 ; *Jakob*, '28), for it receives neuraxes of Purkinje cells (from the vermis, *Jakob*, '28 ; from the hemispheres, *Allen*, '24) and contributes fibers to the brachium conjunctivum. Its characteristic neurons resemble those of the nucleus dentatus, except that they may be slightly larger and are arranged in groups rather than in rows (*Dejerine*, '01 ; *Jakob*, '28, and others). Groups of large cells, similar to those of nucleus emboliformis, but intermingled with clusters of smaller neurons, are found in the nucleus globosus. This nucleus, which lies between the nucleus tecti or fastigii and the nucleus emboliformis, receives impulses from the cerebellar cortex of the vermis and from the medial vestibular nucleus (*Winkler*, '27, tractus vestibulo-globosus) and discharges through both the brachium conjunctivum (*Stilling*, '78) and the corpus restiforme (Russell's fasciculus). According to *Allen* ('24), the afferent impulses reach it from the cortical portions of the hemisphere.

The nucleus tecti (see figs. 415 and 416), often known as the roof nucleus or its German equivalent, the Dachkern, lies near the midline, above the fastigium (hence nucleus fastigii). In man, according to *Jakob* ('28) and others, it begins at the base of the lingula and extends caudalward to the place where the stratum album extends into the pyramis. Both large and small neurons are found in this nuclear mass, a predominance of smaller neurons leading *Brun* ('18) to speak of a large-celled, phylogenetically older portion and a small-celled, phylogenetically younger portion, medially placed. Both *Winkler* ('24) and *Jakob* ('28) have pointed out that the large cells of this nucleus do not equal in size those found in the nucleus dentatus. The primitive relation of the nucleus tecti to the underlying vestibular centers of forms below mammals has been emphasized in earlier portions of the present chapter. Indications of such primitive relations are found in mammals and even in man (*Marburg*, '24 ; *Jakob*, '28). Thus, from the nucleus tecti a strand of gray extends down toward the superior vestibular nucleus. Presumably the nucleus acustico-cerebellosus (*Ramón y Cajal*, '11) is a differentiated portion of this gray band. The nucleus tecti receives impulses from vestibular and other bulbar centers and from the cortex of the vermis (*Horsley* and *Clarke*, '05 ; *Edinger*, '11 ; *Allen*, '24). It gives rise to cerebello-motorius fibers, to Russell's fasciculus, and to cerebello-vestibular fibers.   A considerable part of its efferent fibers decussate before leaving the cerebellum.   All the cerebellar nuclei are interconnected by rich internuclear fibers.

THE FIBER CONNECTIONS OF THE CEREBELLUM

Many of the cerebellar connections have been discussed in the preceding chapters or will be discussed in the chapters that follow.   Therefore, in the following account only a brief résumé of the extracerebellar course and relation of each tract is given, together with references to pages where further details may be found, while emphasis is laid on the intracerebellar relations and connections in so far as these are known.

The mammalian cerebellum has three peduncles on each side and the paths which run to or from the cerebellum lie, with a few exceptions, within these peduncles.   These peduncles are known as the corpus restiforme or inferior cerebellar peduncle, the brachium pontis or middle cerebellar peduncle, and the brachium conjunctivum or superior cerebellar peduncle.   In human anatomy the corpus restiforme proper is divided into two portions, a pars lateralis and a pars corpus juxtarestiforme.   The lateral portion, to which the name corpus restiforme is applied in its more restricted sense, or the oval field of *Winkler*, contains scattered cell clusters constituting the nucleus of the corpus restiforme or the nucleus restiformalis (*Ziehen*, '26).   It is possible that these cells are in synaptic relation with certain, if not all, of the entering fibers, but their function is not clear.   The corpus juxtarestiforme constitutes the more medial region of the peduncle, being separated from the lateral part by a forward prolongation of Deiters' nucleus (*Jakob*, '28, and others).   The main paths entering the lateral portion of the corpus restiforme proper are the dorsal spino-cerebellar tract, the olivo-cerebellar and cerebello-olivary tracts, and the cerebello-petal connections from the reticular nuclei and particularly the lateral reticular nucleus. The more medial corpus juxtarestiforme carries particularly the paths interrelating the vestibular and cerebellar centers but also the cerebello-spinal and other associated paths.

The major fiber connections of the higher mammalian cerebellum may be listed as follows : —

A.   Through the corpus restiforme (and corpus juxtarestiforme of man) : 1.   Dorsal spino-cerebellar tract (*Flechsig*, '76;   *Mott*, '92;   *Neubürger* and *Edinger*, '98;   *Bing*, '07;   *MacNalty* and *Horsley*, '09;   *Vogt* and *Astwazaturow*, '11;   *Strong*, '15;   *Ingvar*, '19;   *Dusser de Barenne*, '24;   *Beck*, '28;   *Jakob*, '28, and others).

2 and 3.   Dorsal and ventral superficial arcuates.   Among authors in favor of either or both of these systems may be mentioned *Darkschewitsch* and *Freud*, '86;   *Ferrier* and *Turner*, '93;   *Klimoff*, '97 and '01;   *Tschermak*, '98;   *Probst*, '02;   *van Gehuchten*, '06;   *von Monakow*, '10;   *Brun*, '25;   *Mussen*, '27.   Various modern texts (such as *Tilney* and *Riley*, '21;   *Winkler*, '21;   *Piersol's* Anatomy, Huber Edition, '30;   *Ranson*, '31;   *Herrick*, '31) favor such connections.   Among authors who have doubted connections with the nucleus gracilis and the nucleus

cuneatus may be mentioned *Vejas* ('85), *Lewandowsky* ('04), and *Horsley* ('06). With the ventral arcuate fibers must also be considered the cerebellar pyramid of Schaffer (see also *Fuse*, '12) and possibly the fibers of Piccolomini, discussed on page 804 (*Fuse*, '12; *von Monakow*, '10; *Winkler*, '21; *Marburg*, '24; *Brun*, 25; *Beck*, '28).

4. Olivo-cerebellar and cerebello-olivary fiber connections (*Held*, '93; *Bechterew*, '94; *Holmes* and *Stewart*, '08; *Edinger*, '08, '11; *Ramón y Cajal*, '11; *Haenel* and *Bielschowsky*, '15; *Brun*, '17 and '18; *Brouwer*, '19 and '27; *Kubo*, '24; *Marburg*, '24; *Schröder* and *Kirschbaum*, '28; *Jakob*, '28, and many others).

5. Fibers from the reticular nuclei of the medulla oblongata (*Schweiger*, '06; *Winkler*, '21; *Marburg*, '24, '24a; *Brun*, '25; *Jakob*, '28, and others). With these connections should be described the path from the corpus ponto-bulbaris, described by *Essick* ('12; see also *Winkler*, '21).

6. Vestibular root fibers. Among contributors who accept the presence of vestibular root fibers to the cerebellum may be mentioned *Edinger* ('86), *Ramón y Cajal* ('11), *Ingvar* ('19), *Gray* ('26), and *Rasmussen* ('32). On the contrary, *Winkler* ('27) stated that such direct vestibular fibers do not occur.

7. Vestibulo-cerebellar fibers. Nearly all of the modern texts on neurology admit the presence of vestibulo-cerebellar fibers; they have received special consideration by *Bruce* ('95), *Klimoff* ('01), *Muskens* ('04; see also '06 and '07), *Schweiger* ('06), *Winkler* ('07 and '21), *Ramón y Cajal* ('11), *Edinger* ('12), *Fuse* ('12), *Löwy* ('14), *Gray* ('26), *Rasmussen* ('32, '32a), *Beck* ('28), and *Jakob* ('28).

8. *Russell's* fasciculus (tractus cerebello-vestibularis et spinalis, faisceau de crochet, faisceau cerebello-bulbaire, tractus uncinatus, the hook bundle or Hakenbündel, fibrae cerebello-tegmentalis). This bundle has been described under different names as here listed by many observers (*Russell*, '94, '97; *Probst*, '02; *Lewandowsky*, '04; *Thomas*, '12; *Winkler*, '21; *Gray*, '26; *Marburg*, '24; *Mussen*, '27 and '29; *Rasmussen*, '32a, '34; *Jakob*, '28).

9. Direct trigeminal root fibers (?) and nucleo-cerebellar or trigemino-cerebellar connections (*Wallenberg*, '05, and others).

10. Cerebello-motorius fibers. The cerebello-motorius fibers are now and again included wholly or in part with the fasciculus of Russell, as in the account of *Mussen* ('27 and '29; see also *Jakob*, '28, page 890).

B. Through the middle cerebellar peduncle or the brachium pontis: The brachium pontis is constituted chiefly by the ponto-cerebellar fibers (*Vejas*, '85; *Lewandowsky*, '04; *Borowiecki*, '11; *Besta*, '12; *Masuda*, '14; *Ingvar*, '19; *Marburg*, '22; *Winkler*, '27; *Jakob*, '28, and many others). In addition to these main paths there are fibers from the reticular nuclei to the cerebellum (*Borowiecki*, '11; *Uemura*, '17; *Brun*, '25), sometimes known as fibrae rectae pontis (*Brun*). Other fibers of this type are the fibrae lemnisco-pontines of *von Monakow*, *Marburg* ('22), *Jakob* ('28), and others. Pedunculo-cerebellar fibers have been described (*Fuse*, '13; *Brun*, '25, and others under the name of the taenia pontis).

C. Through the superior cerebellar peduncle or the brachium conjunctivum:
1. Dento-rubro-thalamic tract. This tract has been recognized by nearly all

the later students of the cerebellum or the midbrain, and it is noted in all of the modern textbooks. In the following brief list only a few of the many possible references are noted : *von Monakow*, '95, '05 ; *Probst*, '01 ; *Preisig*, '04 ; *Edinger*, '11 ; *Ramón y Cajal*, '11 ; *Uemura*, '17 ; *Winkler*, '21 and '27 ; *Marburg*, '24 and '27 ; *Foix* and *Nicolesco*, '25 ; *Rademaker*, '26 ; *Mussen*, '27 and '29 ; *Jakob*, '28, and *Rioch*, '29.

2. Cerebello-tegmental and fastigio-bulbar or fastigio-reticular tracts. These tracts are associated with the dento-rubro-thalamic system, arising in part as collaterals of its fibers (*Wallenberg*, '01 ; *Winkler*, '27 ; *Jakob*, '28, who has given various other citations — *Klimoff, Thomas, Ramón y Cajal*).

3. Collaterals of mesencephalic root fibers (*Wallenberg*, '05 ; *Weinberg*, '28, and others).

4. The ventral spino-cerebellar tract, which appears at the side of the peduncle (*MacNalty* and *Horsley*, '09 ; *Ingvar*, '19 ; *Beck*, '27, and many others).

5. The tecto-cerebellar tract, which lies not within the brachium conjunctivum but between the two brachia in the anterior medullary velum (*Edinger*, '11 ; *Hines*, '25 and '29).

Following this listing of the components of the cerebellar peduncles, it is our purpose in following pages to consider these paths severally in greater detail.

A. Corpus Restiforme and the Ventral Spino-Cerebellar Tract

For convenience in comparing the dorsal and ventral spino-cerebellar tracts, the two systems, which phylogenetically are parts of a great ascending system, are considered together, although the ventral spino-cerebellar tract of higher forms enters the cerebellum at the side of the brachium conjunctivum.

Proprioceptive impulses are brought into the spinal cord by way of the medial division of the dorsal root fibers. Such fibers enter the posterior or dorsal funiculi where they divide into long ascending and shorter descending fibers, which give off collaterals to the dorsal horn of the cord and to nucleus dorsalis of Clarke (7C–2L). Within this latter nucleus lie the cells of origin for the dorsal spino-cerebellar tract. These cells send their neuraxes directly lateralward to the surface of the cord in the region immediately ventral to the dorsal horn, where they turn frontalward. They occupy this position throughout their course in the spinal cord. At the lower end of the medulla oblongata the tract lies ventral to the nucleus of the descending root of the trigeminal nerve but gradually swings lateralward and enters the cerebellum through the corpus restiforme (fig. 422).

The ventral spino-cerebellar tract arises from dorsal horn neurons of the same and opposite sides throughout the cord, but particularly from the levels supplying the extremities. Its fibers are largely of contralateral origin, the decussation occurring through the anterior white commissure. The bundles of the tract take up a superficial position in the cord just ventral to the dorsal spino-cerebellar tract and in close relation with the lateral spino-thalamic tract. The ventral spino-cerebellar tract maintains essentially this same position in its course through the cord and the medulla oblongata. At the level where the dorsal

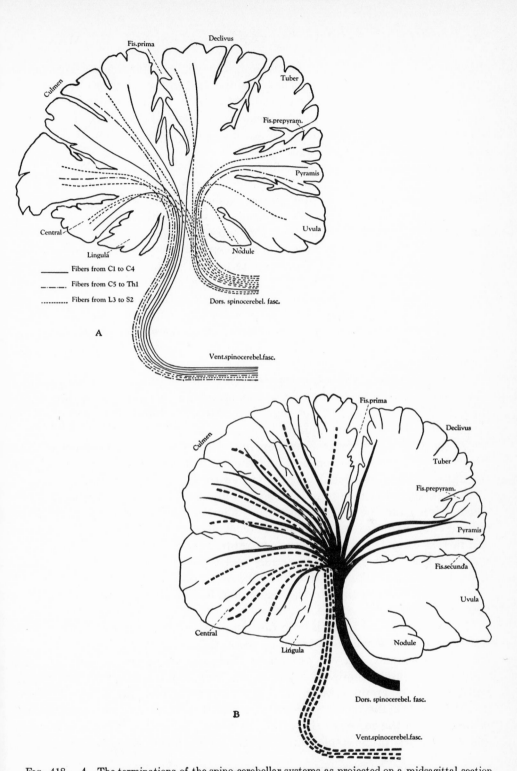

FIG. 418. *A*. The terminations of the spino-cerebellar systems as projected on a midsagittal section of the cerebellum of Cercopithecus cynomolgus. *Salusbury, MacNalty,* and *Horsley.*
B. The terminations of the spino-cerebellar systems in the cortex of the vermis of the cat. *Ingvar.*

spino-cerebellar tract swings dorsalward, the ventral spino-cerebellar courses directly forward. In the pons it lies lateroventral to the superior olive, in close relation to the rubro-spinal, the lateral tecto-spinal, and particularly the lateral spino-thalamic tracts. As upper levels of the pons are reached, it begins to swing dorsalward and then turns backward to enter the cerebellum at the lateral side of the brachium conjunctivum (fig. 422).

The termination of the ascending spino-cerebellar tracts within the cerebellum has received considerable attention. Here may be mentioned particularly the work of *Ingvar* ('18 and '19) on cats and that of *MacNalty* and *Horsley* ('09) on monkeys (fig. 418A). These observers agreed with earlier students (*Mott*, '92, '95, '97; *Bing*, '07, and others) that most of the homolateral fibers of the spino-cerebellar systems terminate in the vermis. Such uncrossed fibers [15] do not enter the hemispheres. The fibers terminate in such a manner that those from the extremities (mainly ventral spino-cerebellar) and those from the trunk (dorsal spino-cerebellar) do not remain entirely separate within the cerebellum. However, according to *MacNalty* and *Horsley* ('09), there is some difference in termination between the dorsal and ventral spino-cerebellar tracts, inasmuch as the ventral reaches farther frontalward than is the case with the dorsal tract. Lingula and nodule do not receive these tracts.

According to *MacNalty* and *Horsley* ('09), the ventral spino-cerebellar tract distributes particularly to the central lobule (lobulus II) but also to the culmen (lobulus III and lobulus IV) and along both lips of the sulcus primarius or fissura prima. The fibers do not appear to show localized distribution within these areas, since the more ventral components of the ventral spino-cerebellar tract (those from the lower extremities) and the more dorsal components (those from the upper extremities) could both be traced to the lobulus centralis.

According to *MacNalty* and *Horsley* ('09), the dorsal spino-cerebellar tract, which arises from the nucleus dorsalis of Clarke, mainly from the trunk region of the cord, distributes also to lobulus II (central) and lobulus III and IV (culmen) and farther caudalward reaches the central portion of the lobulus simplex (declivus), lobulus C_2 of *Bolk* (folia vermis and tuber) and C_1 of *Bolk* (pyramid). According to *MacNalty* and *Horsley* ('09), some of the fibers of the dorsal spino-cerebellar originate in the cervical region and end in the pyramis of the inferior vermis.

Ingvar ('19) found that, in both bird and cat material, spino-cerebellar fibers terminate in very small numbers (if at all) in that portion of the vermis between the lobulus simplex and the pyramis. This intervening region (tuber) is the youngest part phylogenetically of the vermis. The spino-cerebellar fibers, like the vestibular fibers, group themselves in front of and behind this area, in the more primitive parts of the vermis. *Ingvar* (figs. 418B, 419) carried ventral spino-cerebellar fibers to the cortex of the vermis in regions between the precentral fissure and the fissura prima (sulcus primarius). The dorsal spino-cerebellar tract

---

[15] Only one-third of the dorsal spino-cerebellar fibers and one-fifth of the ventral spino-cerebellar fibers are said to cross in the cerebellum — the latter in the decussatio veli; the former in the upper part of the vermis posterior. The reference above is to a lack of crossing in the cerebellum.

reached these regions of the vermis and also the pyramid.   This interpretation implies a sharp distinction between the anterior and posterior lobes on the one hand, and the median lobe on the other hand.   *Ariëns Kappers* ('21) had opportunity to verify the work of *Ingvar* and is convinced of its correctness.   *Ingvar's* results are of great interest both from the standpoint of the function of various parts of the cerebellum and because of their significance in offering an explanation of the development of the hemispheres and their relations with the central portion of the cerebellum.

Beck ('27), working on the cat as *Ingvar* had done, obtained a distribution which differed slightly, though not essentially, from the results obtained by *Ingvar*, in that he found that the ventral spino-cerebellar tract was distributed only medially, reaching in such medial areas not only the culmen and central lobule, but also the lingula.   The dorsal spino-cerebellar tract was thought to reach both medial and lateral areas, but its chief distribution was lateral.   He found that this latter area reached lateralward beyond the subdivisions of the vermis, but not to parts of the tuber.   Medially it appears to extend to the lingula, central, culmen, uvula, pyramid, and a small part of the clivus.   *Beck* also carried a few bundles of the dorsal spino-cerebellar tract to lobulus paramedianus, a distribution which is not in accord with that of other workers and requires further verification.

The nuclei tecti (and probably nuclei globosi) but not the dentate nuclei receive collaterals from the ventral spino-cerebellar but apparently not from the dorsal spino-cerebellar tract.   That the roof nuclei and not the dentate nuclei receive such collaterals of the ventral spino-cerebellar system is in accordance with the fact that the former nuclei are interrelated by neuraxes of Purkinje cells with the anterior lobe and partly with lobulus simplex, while the dentate nuclei receive neuraxes from Purkinje cells situated in the posterior region of the vermis and in the cortex of the hemisphere, including the flocculus (fig. 422).

From the nucleus cuneatus externus, perhaps from the nucleus gracilis and the nucleus of the descending root of the trigeminal, fibers pass dorsolateralward to the corpus restiforme, by way of which peduncle they reach the cerebellum. These constitute the dorsal superficial arcuate system.   Other fibers arising from these nuclei swing downward and medialward, decussate in the midline, and then swing ventralward around the under surface of the pyramids.   Here a very considerable number of the fibers synapse in relation with the neurons forming the arcuate nucleus and, joined by neuraxes from these cells, the composite bundle then swings dorsalward as the ventral superficial arcuate system, along the peripheral surface of the medulla oblongata to the corpus restiforme, and through this to the cerebellum.

The above statements regarding the relations of the dorsal and ventral superficial arcuate systems are in agreement with accounts given in the various texts on the anatomy of the nervous system (see fig. 422), the differences occurring depending on the extent of synapse thought to take place in the arcuate nuclei. Such statements have their basis in a considerable series of observations, on both normal and experimental material, dating over a series of years, among which may be mentioned the early accounts of *Flechsig* ('85), of *Ferrier* and *Turner* ('93), and of *Tschermak* ('98).   *Ferrier* and *Turner* and *Probst* ('02) found homolateral and *Tschermak* both homolateral and contralateral fibers from the nuclei of the dorsal funiculi to the cerebellum through the corpus restiforme.   *Von Monakow* ('10) carried fibers from the external cuneate nucleus to the cerebellum and *van Gehuchten* ('06) described dorsal superficial arcuate fibers.   A quite detailed account of the system is that of *Mussen* ('29), who found that, after degeneration of the nucleus gracilis and the nucleus cuneatus, in addition to the above described dorsal and ventral superficial arcuate fibers, two systems of similar fibers assumed a somewhat different course to reach the corpus restiforme. These are: *a*, transverse arcuato-restiforme fibers which swing slightly ventralward after their origin and then pass almost directly across the upper part of the medulla oblongata, well above the inferior olivary nuclei, to reach the corpus restiforme; and *b*, the crossed arcuato-olivo-cerebellar fibers, which swing ventralward and ventrolateralward from their origin to reach the lateral border of the inferior olivary nucleus, pass through this nucleus and, emerging at the hilus, swing dorsalward and medialward to reach the corpus restiforme.   *Mussen* found the arcuate fibers entering the cerebellum through this peduncle to be distributed to the anterior regions of the vermis.   Connections to the posterior part of the vermis were established by *Mussen* through his transverse arcuato-extra-restiforme fibers, which enter the cerebellum at the side of the ventral spino-cerebellar tract, and through collaterals which pass through the brachium conjunctivum.   But while there appears to be accumulating a considerable amount of evidence favoring the presence of connections between the nucleus gracilis and nucleus cuneatus and the cerebellum by way of the corpus restiforme, there are a number of observers who have denied the presence of such fibers or who have given them a different interpretation (*Lewandowsky*, '04; *Horsley*, '06).   A somewhat different conception of the arcuate system is to be found in the account of *Mingazzini* ('28) who, in addition to fibers from the posterior funicular nuclei through and partly above the contralateral pyramid to the lateral reticular nucleus and the cerebellum and fibers from the posterior funicular nuclei to the contralateral arcuate nuclei, found fibers passing from the cerebellum ventromedially, decussating in the raphé, contributing fibers to the pyramid and terminating in the arcuate nuclei, — thus constituting a cerebellofugal path.

Probably to be considered with these arcuate systems to the cerebellum are the so-called "cerebellar pyramid" of *Schaffer* ('15a) and the tractus arcuato-cerebellaris of *Winkler* ('27).   The cerebellar portion of the pyramidal tract is described as passing across the medulla oblongata and entering the corpus restiforme to distribute to the lateral cerebellar lobes (*Brun*, '25).

Tractus arcuato-floccularis (*Winkler*, '27) arises from the arcuate nuclei but, instead of following the superficial surface of the medulla oblongata, runs dorsalward near the midline, crosses in the raphé, then passes over the floor of the fourth ventricle as the striae medullares acustici (which *von Monakow* had shown are not acoustic) or striae Piccolomini, enters the corpus juxtarestiforme and passes to the flocculus. *Beck* ('28; see also *Jakob*, '28) found, in a case of aplasia of the pons and hypoplasia of the cerebellum, that there were no arcuate nuclei and that the striae Piccolomini were also lacking. However, not all observers have interpreted these fibers as part of an arcuato-floccular path, but have considered them as relating the ponto-cerebellar body to the cerebellum (*Marburg*, '24a; also quoted by *Jakob*, '28) or as constituting a cerebello-fugal system.

The olivo-cerebellar fibers appear to be quite definitely localized in both the inferior olive and in the cerebellum. *Holmes* and *Stewart* ('08), *Brouwer* ('15, '19, and '27), *Haenel* and *Bielschowsky* ('15), *Brun* ('17 and '18), *Brouwer* and *Coenen* ('19), and *Kubo* ('24) studied these relations. Fibers (fig. 422) relating the inferior olivary nucleus of one side with the cerebellar cortex on the other side arise from the characteristic neurons of the inferior olivary nucleus, pass through the hilus, and cross the field to the corpus restiforme, forming a part of the internal arcuate system. From their relations to the nucleus of the descending root of the trigeminal nerve and to the root, in their course across the medulla oblongata, they have sometimes been termed the retrotrigeminal, intratrigeminal, and praetrigeminal internal arcuates (*Mingazzini*, '93). According to *Holmes* and *Stewart* ('08), the olivo-cerebellar fibers reach all parts of the cerebellar cortex with the exception of the flocculus, and they point out that a definite spatial relation exists between these centers. The medial portion of the inferior olive and of the dorsal accessory olive and all of the medial accessory olive send their fibers to the vermis and a small part of the hemispheres. The remainder of the inferior olivary nucleus and of the dorsal accessory olivary nucleus are connected with the cerebellar hemispheres in such fashion that the dorsal part of the olive supplies the superior surface of the contralateral cerebellar hemisphere and the ventral part, the inferior surface (fig. 347).

Brouwer ('19), with whose observations the results of *Haenel* and *Bielschowsky* ('15) and of *Brun* ('17-'18) are in agreement, found only the accessory olives and the mediofrontal part of the chief inferior olive normal in a case of neocerebellar atrophy in which only the vermis and flocculus were normal. Atrophy was present in the mediocaudal and lateral parts of the chief inferior olive. *Brouwer* was able to distinguish a distinct bundle, the fibers of which connect the medial accessory olive with the medial part of the cerebellum. This fascicle, which was termed tractus parolivo-cerebellaris (*Brouwer*, '19; see also *Winkler*, '27), myelinates earlier than do the other olivo-cerebellar bundles. This early myelination is in accordance with the fact that the accessory olives — and more particularly their medial portions — form the most primitive division of the olivary complex and are connected with the more primitive part of the cerebellum, the vermis. *Brouwer* found that the tonsilla and lobulus ansiformis receive particularly connections of the phylogenetically younger portions of the inferior olive, making their appearance in mammals, the so-called neocerebellar portions. In a clinical case of neopontine aplasia *Beck* ('28) found that ponto-cerebellar fibers were destroyed but that the olivo-cerebellar bundles were intact (see also *Jakob*, '28). In this case there was an unequal distribution of olivo-cerebellar fibers to the hemispheres, with more to the tonsil, — results which reopen the question of olivo-cerebellar distribution.   Connections of the flocculus with the olivo-cerebellar system and the spino-cerebellar systems have not as yet been demonstrated.   The lack of such connections is in harmony with the fact that in such animals as the selachians the spino-cerebellar and olivo-cerebellar tracts run past the auricle on their way to the cerebellum (*Voorhoeve*, '17; see bibliography for plagiostomes).   The olivo-cerebellar system medullates later than does the dorsal spino-cerebellar tract.   Not only are there crossed olivo-cerebellar fibers, but uncrossed fibers have been described by *Held* ('93), *Keller* ('01), *Edinger* ('11), *Ramón y Cajal* ('11), *Obersteiner* ('12), and others.   *Brun* thought that such fibers arise from the dorsal portion of the inferior olivary nucleus and the dorsal accessory olive.   Cerebello-olivary fibers are believed to be present by some observers (*Wallenberg*, '01; *Schaffer*, '15 and '15a) although according to *Brun* ('25), if present, they are possibly not numerous.

From the lateral reticular nucleus of the medulla oblongata a bundle of fibers runs dorsalward to terminate in the cerebellum.   This may be termed the tractus reticulo-cerebellaris.   Similar connections, crossed and uncrossed, between the medial reticular cells of the inferior reticular group and the cerebellum have been described (fig. 422).   The ponto-cerebellar body (*Essick*, '07) has a connection with the cerebellum (*Winkler*, '21).

Direct vestibular root fibers (fig. 422) to the cerebellum were described by *Edinger* ('85; also '99).   The presence of such fibers in mammals has been confirmed by a number of observers (see page 487) in both normal and experimental material.   *Ingvar* ('19) was able to trace degenerated fibers of the vestibular nerve toward the cerebellum.   These fibers, after giving off collaterals to the vestibular nucleus, entered the cerebellum to be distributed to the nucleus tecti and to the cortex of the uvula, nodule, flocculus, and lingula.   However, several observers have recorded their doubts as to the existence of such direct root fibers of the vestibular nerve to cerebellar centers, and prominent among these is *Winkler* ('27).   Nearly all students of the vestibular region and the cerebellum agree that important fiber paths interconnect these areas (figs. 419 and 422). *Bruce* ('95) carried vestibulo-cerebellar fibers to the flocculus.   The maturing of the myelin sheaths occurs early along the path from the vestibular area to the flocculus.   *Van Valkenburg* ('13) found that such bundles form the sole connection between the flocculus and the adjoining dorsal region of the medulla oblongata in a 27 cm. human foetus.   The early appearance of myelinated fibers to these specific cerebellar regions was regarded by *Ingvar* ('18 and '19) as evidence of the greater phylogenetic age of these regions.   The superior vestibular nucleus (the angular nucleus of Bechterew) is particularly closely related to the flocculus (*Klimoff*, '01; *Muskens*, '04; *Schweiger*, '06; *Beck*, '28; *Jakob*, '28, and others). Such fibers are in part vestibulo-cerebellar but they are also cerebello-vestibular, as *Beck* found.   From the superior vestibular nucleus, also by way of the corpus juxtarestiforme, fibers pass to the nucleus fastigii (tractus vestibulo-fastigius) and to the nucleus globosus (tractus vestibulo-globosus).   These bundles form two separate tracts, as was emphasized by *Winkler* ('27).

The fasciculus uncinatus or the fasciculus of Russell forms an important efferent system of the cerebellum.   It arises from the contra- and homolateral nuclei tecti (decussating in the commissura ventralis cerebelli) and distributes to the nuclei of the brain stem and upper cord, the differences in the distribution as given by different observers depending somewhat upon the amount included within the fasciculus by the respective observers, particularly whether they included within it the cerebello-motorius fibers.   In the following account the two systems are discussed together.   The tract which bears the name of Russell's fasciculus was first identified by him in 1894 but was not described accurately

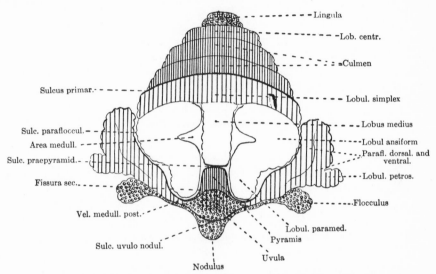

FIG. 419.   A schematic representation of the extent of the vestibulo-cerebellar (circles) and the spino-cerebellar (vertical-lines) systems in the cerebellar cortex. *Ingvar.*

until later, and a thorough understanding of the system, if such may be considered as having been attained, has been reached through the observations of numerous observers. *Probst* ('02) recognized that it had its origin in the contralateral nucleus tecti and that the fibers, after crossing, hooked around the brachium conjunctivum, for a time occupying the most dorsal part of the superior cerebellar peduncle.   The fact that the uncinate fasciculus forms for a time within the cerebellum the most dorsal component of the brachium conjunctivum has been recognized by observers since Russell's description. *Probst* ('02) was unable to trace the fibers to their termination although he saw them turn ventralward, but *Lewandowsky* ('04) divided the uncinate fasciculus, at its position in the superior cerebellar peduncle, into three main bundles : a retropeduncular portion which turned rostralward and which he was unable to trace to its termination, a cerebello-vestibular portion to the superior vestibular nucleus, and a cerebello-tegmental portion to the fasciculus solitarius and the fasciculus of Roller. *Van Gehuchten* ('04b, '05, and '06) divided the fasciculus uncinatus into two bundles, one of which could be related to the reticular formation of the medulla oblongata and a second bundle which could be followed into the corpus restiforme ; he was able to trace fibers of this bundle (in the rabbit) as far as the first cervical segment. *Van Gehuchten* ('20) appears to have regarded the connection with the reticular nuclei as the important part of this fiber tract. *Winkler* ('07, '07a, '21, and '27) has made distinct contributions to the knowledge of this fasciculus. In Marchi preparations of rabbit material he followed the fasciculus from the nucleus tecti (fastigii) and nucleus globosus across the midline and then forward between the brachium conjunctivum and the uvula. It curves around the peduncle, actually for a time its most dorsal component, and then passes to the medial side of the corpus restiforme proper. It enters the medulla oblongata and passes caudalward along the nucleus vestibularis lateralis (Deiters' nucleus) and the spinal or inferior vestibular nucleus, both of which receive fibers from it. Fibers pass off from the bundle at the level of the abducens nerve (*Winkler*, '21) to the reticular gray. *Fuse* ('12) believed that both the contralateral and the homolateral nuclei tecti (fastigii), the nucleus globosus and the nucleus emboliformis, and the phylogenetically older part of the dentate nucleus contribute to this tract. *Fuse* ('12) and *Thomas* ('12) carried fibers of the uncinate fasciculus into the contralateral medial longitudinal fasciculus, and *Fuse* was able to trace them forward as far as the oculomotor nucleus. They reach other parts of the reticular gray. *Rothmann's* ('14) results were in essential agreement with those given above as was also the brief summary of *Marburg* ('24), where the uncinate fasciculus is described as a bundle hooking around the brachium conjunctivum, with its cells of origin in the contralateral roof nucleus and its termination in the vestibular area. *Gray* ('26) analyzed the vestibular connections in the cat and discussed, with other relations, the origin and distribution of the uncinate fasciculus. He traced it to the vestibular nuclei and to certain reticular nuclei of the medulla oblongata and found bundles accompanying the descending vestibular root and extending into the spinal cord as far as the second cervical segment — a cerebello-spinal path possibly comparable to that found in avian forms. A detailed account of the bundle (hook bundle) in the cat was given by *Mussen* ('29), who traced the main fasciculus from the contralateral roof nucleus over the superior cerebellar peduncle to the medial surface of the corpus restiforme. Aberrant fascicles of similar origin may join it during its course. The combined bundles pass to the lateral vestibular nucleus where the major portion terminates. Smaller bundles described by *Mussen* were (1) a medial bundle to the medial and superior vestibular nuclei, the nucleus of the abducens nerve and the medial longitudinal fasciculus, and (2) a ventrolateral bundle dividing at the level of the descending root of the trigeminal into a lateral branch of unknown termination and a medial branch to the region of the facial nucleus — where it is thought to terminate — and to the tecto-spinal tract. *Rasmussen* ('33, J. Comp. Neurol., vol. 57, p. 165) grouped fibers of the brachium conjunctivum to the reticular gray of the pons and midbrain as an ascending limb of the uncinate fasciculus, but found the major part of the bundle passing to the vestibular gray and the reticular gray of the medulla oblongata and the pons. As is to be seen from this review of the literature, the uncinate fasciculus, then, is an important cerebello-fugal path by which impulses are carried from the cerebellum to the underlying vestibular and reticular areas, and undoubtedly it plays an important part in relating the cerebellar activity to the functioning of the labyrinth as *Winkler* ('07) emphasized. The connections of the roof nuclei with the motor nuclei of the brain stem constitute a part of the cerebello-motorius system of lower forms and may be considered as constituting a separate cerebello-motorius or fastigio-bulbar system or as a medial part of the uncinate fasciculus, depending on the limit set for this latter tract. Reference is made to the cerebello-spinal and cerebello-motorius paths diagrammed in figure 422.

Trigemino-cerebellar fibers (fig. 422) from the chief sensory nucleus of the trigeminal nerve and from the nucleus of the descending root are thought to occur in mammals as in lower forms (see, for example, *Huber* and *Crosby* in the revised edition of *Piersol's* Anatomy, '30). They are designated frequently as nucleo-cerebellar fibers. There is quite convincing evidence in normal chrome silver preparations of the presence of direct root fibers of the trigeminal to the cerebellum. These observations await experimental corroboration.

B. BRACHIUM PONTIS OR MIDDLE CEREBELLAR PEDUNCLE

While the spino-cerebellar fibers are related to the cortex of the vermis and the olivo-cerebellar to the cortex of both the vermis and the hemispheres, the ponto-cerebellar fibers, which constitute the main mass of the brachium pontis or middle cerebellar peduncle, are related to the cortex of the hemispheres. According to *Thomas* ('12), *Masuda* ('14), and others, ponto-cerebellar fibers terminate only in the hemispheres; according to *Spitzer* and *Karplus* ('07) and *Besta* ('12) they also have connections with the vermis. As yet evidence is lacking that the flocculus receives such fibers. The fact that in crossed cerebro-cerebellar atrophy it is only the cerebellar hemisphere which decreases in size while the vermis and flocculus do not show the slightest alteration offers strong indication that the cerebro-ponto-cerebellar system is connected only with the cerebellar hemispheres. In any other case it would be necessary to assume either that the vermis and flocculus receive fibers from both sides or that both receive so many other impulses that the disappearance of the pontine connections produces no perceptible change. Moreover, in phylogeny, the development of the cerebellar hemispheres is paralleled by the development of the cerebral hemispheres, the pontine gray, and the brachium pontis. This indicates the existence of a special relationship between the areas named. In monotremes a small brachium pontis and a relatively poorly developed cerebellar hemisphere are present. As the development of these structures is traced from lower to higher animals, they are seen to increase with the increase of the cerebral cortex and more particularly with its association areas.

The first pontine fibers formed lie frontally at about the level of emergence of the trigeminal nerve. In higher mammals the pons is increased caudalward. This affects the root of the trigeminal nerve, which also is shifted somewhat farther caudalward in these forms. Later on, in primates, the root of the facial is forced backward by the enlarged pons (see page 608, Chapter V). Whether caudal pontine fibers are added during this increase or whether the frontal pontine fibers are merely pressed backward by newly added frontal fibers is at present uncertain.   The latter point of view finds support in the fact that in man, at least, the caudal portion of the pontine fibers become myelinated earlier than does the cephalic portion (*Bechterew*, '94a; *Mingazzini*, '08).   The peculiar obliquity of course of the ponto-cerebellar connections, for the caudal part of the pons is connected with the cephalic part of the cerebellar hemispheres, also favors this conception.

Much attention has been given to studies on the origin of the pons.   The work of *Essick* ('12), who, to a considerable extent, made use of the observations of *His* ('91), indicated that there is a common cellular matrix for the inferior olives, the arcuate nuclei, and the pontine gray — thus for all those centers which are dependencies of the cerebellum — and that this common center originates from the dorsolateral, somatic sensory static area of the embryonic medulla oblongata, close behind the rhombic lip of the ventricle. Whereas the inferior olivary cells and those destined to constitute the arcuate nuclei migrate ventralward along the lateral side of the medulla oblongata, the cells which later form the pontine gray shift obliquely frontalward

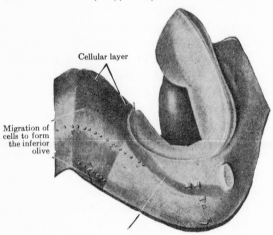

Cellular layer

Migration of cells to form the inferior olive

Migration of pontine gray

FIG. 420.   The dark gray area indicates the line of migration of the cells from the dorsal vestibular area, which enter into the formation of the inferior olive and the pontine nuclei in a human embryo 23 mm. in length. *Essick*.

between the roots of the acoustic and facial nerves and reach the base of the medulla oblongata medial to the roots of the trigeminal.   Thus the neurons which will form the future pontine gray migrate forward under the influence of cortico-pontine tracts.   They afford thus a classical example of an engrammatic neurobiotactic process, a shifting of cells between functionally correlated centers in the direction of the maximal stimulus.   The course of this migration of the pontine gray during embryonic development is said to be still visible in fully developed human brains, through the presence of a so-called corpus ponto-bulbare (*Essick*, '07).   This consists of multipolar cells (figs. 420 and 421).   This body extends along a medullated bundle from a position at the dorsolateral margin of the medulla oblongata, dorsal to the corpus restiforme, between the root fibers of the facial and acoustic nerves, and into the pontine fibers.   *Swank* ('34, J. Comp. Neur., v. 60, p. 309) carried circumolivary pyramidal fibers to it.

The pontine gray receives impulses from the cerebral cortex by way of fronto-pontine and temporo-pontine tracts.   The former are said to arise from the 2nd and 3rd frontal and the latter from the 2nd and 3rd temporal convolutions.   For a further account of their cortical relations and courses see pages 1096 and 1463. They undoubtedly provide means by which the cerebral cortex may exert a regulatory and perhaps frequently an inhibitory influence over the impulses passing through the cerebellum. The exact nature of the impulses carried by them is not as yet understood fully. It is perhaps worthy of note that they come from association areas rather than from projection areas. With regard to the exact termination of cortico-pontine fibers within the pontine gray there is not general agreement. It is generally admitted that they end uncrossed and it is probable, in conformity with their course in the pes pedunculi,

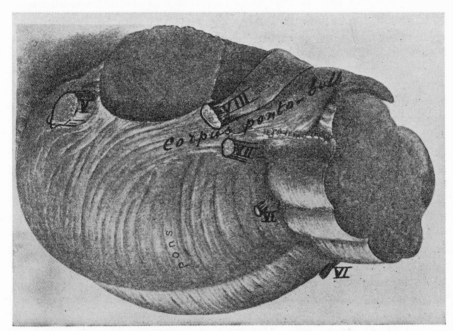

FIG. 421. The brain stem of an adult man with a ponto-bulbar body. *Essick.*

that the temporo-pontine tract (the bundle of Türck) breaks up in the pons more laterally and the fronto-pontine more medially. However, the exact distribution of these tracts is as yet unknown.

Borowiecki ('11) and *Masuda* ('14) stated that in man the fronto-pontine tract is in synaptic relation with pontine gray in the frontal part of the pons, while temporo-pontine fibers distribute only to the posterior third of the area. However, in apes *Spitzer* and *Karplus* ('07) carried the fronto-pontine path farther caudalward than the temporo-pontine. They believed that the latter tract ends in the upper half of the pons. *Thomas* and *Durupt* ('14) also stated that the temporo-pontine path breaks up in the anterior portion of the pons. *Winkler* ('27) carried the fronto-pontine path to the dorsal nucleus and to the lateral part of the ventral pontine nucleus. *Jakob* ('28) carried the fronto-pontine fibers to the oral portion of the pontine gray as *Masuda* ('14) and others had done. Where there is as yet such lack of agreement among observers as to the distribution of the tracts within the pons, it is not possible to determine the localization of impulses reaching the cerebellum by way of the cortico-pontine and the ponto-cerebellar tracts.   The ponto-cerebellar fibers (fig. 422) arise in the pontine gray.   According to a number of observers they all cross in the pons on their way to the cerebellum (*Vejas*, '85; *Borowiecki*, '11; *Masuda*, '14; *Uemura*, '17; *Brun*, '25, and others), while other observers believe that homolateral as well as contralateral fibers are present (*Lewandowsky*, '04; *Marburg*, '22; *Winkler*, '27, and others).   According to *Horsley* ('06), frontal fibers, the taenia pontis, are occasionally found.   Such fibers originate in the gray of the anterior part of the pons.   They run to the dentate nucleus as a distinct band which adjoins the main mass of the pontine fibers along its oral border.   Various earlier observers (*Henle*, '38, and others) regarded it as cere-bello-pontine.   *Brun* ('25) termed these bundles direct pedunculo-cerebellar fibers.   *Fuse* ('12) believed that they could be traced to the retrolenticular portion of the internal capsule (see also *Brun*, '25).   The majority of the ponto-cerebellar fibers pass to the cerebellar cortex.   According to *Masuda* ('14), the projection of the pontine fibers upon the cerebellum is such that those from the dorsal pontine gray distribute to the lobuli quadrangulares (the lateral portions of lobus anterior and lobulus simplex of *Bolk*), those fibers from the lateral pontine gray to the lobulus semilunaris inferior (a part of the crus primum, lobulus ansiformis of *Bolk*), the medial pontine gray to the ventral areas (lobuli gracilis and biventer, hence a part of the crus primum and the entire crus secun-dum of lobulus ansiformis of *Bolk*), and those of the ventral gray to the biventer lobule (crus secundum of lobulus ansiformis of *Bolk*).   By this arrangement the caudal parts of the pons are connected with the oral parts of the cerebellum and vice versa.   It is to be noted that the greater percentage of these connections are with the hemispheric portion of the median lobe of the cerebellum.   A superficial pontine bundle, fasciculus obliquus pontis, is sometimes very promi-nent and indicates clearly the connections of the frontal part of the pons with the caudal part of the cerebellum.   The above statements of *Masuda* ('14) indicate that the ponto-cerebellar system is connected with the hemispheres.   However, other observers (*Spitzer* and *Karplus*, '07; *Besta*, '12; *Winkler*, '27) have re-garded the pontine gray as connected with the cortex of the vermis as well as with the hemispheres.   *Winkler* carried ponto-cerebellar fibers from the ventral pontine gray to the biventer lobule and saw both crossed and uncrossed fibers passing to the vermis from the pontine gray, the proximal portion of the ventral gray supplying the proximal part of the vermis, the dorsal portion the distal part of the vermis.   This ventral portion of the pontine gray is supposedly its oldest part, but *Winkler* made clear that he did not find it connected exclu-sively with any special cerebellar area.   It is obvious that acceptance of these results of *Winkler* raises objections to any sharp subdivision into a neocerebellar and a paleocerebellar area as had been proposed by *Edinger* ('11; and elsewhere). *Jakob* ('28) in discussing a case of neopontine aplasia studied by *Beck* ('28) in which changes in the vermis appeared, made the following pertinent statement: "Daraus gibt Edingersche scharfe Scheidung zwischen Paläo- und Neo-cerebellum nicht anfrecht erhalten kann, sondern dass wir auch in Wurm 'Neuland' annehmen müssen." The termination of these pontine fibers within the cerebellar cortex is believed to be directly upon the Purkinje cells, for the ponto-cerebellar paths end as climbing fibers. Thus a two-neuron path between cerebral cortex and the Purkinje cells of the cerebellar cortex is established (fig. 422).

In addition to these main paths, fiber bundles connect the reticular nuclei of the brain stem with the cerebellum through the middle peduncle (*Borowiecki*, '11; *Masuda*, '14; *Uemura*, '17; *Brun*, '25). Such fibers arise probably from reticular gray in the region of the raphé and the more caudal half of the medial lemnisci bundles (tractus lemnisco-pontines of *von Monakow*, '95; see also *Brun*, '25). Similar fibers pass to the cerebellum from the gray associated with the lateral lemniscus in the pons region (ventrolateral reticular nucleus). *Uemura* ('17) found the nucleus centralis superior connected with the vermis. The medially lying, small reticular cells of the upper pons are connected with the hemispheres (*Brun*, '25; *Jakob*, '28). Such afferent fibers from the tegmental gray to the cerebellum have been termed fibrae rectae pontis; efferent fibers to these reticular nuclei, which are believed to be present in small numbers in the middle peduncle, are termed cerebello-tegmental fibers.

C. BRACHIUM CONJUNCTIVUM, OR SUPERIOR CEREBELLAR PEDUNCLE

The brachium conjunctivum takes origin chiefly from the cerebellar nuclei, the major bundles passing directly out of the hilus of the dentate nucleus. There is evidence (to be considered later) which indicates that other of its efferent components may arise directly from the cerebellar cortex and particularly from the flocculus. Even a cursory examination of the course of the main bundle shows that it passes forward and ventralward from the cerebellum into the region of the midbrain, that it decussates below the ventricle at the level of the inferior colliculus, forming thus the decussation of the brachium conjunctivum (the commissure of Wernicke), and that it then passes forward to terminate in the red nucleus and the dorsal thalamus. The account will begin with the brachium conjunctivum as seen within the cerebellum. At certain levels within the cerebellum the bundle in question includes not only paths which emerge through the brachium conjunctivum, but also fiber systems which leave the cerebellum through other paths, usually by way of the corpus juxtarestiforme (in corpus restiforme in its broadest sense). Thus capping the main mass of brachium conjunctivum fibers (constituting the middle field of *Winkler*, '27) is the uncinate fasciculus, considered on former pages (pages 807 to 809). The uncinate fasciculus leaves the superior cerebellar peduncle as the latter reaches the aqueduct. This middle field carries the main efferent paths. Ventral to this middle field is found the ventrolateral field of *Winkler* ('27), containing a number of short connections, including fascicles of the trigemino-cerebellar connections and the tractus vestibulo-fastigius and tractus vestibulo-globosus of this observer. As the fibers of the peduncle pass along the sides of the peduncle they are bounded medially and laterally by the so-called nuclei of the brachium conjunctivum, which are particularly developed in certain lower mammals such as the rabbit (*Winkler* and *Potter*, '11). These nuclei contribute fibers to the peduncle and probably receive certain incoming impulses, as from the ventral spino-cerebellar tract.

Ramón y Cajal ('03, '11), who studied the decussation of the brachium conjunctivum by the use of silver impregnation methods, found that as these fibers reach their decussation the most dorsal fibers cross first (even well within the pons) and that the decussation is added to ventrally as the bundles are traced forward. In Macacus rhesus, according to the experimental observations of *Mussen* ('27), the most dorsal fibers have their origin from the dorsal cephalic portion of the nucleus emboliformis, while the underlying more central fibers originate from the dorsal cephalic region of the nucleus dentatus.   This observer carried the fibers from the nucleus emboliformis to both the small-celled and the large-celled portions of the red nucleus.   A few bundles could be traced into the field of Forel.   The fibers from the dorsal cephalic portion of the nucleus dentatus *Mussen* ('27) found to be distributed to both the large-celled and small-celled portions of the red nucleus, to the field of Forel, and to the ventral nucleus of the thalamus.   By counting the fibers from these regions of the nucleus emboliformis and the nucleus dentatus through the superior cerebellar peduncle, *Mussen* reached the conclusion that the nucleus parvocellularis of the red nucleus and the thalamic centers received each about one-quarter of such fibers, the remaining half terminating in the large-celled portion of the red nucleus.   Presumably fibers from the more ventral parts of the nucleus emboliformis and the nucleus dentatus may decussate in the ventral portion of the commissure of Wernicke.   These fibers were not investigated by *Mussen* ('27).   However, *Ramón y Cajal* ('03, '11) traced fibers into this more cephalic part of the decussation, which divided and gave off both ascending and descending branches, both before and after crossing.   Many of the ascending branches followed the usual course to the red nucleus and thalamus.   The descending branches formed cerebello-tegmental (and cerebello-motorius) paths, the "voie olivo-bulbaire directe" and "voie olivo-spinale croisée," respectively.   The direct path, according to *Ramón y Cajal*, descends through the pons and medulla oblongata and gives off fibers to the motor nuclei of the trigeminal and facial nerves and may even reach the cord, although of the latter connections he was not entirely certain.   The crossed path *Ramón y Cajal* carried to the facial nucleus and possibly to the cord. This observer emphasized that the fibers nearest the ventricle (that is, the most dorsal fibers) do not bifurcate but decussate and pass forward, and that by no means all of the remaining fibers bifurcate, many of them passing directly forward to the red nucleus and the diencephalic centers.   *Marchi* ('91) and *Thomas* ('97) carried fibers from the superior cerebellar peduncles into the cord.   *Thomas* particularly considered that these arose from the dentate nucleus and could be carried as far as the lumbar cord.   There is some difference of opinion with regard to the caudal extent of these fibers, for while they have been traced into the bulbar regions, not all observers have been able to demonstrate a spinal connection, and there is a distinct tendency to regard such a connection as at least open to question (*Jakob*, '28).   The ascending branches terminate in part, after dividing and redividing, in rich pericellular networks around the neurons of the red nucleus. These are illustrated beautifully for rabbits by *Ramón y Cajal*. Other fibers pass through the red nucleus to the thalamus as has been

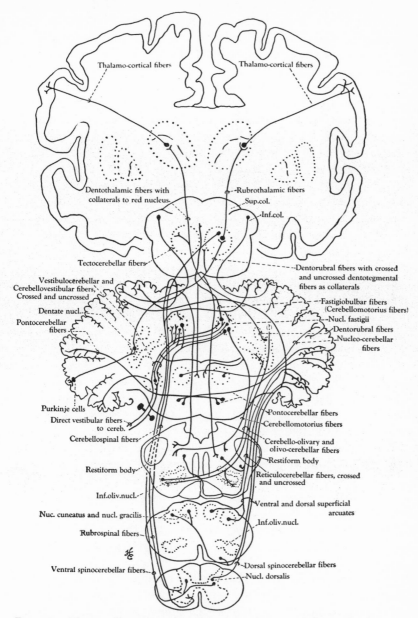

Fig. 422. Diagram illustrating the components of the cerebellar peduncles, with both afferent and efferent cerebellar fibers indicated. *Huber* and *Crosby*.

stated previously. Their exact termination within this latter center is still a matter of some uncertainty. *Von Monakow* ('10) traced them to the medial thalamic nucleus: *Horsley* and *Clarke* ('08) and *Foix* and *Nicolesco* ('25) believed that they reach the lateral thalamic nucleus; *Sachs* ('09) carried them to the lateral thalamic nucleus and the centromedian nucleus; *Vogt* ('11) believed that they distributed to his noyau ventral intermediare and *Ramón y Cajal* ('11) to his noyau anterieur, which is the nucleus ventralis (pars anterior) of various workers. Their termination within the thalamic centers will be discussed later in greater detail (page 1154; see also bibliography of Chapter VIII). The dento-thalamic tract grows progressively larger from lower to higher mammals; with this is associated an increase in the small-celled portion of the red nucleus.

Running forward in the superior cerebellar peduncle, decussating, and passing to the oculomotor nucleus are cerebello-motorius fibers. These are believed to run from the flocculus to the nucleus in question. They are known on occasion as the Wallenberg-Klimoff fibers (*Wallenberg*, '98, and *Klimoff*, '01). Various other observers have identified them, among whom may be mentioned *Lorenz* ('13), *Saito* ('22 and '23), and *Riese* ('25). *Löwy* ('14) demonstrated experimentally that those fibers in the rabbit which arise from that part of the dentate nucleus which extends out into the flocculus are joined by fibers directly from the cortex of the region. Thus, in the rabbit, after a lesion of the cortex of the flocculus which did not involve the dentate nucleus, several small fascicles could be traced into the upper third of the brachium conjunctivum. It was suggested that this may form the bundle to the eye muscle nuclei (*Ariëns Kappers*, '21). It is to be noted that *Kuzume* ('26) found the flocculus connected with the homolateral oculomotor gray and that *Yamamoto* ('29) connected the flocculus to both homolateral and contralateral Edinger-Westphal nuclei, but more particularly to the homolateral nucleus.

From the foregoing account it is evident that the main paths constituting the brachium conjunctivum or superior cerebellar peduncle after it leaves the cerebellum are the dento-rubro-thalamic path, the cerebello-tegmental or cerebello-reticular (and possibly spinal) path, and the cerebello-motorius path. These are illustrated in figure 422. To such fibers must be added collaterals of the mesencephalic root of the trigeminal, which *Wallenberg* ('05) traced into the brachium conjunctivum and *Weinberg* ('28) carried into the cerebellum in the rabbit. The termination within the cerebellum is not known. The lobo-cerebellar and the posterior mesencephalo-cerebellar tracts of fishes apparently have no representatives in mammals.

At the side of the superior cerebellar peduncle the ventral spino-cerebellar tract, discussed with the dorsal spino-cerebellar system (see p. 800), passes to the cerebellum. Between the two superior cerebellar peduncles, through the anterior medullary velum, pass the tecto-cerebellar fibers and possibly also cerebello-tectal fibers. They have been described in forms as low as Ornithorhynchus (*Hines*, '25 and '29), and for a long time have been known to be present in man (*Edinger*, '11, and earlier). Presumably they carry uncrossed and probably also crossed fibers from the inferior colliculus to the cerebellum, and they are said to terminate as climbing fibers in the cerebellar cortex. The details regarding this system, particularly in higher mammals, require further study.

D. Résumé of Certain Connections of the Flocculus

Before leaving the discussion of cerebellar connections it is desirable to consider further certain fiber relations of the flocculus. On the whole, it must be admitted that further work is needed for a complete understanding of the connections of this region, which is one of the most primitive portions of the cerebellum (the paleocerebellum of *Edinger*, '08, and *Comolli*, '10). It is increased in certain mammals such as Echidna, marsupials, and rodents as compared with birds and reptiles, but the reason for such an increase is yet to be explained clearly. *Bolk* ('07) described a relatively very large formatio vermicularis in Phocaena; but *Wilson* ('33), however, described the flocculus as a small lobe and the paraflocculus as large in this animal. Any marked development of it in this water-living mammal would be of particular interest because in fishes, and especially in plagiostomes, there is a very well developed auricle associated with a high degree of development of the peripheral lateral line and vestibular systems. The whale, of course, does not possess a lateral-line system but the vestibular apparatus is well developed and the vestibular nerves are large in this form. Consequently indirect vestibulo-cerebellar fibers, if not direct vestibular root fibers, reach the flocculus and undoubtedly play a prominent part in its development. The enlargement of the flocculus in certain mammals is furthered by its connections with other parts of the cerebellum, providing for intracerebellar conduction, and particularly with the cerebellar nuclei. In such animals, including the whale, the dentate nucleus extends out toward the cortex of the flocculus, an expression of the increased influence of the axons of Purkinje cells of the flocculus upon the gray of the dentate nucleus. Flocculo-fugal fibers related to vestibular nuclei appear to affect thus indirectly the coördination of eye movements, and it is possible that they may affect them more directly through the Wallenberg-Klimoff component of the superior cerebellar peduncle. At all events, in certain mammals there appears to be a direct relation between the degree of eye muscle coördination and the size of the flocculus. However, it must not be forgotten in this connection that the flocculus in primates, and particularly in man, is small, nor that eye movements may be effected by other paths from the cerebellum.[16] Certainly the results of *Bárány* ('14, '17) indicated that in experimental animals stimulation of the floccular cortex led to combinations of eye movements. *Mussen* ('29) found that removal of the flocculus led to interference with righting movements when the animal was laid on the injured side.

Certain connections of the flocculus may be summarized briefly as follows. An interfloccular commissure (*Wallenberg*, '05) has been pointed out in rabbits and, on the basis of its form relations and connections, regarded as homologous

---

[16] For example, *Mussen* ('29) believed that conjugate deviation of the eyes following stimulation of the left vermis is due to impulses passing from the cerebellar cortex to the contralateral roof nucleus and, after a synapse there, by way of the uncinate fasciculus to the abducens nucleus, which supplies the lateral rectus muscle. From the abducens nucleus impulses reach the oculomotor nucleus, which supplies the medial rectus and other extrinsic muscles, over the medial longitudinal fasciculus.

to the interauricular commissure of fishes.   According to some workers, it is uncertain whether the commissural fibers originate from the cortex of the flocculus or from the floccular part of the nucleus dentatus.   *Ingvar* ('19) traced a small bundle of the spino-cerebellar tract to the parafloccular region in cats, a connection which needs further substantiation.   The relations of the flocculus with the vestibular apparatus and possibly directly with eye muscle nuclei have been considered.   Since atrophy of the ponto-cerebellar tracts does not affect the flocculus, and since these tracts do not myelinate until after myelinization of the flocculus, it seems improbable that these fiber bundles reach the floccular area. However, *Wilson* ('33) believed that the parafloccular in the whale owes its size to its reception of about 60 per cent of the pontine fibers.   *Kuzume* ('26), by the use of anatomical and experimental methods, studied the connections of the flocculus and the cerebellar nuclei in rabbits, sixty-five animals being employed. He found association fibers connecting the flocculus with other, and particularly homolateral, regions of the cerebellar cortex.   *Brouwer* and *Coenen* ('21) and *Saito* ('22) described paths between the vermis and the flocculus.   Such connections had been predicted by *Ariëns Kappers* ('21).   However, the existence of vermis-floccular interconnections has been denied by *Clarke* and *Horsley* ('05) and by *Jansen* ('33).   This latter observer was unable to demonstrate connections between the flocculus and the vermis, or association fibers between the flocculus or vermis and the contralateral or homolateral cerebellar hemisphere. *Kuzume* ('26) demonstrated : connections between the flocculus and the nucleus dentatus and between the flocculus and the nucleus fastigii of each side ; homolateral fibers to the nucleus abducens and part of the nucleus oculomotorius ; and a few fibers entering the superior cerebellar peduncle.   *Johnston* ('34, J. Anat., vol. 68, p. 471) connected the flocculus with the pons and possibly the midbrain.

Finally this discussion of the fiber connections may be concluded by a brief mention of the association systems.   *Horsley* and *Clarke* ('05), *Brouwer* and *Coenen* ('21), *Saito* ('22), *Jansen* ('33), and others have recognized short fibers connecting adjacent folia.   The views with regard to certain intracerebellar connections have been reviewed in the preceding paragraph.   Connections from the vermis to the hemispheres have been advocated by *Saito* ('22) and others and denied by *Jansen* ('33).   This latter observer described interhemispheric fibers and connections from the hemisphere to lobulus *C*, and to a less extent to other parts of the vermis.   With *Horsley* and *Clarke*, *Jansen* concluded that : "the study of association fibers in general confirms the impression of mutual independence of the main cerebellar lobes."

THE FUNCTIONAL LOCALIZATION WITHIN THE CEREBELLUM

The foundations of the present knowledge of physiologic localization within the cerebellum were laid particularly by the comparative anatomic researches of *Bolk*, whose deductions have been in part confirmed by later work.   The work of *Bolk* ('03, '06 ; fig. 785), *Adamkiewicz* ('04, '07), *van Rijnberk* ('04, '04a, '08, '12), *Vincenzoni* ('08), *Hulshoff Pol* ('15), *Rothmann* ('10, '13), *Thomas* and

Durupt ('14), *Bárány* ('10, '12, '12a, '12b, '14), *Dusser de Barenne* ('24), and others indicates a physiologic cerebellar localization.

Bolk localized various muscle groups within the different divisions of the cerebellum. He regarded the lobus anterior as the center of coördination for muscles of the head (eyes, tongue, muscles of mastication and those of expression, also laryngeal and pharyngeal muscles). Centers for the coördination of neck musculature are said to lie in the lobulus simplex. The upper part of the lobulus medius medianus (C_1—C_2) contains the coördination centers for bilateral movements of the extremities; in the crura of the lobuli ansiformes and in the lobuli paramediani are the centers for the upper and lower extremities. In the remaining portions of the cerebellum (with the exception of the formatio vermicularis of *Bolk* or the flocculus and paraflocculus of many other observers) the coördination centers for the trunk and tail musculature are said to lie. The flocculus and paraflocculus are superimposed upon the vestibular area and probably have a part in maintaining proper static and kinetic conditions in a fluid medium. The flocculus is related phylogenetically to the auricle of lower forms.

Adamkiewicz obtained abduction of the forepaw in a rabbit following a lesion in the upper quarter of the lobus lateralis, while a lesion in the lower quarter produced a paresis of the hind paw. Between these two areas was a center concerned with turning the head toward the same side. The anterior part of the vermis contained a center for the forepaws and neck; the posterior part a center for the lower extremities. *Pagano* ('05), both by the use of curare and by extirpation methods, localized a center for the coördination of eye and neck movements within the central part of the cerebellum, and a center for the similar coördination of movements of the anterior and posterior extremities in the lateral portions of that organ.

The work of *van Rijnberk* has been more extensive than that of the previously mentioned observers and he has been able, to a considerable extent, to bring his results into line with the observations of *Bolk* and to relate them to the functional divisions established by this latter observer. However, it is necessary to remember that lesions made by *van Rijnberk* were not always confined to the cerebellar cortex. Frequently they involved deeper regions as well.

In his experiments on dogs, *Bárány* found that destruction of the lobulus simplex was followed by an involvement of the muscles of the neck which revealed itself in a continuous shaking of the head from left to right. Injury of the crus primum of the ansiform lobule produced an interference with the movements of the forepaws so that one or both of the paws gave "saluting movements" as the animal approached, which later appeared as a spring-halt (cock-step) when the animal was running. An analogous dysymmetry in walking appeared in the hind paws after a lesion of the crus secundum of the ansiform lobule. Destruction of the paramedian lobule produced rolling movements and pleurothotonus. Ablation of lobulus C_2 of *Bolk* did not appear to affect the walk of the dog, although a similar lesion in the sheep, where C_2 is much better developed, interfered with walking.

The work of *Vincenzoni* ('08) and of *Luna* ('09) in the main confirmed that of *Bárány*. *Hulshoff Pol* ('15), however, obtained incoördinate movements of the posterior extremities after removal of the lobulus medianus posterior, pleurothotonus and " parade " step after lesion of the lobulus paramedianus, and goose step after the destruction of the crus secundum of the ansiform lobule.

After resection of the lobulus ansiformis in dogs, *Rothmann* ('13) observed a disturbance in the movements of the extremities, and, after resection of the lobulus paramedianus in these animals, interference with movements of the trunk, particularly on the contralateral side. Destruction of the flocculus was followed by a disturbance of neck and head movements but by no interference with movements of the extremities. Astasia of the head, a bending of the trunk, due perhaps to the head condition, and interference in the coördination of movements of the limbs were obtained by *Rothmann* after destruction of the anterior lobe. A center for the coördination of the action of the larynx, jaw, and tongue muscles was located in the anterior part of the lobus anterior by *Katzenstein* and *Rothmann*. Destruction of lobulus simplex produced an interference with neck movements, that of lobulus medianus posterior with trunk movements.

The experiments of *Thomas* and *Durupt* ('14) aroused much interest. Their work indicated that injuries to the cerebellum produce interruption in the direction of movements. On the basis of their researches on dogs and monkeys, they came to the following conclusions, which show a remarkable resemblance to the final conclusions of *Bolk*. Static and equilibratory disturbances, as well as instability of the head, are associated with the destruction of the lobulus medianus anterior, while dysymmetry of the extremities is caused by the destruction of the lateral divisions : — lobulus ansiformis, lobulus paramedianus, and formatio vermicularis (flocculus). Lesions of the lobulus simplex are accompanied by a shaking of the head; lesions of the lobulus medianus posterior by interference with equilibrium and by "chutes à la reverse." In the dog, the center for the forepaw lies in front of that for the hind paw, principally in the crus primum of the lobulus ansiformis. *Thomas* and *Durupt* went even further than *Bolk* in their scheme of localization, for they divided these centers into secondary centers associated with antagonistic muscle groups and with special centers for the direction of movements such as bending, stretching, abduction, and adduction. They located the center concerned with abduction of the posterior extremities in the region of the crus secundum lobuli ansiformis, in the lobulus paramedianus, and in the formatio vermicularis (flocculus). These observers pointed out the agreement between their results and those obtained earlier by *Rothmann*. The observations of *Thomas* and *Durupt* on apes are likewise in harmony in general with the conclusions of *Bolk*, since they found that the lobulus quadrangularis and the upper part of the lobus ansoparamedianus exercise a regulatory influence over the upper extremities and the lower part of the lobus ansoparamedianus influences the movements of the lower extremities.

Explanation of the causes underlying these disturbances in movements and the factors involved are to be sought in the work of *Bárány* ('10, '12, '12a), *de Kleijn* and *Magnus* ('20), and others. *Mills* and *Weisenburg* ('14), whose results were tested in the clinic and were further supported by cinematographic reproductions of the interrupted movements, offer confirmation in man of the major principles of *Bolk's* scheme of cerebellar localization.

Comolli ('10) and *Edinger* ('08 and '11) divided the cerebellum into a neo-cerebellar portion (the cerebellar hemispheres) and a paleocerebellar portion (the flocculus and vermis). *Brun* ('25) discussed this subdivision into a neo-cerebellum and a paleocerebellum, which he regarded as of fundamental importance. This paper is of interest since it discusses the fiber paths to and from the several divisions and attempts to establish a " chronogenic localization." *Brun* believed that two types of reflex arcs pass through the cerebellum. Into the paleocerebellum come successive impulses from the proprioceptive centers of the spinal cord, with the generation of the impulses and their continuation due to the many movements of the extremities and trunk. The cerebellum then serves as an inhibitory mechanism, a brake on the movements which result. Changes of tonic character which occur in the cerebrum itself are carried to the cerebellum also and are able to influence or brake the discharge from these centers. The cerebellum exerts an influence of this character over the labyrinthine reflexes since it forms both a primary and a secondary center for vestibular impulses. According to *Brun*, the neocerebellum is intimately related to the cerebral cortex, receiving from that center proprioceptive impulses of the highest order. It seems probable that such connections may involve other than those of proprioceptive character.

Bolk's plan of localization has great theoretical as well as great practical value, for his conclusions to a certain extent actually agree with such neo- and paleo-cerebellar divisions. Thus *Bolk* localized the centers for coördinate movements of the head, neck, and trunk in the anterior lobe, the lobulus simplex, and the vermis portions of the remaining medial and posterior lobes, and such movements, including simple coördinate movements of the fins, are to be found in the lowest vertebrates, in which only the vermis portions of the cerebellum are present.

Bolk regarded the flocculus as a center concerned only with the musculature of the tail. In lower vertebrates, however, the region is an outgrowth of the vestibular area and is not concerned with somatic musculature. The researches of *Bárány* ('14) strongly suggest that in higher vertebrates the flocculus exerts a considerable influence over movements of the eyes, in part, at least, through its connections with the vestibular regions (see page 817). That the two points of view are not at utter variance is seen from the fact that in animals in which the neck is rigid, fibers from the vestibular nuclei (through Mauthner's cells) send impulses over motor neurons which affect greatly the movements of the body and tail of the animal.

MacNalty and *Horsley* ('09) believed that the results obtained by them with regard to the distribution of the spino-cerebellar tracts within the cerebellum contradicted the scheme of cerebellar localization as presented by *Bolk*. Their results, based on a study of monkeys, indicate that the fibers from the whole cervical cord (C1–T1) distribute chiefly in front of the sulcus primarius, to central and culmen of the anterior lobe, but a few fibers reach the uppermost part of the pyramis.   These authors stated explicitly that fibers from the anterior extremities reach the lobulus centralis as well as the pyramis.   (See pages 788 and 789 for a comparison of the terminologies.)

From these facts it is evident that a great correlation of perceptions from various regions of the body and head takes place in the cortex of the vermis.   In particular there is a correlation of impulses from the extremities and the interrelation of these with impulses arising within the neck and trunk musculature. The pronounced overlapping of different areas supplied by spino-cerebellar tracts within the cortex of the vermis and the consequent correlation is not surprising since it is scarcely possible to alter to any great extent the position of any one portion of the body without affecting to some extent the position and relations of other parts as well.   Such intimate correlation has received recognition in *Bolk's* plan of localization, for not only movements of the trunk but associated movements of the anterior and posterior extremities are localized by this observer in the tuber and in the pyramid of the cerebellum.   The pronounced overlapping then raises the question as to whether or not localization of function, as far as it may be applied to the cerebellum, may not depend upon the maximum impulses reaching a particular region.   In other words, the localization within a given area is an indication that the predominant or maximum impulses to that area arise from such portions of the body as are there localized, but does not take account of a minimal number of impulses from other body regions which may reach the area.

To attempt to relate in detail the results obtained on spino-cerebellar distribution to the plan of cerebellar localization as presented by *Bolk* is at present more or less futile.   There is no direct agreement between the two plans, but it must be emphasized again that this does not necessarily imply that either set of conclusions is incorrect.   It simply means that much more must be known with respect to all phases of the problem before what appear to be conflicting results can be reconciled.   The following brief survey is intended to indicate merely that there is more possibility of correlation than is sometimes believed to be the case.

The results of *MacNalty* and *Horsley* indicate that the spino-cerebellar fibers from the neck region (C1–C4) are localized in the lobulus centralis and the culmen. Fibers from the chief sensory nucleus of the trigeminal also reach this region. The upper cervical fibers carry impulses from the neck region and from the head through the descending root of the trigeminal nerve.   All the facts appear to indicate that the part of the cerebellum receiving these fibers is the center for head and neck regions.   That the neck centers are not confined to the lobulus simplex (*Bolk*) appears clear, since stability of the neck in animals such as the giraffe, where it is very long, obviously is dependent upon the relation of these muscles to certain trunk muscles.   An hypertrophy of the lobulus simplex with an accompanying great development of the neck musculature is associated with a similar hypertrophy of the middle lobe.

According to *MacNalty* and *Horsley*, the fibers of the dorsal spino-cerebellar tract, which arise chiefly from the trunk (Th. 1–L1), are projected to some extent on the region in front of the sulcus primarius, but are distributed chiefly to the areas behind that fissure, and particularly to the pyramis. That the centers for the trunk regions below the neck are localized in the vermis in a region caudal to the centers for the head and neck is also generally accepted. That the center for neck musculature does not lie entirely between those for head and trunk, but is somewhat intermingled with the center for the head musculature on the one hand and with the center for the trunk musculature on the other, while presenting difficulties, is not of necessity at variance with the results of *Bolk*. It is also probable that the lingula does not receive head fibers only.

The localization of the extremity centers presents the greatest difficulties. Presumably such centers must lie in relation both to the head and neck centers of the anterior lobe and to the trunk centers as represented in the pyramid. The correlation of the centers for the extremities with those of the trunk in the lobulus medianus posterior was predicated by *Bolk*. *MacNalty* and *Horsley* and also *Ingvar* found that no spino-cerebellar fibers passed to the tuber or clivus, and these results suggest that the region is associative in character and that it has to do with bilaterally associated movements. Such a function for these regions is not of necessity denied by *Bolk's* scheme of localization. This latter observer did localize the centers for the more delicate unilateral movements within the cerebellar hemispheres. This latter localization is not called into question by the results of *MacNalty* and *Horsley*, for these latter observers traced no spino-cerebellar tracts to hemispheric regions. The pontocerebellar fibers distribute to the hemispheres, and it seems altogether probable that they may bring from the cerebral cortex such finer proprioceptive impulses as are necessary for the finer regulation of certain movements of unilateral character. It would appear, then, that the two sets of results, those of *MacNalty* and *Horsley* and those of *Bolk*, can be harmonized to a certain extent, though not completely or satisfactorily, from the data at hand.

A somewhat different plan of localization within the cerebellar cortex of the cat has been offered by *Mussen* ('27), but in the present state of our knowledge this plan does not appear to accord any more closely with the fiber distribution as given for the vermis by *MacNalty* and *Horsley* and by *Ingvar* ('19) than does the localization pattern of *Bolk*. *Mussen's* work is of particular interest for the study of cerebellar localization because his results were obtained by stimulation of the cortex. *Horsley* and *Clarke* ('08) had believed that the surface of the cerebellum could not be stimulated by electrical current, although results of stimulation appear if the electrodes are sunken more deeply into the substance of the cerebellum. According to *Bárány* ('14), faradization of the cortex of the flocculus produces eye movements, but some have thought this to be due to a deeper penetration of the current. *Mills* and *Weisenburg* ('14), *Cobb, Bailey, and Holtz* ('17), and *Miller* and *Banting* ('22 and '22a; see also *Miller*, '29) obtained results from stimulation of the cerebellar cortex. In this connection a remark made by *van Valkenburg* (*Ariëns Kappers*, '21) offers much food for thought. It was to the effect that the localization, as based upon the endings of the spino-cerebellar tracts, is the localization of the afferent stimuli, whereas the functional localization, as given by *Bolk*, is a localization based on the origin of efferent paths.   Perhaps more than any other suggestion this opens a way for relating the various and apparently conflicting observations which have grown out of the studies on the cerebellum.

Any consideration of the general nature of cerebellar function must include some mention of the researches of *Luciani* ('91 and '93).   This observer analyzed the character of these functions in the hand of a patient following cerebellar destruction.   It was he who first pointed out the appearance of hypotonia, hyposthenia, and ataxia of the muscles, phenomena which, in so far as they are due to the cerebellar lesions, are not entirely incontestable, as the later work of *Gordon Holmes* ('17), *Miller* ('29), and others have indicated, and as has been confirmed in many respects.   *Miller* ('29) pointed out that the hypertonia which often follows close on the cerebellar lesion and which was regarded as a release phenomenon by *Luciani*, is due to the removal of the inhibitory action of certain regions of the cerebellum.   Neither *Dusser de Barenne* ('24) nor *Rademaker* ('26; *Miller*, '29, p. 362) found hypotonia following removal of part or all of the cerebellum, but in the cases studied by *Holmes* ('17) hypotonia was present. *Miller* ('29) offered as explanation of this that "some parts of the cerebellum have an augmentor, others an inhibitory action on postural tone."   *Holmes* ('17) and *Dusser de Barenne* ('24) both found that muscular tremors (astasia) frequently follow cerebellar lesions.   *Holmes* ('17) looked upon the cerebellum as a center for motor reënforcement.   In its action over the motor centers of the brain stem and cord it prepares them — tunes them — so that the response may be carried out on receipt of the stimulation from higher centers and that it may be effective and sufficiently forceful.   *Wertham* and *Lyman* ('29) found the conclusions of *Holmes* confirmed in their study of arrhythmokinesis.   *Holmes* emphasized that in his cases nystagmus was present and that often the patients showed an inability to carry out acts which involved the association of separate muscle groups in the rapid performance of alternate movements such as flexion and extension or pronation and supination.   In line with this is the work of *Tilney* and *Pike* ('25), who showed that cerebellar lesions affect the coöperative activity of the muscles on the two sides of a limb (*i.e.* the so-called antagonistic muscles), the degree depending on the depth of the lesion.   Also, according to *Tilney* ('19), action of the cerebellum is synergic, for this organ exerts a controlling and checking influence over the agonistic and antagonistic muscles. *André-Thomas* ('14, quoted from *Hunt*, '29) had conceived of cerebellar functions as finding expression in the hyposthenia and hypersthenia of the muscle groups (the antagonistic and the agonistic).   *Mills* and *Weisenburg* ('14) and *Weisenburg* ('27 and '29) considered that the essential function of the cerebellum is synergia.   *Weisenburg* ('27 and '29) stated that the cerebellum has a synergic action over motor activity and that cerebellar lesions of various types find the patient unable to carry out synergic movements in the normal manner. This observer believed that there is a definite pattern of functional localization within the cerebellum along the accepted line, but no centers producing deviations.   He found atonia and asthenia present in acute lesions of the cere-

bellum, but regarded these defects as due to some more or less temporary interference with the functioning of other centers and probably efferent centers.   He
stated definitely that "the fundamental defect of a cerebellar lesion is asynergia."
Hunt ('29) stated that "I, too, would reduce its (the cerebellum's) manifestations
to a single essential syndrome, namely, the regulation of posture and postural
tone."

The influence of the cerebellum over muscle tonus is not explained easily.
Certain studies on tonic and righting reflexes in decerebrate animals appear to
have shown that these are abolished when certain regions of the tegmental part
of the midbrain and the bulb are destroyed.   *Sherrington* ('98), *Beritoff* and
Magnus ('14), and *de Kleijn* and *Magnus* ('20) showed that decerebrate rigidity
is not abolished by the removal of the cerebellum.   This rigidity can be inhibited
by stimulation of the cerebellar cortex (also by stimulation of deeper portions of
the cerebellum) and the superior cerebellar peduncles (*Sherrington*, '98; *Cobb*,
Bailey, and *Holtz*, '17; *Miller* and *Banting*, '22).   Recently *Pollock* and *Davis* ('29)
arrived at the same conclusions.   They studied a number of cats in which decerebration was accomplished by the anemic method and in which the cerebellum was removed.   They obtained a much greater degree of opisthotonus than
in animals in which decerebration alone occurred.   This opisthotonus could be
abolished if the labyrinths were destroyed.   They concluded "that the cerebellum as a whole inhibits tonic labyrinthine reflexes which are responsible for
the production of the marked increase in rigidity when the head is turned vertex
down and for the extreme opisthotonus."   *Rademaker* ('26) showed that active
uninhibited labyrinthine righting reflexes and static impulses occur in animals
without a cerebellum, but he found in normal animals the condition described
by *Pollock* and *Davis* ('29) in decerebrate animals — that the cerebellum has
some sort of a regulatory or inhibitory action over certain postural reflex activities.
Thus *Magnus* and *de Kleijn* (*Magnus*, '24) believed that destruction of the
red nucleus or of the decussation of the rubro-spinal tract (decussation of Forel)
resulted in the loss of righting reflexes and the onset of rigidity, but *Magnus* ('25)
stated that there was no positive evidence for the influence of the cerebellum
on postural activity.   The experiments of *Magnus* and *de Kleijn* were based
on thalamic and decerebrate animals, that is, on animals which possessed only
the brain stem.   *Mussen* ('29) studied animals which were uninjured except
for certain minute lesions and obtained almost diametrically opposite results
(this matter is discussed further in the account of the mesencephalon, Chapter
VIiI, pages 1087 to 1091).

What are the underlying factors which enable the normal cerebellum to influence the normal tonus and the normal sthenia and taxis?   In order to answer
these questions it is necessary to discover in the first place what characteristics
these normal activities have in common, or, better yet, what impulses acting in
or on the body are dominated by the cerebellum.

Ingvar ('19; see also '18, 18a) considered these matters and came to the conclusion that the cerebellum plays a great rôle in maintaining the effectiveness of
the body and in adapting its parts to the play of gravity and to inertia.   As a

consequence of the inertia of all bodies kinetic energy appears, a fact which is important in the maintenance of equilibrium.   It follows that the cerebellum must receive impulses of a static as well as of a kinetic character and has to control or neutralize static as well as kinetic energy.   Furthermore, it is clear that animals, such as the majority of mammals, which must maintain their balance on four extremities — all of which have joints — are predisposed toward a very labile type of equilibrium.   Thanks to the very intricate interrelations which produce great inertia of the muscles, and likewise to certain anatomic attributes of the joint surfaces which must be present in order that the bones may interlock, the system as a whole is always stable in its effect in the normal animal.   Naturally the muscles are of the greatest importance in accomplishing this.

In order to carry on its many, varied motor functions, an animal must always be able to put into practical effect a constant stable equilibrium.   In every movement of the extremity of an animal, the resultants of the parallelogram of forces of gravity acting on the parts of the body shift, and every change must be regulated and compensated for through the inertia of the muscles of the part, with due consideration for the influence exerted by the force of gravity on the whole body.   In the changing life of the animal such changes in the parallelogram of forces continually occur, and for these there must be compensation.   This goes on unconsciously, in a reflex manner.   It is very easy to recognize the use of unconscious regulation and the combating of the forces which act unceasingly on the individual.

The oldest afferent paths to the cerebellum are those of the vestibular and, in fishes, of the lateral-line systems.   Consequently the most primitive forms of cerebella (as in Petromyzon) are connected primarily with the nuclei of these nerves.   Physiologically there is also a certain relationship between the vestibular apparatus and the cerebellum, although the old notion that the labyrinth reflex in large part passes through the cerebellum has been disproved (*de Kleijn* and *Magnus*, '20; *Rademaker*, '26, and others).   *Bárány* ('12a) demonstrated that vestibular reaction movements are carried into the cerebellar cortex.   If the elementary impulses, which stream centralward from the peripheral vestibular apparatus, are more closely analyzed, it will be found that static and kinetic energy are concerned in the impulses.   The vestibular apparatus is a sense organ for the perception of mass from the standpoint of its two physico-mechanical functions : gravitation and inertia.   It is also apparent that these functions preserve in themselves a fundamental principle of cerebellar activity.   Relatively early phylogenetically, spino-cerebellar paths become the greatest afferent cerebellar systems.   A consideration of the physiologic importance of the impulses which stream over these paths to the cerebellum forces the admission that not much of a precise nature is known regarding these impulses.   With regard to the true function of these paths, the work of *Marburg* ('04) and *Bing* ('06) indicates that disturbances of these systems ("Hypotonie und Regulationsstörung der Prinzipialbewegungen an den Extremitätenwinzeln") which appear in cerebellar syndromes suggest to a certain degree vestibular disturbances.   The peripheral end-organs (neuromuscular and neurotendinous and Pacinian corpuscles) which send these impulses through the spino-cerebellar tracts are in need of further investigation.

One sensory disturbance, which according to certain observers is apparent after cerebellar lesions and disease, is the destruction in the extremities of an ability to estimate weight. This symptom was described first by *Lotmar* ('08) as dependent upon the cerebellum. The observations of *Maas* ('13) and *Goldstein* and *Reichmann* ('16) have confirmed this. The last mentioned authors speak of an undervaluing of weight as a deficiency symptom and an overvaluing of weight as an initiation symptom.

Freund ('14) also found such disturbances. He arrived at the conclusion that the cerebellum serves as a way station for impulses concerned with an appreciation of weight, which must involve the cerebral cortex for conscious appreciation. However, *Holmes* ('17) denied that any disturbance so simple makes its appearance after cerebellar lesions. He found that if he permitted his patients with only a cerebellotatic arm and cerebellotatic hand to estimate weights they gave correctly the relations of the weights (indeed, one patient recognized the relation better and more correctly with the atatic than with the well hand), but if the patients compared weights held in both hands at the same time, *Holmes* found a disturbance of the ability to appraise the weight held in the atatic hand. Undoubtedly further research is necessary along this line. From the present knowledge it appears to follow that the ability to estimate weights correctly is disturbed in some manner after cerebellar lesions. This will also include a disturbance of the appreciation of the effects of gravity, this time through impulses from the extremities. Consequently it suggests that the elementary impulses which stream from the spinal cord to the cerebellum may be of the same character as the static and kinetic impulses which arise from the vestibular apparatus. The fiber systems which presumably convey these impulses are the spino-cerebellar tracts. Nearly all observations indicate that the terminations of the spino-cerebellar paths within the cerebellum do not correspond sufficiently well with centers for the extremities as laid down in this brain area by *Bolk* ('03, '06, etc.) and by others, since these paths end only in the vermis. It is not tenable that these impulses from the spinal cord pass directly to such centers. They must be carried there in some way. In exactly what way this is brought about is not known, but it is established clearly that a destruction of the appreciation of weights, that is, a disturbance of the appreciation of gravity, is associated with cerebellar lesions. Moreover, this perception of the force of gravity is related to the state of tension of the muscles and tendons. The subjective perception of weight is a particular type of perception of resistance in general. Perception of resistance is often associated with muscle contractions. Though skin and joint sensibility play a rôle in this type of perception, it is difficult indeed to deny the part taken by specific muscle sensibility (*Nagel*, '05). In this way the conclusion is reached that the cerebellum is concerned in some sensory fashion in muscle contractions in general. It is to be expected that the impulses which are released through muscle contraction pass into the cerebellum in order that they may be utilized.

Assembled clinical cases of cerebellar lesions and atrophies appear to be explainable from the point of view, that the reflex functions of the cerebellum depend upon peripheral innervations which are associated with the state of tension of the muscle and upon the paths which convey such sensations to the cerebellum.   Thus *Hoshino* ('19) found, in his study of the spinal cords and brains of a family of ataxic pigeons, that the molecular layer was greatly reduced and that microgyri were present throughout but that there was no definite localization of this reduction, although it was very distinctly evident in the lateral part of the body of the cerebellum.   The Purkinje cells showed no significant reduction nor did the cerebellar nuclei, but Clarke's nucleus, the dorsal spino-cerebellar tract, and other associated tracts and centers showed a marked decrease in size. His results resemble in general those obtained by *Marie* ('93), who found that in two cases of human hereditary ataxia marked atrophy of the cerebellum and reduction of the inferior and middle cerebellar peduncles occurred.   In the ataxia of *Friedreich* ('63) there is a degeneration or atrophy and consequent secondary sclerosis of the posterior and lateral funiculi of the spinal cord and the spino-cerebellar tracts while the fasciculus gracilis and fasciculus cuneatus are especially involved.

Such reflex functions must not be confused with conscious muscle sense ; that is, the stereognostic sense of the posterior columns which is carried forward largely by way of the medial lemniscus to the thalamus and, after synapse there, to the cortex (fig. 521).   The proprioceptors concern themselves also with endogenous changes in condition and the cerebellum is their chief center for such activities.   *Sherrington* ('06) has indicated this in his discussion of the many parallels between the functions of the labyrinth and of the proprioceptors of the extremities.   Both groups are thought to exercise a very important influence over muscle tonus and particularly over body position, which is maintained by a steady struggle against gravity.   The proprioceptive impulses from body regions are those, then, which reach the cerebellum by way of the spino-cerebellar paths.   Gravity will provide a very strong incentive for the action of these proprioceptors, according to *Sherrington*.   This again gives a basis for considering that the spino-cerebellar fibers are functionally equivalent to vestibular, in the sense that both fiber systems function under the influence of gravity.

The plan of functional localization must depend, according to *Ingvar* ('19), on the direction of the movement.   According to this interpretation the cerebellum is not content with centers for anterior, posterior, and lateral portions of the body.   It must have centers for these in all possible muscle combinations. It is most probable that there is a cyclic (circular) arrangement of paths.

If it be called to mind that the anterior and posterior lobes of the cerebellar complex lie close to each other and to a certain extent form a basal plate, and that these basal plates are closely related in their fiber connections (vestibular nerve) and form the oldest part of the cerebellum, then it is very apparent that here is found the anatomic substratum for a cyclic center.   It is easy to see how in such a cyclic fundament the different impulses due to the movements and the shifting of the center of gravity of the body are distributed in all directions for the maintenance of equilibrium.

According to *Ingvar's* experiments, an ablation of the posterior lobe produced a tendency to fall backward, while the destruction of the anterior lobe had an opposite effect — produced a tendency to fall forward. If a defect in the basal balance cycle shows deficiencies in backward and forward direction of movements, then it is logical to suppose that a lesion in a given place will give a deficiency in this ability to direct the movements. These centers must lie near the basal part of the cerebellum and pass over into each other.

In connection with this question, *Ingvar* ('19) mentioned an observation that he had made on an operated rabbit in which only the anterior cerebellar lobe on the right side was injured. This led him to the conclusion that extremity centers were also to be sought in part in the lateral portion of the anterior lobe. The single abnormality observable in the animal consisted in a giving away of the right forelimb in running; the animal threatened to fall forward to the right. This appearance could not be explained on the basis of the localization scheme of *Bolk;* on the contrary, it is in complete accord with the acceptance of a cyclic representation of body relations in the basal parts of the cerebellum. A break in the ring forward and to the right produces an appearance of falling forward to the right.

The basal "ring" arrangement of *Ingvar* is indicated in the static and kinetic shifting of the center of mass of the whole body, or more correctly, of its vertical resultant, the weight line. To the body, then, are added the extremities, which, within certain limits, represent special, movable, dynamic systems. Each has its own center of mass, the static and kinetic functions of which must be adjusted constantly with reference to the chief center of mass of the whole system, the center of gravity of the body. Since these are also in part independent systems, they also require independent representation within the cerebellar cortex. That the centers for the individual extremity lie in the lobulus ansoparamedianus in *Bolk's* sense, experimental physiologic studies of the cerebellum teach in a satisfactory way. But according to this interpretation these extremity centers must be situated so that they have an intimate relation with the system for maintaining equilibrium of the center of mass of the whole body. Such a situation appears to be present. Indeed the manner in which the centers for the extremities are built up about the centers for the main (body) system (as indicated in *Bolk's* scheme of localization) accords well with such a relation. Just as, in a certain sense, the extremities are placed on the trunk, so their cerebellar cortical portions are placed on those parts of the hemisphere which are in relation with centers in the vermis for the trunk muscles, with the localization for the different extremities carried out according to the direction of the movements in which they particularly participate. From the standpoint of such a localization, the anterior extremities, which play a much more important rôle in maintaining the balance of the forward end of the body than do the posterior extremities, should be, and apparently are, located in the cerebellum in the region in front of the centers for the posterior extremities. The crus primum of the ansiform lobule, which contains the centers for the anterior extremity, lies close behind the lobulus simplex. For maintenance of the balance of the posterior part of the body the posterior extremities are the more important. Every tendency of the body to fall backward is met reflexly by bracing the hind paws against the ground and extending them. In accordance with this fact, the centers which are concerned with the posterior extremities (the crus secundum of the ansiform lobule and paramedian lobule) lie nearer the posterior lobe. The maintenance of balance lateralward is also dependent upon extremity musculature, and particularly upon the abductors and adductors. For each of these two groups centers have been pointed out. The impulses which stream into the cerebellum, as the chief center of this inertia, and which are released as static and kinetic impulses, are regarded, then, as specific for the cerebellum, and as these impulses are associated with the conception of mass and their functions with gravitation and inertia, the conclusion is reached that the cerebellum is in the service of a specific perception, a "mass" perception (*Ingvar*, '19; *Ariëns Kappers*, '21). In diseases of the cerebellum an insufficient regulation of this sense appears, a fact that shows itself in overreactions, in a too great elevation of the extremities (parade step and goose step), in overreaching in the effort to carry out an act (*Bárány*), or in the rebound phenomena of *Gordon Holmes*, since then the true appreciation of the inertia and of the force acting against it is lacking.

From the foregoing account it is evident that *Ingvar* conceived of the cerebellum as a center, the chief concern of which is the regulation of the dynamic and of the static equilibriums of the body masses. It is a synergic center which overcomes the inertia of the organ. In many respects his conceptions have the support of various experimental, clinical, and pathological studies. With regard to its action as a synergic center, many modern observers are in agreement. Perhaps the criticism to be made of *Ingvar's* studies is the fact that he did not emphasize sufficiently the part which the striatum and cerebral cortex play in movements or in the maintenance of posture. *Weisenburg* ('27) voiced this same objection and emphasized other points which he regarded as faulty in the reasoning of *Ingvar*. In considering certain clinical aspects of the matter, *Weisenburg* stated "that the cause of the deviation of a trunk or a limb is a destruction of certain synergic units and that whatever movement occurs is the result of the activity of cortical and midbrain levels and the uninjured portion of the cerebellum, expressed through the lowest motor levels in the spinal cord."

In his consideration of the cerebellar function, *Ramón y Cajal* ('11) emphasized another phase of the structure of the cerebellum. This relates to the highly complex cytoarchitecture of its cortex. An impulse entering by way of mossy fibers distributes to neurons of the granular layer. These cells of the granular layer send their neuraxes to the molecular layer where they divide, and running parallel with the folia come into synaptic relations with the dendrites of many Purkinje cells. Similarly, basket cells within the molecular layer (presumably having received impulses from the granular layer by way of collaterals) form, through their neuraxes, pericellular synapses around cell bodies of the Purkinje cells. The neuraxes of such basket cells distribute at each level at right angles to the planes of distribution of the neuraxes from the granular cell layer.   By such mechanisms impulses entering the cerebellum over relatively few fibers may be discharged to many Purkinje cells.   These latter are large neurons, the cell bodies of which are rich in Nissl substance, and the whole mechanism was conceived of by *Ramón y Cajal* as a means of increasing the response and was termed by him an avalanche type of conduction.   No account of cerebellar function can fail to take account of certain cytological facts — (*a*) that the cerebellar cortex has a uniform structure throughout, which bespeaks some common functional quality (see also *Herrick*, '31), and (*b*) that in its cellular organization it presents the structural basis for building up or reënforcing stimuli in the sense implied by *Ramón y Cajal* ('11) in the term "avalanche conduction" as above outlined. In this connnection should be mentioned the work of *Moruzzi* ('30) and *Pensa* ('31), who recognized a rich anastomosing plexus internal to the Purkinje cells which receives processes of cerebellar cells and collaterals of all types of entering fibers.   They regarded this rete as a dominant factor in the determination of cerebellar function.   *Pensa* ('31) questioned certain of *Ramon y Cajal's* observations and the conclusions drawn from them with regard to avalanche conduction.   For details the original papers should be consulted.

Herrick wrote of the cerebellar cortex that it represents "a great reservoir of nervous energy."   *Herrick's* point of view with regard to the cerebellum perhaps is expressed best in the following quotations.   In "Neurological Foundations of Animal Behavior" ('24), page 242, he spoke of it as a "proprioceptive adjuster," and again he stated that since it is a phylogenetic derivative of the vestibular apparatus, "it is primarily a balancing brain," but that in conjunction with this function of maintaining equilibrium are "control of posture, regulation and coördination of all movements of precision of the skeletal musculature, and the maintenance of muscular tone."   He compared its function to that of a gyroscope, which stabilizes the movements of the ship against the action of the elements.   Not unlike *Herrick's* interpretation is that of *Jakob* ('28), who believed that the functions of the cerebellum fall into two general types: 1, a more primitive type concerned with the maintenance of equilibrium and 2, a type concerned with the regulation of movements.

Goldstein ('27) believed that the cerebellum is not to be considered a coördinating apparatus although it does function by virtue of its position between the cerebral and the peripheral motor apparatus.   He regarded it as exerting an automatic regulation and stabilization over the course of movements carried on under "cerebral" innervation.   He felt that the cerebellum is concerned in strengthening the cerebral impulses, most particularly where the primitive automatism would produce different or opposite effects.   He spoke of the cerebellum as producing a flexion check (Beugezügel) against a primitive tendency toward extension; in carrying out such a function the action of the cerebellum on lower centers may be inhibitory in character.   *Goldstein* appears to have agreed with the conclusions of *Jelgersma* ('18a) that the cerebellum represents a "Grosshirnganglion" which carries over to the motor centers the movement pattern (Bewegungsbilder) formed within the forebrain.   *Jelgersma* ('18, '18a,

'20 and '20a) spoke of the cerebellum as a reflex apparatus and regarded it as exerting a "corrective" influence over the forebrain innervation to motor centers. To quote more directly, *Jelgersma* regarded the cerebellum as having a reflex function, "welche nicht die einfachen Koordinationen betrifft, sondern diese als Elemente zu einer höheren Koordination, wie sie durch dass Grosshirn zusammen gefügt sind, korrigiert" (see *Jelgersma*, '18a, page 76; quoted also by *Goldstein*, '27, page 315). *Goldstein's* objection to the use of the word "corrective" seems quite justified, since the impulse arising from any motor center is the resultant of all the impulses acting upon it.

Experimental stimulation of the medial cerebellar nuclei (*Sachs* and *Fincher*, '27; *Mussen*, '29; see also p. 796) has led to nystagmoid movements, and *Miller* and *Laughton* ('28) obtained ocular movements from stimulation of the nucleus emboliformis and the nucleus globosus. *Tilney* ('27) considered that the medial group of cerebellar nuclei are archikinetic, concerned with balance, and that the lateral group are neokinetic in function, promoting associated movements of the extremities and the face.

In the foregoing pages, the views of various investigators of cerebellar structure and function have been presented. Such references might be increased many fold, for the literature on various phases of cerebellar function is very large. Yet in spite of all the work that has been carried on, the problems concerned with cerebellar function are by no means solved. However, there are certain statements which appear to us justified and which may be made with a fair degree of certainty (*Huber* and *Crosby*).

1. From its phylogenetic and ontogenetic history and from its fiber connections, the cerebellum is in intimate connection on the afferent side of the arc, (*a*) with the vestibular system and (*b*) with various conductors of proprioceptive impulses which have their origin from neuromuscular and neurotendinous nerve endings and the Pacinian corpuscles. Such incoming impulses are discharged to some extent to the cerebellar nuclei but also to the cerebellar cortex.

2. The cerebellum is under the control of the cerebral cortex, the major part of its hemisphere, and particularly the middle lobe, developing hand in hand with the cerebral cortex. The termination of the ponto-cerebellar neurons of the two neuron cortico-ponto-cerebellar chain is as climbing fibers directly on Purkinje cell dendrites.

3. Discharge paths from the cerebellum fall into two major groups. To the first group belong those paths that pass either directly to the motor centers of the brain stem and upper spinal cord or indirectly to such centers by way of the vestibular nuclei, the tegmental gray, or the red nucleus. To the second group are allocated fibers which pass forward to convey impulses to the thalamus, either with or without relay in the red nucleus. The vast majority of these fibers arise from the cerebellar nuclei, though a certain few may arise from the cortex directly.

4. The histological structure indicates that the impulses brought into the cerebellum are built up and strengthened along the lines of *Ramón y Cajal's* ('11) theory of avalanche conduction. This admission of a mechanism for strengthening the impulses in no way implies that an increased motor response or a com-

plete inhibition of a motor response necessarily results from the discharge of the cerebellum into the centers, but rather that there is regulation of the impulses which pass through the motor nuclei of the brain stem and the spinal cord and over the peripheral fibers arising from their neurons. This action of the cerebellum tends to make the responses of the neuromotor mechanisms of the body adequate to the demands made upon them and finds partial expression at least in the regulation of posture and postural tone. The action of the cerebellum is synergic, then, and is concerned with the maintenance of equilibrium, static and dynamic, of the body masses, probably somewhat after the mode advocated by *Ingvar* ('18). That in carrying out this regulation its action on the lower centers may often be inhibitory is probable. It is certain that the cerebellum acts in correlation with the striatum and cerebral cortex.

5. The localization scheme, whether that of *Bolk* or of others be ultimately accepted, is an efferent localization pattern, representative of the distribution of impulses from the cerebellum rather than the regional projection of afferent cerebellar paths. The dominance of this efferent pattern is indicated structurally within the cerebellum by the relative uniformity of its cortical patterns throughout. In this connection one must be reminded that the different histologic areas of the cerebral cortex serve to demark functionally different regions.

6. The details of the interrelation between the areas of the cerebellum receptive for incoming paths, as indicated by the various observations quoted, and the efferent centers concerned with muscle groups are not known with sufficient detail to make clear the entire course of the impulses through this center. As contributory to an understanding of such relations are the studies of *Jansen* ('33) and others on the intrinsic paths of the cerebellum and the "rete" formation of *Moruzzi* ('30) and *Pensa* ('31).

RÉSUMÉ OF THE PHYLOGENETIC DEVELOPMENT OF THE CEREBELLUM

CYCLOSTOMES

The phylogenetic history of the cerebellum indicates that this organ develops in relation with the area acustico-lateralis between this center and the optic tectum. Even in Petromyzon, the cerebellum is not a mere continuation of the area vestibulo-lateralis but a region of interrelation between vestibulo-lateral stimuli on the one hand, and stimuli from more frontal regions, by way of the tractus lobo-cerebellaris and the tractus tecto-cerebellaris, on the other. This primitive correlation of the vestibulo-lateral stimuli with those arising from more frontal regions is possibly the cause of the differentiation of the cerebellum at the anterior and not at the posterior part of the area vestibulo-lateralis. Proprioceptive sensibility from the upper part of the body reaches the cerebellum over bulbo- and spino-cerebellar fibers (*Pearson*). Morphologically the cerebellum is plate-like in form in Petromyzon and is not differentiable into a central and lateral portions. Histologically it resembles greatly the static area. Its granular layer forms a small protrusion by which it is raised somewhat dorsally. Over the outer part a primordial crista cerebellaris, a continuation of the molecular layer, covers the nuclei of the vestibular and particularly of the lateral-line nerves.

PLAGIOSTOMES

The cerebellum is much better developed in plagiostomes than in cyclostomes. Two lateral parts, the auricles, and a central part, the corpus cerebelli, can be distinguished. These exhibit a certain independence of each other both in their morphologic relations and in their fiber connections. The auricles are evidently dependent upon the impulses brought to the brain through lateral line and vestibular nerves. The upper lip of the cerebellum extends medialward and forms below and behind the corpus cerebelli a central portion which is connected with the lower lobe of the cerebellum. However, in its connections, this fused central portion is more directly related to the auricles than to the corpus cerebelli, the posterior lobe of which it forms. The sulcus paraauricularis, which separates the body from the auricle, passes here over the midline into its fellow of the opposite side, the communicating fissure being termed fissura postrema. This latter fissure marks the boundary between the lower lobe and the remainder of the corpus cerebelli. The corpus cerebelli receives impulses brought in over spino- and olivo-cerebellar tracts. Such impulses enter into relation with those received over such frontal tracts as the tractus lobo-cerebellaris and the tractus mesencephalo-cerebellaris superior. It appears that it is chiefly the increase of the spino-cerebellar and olivo-cerebellar fiber connections, which reach the central and not the auricular portions of the cerebellum, that is responsible for the development of the corpus cerebelli. This latter portion becomes a correlation center for impulses carried by fiber tracts from the spinal cord and the inferior olivary nucleus, and from mesencephalic and diencephalic centers. The corpus cerebelli varies in the number of its fissures in the different plagiostomes. In the more primitive members of the type it is smooth or shows only a medial sagittal fissure which betrays its bilateral origin. Among the less primitive plagiostomes smooth cerebella are found only in the smallest sharks. In the larger sharks and the rays there is a distinct fissure pattern which increases both in the degree of ts development and of its complexity with the size of the animal. The first transverse fissure to make its appearance is the sulcus transversus primus. This corresponds in position to the place where the ventriculus cerebelli communicates with the ventriculus rhomboidalis (a locus minoris resistentiae). In front of it a sulcus anterior is found in larger animals while behind the sulcus transversa prima is the sulcus posterior cerebelli and still farther caudal is the fissura postica, separating off a posterior paired lobe. The major subdivisions thus formed are divided further, in the larger animals of the group, by a series of shallow grooves, the cortical surface thus increasing in proportion to the size of the animal in accordance with the law of Baillarger and Dareste. The efferent bundles arise chiefly from the cerebellar cortex in plagiostomes. However, certain of the paths, such as the tractus cerebello-motorius, arise from subcerebellar cells which are situated in a swelling at the lateral lower border of the cerebellum, the eminentia ventralis cerebelli.

GANOIDS AND TELEOSTS

In ganoids there is a well-developed auricle which terminates, as in plagiostomes, in a blind sac. A well-developed corpus cerebelli forms the main mass of the cerebellum between the auricles and is continued forward within the optic ventricle as the valvula. In the lateral part of the corpus cerebelli is found a mass of granular cells, presumably homologous to the structure so designated in teleosts, but not appearing on the surface except at the level of the trochlear decussation. The massa granularis forms the upper medial part of the auricle in ganoids. The connections of the cerebellum of ganoids are essentially the same as those described for teleosts.

In teleosts the cerebella exhibit certain marked variations when compared with those of other fishes. These changes are due in part to a compression exerted on this region by the skull during larval development. Though the cerebellum is a simple plate in the beginning, the granular layer, which protrudes more or less as in petromyzonts, soon forms a body which extends posteriorly. The cavity narrows down with the great lateral growth of the granular layer. Teleosts do not have a well-developed auricle containing a lateral continuation of the fourth ventricle such as is found in lower fishes, although occasionally traces of such a structure have been described. Instead of a well-marked auricle there is a thickening of the lateral wall due to a great increase of the massa granularis during development so that the ventricle is almost or quite obliterated. The medial and upper leaf of the auricle in ganoids such as Polyodon is formed by the massa granularis. With the great increase in the massa granularis in teleosts, the region becomes massive and the ventricle becomes obliterated. The cells, which are homologous to those forming the auricle of cyclostomes and amphibians, are confined to the under leaf of the teleostean auricle. The corpus cerebelli extends forward into the optic ventricle as the valvula, which in many of these animals is very highly developed. The eminentia granularis extends forward on either side to become continuous with the valvula. Caudally it is continuous with the cerebellar crest, which overlies the lateral line area of the medulla oblongata. The corpus cerebelli almost completely loses its ventricular space but does not have fissures, with the exception of that portion which grows into the tectal region as the valvula cerebelli. The spino-cerebellar and olivo-cerebellar fibers to the corpus cerebelli have not increased in teleosts as compared with sharks.

The increase in the frontal part of the corpus cerebelli, the valvula cerebelli, is dependent largely upon the presence of a tractus mesencephalo-cerebellaris posterior, which enters the cerebellum through the valvula, where it in part distributes and in part passes through to other regions of the corpus cerebelli. The greatest development of the valvula cerebelli is found in Mormyridae. The associated hypertrophy of the tractus mesencephalo-cerebellaris posterior appears to be dependent upon the great degree of development of the lateral-line organs. Spino- or olivo-cerebellar tracts have not been observed in the valvula. It is probable that this frontal part of the cortex, like the auricle, serves static more than general body functions. The efferent cerebellar systems are the same in principle in teleosts as in sharks. They originate principally from the cortex of the cerebellum itself. True intracerebellar nuclei are still absent in teleosts, but subcerebellar cell groups are present, as in sharks, in the eminentia ventralis cerebelli and appear to give off the major portion of the frontally directed efferent fibers of the cerebellum, the primitive brachium conjunctivum.

AMPHIBIANS

Among amphibians considerable differences in the degree of development of the cerebellum are to be found depending upon whether the form under consideration belongs to the tailed or tailless type. Morphologically the difference is particularly evident in the corpus cerebelli, which is much more developed in tailless amphibians, such as Rana, than in tailed forms. In the latter the auricles are particularly well developed and the corpus cerebelli is represented often only by a commissural layer which carries a few scattered cells and is somewhat enlarged on either side.

As in sharks, the spino-cerebellar and olivo-cerebellar fibers in amphibians pass through the auricle and enter the corpus cerebelli, while the vestibular and the lateral-line components (where present) run to the base of the auricle where they distribute and do not pass to any extent to the corpus cerebelli. The tractus mesencephalo-cerebellaris posterior of fishes is entirely lacking in amphibians, a condition which is not surprising in view of the relatively poor development of the lateral-line system in these latter animals. The tractus lobo-cerebellaris is present, but less well developed than in most fishes; a tractus tecto-cerebellaris from the corpus posterius is demonstrable. Taking it all in all, the cerebello-petal fibers are much less developed in amphibians than in fishes. Intracerebellar nuclei are not present in amphibians. Cells contributing fibers to the brachium conjunctivum have a subcerebellar position in the eminentia ventralis. The greater size of the corpus cerebelli and the smaller size of the auricles in frogs as compared with the size of these structures in tailed amphibians is undoubtedly to be sought in the greater size of the spino-cerebellar and tecto-cerebellar tracts in the frog and the absence of lateral line centers in the adult form of this latter animal, for the spino-cerebellar and tecto-cerebellar tracts distribute particularly to the corpus cerebelli while the lateral line and vestibular centers are intimately associated with the auricular portions. The corpus cerebelli in amphibians is not divisible into secondary portions. As in Petromyzon, so in the frog, this part of the cerebellum shows a slight protrusion of the granular layers and a consequent arching dorsalward of its posterior margin.

REPTILES

The cerebellum differs in different reptiles depending upon the order under consideration. In Sphenodon and saurians the entire cerebellar plate shows a marked eversion. In all other reptiles its tip extends backward over the ventricle as in the sharks. Whereas the cerebellum is a flat plate in the snakes, it is a high, vaulted organ in turtles and in crocodiles, with a sulcus parafloccularis indicating fairly clearly a separation between an auricular or floccular portion and a corpus cerebelli. The corpus cerebelli is smooth in turtles, but in crocodiles two transverse fissures are present, a sulcus anterior and a sulcus posterior, the latter of which is continuous with the sulcus paraauricularis. These transverse fissures divide the corpus cerebelli into three parts, a lobus anterior, a lobus medius, and a lobus posterior. The last portion is connected with the auricles. In all reptiles the corpus cerebelli is much better developed than is the auricle or flocculus, a condition which is to be expected in the entire absence of lateral-line nerves and in the presence of better developed spino-cerebellar systems than are to be found in lower forms. This increase in the spino-cerebellar tracts is due to the terrestrial life of the animals and to the particular demands made upon the trunk and, in many reptiles, upon the extremity musculature, for orientation in space and the maintenance of equilibrium. According to *Larsell*, the development of the trunk musculature in forms which lack extremities, such as snakes, in contrast to the well-developed musculature of the extremities in certain lizards and in crocodilian forms is reflected in the type of development of the cerebellum in these different reptiles. This observer recognized a median portion, a pars intercalata, which is particularly well developed in legless forms, and paired lateral parts, the relative size of which depends not only upon the presence of legs but, to some extent, upon their specialization as means of rapid locomotion. These subdivisions in the reptilian cerebellum, which require further corroboration, are suggestive of the cerebellar localization pattern which develops in higher forms.

The afferent connections of the reptilian cerebellum are relatively rich, consisting of spino- and olivo-cerebellar tracts, the usual vestibular connections, trigemino-cerebellar systems, tecto-cerebellar paths, and certain other connections. The major efferent paths are vestibulo-cerebellar tracts, the uncinate fasciculus, the cerebello-motorius and cerebello-tegmental fascicles, and a primordial cerebello-rubral tract.

The subcerebellar nuclear group of lower forms has shifted in reptiles into the cerebellum itself, and is represented by two indistinctly separated nuclei — a medial and a lateral nucleus. This is brought about by the growth dorsalward and medialward of the eminentiae granulares of the two sides which in part meet in the midline above the ventriculus rhomboidalis. These eminences represent the lower part of the corpus cerebelli. The shifting dorsalward of the primitively subcerebellar nuclei into the cerebellum itself is due to the neurobiotactic stimuli of the Purkinje cells, the neuraxes of which end around the neurons of the future cerebellar nuclei.

BIRDS

In birds the development of the flocculi (auricles) varies greatly, but these cerebellar structures are always demonstrable. They are separated by the sulcus paraflocculares or paraauricularis from the body of the cerebellum, and always are in close relationship to the vestibular region, but do not receive spino- and olivo-cerebellar fibers.

The corpus cerebelli is much more highly developed in birds than in reptiles. In contrast to the conditions in reptiles are the greater massiveness and the elaborate fissuration of this part of the cerebellum in birds. The sulcus posterior, separating the posterior lobe from the rest of the cerebellum, is especially easily recognized in smaller birds. At the sides the posterior lobe borders on the flocculus and paraflocculus. The region in front of the sulcus posterior is secondarily divisible into two major portions, an anterior lobe and a median lobe. According to the work of *Ingvar*, these three lobes may be subdivided in turn into lobules by bounding fissures comparable to those found in the vermis of mammals. The enlargement of the corpus cerebelli is a consequence chiefly of the increase in spino-cerebellar fibers which terminate only in this portion. Its greater size in larger birds is associated with the increased number of such fiber bundles. These spino-cerebellar fibers arise from the entire cord, including the lumbar region, and they distribute to the corpus cerebelli. The region corresponding to the mammalian tuber remains practically free of them. It is a correlation area. No olivo-cerebellar fibers reach the pars postrema or the flocculus. Somewhat in contrast with the conditions in birds are those described for teleosts, where the frontal connections (the tractus lobo-cerebellaris and tractus mesencephalo-cerebellaris posterior) are the dominant connections. The frontal afferent cerebellar tracts thus far described for birds are the tractus tecto-cerebellaris and tractus strio-cerebellaris, which latter may conduct in part at least in the opposite direction.

The subcerebellar nuclei of lower forms have become cerebellar nuclei in birds as in reptiles, but still betray their origin from subcerebellar vestibular regions by connecting gray bands. These nuclei are highly developed in avian forms. The efferent cerebellar tracts arise chiefly from these nuclei, but a part of the cerebello-fugal fibers appear still to originate from the cerebellar cortex (tractus cerebello-motorius?). A very well developed descending system to the medulla oblongata and the spinal cord, the uncinate fasciculus or the fasciculus of Russell, takes its origin from the nucleus tecti. The brachium conjunctivum arises mainly from the homologue of the nucleus dentatus.

MAMMALS

The cerebellum of mammals as compared with that of lower forms is remarkable for its considerable increase in width and for the presence of lateral portions, the cerebellar hemispheres, differentiable from a medial portion, the vermis. The auricle, which is known as the lobulus floccularis, has remained, and in many mammals has increased in size, particularly through the increase of the paraflocculus. The newly added cerebellar hemispheres, the so-called neocerebellum, are separable from the phylogenetically older vermis and flocculus, the paleocerebellum (of *Edinger*). Of the two portions of the paleocerebellum, pathologic and, to a certain extent, comparative anatomic evidence indicates that the flocculus is the older portion. The development of the neocerebellum, which joins the lobus medius of the corpus cerebelli of lower animals, is dependent upon increased connections with the inferior olivary complex and also on fiber relations with the cerebral cortex by way of the cortico-ponto-cerebellar tracts.

Differences between the paleocerebellum and the neocerebellum are found ontogenetically in the earliest histologic development of the paleocerebellum. Moreover, pathologico-anatomical studies indicate that in an atrophy of the cerebellum, where there is an involvement of the cortico-ponto-cerebellar connections, only the neocerebellar portions are affected. The conception of the subdivision of the cerebellum into neocerebellum and paleocerebellum has been discussed on page 821.

That too sharp a line must not be drawn between the vermis and the hemispheres is evidenced by the fact that many fissures of the cerebellum run through both the vermis and the hemisphere, dividing these into blocks which extend across both portions of the cerebellum, as is the case with the lobus anterior and the lobulus simplex. These fissures follow a definite plan in their development in mammals. In addition to the sulcus parafloccularis a transverse fissure soon appears at the posterior part of the cerebellum, which is the sulcus uvulo-nodularis. As its name implies, this separates the uvula from the nodule. In some animals this is the first fissure to make its appearance. It is homologous to the fissura postrema of birds and reptiles. The nodulus lying posterior to it forms the pars postrema cerebelli. In front of this portion a transverse fissure appears very early, the sulcus primarius or fissura prima, which forms the boundary between the lobus anterior and the lobus medius. Soon a fissura secunda makes its appearance. This forms the boundary in the vermis between the pyramis and uvula and is the caudal boundary of the middle lobe in this region, as recognized by *Elliot Smith*. Shortly after this, the fissura prepyramidalis of *Ingvar* (see page 785) makes its appearance. This fissure separates the tuber from the pyramis and from the caudal border of the middle lobe within the vermis as defined by *Ingvar*. Then the other fissures appear until the typical adult pattern is reached. A comparison of the mammalian cerebellum with the avian cerebellum indicates that like areas are present in the vermis in the two classes, but that the middle lobe has developed greatly in mammals and that its great development in the hemispheres is a mammalian characteristic. The middle lobe was concerned in the interrelation and correlation of impulses in birds. In mammals, with the development of the ponto-cerebellar system, the hemisphere portion of the lobe enlarges to form the region of development of the mesocerebellum. This enlargement of the hemisphere portion of the middle lobe involves particularly the lobus or lobulus complicatus of *Bolk*, which shows great variation in different mammals.

The spino-cerebellar systems are distributed in mammals, as in birds, to the vermis of the cerebellum. Probably they do not reach the hemispheres in mammals — certainly to no appreciable extent. Opinions differ as to the exact distribution within the vermis (pp. 802 and 803), but the consensus of opinion appears to be that they distribute little if any to the tuber and probably do not reach the lingula and nodule (see *Beck*, p. 803). The olivo-cerebellar fibers distribute to the whole cerebellum, paleocerebellar, and neocerebellar parts as well, with the exception of the flocculus. Definite regions of the inferior olivary nucleus have a definite localization within the cerebellum. This is of such a sort that the more primitive portions of the olive, including the medial and dorsal accessory olive as well, are connected with the cortex of more primitive parts of the cerebellum (vermis), while the later developed portions of the inferior olivary nucleus are related with the neocerebellar cortex.

The cortico-ponto-cerebellar fibers which discharge to the Purkinje cell dendrites of the cerebellar hemispheres as climbing fibers are new in mammals, or at least they have not been described in lower forms. Their degree of development is an index of the degree of development of the cerebral cortex (particularly of its association areas) and of the cerebellar hemispheres. Opinions still differ as to whether or not these fibers may also reach the cortex of the vermis, particularly of the middle lobe. The great increase in the hemisphere portion of the middle cerebellar lobe indicates a particular relation between the development of this cerebellar portion and the cerebral cortex associated with it through the cortico-ponto-cerebellar system. This connection places the cerebellum under the more or less direct control of the cerebral cortex, making possible an increasing or inhibiting of its activities within certain limits. It also provides a portion of the path for discharging cerebellar impulses into motor centers in movements initiated within the cortex.

Efferent tracts of the cerebellum may possibly originate to some slight extent in mammals from the cerebellar cortex, particularly from the flocculus. However, the great majority of such efferent tracts take origin from the cerebellar nuclei, which in mammals lie entirely within the cerebellum. In lower mammals two main nuclear masses are evident; gradually an intermediate mass of gray appears (sometimes termed the nucleus intercalatus); in higher mammals and man four main nuclear masses are present, — nucleus tecti, nucleus emboliformis, nucleus globosus, nucleus dentatus. However, even in man, these masses are somewhat interconnected, the nucleus tecti and the nucleus emboliformis forming a medial group and the other two nuclei forming a lateral group. On the whole, the topographic relations of the nuclei are of such character that the different regions of the nuclei are related to corresponding cerebellar cortical areas. This is an indication, of course, of the neurobiotactic influence of the cerebellar cortex upon the development of these nuclei. The nucleus tecti receives its impulses mainly from the lobus anterior and the vermis, the dentate nucleus receives its impulses from the hemisphere, particularly the hemispheric portions of the lobus medius, and also from the flocculus, into which it partly extends in certain mammals. Its dorsomedial, frontal limb receives fibers from the vermis and flocculus, according to *Brun*. There are differences of opinion with regard to the relative distribution of hemisphere and vermis fibers to the nucleus globosus and the nucleus emboliformis (see discussion on p. 797).

The flocculus has retained its direct relations with the vestibular apparatus in mammals. Probably it is also related to coördinated eye movements. It apparently is in connection with the nodulus.

The efferent cerebellar paths taking origin in the nucleus tecti (nucleus fastigii) pass by both inferior and superior cerebellar peduncles to the motor nuclei of the cranial nerves, to various tegmental centers in the brain stem, and to efferent centers of the cord. Those efferent cerebellar paths arising in the nucleus dentatus pass by way of the superior peduncle to the red nucleus and the dorsal thalamus, and, to some extent, to tegmental areas of the brain stem (see fig. 422). These provide tracts over which the cerebellum may regulate the impulses passing through these centers, since it appears at least probable that the cerebellum is a synergic center which exerts a regulatory effect over impulses passing through the lower efferent centers, and this is exhibited in its regulation of posture and postural tone. The cerebellum also is a most important proprioceptive center for both vestibular impulses and impulses from neuromuscular and neurotendinous endings. The path forward to the diencephalon (dento-rubro-thalamic tract) provides a means for proprioceptive impulses, including the vestibular impulses, to reach the thalamus and, after a synapse, the cortex by way of cerebellar centers.

Although at the present time the data available appear to be somewhat conflicting, or at least difficult to reconcile, the indications are that there is a degree of localization within the cerebellum, not only along the lines indicated by the distribution of incoming fiber systems, but also in terms of the efferent systems as represented in localization of head, neck, trunk, and extremity centers, and also, in some cases, of a center for the tail, within the cerebellum. That the two patterns do not agree does not imply that either one or the other pattern is incorrect, but merely that the means of reconciling them have not been found. For a further discussion of cerebellar functions, reference should be made to pages 818 to 833.

BIBLIOGRAPHY

The Finer Histology of the Cerebellum

In this chapter, the literature referred to under this subdivision is quoted with the literature on mammals unless specific statement to the contrary is made in the text.

CYCLOSTOMES

ADDISON, W. H. 1929. The phylogeny of the afferent cerebellar pathways. The Cerebellum. VIth Research Publ. of Assoc. for Research in Nerv. and Ment. Dis., p. 329. Williams and Wilkins Co., Baltimore.

AHLBORN, F. 1883. Untersuchungen über das Gehirn der Petromyzonten. Zeitschr. f. wissensch. Zool., Bd. 39, S. 191.

ARIËNS KAPPERS, C. U. 1920–21. Vergleichende Anatomie des Nervensystems. (German edition of present text.) E. F. Bohn, Haarlem.

CLARK, W. B. 1906. The cerebellum of Petromyzon fluviatilis. J. Anat., vol. 40, p. 318.

CONEL, J. LeR. 1929. The development of the brain of Bdellostoma stouti. I. External growth changes. J. Comp. Neurol., vol. 47, p. 343.

FALCONE, C. 1893. La corteccia del cervelletto. F. Giannini e figli, Napoli.

HAUSMAN, L. 1929. The comparative morphology of the cerebellar vermis, the cerebellar nuclei and the vestibular mass. The Cerebellum. VIth Research Publ. of Assoc. for Research in Nerv. and Ment. Dis., p. 193. Williams and Wilkins Co., Baltimore.

HERRICK, C. J.   1924.   Origin and evolution of the cerebellum.   Arch. Neurol. and Psychiat., vol. 11, p. 621.

JANSEN, J.   1930.   The brain of Myxine glutinosa.   J. Comp. Neurol., vol. 49, p. 359.

JELENEFF, 1879.   Histologische Untersuchung des kleinen Gehirnes der Neunauge (Petromyzon fluviatilis).   Bull. d. l'Acad. Imper. d. Sc. D. St. Petersburg, vol. 25 (quoted from Clark, '06).

JOHNSTON, J. B.   1902.   The brain of Petromyzon.   J. Comp. Neurol., vol. 12, p. 1.

VON KUPFFER, C.   1899.   Zur Kopfentwicklung von Bdellostoma.   Sitzungsb. d. Gesellsch. f. Morphol. u. Physiol. in München, Heft I.

——.   1906.   Die Morphogenie des Centralnervensystems.   O. Hertwig's Handbuch der vergleichenden und experimentellen Entwickelungslehre der Wirbeltiere, Bd. 2, Teil 3, S. 1.   G. Fischer, Jena.

LARSELL, O.   1929.   The comparative morphology of the membranous labyrinth and the lateral line organs in their relation to the development of the cerebellum.   The Cerebellum, VIth Research Publ. of Assoc. for Research in Nerv. and Ment. Dis., p. 297.   Williams and Wilkins Co., Baltimore.

PEARSON, A. A., JR.   1933.   The acustico-lateral centers and the cerebellum of certain fishes, with a consideration of their fiber connections.   Dissertation.

SCHAPER, A.   1899.   Zur Histologie des Kleinhirns der Petromyzonten.   Anat. Anz., Bd. 16, S. 439.

SCHILLING, K.   1907.   Ueber das Gehirn von Petromyzon fluviatilis.   Abhandl. d. Senckenb. nat. Gesellsch., Frankfurt am Main, Bd. 30.

TRETJAKOFF, D.   1909.   Das Nervensystem von Ammocoetes.   II.   Gehirn. Arch. f. mikr. Anat., Bd. 74, S. 636.

PLAGIOSTOMES

ADDISON, W. H.   1929.   The phylogeny of the afferent cerebellar pathways.   The Cerebellum, VIth Research Publ. of Assoc. for Research in Nerv. and Ment. Dis., p. 329.   Williams and Wilkins Co., Baltimore.

ARIËNS KAPPERS, C. U.   1906.   The structure of the teleostean and selachian brain.   J. Comp. Neurol., vol. 16, p. 1.

——.   1920–21.   Vergleichende Anatomie des Nervensystems.   (German edition of present text.)   E. F. Bohn, Haarlem.

BURCKHARDT, R.   .1897.   Beitrag zur Morphologie des Kleinhirns der Fische.   Arch. f. Anat. u. Physiol., Anat. Abt., Suppl.-Bd., S. 111.

——.   1907.   Das Zentral-Nervensystem der Selachier als Grundlage für eine Phylogenie des Vertebratenhirns.   I. Teil: Einleitung und Scymnus lichia.   Nov. Act. Acad. Leopoldino-Carolinae nat. curios., vol. 73, p. 241.

——.   1911.   Idem., II.   Teil: Die übrigen Palaeoselachier.   Nov. Act. Acad. Leopoldino-Carolinae nat. curious., vol. 94, p. 1.

CATOIS, E. M.   1901.   Recherches sur l'histologie et l'anatomie microscopique de l'encephale chez les poissons.   Bull. scient. de la France et de la Belgique, vol. 36, p. 1.

EDINGER, L.   1908.   Vorlesungen über den Bau der nervösen Centralorgane des Menschen und der Thiere.   7te Aufl., F. C. W. Vogel, Leipzig.

HAUSMAN, L.   1929.   The comparative morphology of the cerebellar vermis, the cerebellar nuclei, and the vestibular mass.   The Cerebellum, VIth Research Publ. of Assoc. for Research in Nerv. and Ment. Dis., p. 193.   Williams and Wilkins Co., Baltimore.

HERRICK, C. J.   1924.   Origin and evolution of the cerebellum.   Arch. Neurol. and Psychiat., vol. 11, p. 621.

VAN HOEVELL, J. J. L. D.   1916.   The phylogenetic development of the cerebellar nuclei.   Kon. Akad. v. Wetensch. te Amsterdam, Proc. sect. sc., vol. 18, pt. 2, p.1421.

HOUSER, G. L. 1901. The neurones and supporting elements in the brain of a selachian. J. Comp. Neurol., vol. 11, p. 65.

LARSELL, O. 1929. The comparative morphology of the membranous labyrinth and the lateral line organs in their relation to the development of the cerebellum. The Cerebellum, VIth Research Publ. of Assoc. for Research in Nerv. and Ment. Dis., p. 297. Williams and Wilkins Co., Baltimore.

PEARSON, A. A., JR. 1933. The acustico-lateral centers and the cerebellum of certain fishes, with a consideration of their fiber connections. Dissertation.

SAUERBECK, E. 1896. Beiträge zur Kenntnis vom feineren Bau des Selachierhirns. Anat. Anz., Bd. 12, S. 41.

SCHAPER, A. 1898. The finer structure of the selachian cerebellum (Mustelus vulgaris) as shown by chrome-silver preparations. J. Comp. Neurol., vol. 8, p. 1.

STERZI, G. 1912. Il sistema nervoso centrale dei vertebrati. Vol. 2. A. Draghi, Padova.

VOORHOEVE. 1917. Over den bouw van de kleine hersenen der Plagiostomen. Inaugural Dissertation, Amsterdam.

WALLENBERG, A. 1907. Beiträge zur Kenntnis des Gehirns der Teleostier und Selachier. Anat. Anz., Bd. 31, S. 369.

GANOIDS AND TELEOSTS

ADDISON, W. H. 1923. A comparison of the cerebellar tracts in three teleosts. J. Comp. Neurol., vol. 36, p. 1.

——. 1929. The phylogeny of the afferent cerebellar pathways. The Cerebellum, VIth Research Publ. of Assoc. for Research in Nerv. and Ment. Dis., p. 329. Williams and Wilkins Co., Baltimore.

ARIËNS KAPPERS, C. U. 1906. The structure of the teleostean and selachian brain. J. Comp. Neurol., vol. 16, p. 1.

——. 1907. Das Gehirn der Ganoiden, Amia calva und Lepidosteus osseus. Abhandl. d. Senckenb. nat. Gesellsch., Frankfurt am Main.

——. 1920–21. Vergleichende Anatomie des Nervensystems. (German edition of present text.) E. F. Bohn, Haarlem.

ARIËNS KAPPERS, C. U., AND CARPENTER, F. W. 1911. Das Gehirn von Chimaera monstrosa. Folia neuro-biol., Bd. 5, S. 127.

BANCHI, A. 1903. Sulle vie di connessione del cervelletto. Arch. ital. di anat. e di embriol., vol. 2, p. 426.

BERKELBACH VAN DER SPRENKEL, H. 1915. The central relations of the cranial nerves of Silurus glanis and Mormyrus caschive. J. Comp. Neurol., vol. 25, p. 5.

BING, R., AND BURCKHARDT, R. 1904. Das Centralnervensystem von Ceratodus Forsteri. Anat. Anz., Bd. 20, S. 588.

BRICKNER, R. M. 1929. A description and interpretation of certain parts of the teleostean midbrain and thalamus. J. Comp. Neurol., vol. 47, p. 225.

BURR, H. S. 1928. The central nervous system of Orthagoriscus mola. J. Comp. Neurol., vol. 45, p. 33.

CATOIS, E. M. 1901. Recherches sur l'histologie et l'anatomie microscopique de l'encephale chez les poissons. Bull. scient. de la France et de la Belgique, vol. 36, p. 1.

FRANZ, V. 1911. Das Kleinhirn der Knochenfische. Zool. Jahrb., Abt. f. Anat., Bd. 32, S. 401.

FUSARI, R. 1887. Untersuchungen über die feinere Anatomie des Gehirnes der Teleostier. Internat. Monatschr. f. Anat. u. Physiol., Bd. 4, S. 275.

GOLDSTEIN, K. 1905. Untersuchungen über das Vorderhirn und Zwischenhirn einiger Knochenfische (nebst einigen Beiträgen über Mittelhirn und Kleinhirn derselben). Arch. f. mikr. Anat., Bd. 66, S. 135.

HAUSMAN, L.   1929.   The comparative morphology of the cerebellar vermis, the cere-bellar nuclei and the vestibular mass.   The Cerebellum, VIth Research Publ. of Assoc. for Research in Nerv. and Ment. Dis., p. 193.   Williams and Wilkins Co., Baltimore.

HERRICK, C. J.   1907.   The tactile centers in the spinal cord and brain of the sea robin, Prionotus carolinus.   J. Comp. Neurol., vol. 17, p. 307.

——.   1924.   Origin and evolution of the cerebellum.   Arch. Neurol. and Psychiat., vol. 11, p. 621.

HOCKE HOOGENBOOM, K. J.   1929.   Das Gehirn von Polyodon folium Lacép.   Jahrb. f. Morphol. u. mikr. Anat.; Abt. 2, Zeitschr. f. mikr.-anat. Forschung, Bd. 18, S. 311.

HOLMGREN, N., AND VAN DER HORST, C. J.   1925.   Contribution to the morphology of the brain of Ceratodus.   Acta Zool., Bd. 6, S. 59.

VAN DER HORST, C. J.   1919.   Das Kleinhirn der Crossopterygii.   Bijdragen tot de Dierkunde van het Kon. Zool. Genootschap Natura Artis Magistra.   Aflevering 21. Amsterdam.

——.   1925.   De myelencephalonklier van Polyodon, Acipenser en Amia.   Verslag. kon. Akad. v. Wetensch. te Amsterdam, vol. 34, pt. 1, p. 428.

——.   1925a.   Het Cerebellum der Visschen.   I.   Algemeene morphologie van het cerebellum.   Verslag. kon. Akad. v. Wetensch. te Amsterdam, vol. 34, pt. 2, p. 816.

HUET, W. G.   1911.   Notes on the trochlear and oculomotor nuclei and the trochlear root in the lower vertebrates.   Kon. Akad. v. Wetensch. te Amsterdam, Proc. sect. sc., vol. 13, pt. 2, p. 897.

JOHNSTON, J. B.   1901.   The brain of Acipenser; a contribution to the morphology of the vertebrate brain.   G. Fischer, Jena.

KOOY, F. H.   1917.   The inferior olive in vertebrates.   Folia neuro-biol., Bd. 10, S. 205.

LARSELL, O.   1929.   The comparative morphology of the membranous labyrinth and the lateral line organs in their relation to the development of the cerebellum.   The Cerebellum, VIth Research Publ. of Assoc. for Research in Nerv. and Ment. Dis., p. 297.   Williams and Wilkins Co., Baltimore.

MALME.   1892.   Studien über das Gehirn der Knochenfische.   Stockholm.

MAYSER, P.   1881.   Vergleichend anatomische Studien über das Gehirn der Knochen-fische mit besonderer Berücksichtigung der Cyprinoiden.   Zeitschr. f. wissensch. Zool., Bd. 36, S. 259.

PALMGREN, A.   1921.   See bibliography for amphibians.

PEARSON, A. A., JR.   1933.   The acustico-lateral centers and the cerebellum of certain fishes, with a consideration of their fiber connections.   Dissertation.

RAMÓN Y CAJAL, S.   1894.   Notas preventivas sobre la estruttura del encefalo de los Teleósteos : I.   Cerebelo.   Anales de la sociedad Espânol de Historia Natural, vol. 23.

——.   1904.   Textura del sistema nervioso del hombre y de los vertebrados.   Vol. 2. N. Moya, Madrid.

——.   1909–11.   Histologie du système nerveux de l'homme et des vertébrés. A. Maloine, Paris.

SCHAPER, A.   1893.   Zur feineren Anatomie des Kleinhirns der Teleostier.   Anat. Anz., Bd. 8, S. 705.

——.   1894.   Die morphologische und histologische Entwickelung des Kleinhirns der Teleostier.   Anat. Anz., Bd. 9, S. 489.   Morphol. Jahrb., Bd. 21, p. 625.

STENDELL, W.   1914.   Die Faseranatomie des Mormyriden-Gehirns.   Abhandl. d. Senckenb. nat. Gesellsch., Frankfurt am Main, Bd. 36.

TELLO, F.   1909.   Contribución al conocimiento del encéfalo de los Teleósteos.   Los núcleos bulbares.   Trab. d. lab. de invest. biol. Univ. de Madrid, vol. 7, p. 1.

TUGE, H.   1934.   J. Comp. Neurol., vol. 60, pp. 201 and 225.

WALLENBERG, A.   1907.   Beiträge zur Kenntnis des Gehirns des Teleostier und Selachier.   Anat. Anz., Bd. 31, S. 369.

AMPHIBIANS

ADDISON, W. H.   1929.   The phylogeny of the afferent cerebellar pathways.   The
Cerebellum, VIth Research Publ. of Assoc. for Research in Nerv. and Ment. Dis.,
p. 329.   Williams and Wilkins Co., Baltimore.
ARIËNS KAPPERS, C. U.   1920–21.   Vergleichende Anatomie des Nervensystems.
(German edition of present text.)   E. F. Bohn, Haarlem.
ARIËNS KAPPERS, C. U., AND HAMMER, E.   1918.   Das Zentralnervensystem des Ochsen-
frosches (Rana catesbyana).   Psychiat. en neurol. Bl., Amsterdam, vol. 22, p. 368.
BINDEWALD, C.   1911.   Eine commissura intertrigemina im Amphibiengehirn.   Anat.
Anz., Bd. 40, S. 243.
ECKER, A., WIEDERSHEIM, R., AND GAUPP, E.   1894.   Anatomie des Frosches.   Zweite
Abteilung.   F. Vieweg u. Sohn, Braunschweig.
HAUSMAN, L.   1929.   The comparative morphology of the cerebellar vermis, the cere-
bellar nuclei and the vestibular mass.   The Cerebellum, VIth Research Publ. of Assoc.
for Research in Nerv. and Ment. Dis., p. 193.   Williams and Wilkins Co., Baltimore.
HERRICK, C. J.   1914.   The cerebellum of Necturus and other urodele Amphibia.
J. Comp. Neurol., vol. 24, p. 1.
——.   1914a.   The medulla oblongata of larval Amblystoma.   J. Comp. Neurol.,
vol. 24, p. 343.
——.   1917.   The internal structure of the midbrain and thalamus of Necturus.
J. Comp. Neurol., vol. 28, p. 215.
——.   1924.   Origin and evolution of the cerebellum.   Arch. Neurol. and Psychiat.,
vol. 11, p. 621.
——.   1924a.   Neurological foundations of behavior.   H. Holt and Co., New York.
——.   1930.   The medulla oblongata of Necturus.   J. Comp. Neurol., vol. 50, p. 1.
HIRSCH-TABOR, O.   1908.   Ueber das Gehirn von Proteus anguineus.   Arch. f. mikr.
Anat., Bd. 72, S. 719.
KINGSBURY, B. F.   1895.   On the brain of Necturus maculata.   J. Comp. Neurol.,
vol. 5, p. 139.
LARSELL, O.   1920.   The cerebellum of Amblystoma.   J. Comp. Neurol., vol. 31, p. 259.
——.   1923.   The cerebellum of the frog.   J. Comp. Neurol., vol. 36, p. 89.
——.   1925.   The development of the cerebellum in the frog (Hyla regilla) in relation
to the vestibular and lateral line systems.   J. Comp. Neurol., vol. 39, p. 249.
——.   1929.   The comparative morphology of the membranous labyrinth and the
lateral line organs in their relation to the development of the cerebellum.   The
Cerebellum, VIth Research Publ. of Assoc. for Research in Nerv. and Ment. Dis.,
p. 297.   Williams and Wilkins Co., Baltimore.
——.   1931.   The cerebellum of Triturus torosus.   J. Comp. Neurol., vol. 53, p. 1.
——.   1932.   The development of the cerebellum in Amblystoma.   J. Comp. Neurol.,
vol. 54, p. 357.
——.   1934.   See bibliography for the mammalian cerebellum.
PALMGREN, A.   1921.   Embryological and morphological studies on the midbrain and
cerebellum of vertebrates.   Acta Zool., Bd. 2, S. 1.
RÖTHIG, P.   1927.   Beiträge zum Studium des Zentralnervensystems der Wirbeltiere.
XI.   Ueber die Faserzüge im Mittelhirn, Kleinhirn und der Medulla oblongata der
Urodelen und Anuren.   Jahrb. f. Morphol. u. mikr. Anat.; Abt. 2, Zeitschr. f. mikr.-
anat. Forschung, Bd. 10, S. 381.
WLASSAK, R.   1887.   Das Kleinhirn des Frosches.   Arch. f. Anat. u. Physiol., Physiol.
Abt., Suppl.-Bd., S. 109.

846 NERVOUS SYSTEMS OF VERTEBRATES AND OF MAN

REPTILES

Addison, W. H. 1929. The phylogeny of the afferent cerebellar pathways. The Cerebellum, VIth Research Publ. of Assoc. for Research in Nerv. and Ment. Dis., p. 329. Williams and Wilkins Co., Baltimore.

Ariëns Kappers, C. U. 1920–21. Vergleichende Anatomie des Nervensystems. (German edition of present text.) E. F. Bohn, Haarlem.

——. 1929. The evolution of the nervous system. E. F. Bohn, Haarlem.

Banchi, A. 1903. Sulle vie di connessione del cervelletto. Arch. ital. di anat. e di embriol., vol. 2, p. 426.

Beccari, N. 1912. La costituzione, i nuclei terminali, e le vie di connessione del nervo acustico nella Lacerta muralis, Merr. Arch. ital. di anat. e di embriol., vol. 10, p. 646.

Edinger, L. 1908. Vorlesungen über den Bau der nervösen Centralorgane des Menschen und der Thiere. 7te Aufl., F. C. W. Vogel, Leipzig.

Frederikse, A. 1931. The lizard's brain. An investigation of the histological structure of the brain of Lacerta vivipara. Dissertatie, Amsterdam.

Hausman, L. 1929. The comparative morphology of the cerebellar vermis, the cerebellar nuclei and the vestibular mass. The Cerebellum, VIth Research Publ. of Assoc. for Research in Nerv. and Ment. Dis., p. 193. Williams and Wilkins Co., Baltimore.

Herrick, C. J. 1924. Origin and evolution of the cerebellum. Arch. Neurol. and Psychiat., vol. 11, p. 621.

Hindenach, J. C. R. 1931. The cerebellum of Sphenodon punctatum. J. Anat., vol. 45, p. 19.

van Hoevell, J. J. L. D. 1916. The phylogenetic development of the cerebellar nuclei. Kon. Akad. v. Wetensch. te Amsterdam, Proc. sect. sc., vol. 18, pt. 2, p. 1421.

Huber, G. Carl, and Crosby, E. C. 1926. On thalamic and tectal nuclei and fiber paths in the brain of the American alligator. J. Comp. Neurol., vol. 40, p. 97.

——. 1933. The reptilian optic tectum. J. Comp. Neurol., vol. 57, p. 57.

Ingvar, S. 1919. Zur Phylo- und Ontogenese des Kleinhirns. Folia neuro-biol., Bd. 11, S. 205.

de Lange, S. J. 1917. Das Hinterhirn, das Nachhirn und das Rückenmark der Reptilien. Folia neuro-biol., Bd. 10, S. 385.

Larsell, O. 1926. The cerebellum of reptiles: lizards and snake. J. Comp. Neurol., vol. 41, p. 59.

——. 1929. The comparative morphology of the membranous labyrinth and the lateral line organs in their relation to the development of the cerebellum. The Cerebellum, VIth Research Publ. of Assoc. for Research in Nerv. and Ment. Dis., p. 297. Williams and Wilkins Co., Baltimore.

——. 1932. The cerebellum of reptiles: chelonians and alligator. J. Comp. Neurol., vol. 56, p. 299.

——. 1934. See bibliography for the mammalian cerebellum.

Ramón y Cajal, S. 1909–11. Histologie du système nerveux de l'homme et des vertébrés. A. Maloine, Paris.

Shanklin, W. M. 1930. The central nervous system of Chameleon vulgaris. Acta Zool., Bd. 11, S. 425.

Weston, J. K. 1933. The reptilian vestibular and cerebellar gray with fiber connections. Dissertation.

BIRDS

Addison, W. H. 1929. The phylogeny of the afferent cerebellar pathways. The Cerebellum, VIth Research Publ. of Assoc. for Research in Nerv. and Ment. Dis., p. 329. Williams and Wilkins Co., Baltimore.

ARIËNS KAPPERS, C. U. 1920–21. Vergleichende Anatomie des Nervensystems. (German edition of present text.) E. F. Bohn, Haarlem.

BANCHI, A. 1903. Sulle vie di connessione del cervelletto. Arch. ital. di anat. e di embriol., vol. 2, p. 426.

BIONDI, G. 1913. I nuclei d'origine e terminale del nervo trigemino nel pollo. Rev. ital. di neuropat., psichiat. ed elettrot., vol. 6. (Quoted from Craigie '28.)

BOK, J. T. 1915. Die Entwicklung der Hirnnerven und ihrer zentralen Bahnen. Die Stimulogene Fibrillation. Folia neuro-biol., Bd. 9, S. 475.

BRANDIS, F. 1894. Untersuchungen über das Gehirn der Vögel. II. Theil: Das Kleinhirn. Arch. f. mikr. Anat., Bd. 43, S. 787.

——. 1894–6. Das Kleinhirn der Vögel in seiner Beziehung zur Systematik. J. f. Ornithol., Bd. 44.

BROUWER, B. 1913. Ueber das Kleinhirn der Vögel, nebst Bemerkungen über das Lokalisationsproblem im Kleinhirn. Folia neuro-biol., Bd. 7, S. 349.

CRAIGIE, E. H. 1928. Observations on the brain of the humming bird (Chrysolampis mosquitus Linn. and Chlorostilbon caribaeus Lawr.). J. Comp. Neurol., vol. 48, p. 377.

DOGIEL, A. S. 1896. Die Nervenelemente im Kleinhirne der Vögel und Säugethiere. Arch. f. mikr. Anat., Bd. 47, S. 707.

EDINGER, L. 1908. Vorlesungen über den Bau der nervösen Centralorgane des Menschen und der Thiere. 7te Aufl., F. C. W. Vogel, Leipzig. See 1900 edition also.

FRENKEL, B. 1909. Die Kleinhirnbahnen der Taube. Bull. internat. Acad. d. sc. de Cracovie, vol. 2, p. 123.

FRIEDLANDER, A. 1898. Untersuchungen über das Rückenmark und das Kleinhirn der Vögel. Neurol. Centralbl., Bd. 17, S. 351 u. S. 397.

GROEBBELS, F. 1927. Die Lage- und Bewegungsreflexe der Vögel. V. Mitteilung. Die physiologische Gruppierung der Lage- und Bewegungsreflexe der Haustaube und ihre weitere Analyse durch Labyrinthentfernung und galvanische Reizung nach Entfernung des Labyrinth und seiner Teile. Arch. f. d. ges. Physiol. (Pflüger's), Bd. 217, S. 631.

——. 1927. Idem. VI. Mitteilung. Degenerationsbefunde im Zentralnervensystem der Taube nach Entfernung des Labyrinths und seiner Teile. Arch. f. d. ges. Physiol. (Pflüger's), Bd. 218, S. 89.

——. 1928, 1928a. See bibliography for birds, Chapter IV.

HAUSMAN, L. 1929. The comparative morphology of the cerebellar vermis, the cerebellar nuclei and the vestibular mass. The Cerebellum, VIth Research Publ. of Assoc. for Research in Nerv. and Ment. Dis., p. 193. Williams and Wilkins Co., Baltimore.

HERRICK, C. J. 1893. Laboratory notes from Denison University. VI. Illustrations of the surface anatomy of the brain of certain birds. J. Comp. Neurol., vol. 3, p. 171.

——. 1924. Origin and evolution of the cerebellum. Arch. Neurol. and Psychiat., vol. 11, p. 621.

——. 1931. An introduction to neurology. 5th edition, W. B. Saunders Co., Philadelphia and London.

VAN HOEVELL, J. J. L. D. 1916. The phylogenetic development of the cerebellar nuclei. Kon. Akad. v. Wetensch. te Amsterdam, Proc. sect. sc., vol. 18, pt. 2, p. 1421.

HUBER, G. CARL, AND CROSBY, E. C. 1929. The nuclei and fiber paths of the avian diencephalon, with consideration of telencephalic and certain mesencephalic centers and connections. J. Comp. Neurol., vol. 48, p. 1.

INGVAR, S. 1919. Zur Phylo- und Ontogenese des Kleinhirns. Folia neuro-biol., Bd. 11, S. 205.

KALISCHER, O.   1905.   Das Grosshirn der Papageien in anatomischer und physiologischer Beziehung.   Abhandl. d. kön. preuss. Akad. d. Wissensch., Abh. 4, S. 1. Berlin.

LARSELL, O.   1929.   The comparative morphology of the membranous labyrinth and the lateral line organs in their relation to the development of the cerebellum.   The Cerebellum, VIth Research Publ. Assoc. for Research in Nerv. and Ment. Dis., p. 297.   Williams and Wilkins Co., Baltimore.

MESDAG, T. M.   1909.   Bijdrage tot de ontwikkelingsgeschiedenis van de structuur der hersenen bij het kip.   Dissertation, Groningen.

MÜNZER, E., AND WIENER, H.   1898.   Beiträge zur Anatomie und Physiologie des Centralnervensystems der Taube.   Monatschr. f. Psychiat. u. Neurol., Bd. 34, S. 379.

MURPHY.   1900.   Die morphologische und histologische Entwicklung des Kleinhirns der Vögel.   Inaugural Dissertation, Berlin.

MUSKENS, L. J. J.   1930.   On tracts and centers involved in the upward and downward associated movements of the eyes after experiments in birds.   J. Comp. Neurol., vol. 50, p. 289.

PIERSOL, G. A.   1930.   Human anatomy.   9th edition revised under the supervision of G. Carl Huber.   J. B. Lippincott Co., Philadelphia and London.

RAMÓN Y CAJAL, S.   1904.   Textura del sistema nervioso del hombre y de los vertebrados.   Vol. 2.   N. Moya, Madrid.

——.   1908.   Los ganglios centrales del cerebelo de los aves.   Trab. d. lab. de invest. biol. Univ. de Madrid, vol. 6, p. 177.

——.   1909–11.   Histologie du système nerveux de l'homme et des vertébrés. A. Maloine, Paris.

RANSON, S. W.   1931.   The anatomy of the nervous system.   4th edition. W. B. Saunders Co., Philadelphia and London.

REISINGER, L.   1916.   Das Kleinhirn der Hausvögel.   Zool. Anz., Bd. 47, S. 189.

SANDERS, E. B.   1929.   A consideration of certain bulbar, midbrain, and cerebellar centers and fiber tracts in birds.   J. Comp. Neurol., vol. 49, p. 155.

SCHROEDER, K.   1911.   Der Faserverlauf im Vorderhirn des Huhnes.   J. f. Psychol. u. Neurol., Bd. 18, S. 115.

SHIMAZONO, J.   1912.   Das Kleinhirn der Vögel.   Arch. f. mikr. Anat., Bd. 80, S. 397.

TURNER, C. H.   1891.   Morphology of the avian brain.   I. Taxonomic value of the avian brain and the histology of the cerebrum.   J. Comp. Neurol., vol. 1, p. 39.

WALLENBERG, A.   1900.   Ueber centrale Endstätten des Nervus octavus der Taube. Anat. Anz., Bd. 17, S. 102.

WINKLER, C.   1907.   The central course of the nervus octavus and its influence on motility.   Verhandl. d. kon. Akad. v. Wetensch. te Amsterdam, Tweede Sectie, Deel 14, no. 1.

MAMMALS

ADDISON, W. H.   1911.   The development of the Purkinje cells and of the cortical layers in the cerebellum of the albino rat.   J. Comp. Neurol., vol. 21, p. 259.

——.   1929.   The phylogeny of the afferent cerebellar pathways.   The cerebellum. VIth Research Publ. of Assoc. for Research in Nerv. and Ment. Dis., p. 329.   Williams and Wilkins Co., Baltimore.

ALLEN, W. F.   1924.   Distribution of fibers originating from the different basal cerebellar nuclei.   J. Comp. Neurol., vol. 36, p. 399.

ANTON, G., AND ZINGERLE, H.   1914.   Genaue Beschreibung eines Falles von beiderseitigem Kleinhirnmangel.   Arch. f. Psychiat., Bd. 54, S. 8.

ARIËNS KAPPERS, C. U. 1914. Ueber das Rindenproblem und die Tendenz innerer Hirnteile sich durch Oberflächen-Vermehrung statt Volumzunahme zu vergrösseren. Folia neuro-biol., Bd. 8, S. 507.

——. 1920–21. Vergleichende Anatomie des Nervensystems. (German edition of present text.) E. F. Bohn, Haarlem.

BÁRÁNY, R. 1910. Der Vestibularapparat und seine Beziehungen zum Rückenmark, Kleinhirn und Grosshirn. Neurol. Centralbl. Bd. 29, S. 748.

——. 1912. Weitere Untersuchungen und Erfahrungen über die Beziehungen zwischen Vestibularapparat und Zentralnervensystem. Hachbarschafts- und Fernwirkungen auf Kleinhirn und Vestibularapparat bei Hirntumoren. Deutsche Zeitschr. f. Nervenh., Bd. 45, S. 353.

——. 1913. Lokalisation in der Rinde der Kleinhirnhemisphären des Menschen. Wien. klin. Wochenschr., Bd. 39, S. 637.

——. 1914. Untersuchungen über die Funktion des Flocculus am Kaninchen. Jahrb. f. Psychiat. u. Neurol., Bd. 36, S. 631.

——. 1916. Die Bedeutung der Assoziationszellen im Kleinhirn. Internat. Zentralbl. f. Ohrenh., Bd. 14, S. 161.

——. 1917. Theoretisches zur Funktion der Bogengänge und speciell des Flocculus beim Kaninchen. Nordisk Tidskrift för Oto-Laryngologi, Bd. 2.

——. 1922. Vad som medsäkerhet är fastställt och vad som ännu är ovisst vis à vis lokalisationen i lillhjärnen. Hygiea, vol. 84, p. 369. (Quoted from Miller '29.)

VON BECHTEREW, W. 1885. Ueber eine bisher unbekannte Verbindung der grossen Oliven mit dem Grosshirn. Neurol. Centralbl., Bd. 4, S. 194.

——. 1885a. Zur Anatomie der Schenkel des Kleinhirns. Neurol. Centralbl., Bd. 4, S. 121.

——. 1886. Ueber die Bestandtheile des Corpus restiforme. Arch. f. Anat. u. Physiol., Anat. Abt., S. 403.

——. 1892. Zur Frage über die Striae medullares des verlängerten Markes. Neurol. Centralbl., Bd. 11, S. 297.

——. 1894. Ueber das Olivenbündel des zervikalen Teils vom Rückenmark. Neurol. Centralbl., Bd. 13, S. 433.

——. 1894a. Die Leitungsbahnen im Gehirn und Rückenmark. 2te Aufl. 1899.

BECK, G. M. 1927. The cerebellar terminations of the spino-cerebellar fibers of the lower lumbar and sacral segments of the cat. Brain, vol. 50, p. 60.

——. 1928. A case of aplasia of the pons with hypoplasia of the cerebellum. Arch. Neurol. and Psychiat., vol. 20.

BERLINER, K. 1905. Beiträge zur Histologie und Entwicklungsgeschichte des Kleinhirns, nebst Bemerkungen über die Entwicklung der Funktionstüchtigkeit desselben. Arch. f. mikr. Anat., Bd. 66, S. 220.

BESTA, C. 1912. Ueber die zerebro-zerebellaren Bahnen. Arch. f. Psychiat., Bd. 50, S. 323.

BIELSCHOWSKY, M. 1905. Die histologische Seite der Neuronlehre. J. f. Psychol. u. Neurol., Bd. 5, S. 128.

BIELSCHOWSKY, M., AND WOLFF, M. 1904. Zur Histologie der Kleinhirnrinde. J. f. Psychol. u. Neurol., Bd. 4, S. 1.

BING, R. 1907. Die Bedeutung der spino-cerebellaren Bahnen. Wiesbaden.

——. 1911. Die Lokalisation der Kleinhirnläsionen. Cor.-Bl. f. Schweiz. Aerzte, Basil, Bd. 42, S. 206.

BOLK, L. 1902. Hoofdlijnen der vergelijkende Anatomie van het Cerebellum der zoogdieren voornamelijk in verband met den bouw der kleine hersenen van den mensch. Psychiat. en neurol. Bl., Amsterdam, vol. 6, p. 175.

——. 1902a. Beiträge zur Affen-Anatomie. IV. Das Kleinhirn der Neuweltaffen. Morphol. Jahrb., Bd. 31, S. 44.

BOLK, L. 1902b. Hauptzüge der vergleichenden Anatomie des Cerebellum der Säugetiere, mit besonderer Berücksichtigung des menschlichen Kleinhirns. Monatschr. f. Psychiat. u. Neurol., Bd. 12, S. 432.

——. 1903. Over de physiologische beteekenis van het cerebellum. E. F. Bohn, Haarlem.

——. 1905. On the development of the cerebellum in man. Kon. Akad. v. Wetensch. te Amsterdam, Proc. sect. sc., vol. 8, pt. 1, pp. 1 and 85.

——. 1906, 1907. Das Cerebellum der Säugetiere. G. Fischer, Haarlem u. Jena. See also Petrus Camper, Nederl. Bijdr. t. de anat., Erster Teil in vol. 3, p. 1; Zweiter Teil, p. 485; Dritter Teil, 1907, vol. 4, p. 115.

BOROWIECKI, S. 1911. Vergleichend-anatomische und experimentelle Untersuchungen über das Brückengrau und die wichtigsten Verbindungen der Brücke. Arb. a. d. hirnanat. Inst. in Zürich, Bd. 5, S. 43.

BRADLEY, O. C. 1903. On the development and homology of the mammalian cerebellar fissures. J. Anat., vol. 37, p. 112.

BROUWER, B. 1913. Ueber Hemiatrophia neocerebellaris. Arch. f. Psychiat. Bd. 51, S. 539.

——. 1915. Anatomische Untersuchung über das Kleinhirn des Menschen. Psychiat. en neurol. Bl., Amsterdam, Bd. 19, S. 104.

——. 1919. Beitrag zur Kenntnis der diffusen chronischen Kleinhirnerkrankungen. Neurol. Centralbl., Bd. 3, S. 674.

——. 1924. Hypoplasia ponto-neocerebellaris. Psychiat. en neurol. Bl., Amsterdam. Bd. 28, S. 461.

——. 1927. Anatomical, phylogenetical, and clinical studies on the central nervous system. Heiter Foundation Lectures, Johns Hopkins University, School of Medicine. Williams and Wilkins, Baltimore.

BROUWER, B., AND COENEN, L. 1919. Ueber die Oliva inferior. J. f. Psychol. u. Neurol., Bd. 25, S. 52.

——. 1921. Untersuchung über das Kleinhirn. Psychiatr. en neurol. Bl., Bd. 25, S. 201.

BRUCE, A. 1895. On the flocculus. Brain, vol. 18, p. 227.

——. 1910. The tract of Gowers. Quart. J. Exper. Physiol., vol. 3, p. 391.

BRUN, R. 1912. Ein Fall von doppelseitigen Erweichungscysten im verlängenten Mark. Arb. a. d. neurol. Instit. am Zürich., Bd. 6, S. 269.

——. 1917–1918. Zur Kenntnis der Bildungsfehler des Kleinhirns. Schweiz. Arch. f. Neurol. u. Psychiat., Bd. 1, S. 61; Bd. 2, S. 48; Bd. 3, S. 13.

——. 1925. Das Kleinhirn. Anatomie, Physiologie und Entwicklungsgeschichte. Schweiz. Arch. f. Neurol. u. Psychiat., Bd. 16, S. 183, also Bd. 17, S. 89.

BRUNNER, H. 1919. Die zentralen Kleinhirnkerne bei den Säugetieren. Arb. a. d. neurol. Inst. a. d. Wien. Univ. (Obersteiner's), Bd. 20, S. 200.

COBB, S., BAILEY, A. A., AND HOLTZ, P. R. 1917. On the genesis and inhibition of extensor rigidity. Am. J. Physiol., vol. 44, p. 239.

COMOLLI, A. 1910. Per una nuova divisione del cerveletto dei mammiferi. Arch. ital. di anat. e di embriol., vol. 9, p. 247.

CRAIGIE, E. H. 1926. Notes on the morphology of the mossy fibers in some birds and mammals. Trav. du laborat. de recherch. biol. de l'Univ. de Madrid, T. 24.

DARKSCHEWITSCH, L., AND FREUD, S. 1886. Ueber die Beziehung des Strickkörpers zum Hinterstrang und Hinterstrangskern nebst Bemerkungen über zwei Felder der Oblongata. Neurol. Centralbl., Bd. 5, S. 121.

DEITERS, O. 1865. Untersuchungen über Gehirn und Rückenmark des Menschen und der Säugetiere. Braunschweig.

DEJERINE, J. 1901. Anatomie des centres nerveux., vols. I–II, Reuff et Cie. Paris.

DEMOLE, V. 1927. Structure et connexions des noyaux denteles du cervelet. Schweiz. Arch. f. Neurol. u. Psychiat., Bd. 21, S. 73.

DOGIEL, A. S. 1896. Die Nervenelemente im Kleinhirne der Vögel und Säugethiere. Arch. f. mikr. Anat., Bd. 47, S. 707.

DOWD, L. W. 1929. The development of the dentate nucleus in the pig. J. Comp. Neurol., vol. 48, p. 471.

DUSSER DE BARENNE, J. G. 1924. Die Funktionen des Kleinhirns. Handb. d. Neurol. d. Ohres, Bd. 1, S. 589.

EDINGER, L. 1885. Zur Kenntnis des Verlaufes der Hinterstrangfasern in der Medulla oblongata und im unteren Kleinhirnschenkel. Neurol. Centralbl., Bd. 3, S. 73.

——. 1886. Ueber die Ursprungverhältnisse der Acusticus und die direkte sensorische Kleinhirnbahn. Neurol. Centralbl., Bd. 5, S. 286.

——. 1899. Anatomische und vergleichende-anatomische Untersuchungen über die Verbindung der sensorischen Hirnnerven mit dem Kleinhirn. Direkte sensorische Kleinhirnbahn, etc. Neurol. Centralbl., Bd. 18, S. 914.

——. 1908 and 1911. Vorlesung über den Bau der nervösen Centralorgane des Menschen und der Thiere. (1908– 7te Aufl.) F. C. W. Vogel, Leipzig. (Other editions — 1887, 1899, etc.)

——. 1909. Ueber die Einteilung des Cerebellums. Anat. Anz., Bd. 35, S. 319.

——. 1912. Ueber das Kleinhirn und den Statotonus. Deutsche Zeitschr. f. Nervenh., Bd. 45, S. 300.

ELLIOT SMITH, G. 1902. The primary subdivisions of the mammalian cerebellum. J. Anat., vol. 36, p. 381.

——. 1903. Further observations on the natural mode of subdivision of the mammalian cerebellum. Anat. Anz., Bd. 23, S. 368.

——. 1903a. Notes on the morphology of the cerebellum. J. Anat., vol. 37, p. 329.

ESSICK, C. R. 1907. The corpus ponto-bulbare — a hitherto undescribed nuclear mass in the human hind brain. Am. J. Anat., vol. 7, p. 119.

——. 1912. The development of the nuclei pontis and nucleus arcuatus in man. Am. J. Anat., vol. 13, p. 25.

ESTABLE, C. 1923. Notes sur la structure comparative de l'ecorce cerebelleuse et derevees physiologiques possibles. Trav. du laborat. de recherche biol. de l'univ. de Madrid, Bd. 21, S. 169.

FALCONE, C. 1893. La corteccia del cervelletto. Napoli.

FERRIER, D., AND TURNER, W. A. 1893. A record of experiments illustrative of the symptomatology and degenerations following lesions of the cerebellum and its peduncles and related structures in monkeys. Proc. Roy. Soc., London, vol. 54, p. 476.

FLECHSIG, P. E. 1876. Die Leitungsbahnen im Gehirn und Rückenmark des Menschen. W. Engelmann, Leipzig.

——. 1885. Ueber die Verbindungen der Hinterstränge mit dem Gehirn. Neurol. Centralbl., Bd. 3, S. 97.

——. 1903. Weitere Mittheilungen über die Entwicklungsgeschlichtlichen (myologenetischen) Felder in der menschlichen Grosshirnrinde. Neurol. Centralbl., Bd. 22, S. 202.

——. 1920. Anatomie des menschlichen Gehirns und Rückenmarks. Bd. 1. Thieme, Leipzig.

FOIX, C., AND NICOLESCO, J. 1925. Anatomie cérébrale. Les noyaux gris centraux et la region mésencephalo-sous-optique. Masson et Cie., Paris.

FUSARI, R. 1883. Sull'origine delle fibre nervose nello strato molecolare delle circonvoluzioni cerebellari dell'uomo. Atti d. R. Accad. d. Sc. di Torino, vol. 19, p. 47.

FUSE, G. 1912. Die innere Abteilung des Kleinhirnsteils (Meynert, IAK.) und der Deiterssche Kern. Arb. a. d. hirnanat. Inst. in Zürich, Bd. 6, S. 29.

Gans, A. 1924. Beitrag zur Kenntnis des Aufbaues des Nucleus dentatus aus zwei Teilen, namentlich auf Grund von Untersuchungen mit der Eisenreaktion. Zeitschr. f. d. ges. Neurol. u. Psychiat., Bd. 113, S. 750.

van Gehuchten, A. 1891. La structure des centres nerveux. La moelle épinière et le cervelet. La Cellule, vol. 7, p. 81.

——. 1893. Le système nerveux de l'homme. Louvain.

——. 1904. Le corps restiforme et les connexions bulbo-cérébelleuses. Le Névraxe, vol. 6, p. 125.

——. 1904a. Connexions centrales du noyau de Deiters. Le Névraxe, vol. 6, p. 19.

——. 1904b. Le faisceau en crochet de Russell ou faisceau cerebello-bulbaire. Le Névraxe, vol. 6, p. 117.

——. 1905. Les pédoncules cérébelleux supérieurs. Le Névraxe, vol. 7, p. 29.

——. 1906. Anatomie du système nerveux de l'homme. A. Uyspruyst-Dieudonné, Louvain.

——. 1920. Les Maladies nerveusis. Louvain.

Goldstein, K. 1910. Ueber die aufsteigende Degeneration nach Querschnittsunterbrechung des Rückenmarks (Tractus spino-cerebellaris posterior, Tractus spino-olivaris, Tractus spino-thalamicus). Neurol. Centralbl., Bd. 29, S. 898.

——. 1927. Das Kleinhirn. Handb. d. norm. u. path. Physiol., Bd. 10, S. 222.

Golgi, C. 1886. Sulla fina Anatomia degli organi centrali del sistema nervoso. U. Hoepli, Milano.

——. 1898. Intorno alla struttura delle cellule nervose. Boll. d. soc. med. chirurg. d. Pavia.

Golgi, C., and Fusari, R. 1886. Sull'origine delle fibre nervose nello strato moleculare delle circumvoluzione cerebrali dell'uomo. Atti. d. Reale Accad. di scienze di Torino, Bd. 19.

Gray, L. P. 1926. Some experimental evidence on the connections of the vestibular mechanism in the cat. J. Comp. Neurol., vol. 41, p. 319.

Groebbels, F. 1927. Zur feineren Analyse der Beziehungen zwischen Labyrinth und Kleinhirn. Klin. Wochenschr., Bd. 6, no. 38, S. 1806.

Haenel, H., and Bielschowsky, M. 1915. Olivocerebellare Atrophie unter dem Bilde des familiaren Paramyoklonus. J. f. Psychol. u. Neurol., Bd. 21, S. 385.

Hatschek, R. 1907. Zur vergleichenden Anatomie des Nucleus ruber tegmenti. Arb. a. d. neurol. Inst. a. d. Wien. Univ. (Obersteiner's), Bd. 15, S. 89.

Hausman, L. 1929. The comparative morphology of the cerebellar vermis, the cerebellar nuclei and the vestibular mass. The Cerebellum, VIth Research Publ., of Assoc. for Research in Nerv. and Ment. Dis., p. 193. Williams and Wilkins Co., Baltimore.

Held, H. 1893. Beiträge zur feineren Anatomie des Kleinhirns und des Hirnstammes. Arch. f. Anat. u. Physiol., Anat. Abt., S. 435.

——. 1897. Beiträge zur Structur der Nervenzellen und ihrer Fortsätze. Zweite Abhandlung. Arch. f. Anat. u. Physiol., Anat. Abt., S. 204.

Henle, J. 1879. Handbuch der Nervenlehre des Menschen. Braunschweig.

Henschen, F. 1907. Seröse Zyste und partieller Defekt des Kleinhirns. Zeitschr. f. klin. Med., Bd. 63, S. 115.

Herrick, C. J. 1895. The histogenesis of the cerebellum. J. Comp. Neurol., vol. 5, p. 66.

——. 1924. Origin and evolution of the cerebellum. Arch. Neurol. and Psychiat., vol. 11, p. 621.

——. 1931. An introduction to neurology. 5th edition. W. B. Saunders Co., Philadelphia and London.

Hines, M. 1925. The midbrain and thalamus of Ornithorhynchus paradoxus. Proc. Amer. Assoc. Anat., Anat. Rec., vol. 24, p. 361.

HINES, M. 1929. The brain of Ornithorhynchus anatinus. Phil. Tr. Roy. Soc., London, Ser. B, vol. 217, p. 155.

HIS, W. 1891. Die Entwickelung des menschlichen Rautenhirns vom Ende des ersten bis zum Beginn des dritten Monats. Abhandl. d. math.-phys. Klasse d. kön. sächs. Gesellsch. d. Wissensch., Bd. 17, no. 1, S. 1.

———. 1904. Die Entwicklung des menschlichen Gehirns während der ersten Monate. S. Hirzel, Leipzig.

HOLMES, G. The symptoms of acute cerebellar injuries due to gunshot injuries. Brain, vol. 40, p. 461.

HOLMES, G., AND STEWART, T. G. 1908. On the connection of the inferior olives with the cerebellum in man. Brain, vol. 31, p. 125.

HORSLEY, V. 1906. Note on the taenia pontis. Brain, vol. 29, p. 28.

HORSLEY, V., AND CLARKE, R. H. 1905. On the intrinsic fibres of the cerebellum, its nuclei and its efferent tracts. Brain, vol. 28, p. 13.

———. 1908. The structure and functions of the cerebellum examined by a new method. Brain, vol. 31, p. 45.

INGVAR, S. 1918. Beitrag zur Kenntnis der Lokalisation im Kleinhirn. (Zweite und dritte Mitteilung über das Kleinhirn.) I. Ein Fall von Solitärtuberkel im Kleinhirn. Psychiat. en neurol. Bl., Amsterdam, vol. 22, p. 312.

———. 1919. Zur Phylo- und Ontogenese des Kleinhirns. Folia neuro-biol., Bd. 11, S. 205.

———. 1923. On cerebellar localization. Brain, vol. 46, p. 301.

JAKOB, A. 1923. Die extrapyramidalen Erkrankungen. J. Springer, Berlin.

———. 1925. The anatomy, clinical syndromes and physiology of the extrapyramidal system. Arch. Neurol. and Psychiat., vol. 13, p. 596.

———. 1928. Das Kleinhirn. In G. von Möllendorf's Handbuch der mikroskopischen Anatomie des Menschen. Das Zentralnervensystem, Bd. 4, S. 674.

JANSEN, J. 1933. Experimental studies on the intrinsic fibers of the cerebellum. I. The arcuate. J. Comp. Neurol., vol. 57, p. 369.

JELGERSMA, C. 1917. Drei Fälle von Cerebellar-atrophie bei der Katze; nebst Bemerkungen über das cerebro-cerebellare Verbindungssystem. J. f. Psychol. u. Neurol., Bd. 33, S. 105.

———. 1918. Die Funktion des Kleinhirns. J. f. Psychol. u. Neurol., Bd. 23, S. 137.

———. 1918a. Zur Theorie der zerebellaren Koordination. J. f. Psychol. u. Neurol., Bd. 24, S. 53.

———. 1920. Eine Systemerkrankung im Kleinhirn. J. f. Psychol. u. Neurol., Bd. 25, S. 42.

———. 1920a. Weiterer Beitrag zur Funktion des Kleinhirns. J. f. Psychol. u. Neurol., Bd. 25, S. 12.

———. 1921. De kleine hersenen. Anatomisch, physiologisch en pathologische beschoud. Amsterdam.

KAPLAN, M. 1916. Ueber die Beziehung der Ursprungskerne der motorischen Nerven zu den supraponierten Zentren. Arb. a. d. neurol. Inst. a. d. Wien. Univ. (Obersteiner's), Bd. 21, S. 383.

KELLER, R. 1901. Ueber den Folgen von Verletzungen in der Gegend der unteren Olive. Arch. f. Anat. u. Entwicklungsgesch, S. 177.

KLIMOFF, J. 1899. Ueber die Leitungsbahnen des Kleinhirns. Arch. f. Anat. u. Physiol., Anat. Abt., S. 11. Dissertation, Kasam, 1897. (Arch. f. mikr. Anat., 1901.)

VON KÖLLIKER, A. 1890. Zur feineren Anatomie des centralen Nervensystems. Erster Beitrag. Das Kleinhirn. Zeitschr. f. wissensch. Zool., Bd. 49, S. 663.

———. 1900. Sulla presenza di un gran numero di fibre nervoro e mielina nello strato molecolare del cervelletto dei Monotremi e di un Marsupiale. Milan.

Kononova, E.   1912.   L'atrophie croisée du cervelet consécutive aux lésions cérébrales chez l'adulte.   Steinheil, Paris.

Koschewnikoff, A.   1869.   Axencylinderforsatz der Nervenzellen im Kleinhirn des Kalbes.   Arch. f. mikr. Anat., Bd. 5, S. 332.

Kraus, W. M., and Weil, A.   1929.   The measurement of the human cerebellar surface. The Cerebellum, VIth Publ., Research Publ. of Assoc. for Research in Nerv. and Ment. Dis.   Williams and Wilkins Co., Baltimore.

Kubo, K.   1924.   Ueber den sogenannten Nucleus postpyramidalis (Cajal's); retropyramidalis (Déjerines); conterminalis (Ziehens).   Arb. a. d. neurol. Inst. a. d. Wien. Univ. (Obersteiner's), Bd. 25, S. 261.

Kuithan, W.   1895.   Die Entwicklung des Kleinhirns bei Säugetieren.   Münchener med. Abhandl., Bd. 7, Heft 6, S. 1.

von Kupffer, K.   1906.   Die Morphogenie des Centralnervensystems.   O. Hertwig's Handbuch der vergleichenden und experimentellen Entwickelungslehre der Wirbeltiere, Bd. 2, Teil 3, S. 1.   G. Fischer, Jena.

Kuzume, G.   1926.   Experimentell-anatomische Untersuchungen über die inneren und äusseren Verbindungen des Flocculus und der Kleinhirnkerne (häuptsächlich des Dachkerns).   Folia Anat. Japon., Bd. 4, S. 75.

——.   1926a.   Experimental anatomical studies on the nerve fibers of the flocculus cerebelli and nucleus cerebelli (mainly nucleus tecti).   Japan Med. World, Tokyo, vol. 6, p. 137.

de Lange, S. J.   1918.   Quoted from Ariëns Kappers '21.

Langelaan, J. W.   1908.   Description of a stage in the development of the human cerebellum.   Anat. Anz., Bd. 32, S. 421.

——.   1919.   On the development of the external form of the human cerebellum. Brain, vol. 42, p. 130.

Larsell, O.   1929.   The comparative morphology of the membranous labyrinth and the lateral line organs in their relation to the development of the cerebellum.   The Cerebellum, VIth Research Publ. of Assoc. for Research in Nerv. and Ment. Dis.

——.   1934.   Arch. of Neurol. and Psychiatr., vol. 31, p. 373.

Lewandowsky, M.   1904.   Untersuchungen über die Leitungsbahnen des Truncus cerebri und ihren Zusammenhang mit denen der Medulla spinalis und des Cortex cerebri.   G. Fischer, Jena.

Lorenz, A.   1913.   Zur alten und modernen Behandlung der spastischen Paralysen. Wien. med. Wochenschr., Bd. 63, S. 2497.

Löwy, R.   1910.   Zur Frage der superfiziellen Körnerschichte und Markscheidenbildung des Kleinhirns.   Arb. a. d. neurol. Inst. a. d. Wien. Univ. (Obersteiner's), Bd. 18, S. 253.

——.   1911.   Zur Lokalisation im Kleinhirn.   Neurol. Centralbl., Bd. 30, S. 184.

——.   1914.   Ueber die Faseranatomie und Physiologie des Formatio vermicularis cerebelli.   Arb. a. d. neurol. Inst. a. d. Wien. Univ. (Obersteiner's), Bd. 21, S. 259.

Luciani, L.   1891.   Il cervelletto.   Florence.

Lugaro, E.   1894.   Ueber die Histogenese der Körner der Kleinhirnrinde.   Anat. Anz., Bd. 9, S. 710.

——.   1895.   Sulla istogenesi dei granuli della corteccia cerebellare.   Monit. coll. ital. t. v. nos., Bd. 6 u. 7.   (Quoted from Jakob, '28.)

Luna, E.   1909.   Contributo allo studio sulla morfologia del cervelletto di alcuni mammiferi.   Folia neuro-biol., Bd. 3, S. 313.

MacNalty, A. S., and Horsley, V.   1909.   On the cervical spino-bulbar and spinocerebellar tracts and on the question of topographical representation in the cerebellum.   Brain, vol. 32, p. 237.

Magnus, R.   1924.   Körperstellung.   J. Springer, Berlin.

MAHAIM. 1894. Recherches sur la structure anatomique du noyau rouge et ses connexions avec le pedoncule cerebelleux superieur. Bruxelles.

MARBURG, O. 1903. Zur Frage des "Anterolateral-Traktes von Gowers." Monatschr. f. Psychiat. u. Neurol., Bd. 13, S. 486.

——. 1904. Die physiologische Funktion der Kleinhirnseitenstrangbahn. Arch. f. Anat. u. Physiol., Physiol. Abt., Suppl., S. 457.

——. 1914. Das Kleinhirn beim angeborenen Hydrocephalus. Arb. a. d. neurol. Inst. a. d. Wien. Univ. (Obersteiner's), Bd. 21, S. 213.

——. 1922. Studien über den Kleinhirnbrückenwinkel und den hinteren Kleinhirnabschnitt. Arb. a. d. neurol. Inst. a. d. Wien. Univ. (Obersteiner's), Bd. 24, S. 1.

——. 1924. Die Anatomie des Kleinhirns. Deutsche Zeitschr. f. Nervenh., Bd. 81, S. 8.

——. 1924a. Entwicklungsgeschichte, makroscopische und microscopische Anatomie des Kleinhirns. In Marburg's Handbuch der Neurologie des Ohres, Bd. 1, S. 175. Urban u. Schwarzenberg, Berlin u. Wien.

——. 1927. Mikroskopisch-topographischer Atlas des menschlichen Zentralnervensystems. S. 1–226. F. Deuticke, Wien.

MARCHI, V. 1891. Sull'origine e decorso dei peduncoli cerebellari e sui loro rapporti cogli altri centri nervosi. Riv. sper. di freniat., vol. 17, p. 357.

MASUDA, N. 1914. Ueber das Brückengrau des Menschen (Griseum Pontis) und dessen nähere Beziehungen zum Kleinhirn und Grosshirn. Arb. a. d. hirnanat. Inst. in Zürich, Bd. 9, S. 1.

MEYER, A. 1907. The connections of the occipital lobes and the present status of the cerebral visual affections. Tr. A. Am. Phys., vol. 22, p. 7.

MILLER, F. 1929. The physiology of the cerebellum. The Cerebellum, VIth Research Publ. of Assoc. for Research in Nerv. and Ment. Dis., p. 361. Williams and Wilkins Co., Baltimore. See also Physiol. Rev., vol. 6, p. 124.

MILLER, F. R., AND BANTING, F. G. 1922. Observations on cerebellar stimulations. Am. J. Physiol., vol. 59, p. 478. Proc. Am. Physiol. Soc., 1921. Brain, vol. 45, p. 104.

MILLER, F. R., AND LAUGHTON, N. B. 1928. The functions of the cerebellar nuclei as determined by faradic stimulation. Arch. neurol. and Psychiat., vol. 19, p. 47.

MINGAZZINI, G. 1893. Ulteriori ricerche intorno alle fibrae arciformes ed al raphe della oblongata nell'uomo. Internat. Monatschr. f. Anat. u. Physiol., Bd. 10, S. 105. Republished, Folia neuro-biol., Bd. 7, 1913.

——. 1905. Klinischer und pathologisch-anatomischer Beitrag zum Studium der Kleinhirnatrophien des Menschen. Monatschr. f. Psychiat. u. Neurol., Bd. 18, S. 76, 113 u. 261.

——. 1908. Sul decorso delle vie cerebro-cerebellari nell'uomo. Riv. di pat. nerv., vol. 13, p. 28.

——. 1928. Medulla oblongata und Brücke. G. von Möllendorf's Handbuch der mikroskopische Anatomie des Menschen. Nervensystem, Bd. 4, S. 579. J. Springer, Berlin.

VON MONAKOW, C. 1883. Experimentalle Beitrag zur Kenntnis des Corpus restiforme. Arch. f. Psychiat., Bd. 14, S. 1.

——. 1895. Experimentalle und pathologische-anatomische Untersuchungen über die Haubenregion den Sehhügel und die Regio subthalamica nebst Beiträgen zur Kenntnis früherworbener Gross- und Kleinhirndefekte. Arch. f. Psychiat., Bd. 27, S. 1.

——. 1899. Ueber die Missbildungen des Centralnervensystems. Ergeb. d. allg. Path. u. path. Anat., Bd. 6, S. 513.

——. 1905. Gehirnpathologie. 2te Aufl., A. Hölder, Wien.

——. 1909. Der rote Kern, die Haube und die Regio hypothalamica bei einigen Säugetieren und beim Menschen. Teil I. Arb. a. d. hirnanat. Inst. in Zürich, Bd. 3, S. 49.

von Monakow, C. 1910. Idem. Teil II. Arb. a. d. hirnanat. Inst. in Zürich, Bd. 4, S. 103.

———. 1911. Aufbau und Lokalisation der Bewegungen beim Menschen. Arb. a. d. hirnanat. Inst. in Zürich, Bd. 5, S. 1.

———. 1912. Ueber eine bis jetzt noch nicht beschriebene Missbildung des Kleinhirns. Neurol. Centralbl., Bd. 31, S. 1472.

Mott, F. W. 1892. Ascending degeneration resulting from lesions of the spinal cord in monkeys. Brain, vol. 15, p. 215.

———. 1895. Experimental enquiry upon the afferent tracts of the central nervous system of the monkey. Brain, vol. 18, p. 1.

———. 1897. Die zuführenden Kleinhirnbahnen des Rückenmarks bei dem Affen. Monatschr. f. Psychiat. u. Neurol., Bd. 1, S. 104.

Muskens, L. J. J. 1904. Degenerations in the central nervous system after removal of the flocculus cerebelli. Kon. Akad. v. Wetensch. te Amsterdam, Proc. sect. sc., vol. 7, pt. 1, p. 282.

———. 1906, 1907. Anatomical research about cerebellar connections. Kon. Akad. v. Wetensch. te Amsterdam, Proc. sect. sc., vol. 8, pt. 2, p. 563.

Mussen, A. T. 1927. Experimental investigations on the cerebellum. Brain, vol. 50, p. 313.

———. 1929. Experimental investigations of the cerebellum. The Cerebellum, VIth Research Publ. of Assoc. for Research in Nerv. and Ment. Dis., p. 381. Williams and Wilkins, Baltimore.

Neubürger, T., and Edinger, L. 1898. Einseitiger, fast totaler Mangel des Cerebellum. Berliner klin. Wochenschr., Bd. 35, S. 100.

Obersteiner, H. 1909. Ueber die Bedeutung der Körnerschichte des Kleinhirns. Jahrb. f. Psychiat. u. Neurol., Bd. 30, S. 192.

———. 1912. Anleitung beim Studium des Baues der nervösen Zentralorgane im gesunden und kranken Zustände. 5te Aufl., F. Deuticke, Leipzig u. Wien. (Also earlier edition, 1888.)

Oudendal, A. J. F. 1912. Ueber den Zusammenhang der Ausläufer der Korbzellen mit den Zellen von Purkinje in der Rinde des Kleinhirns. Psychiat. en neurol. Bl., Amsterdam, vol. 16, p. 10.

Papez, J. 1929. Comparative neurology. T. Y. Crowell Co., New York. Reference is made particularly to Chapter X, page 92.

Piersol, G. A. 1930. Human anatomy. 9th edition revised under the supervision of G. Carl Huber. J. B. Lippincott Co., Philadelphia and London.

Pollock, L. J., and Davis, L. 1927. The influence of the cerebellum upon the reflex activities of the decerebrate animal. Brain, vol. 50, p. 277.

———. 1929. The influence of the cerebellum upon reflex activities. The Cerebellum, VIth Research Publ. of Assoc. for Research in Nerv. and Ment. Dis. Williams and Wilkins, Baltimore.

Preisig, H. 1904. Le noyau rouge et le péduncle cérébelleux supérieur. J. f. Psychol. u. Neurol., Bd. 3, S. 215.

———. 1912. Étude anatomique et anatomo-pathologique sur un cas d'atrophie du cervelet. J. f. Psychol. u. Neurol., Bd. 19, S. 1.

Probst, M. 1899. Ueber vom Vierhügel, von der Brücke und vom Kleinhirn absteigende Bahnen. Deutsche Zeitschr. f. Nervenh., Bd. 15, S. 192.

———. 1901. Zur Kenntnis des Bindearmes, der Haubenstrahlung und der Regio subthalamica. Monatschr. f. Psychiat. u. Neurol., Bd. 10, S. 288.

———. 1902. Zur Anatomie und Physiologie des Kleinhirns. Arch. f. Psychiat., Bd. 35, S. 692.

Purkinje, J. E. 1837. Ueber die gangliösen Körperchen in verscheidenen Theilen des Gehirns. Berichte u. d. Versamml. d. deutsch. Naturf., S. 179.

RADEMAKER, G. G. J. 1926. Die Bedeutung der roten Kerne und des übrigen Mittelhirns für Muskeltonus, Körperstellung und Labyrinthreflexe. J. Springer, Berlin.

RAMÓN Y CAJAL, S. 1888. Sobre las fibras nerviosas de la capà molecular del cerebelo. Rev. trimest. micrograf., vol. I, p. 1.

——. 1889. Sur l'origine et la direction des prolongations nerveuses de la couche moléculaire du cervelet. Internat. Monatschr. f. Anat. u. Physiol., Bd. 6, S. 158.

——. 1890. Sur les fibres nerveuses de la couche granuleuse du cervelet et sur l'évolution des éléments cerebelleux. Internat. Monatschr. f. Anat. u. Physiol., Bd. 7, S. 12.

——. 1890. A propos de certains elements bipolaires du cervelet. Internat. Monatschr. f. Anat. u. Physiol., Bd. 7, S. 102.

——. 1896. El azul de metileno en los centros nerviosos. Rev. trimest. micrograf., vol. 1, p. 68.

——. 1896a. Sobre las relaciones de las células nerviosas con las neuróglicas. Rev. trimest. micrograf., vol. 1, p. 96.

——. 1900. Pequenas comunicaciones tecnicas. Rev. trimest. micrograf., vol. 5, p. 95.

——. 1903. La doble via descendente del pedonculo cerebelloso superior. Trab. d. lab. de invest. biol. Univ. de Madrid, vol. 2, p. 167.

——. 1904. Textura del sistema nervioso del hombre y de los vertebrados. Vol. 2. N. Moya, Madrid.

——. 1909-11. Histologie du système nerveux de l'homme et des vertébrés. A. Maloine, Paris.

RAMÓN Y CAJAL, S., AND ILLERA. 1907. Quelques nouveaux details sur la structure de l'écorce cérébelleuse. Trab. d. lab. de invest. biol. Univ. de Madrid, vol. 5, p. 71.

RANSON, S. W. 1931. The anatomy of the nervous system. 4th edition. W. B. Saunders Co., Philadelphia and London.

RASMUSSEN, A. T. 1932. Secondary vestibular tracts in the cat. J. Comp. Neurol., vol. 54, p. 143.

——. 1932a. The principal nervous pathways. The Macmillan Co., New York.

RETZIUS, G. 1892. Die nervösen Elemente der Kleinhirnrinde. Biol. Untersuch., N. F., Bd. 3, S. 17.

——. 1892a. Kleinere Mitteilungen von dem Gebiete der Nervenhistologie. I. Ueber die Golgi'schen Zellen und die Kletterfasern Ramón y Cajal's in der Kleinhirnrinde. Biol. Untersuch., N. F., Bd. 4, p. 57.

——. 1894. Neuroglia des Gehirns beim Menschen und bei Säugetieren. II. Die Neuroglia des Kleinhirns. Biol. Untersuch., N. F., Bd. 6, p. 60.

RHEIN, J. H. 1911. A pathologic study of Türck's bundle. J. Nerv. and Ment. Dis., vol. 38, p. 522.

——. 1922. An anatomic study of the Faisceau du Türck in relation to the temporal lobe. Arch. Neurol. and Psychiat., vol. 8, p. 608.

RIESE, W. 1925. Ueber die Markreizung im Kleinhirn. Zeitschr. f. d. ges. Neurol. u. Psychiat., Bd. 94, S. 629.

RILEY, H. A. 1929. The mammalian cerebellum. A comparative study of the arbor vitae and folial pattern. The Cerebellum, VIth Research Publ. of Assoc. for Research in Nerv. and Ment. Dis., p. 37. Williams and Wilkins, Baltimore.

RIOCH, D. M. 1929. Studies on the diencephalon of Carnivora. I. The nuclear configuration of the thalamus, epithalamus, and hypothalamus of the dog and cat. J. Comp. Neurol., vol. 49, p. 1.

ROTHMANN, M. 1914. See bibliography, p. 863.

RUSSELL, J. S. R. 1894. Degenerations consequent on experimental lesions of the cerebellum. Proc. Roy. Soc., London, vol. 56, p. 303.

——. 1897. The origin and destination of certain afferent and efferent tracts in the medulla oblongata. Brain, vol. 20, p. 409.

RUSSELL, J. S. R.   1898.   Contributions to the study of some of the afferent and efferent tracts in the spinal cord.   Brain, vol. 21, p. 145.

SACCOZZI, A.   1887.   Sul nucleo dentato del cerveletto.   Riv. sper. di freniat., vol. 13, p. 93.

SACHS, E. A., AND FINCHER, E. F.   1927.   Anatomical and physiological observations on lesions in the cerebellar nuclei in Macacus rhesus.   Brain, vol. 50, p. 350.

SAITO, M.   1922, 1923.   Experimentelle Untersuchungen über die inneren Verbindungen der Kleinhirnrinde und deren Beziehungen zu Pons und Medulla oblongata.   Arb. a. d. neurol. Inst. a. d. Wien. Univ. (Obersteiner's), Bd. 23, Heft. 3, S. 74; also Bd. 24, S. 77.

SAUER, W.   1914.   Ein Beitrag zur Kenntnis der Kleinhirnbahnen beim Menschen.   Folia neuro-biol., Bd. 8, S. 395.

SCHAFFER, K.   1914.   Der Kleinhirnanteil der Pyramidenbahn (die cerebellare Pyramide).   Zeitschr. f. d. ges. Neurol. u. Psychiat., Bd. 27, S. 435.

——.   1915.   Gibt es eine cerebello-oliviäre Bahn?   Zeitschr. f. d. ges. Neurol. u. Psychiat., Bd. 27, p. 86.

——.   1915a.   Der Kleinhirnanteil der Pyramidenbahn.   Zeitschr. f. d. ges. Neurol. u. Psychiat., Bd. 27, p. 86.

SCHRÖDER, A. H., AND KIRSCHBAUM, W.   1928.   See bibliography, p. 863.

SCHWEIGER, L.   1906.   Zur Kenntnis der Kleinhirnsklerose.   Arb. a. d. neurol. Instit., a. d. Wien. Univ. (Obersteiner's), Bd. 13, S. 260.

SHERRINGTON, C. S.   1898.   Decerebrate rigidity and reflex coördination of movements.   J. Physiol., vol. 22, p. 319.

SMITH, G. ELLIOT.   See bibliography under Elliot Smith, G.

SPITZER, A., AND KARPLUS, J. B.   1907.   Ueber experimentelle Läsionen an der Gehirnbasis.   Arb. a. d. neurol. Inst. a. d. Wien. Univ. (Obersteiner's), Bd. 16, S. 348.

STILLING, B.   1864–1878.   Untersuchungen über den kleinen Gehirns.   Kassel.   Bd. 1, 1864; Bd. 2, 1867; Bd. 3, 1878.

STREETER, G. L.   1912.   The development of the nervous system.   In the Manual of human embryology by Keibel, F., and Mall, F. P.   J. B. Lippincott Co., Philadelphia and London.

STRONG, O. S.   1913.   A case of hemicerebellar atrophy in a child.   Proc. Am. A. Anatomists, Philadelphia.   In Anat. Rec., vol. 8, p. 107, 1914.

——.   1915.   A case of unilateral cerebellar agenesia.   J. Comp. Neurol., vol. 25, p. 361.

STROUD, B. B.   1895.   The mammalian cerebellum.   Part I.   The development of the cerebellum in man and the cat.   J. Comp. Neurol., vol. 5, p. 71.

——.   1897.   A preliminary account of the comparative anatomy of the cerebellum.   Proc. A. Am. Anatomists.

SYMINGTON.   Quoted from Herrick '31.

TERRAZAS.   1897.   Notas sobre la neuroglia del cerebelo.   Revist. trimestr. microg., vol. 2.

TESTUT, L.   1921–23.   Traité d'anatomie humaine.   O. Doin, Paris.   (See also edition of 1911.)

THOMAS, A.   1897.   Le cervelet.   These, Paris.   (Quoted from Ramón y Cajal '11.)

——.   1899.   Étude sur quelques faisceaux descendants de la moelle.   J. de physiol. et de path. gén., vol. 1, p. 47.

——.   1912.   Cerebellar functions.   New York.

THOMAS, A., AND DURUPT, A.   1914.   Les localisations cérébelleuses.   Vigot, Paris.

TILNEY, F.   1923.   Genesis of cerebellar functions.   Arch. Neurol. and Psychiat., Bd. 9, p. 138.

——.   1927.   The chief intracerebellar and precerebellar nuclei.   Brain, vol. 50, p. 275.

TILNEY, F., AND RILEY, H.   1921.   The form and functions of the central nervous system.   P. Hoeber, New York.

TSCHERMAK, A. 1898. Notiz beheffs des Rindenfeldes der Hinterstrangbahnen. Neurol. Centralbl., Bd. 17, S. 159.

TÜRCK, L. 1851. Ueber sekundäre Erkrankung einzelner Rückenmarkstränge und ihrer Fortsetzungen zum Gehirns. Sitzungsb. d. K. Akad. d. wissensch. zu Wien, Math.-nat. Cl., Bd. 6, S. 288.

———. 1910. Gesammelte neurologische Schriften. Leipzig.

UEMURA, H. 1917. Pathologische-anatomische Untersuchungen über die Verbindungs-bahnen zwischen dem Kleinhirn und dem Hirnstamm. Schweiz. Arch. f. Neurol. u. Psychiat., Bd. 1, S. 151 u. 342.

VAN VALKENBURG, C. T. 1913. Bijdrag tot de kennis eener localisatie in de men-schelijke kleine hersenen. Nederl. tijdschr. v. geneek., Heft 1, S. 6.

VEJAS, P. 1885. Verbindungsbahnen des Kleinhirns. Arch. f. Psychiat., Bd. 16, S. 200.

DE VILLAVERDE, J. M. 1920. Las degeneraciones secundarias consecutivas a lesiones experimentales del cerebelo. Trab. d. lab. de invest. biol. Univ. Madrid, vol. 18, p. 143.

VOGT, H., AND ASTWAZATUROW, M. 1911. Ueber angeborene Kleinhirnerkrankungen mit Beitragen zur Entwickelungsgeschichte des Kleinhirns. Arch. f. Psychiat., Bd. 49, S. 75.

WALLENBERG, A. 1898. Die sekundäre Acusticusbahn der Taube. Anat. Anz., Bd. 14, S. 353.

———. 1901. Anatomischer Befund in einem als akute Bulbar affektion beschriebenen Falle. J. Psychol. u. Neurol., Bd. 34, S. 923.

———. 1905. Sekundäre Bahnen aus dem frontalen sensibeln Trigeminuskerne des Kaninchens. Anat. Anz., Bd. 26, S. 145.

WEIDENREICH, F. 1899. Zur Anatomie der centralen Kleinhirnkerne der Säuger. Zeitschr. f. Morphol. u. Anthropol., Bd. 1, S. 259.

WEINBERG, E. 1928. The mesencephalic root of the fifth nerve. A comparative ana-tomical study. J. Comp. Neurol., vol. 46, p. 249.

WEISENBURG, T. H. 1927. Cerebellar localization and its symptomology. Brain, vol. 50, p. 357.

WILSON, R. B. 1933. The anatomy of the brain of the whale (Balaenoptera sulfurea). J. Comp. Neurol., vol. 58, p. 419.

WINKELMAN, N. W., AND ECKEL, J. 1929. Origin of the corticocerebellar system as determined in human pathological material. The cerebellum, VIth Research Publ. of Assoc. for Research in Nerv. and Ment. Dis., p. 481. Williams and Wilkins, Baltimore.

WINKLER, C. 1907. The central course of the nervus octavus and its influence on motility. Verhandl. d. kon. Akad. v. Wetensch. te Amsterdam, Tweede Sectie, Deel 14, no. 1.

———. 1907a. L'influence du N. octavus sur les mouvements. Handl. Ned. Nat. en Gen. Congres, vol. 11, p. 546.

———. 1921. Anatomie du systeme nerveux. Bd. 2. E. F. Bohn, Haarlem.

———. 1923. A case of olivo-pontine cerebellar atrophy and our conception of neo- and palaio-cerebellum. Schweiz. Arch. f. Neurol. u. Psychiat., Bd. 13, S. 684

———. 1927. Anatomie du système nerveux. Le cervelet. Bd. 3, chapt. 7, p. 108. E. F. Bohn, Haarlem.

WINKLER, C., AND POTTER, A. 1911. An anatomical guide to experimental researches on the rabbit's brain. W. Versluys, Amsterdam.

———. 1914. An anatomical guide to experimental researches on the cat's brain. W. Versluys, Amsterdam.

YAMAMOTO, T. 1929. Über die äussere und innere Organisation des Kleinhirns mit besondere Berücksichtigung der Wechselbeziehung zwischen dem Kleinhirn und den Koordinationskerne. Folia Anat. Japon., vol. 7, p. 223.

ZIEHEN, T. 1899, 1913, and 1926. Nervensystem. In K. von Bardeleben's Handbuch der Anatomie des Menschen. G. Fischer, Jena.

——. 1901. Ueber die Furchen und Lappen des Kleinhirns bei Echidna. Monatschr. f. Psychiat. u. Neurol., Bd. 10, S. 143.

——. 1906. Die Morphogenie des Centralnervensystems der Säugetiere. O. Hertwig's Handbuch der vergleichenden und experimentellen Entwickelungslehre der Wirbeltiere. Bd. 2, Teil 3, S. 273. G. Fischer, Jena.

LITERATURE CONCERNED WITH PROBLEMS OF CEREBELLAR FUNCTIONAL LOCALIZATION AND PHYSIOLOGY

ADAMKIEWICZ, A. 1904. Die wahren Centren der Bewegung. Neurol. Centralbl., Bd. 23, S. 546.

——. 1907. Der Doppelmotor im Gehirn. Neurol. Centralbl., Bd. 26, S. 690.

ARIËNS KAPPERS, C. U. 1920–21. Vergleichende Anatomie des Nervensystems. (German edition of present text.) E. F. Bohn, Haarlem.

BÁRÁNY, R. 1910. Neue Untersuchungsmethoden die Beziehungen zwischen Vestibularapparat, Kleinhirn und Rückenmark betreffend. Wien. klin. Wochenschr., Bd. 23, S. 225.

——. 1912. Beziehungen zwischen Bau und Funktion des Kleinhirns nach Untersuchungen am Menschen. Wien. klin. Wochenschr., Bd. 25, S. 1737.

——. 1912a. Eine operierte und geheilte Kleinhirnzyste, mit Ausfall der vestibularen Zeigereaktion beider oberer Extremitäten nach abwärts, bei operativer Läsion der hintersten Anteile der Lobi semilunares superior und inferior beiderseits. Wien. klin. Wochenschr., Bd. 25, S. 432.

——. 1912b. Lokalisation in der Rinde der Kleinhirnhemisphären des Menschen. Wien. klin. Wochenschr., Bd. 25, S. 2033.

——. 1914. Untersuchungen über die Funktion des Flocculus am Kaninchen. Jahrb. f. Psychiat. u. Neurol., Bd. 36, S. 631.

BERITOFF, J. S., AND MAGNUS, R. 1914. Zusatz bei der Korrektur. Arch. f. d. ges. Physiol. (Pflüger's) vol. 178, p. 124.

BEYERMAN. 1916. Over aangeboren kleine hersenen-stoornissen. Dissertatie. Leiden.

BING, R. 1906. Experimentalles zur Physiologie des Tractus spinocerebellares. Arch. f. Anat. u. Physiol., Physiol. Abt., S. 250.

BLACK, D. 1916. Cerebellar localization in the light of recent research. J. Lab. and Clin. Med., vol. 1, p. 467.

BOLK, L. 1903. Over de physiologische beteekenis van het cerebellum. E. F. Bohn, Haarlem.

——. 1906. Das Cerebellum der Säugetiere. E. F. Bohn, Haarlem and G. Fischer, Jena.

BROUWER, B. 1913. Ueber Hemiatrophia neocerebellaris. Arch. f. Psychiat., Bd. 51, S. 539.

——. 1915. Anatomische Untersuchung über das Kleinhirn des Menschen. Psychiat. en Neurol. Bl., Amsterdam, vol. 19, p. 104.

——. 1927. Anatomical, phylogenetical and clinical studies on the central nervous system. Heiter Foundation Lectures, Johns Hopkins Univ., School of Medicine. Williams and Wilkins, Baltimore.

BRUN, R. 1925. Das Kleinhirn. Anatomie, Physiologie und Entwicklungsgeschichte. Schweiz. Arch. f. Neurol. u. Psychiat., Bd. 16, S. 183.

COBB, S., BAILEY, A. A., AND HOLTZ, P. R. 1917. On the genesis and inhibition of extensor rigidity. Am. J. Physiol., vol. 44, p. 239.

COMOLLI, A. 1910. Per una nuova divisione del cervelletto dei mammiferi. Arch. ital. di anat. e di embriol., vol. 9, p. 247.

DUSSER DE BARENNE, J. G. 1924. Die Funktionen des Kleinhirns. Handb. d. Neurol. d. Ohres, Bd. 1, S. 589.

EDINGER, L. 1908. Vorlesungen über den Bau der nervösen Centralorgane des Menschen und der Thiere. 7te Aufl., F. C. W. Vogel, Leipzig. See also 1911 edition.

FREUND, C. S. 1914. Zur Stöhrung der Schwerempfindung. Zeitschr. f. Nervenh., Leipzig, Bd. 1, S. 297. Referred to in Zeitschr. f. d. ges. Neurol. u. Psychiat., Bd. 8, 1914. VIIte Jahrerversamml. d. Gesellsch. Deutscher Nervenärzte.

FRIEDREICH, N. 1863. Ueber degenerative Atrophie der spinalen Hinterstränge. Virchow's Arch. f. path. Anat., Bd. 26, S. 391 u. 433; Bd. 27, S. 1.

GOLDSTEIN, K. 1913. Ueber Störungen der Schwereempfindung bei gleichseitiger Kleinhirnaffektion. Neurol. Centralbl., Bd. 32, S. 1082.

——. 1927. Das Kleinhirn. Handb. d. norm. u. path. Physiol., Bd. 10, S. 222.

GOLDSTEIN, K., AND REICHMANN, F. 1916. Beiträge zur Kasuistik und Symptoma-tologie der Kleinhirnerkrankungen (im besonderen zu den Störungen der Bewe-gungen, der Gewichts-, Raum- und Zeitschätzung). Arch. f. Psychiat., Bd. 56, S. 466.

HERRICK, C. J. 1924. The neurological foundations of behavior. Henry Holt and Co., New York.

——. 1931. An introduction to neurology. 5th edition. W. B. Saunders Co., Phila-delphia and London.

HOLMES, G. 1917. The symptoms of acute cerebellar injuries due to gunshot injuries. Brain, vol. 40, p. 461.

——. 1922. The clinical symptoms of cerebellar disease and their interpretation. Lancet, pp. 59, 111, 1177, and 1231.

HORSLEY, V., AND CLARKE, R. H. 1908. The structure and functions of the cerebellum examined by a new method. Brain, vol. 31, p. 45.

HOSHINO, T. 1919. A study of the brains and spinal cords in a family of ataxic pigeons. J. Comp. Neurol., vol. 31, p. 111.

HULSHOFF POL, D. J. 1909. Cerebellair Ataxie. Psychiat. en neurol. Bl., Amster-dam, vol. 13, p. 273.

——. 1915. Cerebellaire functies in verband met hun localisatie. Psychiat. en neurol. Bl., Amsterdam, vol. 19, p. 181.

HUNT, J. R. 1929. The static system and its relation to cerebellar function. The Cerebellum, VIth Research Publ. of Assoc. for Research in Nerv. and Ment. Dis., p. 345. Williams and Wilkins, Baltimore.

INGVAR, S. 1918. Beitrag zur Kenntnis der Lokalisation im Kleinhirn. I. Ein Fall von Solitärtuberkel im Kleinhirn. Psychiat. en neurol. Bl., Amsterdam, vol. 22, p. 312.

——. 1918a. Zur Kenntnis vom Einfluss des Kleinhirns auf die Sprache. Psychiat. en neurol. Bl., Amsterdam, vol. 22, p. 329.

——. 1919. Zur Phylo- und Ontogenese des Kleinhirns. Folia neuro-biol., Bd. 11, S. 205.

JACOB, A. 1928. Das Kleinhirn. In F. von Möllendorf's Handbuch der mikrosko-pischen Anatomie des Menschen. Das Zentralnervensystem, Bd. 4, S. 674. J. Springer, Berlin.

JANSEN, J. 1933. Experimental studies on the intrinsic fibers of the cerebellum. I. The arcuate fibers. J. Comp. Neurol., vol. 57, p. 369.

JELGERSMA, G. 1904. De physiologische beteekenis van het cerebellum. Scheltema en Holkema, Amsterdam.

——. 1918. Die Funktion des Kleinhirns. J. f. Psychol. u. Neurol., Bd. 23, S. 137.

——. 1918a. Zur Theorie der zerebellaren Koordination. J. f. Psychol. u. Neurol., Bd. 24, S. 53.

——. 1920. Eine Systemerkrankung im Kleinhirn. J. f. Psychol. u. Neurol., Bd. 25, S. 42.

JELGERSMA, G.   1920a.   Weiterer Beitrag zur Funktion des Kleinhirns.   J. f. Psychol. u. Neurol., Bd. 25, S. 12.

KATZENSTEIN, J., AND ROTHMANN, M.   1911.   Zur Localisation der Kehlkopfinnervation in der Kleinhirnrinde.   Neurol. Centralbl., Bd. 30, S. 1146.

DE KLEIJN, A., AND MAGNUS, R.   1920.   Ueber die Unabhängigkeit der Labyrinthreflexe vom Kleinhirn und über die Lage der Zentren für die Labyrinthreflexe im Hirnstamm.   Arch. f. d. ges. Physiol. (Pflüger's), Bd. 178, S. 124.   See also München er med. Wochenschr., no. 20, 1919.

KUBO, K.   1924.   Quoted from Jakob '28.

LOTMAR, F.   1908.   Ein Beitrag zur Pathologie des Kleinhirns.   Monatschr. f. Psychiat. u. Neurol., Bd. 24, S. 217.

LUCIANI, L.   1891.   Il cervelletto.   Florence.

——.   1893.   Das Kleinhirn.   E. Besold, Leipzig.

LUNA, E.   1909.   Contributo allo studio sulla morfologia del cervelletto di alcuni mammiferi.   Folia neuro-biol., Bd. 3, S. 313.

MACNALTY, A. S., AND HORSLEY, V.   1909.   On the cervical spino-bulbar and spino-cerebellar tracts and on the question of topographical representation in the cerebellum.   Brain, vol. 32, p. 237.

MAAS, O.   1913.   Störung der Schwereempfindung bei Kleinhirnerkrankung.   Neurol. Centralbl., Bd. 32, S. 405.

MAGNUS, R.   1924.   Körperstellung.   J. Springer, Berlin.

MARASSINI, A.   1907.   Sur les phénomènes consécutifs aux extirpations partielles du cervelet.   Arch. ital. de biol., vol. 47, p. 135.

MARBURG, O.   1904.   Die physiologische Funktion der Kleinhirnseitenstrangbahn (Tractus spino-cerebellaris dorsalis) nach Experimenten am Hunde.   Arch. f. Anat. u. Physiol., Physiol. Abt., Suppl.-Bd., S. 457.

MARIE, P.   1893.   Sur l'hérédo-ataxie cérébelleuse.   Semaine méd., no. 56, p. 444.

MILLER, F.   1929.   The physiology of the cerebellum.   The Cerebellum, VIth Research Publ. of Assoc. for Research in Nerv. and Ment. Dis., p. 361.   Williams and Wilkins Co., Baltimore.   See also Physiol. Rev., vol. 6, p. 124.

MILLER, F. R., AND BANTING, F. G.   1922.   Observations on cerebellar stimulations.   Am. J. Physiol., vol. 59, p. 478.   Proc. Am. Physiol. Soc., 1921.   1922a.   Brain, vol. 45, p. 104.

MILLS, C. K., AND WEISENBURG, T. H.   1914.   Cerebellar symptoms and cerebellar localization, including kinematographic observations on cerebellar phenomena.   J. A. M. A., vol. 63, p. 1813.

MORUZZI, G.   1930.   La rete nervosa diffusa (Golgi) dello strato dei granuli del cervelletto.   Arch. Ital. di Anat. ed Embriol., vol. 28, p. 238.

MUNK, H.   1906, 1907, 1908.   Ueber die Functionen des Kleinhirns.   Sitzungsb. d. kon. preuss. Akad. d. Wissensch., Berlin, Bd. 1, 1906, S. 443; Bd. 1, 1907, S. 16; Bd. 1, 1908, S. 294.

MUSSEN, A. T.   1927.   Experimental investigations on the cerebellum.   Brain, vol. 50, p. 313.

——.   1929.   Experimental investigations of the cerebellum.   The Cerebellum, VIth Research Publ. of Assoc. for Research in Nerv. and Ment. Dis., p. 381.   Williams and Wilkins, Baltimore.

NAGEL, W. A.   1905.   Die Lage-, Bewegungs- und Widerstandsempfindungen.   Handbuch der Physiologie des Menschen, Bd. 3, S. 735, 748 u. 755.   Vieweg u. Sohn, Braunschweig.

PAGANO, G.   1905.   Essai de localisations cérébelleuses.   Arch. ital. de biol., vol. 43, p. 139.

PENSA, A.   1931.   Osservazioni e considerazioni sulla struttura della corteccia cerebellare dei mammiferi.   Reale Accad. Nazionale dei Lincei, vol. 5, fasc. 2, p. 25.

POLLOCK, L. J., AND DAVIS, L. 1927. The influence of the cerebellum upon the reflex activities of the decerebrate animal. Brain, vol. 50, p. 277.

——. 1929. The influence of the cerebellum upon reflex activities. The Cerebellum, VIth Research Publ. of Assoc. for Research in Nerv. and Ment. Dis., p. 424. Williams and Wilkins, Baltimore.

PROBST, M. 1902. Zur Anatomie und Physiologie des Kleinhirns. Arch. f. Psychiat., Bd. 35, S. 692.

PRUS, J. 1901. Sur les localisation des centres moteurs dans l'écorce du cervelet. Arch. pol. d. sc. biol. et med., vol. 1.

RADEMAKER, G. G. J. 1926. Die Bedeutung der roten Kerne und des übrigen Mittelhirns für Muskeltonus, Körperstellung und Labyrinthreflexe. J. Springer, Berlin.

RAMÓN Y CAJAL, S. 1909–11. Histologie du système nerveux de l'homme et des vertébrés. A. Maloine, Paris.

VAN RIJNBERK, G. 1904. Tentativi di localizzazioni funzionali nel cervelletto. 1°. Il lobulo semplice. Arch. di fisiol., vol. 1, p. 569.

——. 1904a. Idem. 2°. Il centro per gli arti anteriori. Arch. di fisiol., vol. 2, p. 18.

——. 1908. Die neueren Beiträge zur Anatomie und Physiologie des Kleinhirns der Säuger. Folia neuro-biol., Bd. 1, S. 46, 403 u. 535.

——. 1912. Weitere Beiträge zum Lokalisationsproblem im Kleinhirn. Folia neuro-biol., Sommerergänzungsheft, Bd. 6, S. 143.

ROTHMANN, M. 1910. Demonstration zur Lokalisation im Kleinhirn des Affen. Sitzungsb. d. Berliner Gesellsch. f. Psychiat. u. Nervenkrankh., 1910. Referred to in Neurol. Centralbl., Bd. 29, S. 389.

——. 1913. Die Funktion des Mittellappens des Kleinhirns. Monatschr. f. Psychiat. u. Neurol., Bd. 34, S. 389.

——. 1913a. Zur Kleinhirnlokalisation. Berliner klin. Wochenschr., Bd. 50, no. 8, S. 336.

——. 1913b. The symptoms of cerebellar disease and their significance. Report XVIIth Internat. Congress, London.

——. 1914. Die symptome der Kleinhirnkrankheiten und ihre Bedeutung. Monatschr. f. Psychiat. u. Neurol., Bd. 35, S. 43.

——. 1914a. Demonstration zur Rindenexstirpation des Kleinhirns. Neurol. Centralbl., Bd. 33, S. 1010.

RUSSELL, P. 1894. Experimental researches into the function of the cerebellum. Phil. Tr. Roy. Soc., London, Ser. B, vol. 185, p. 819.

SAITO, M. 1922. Experimentelle Untersuchungen über die inneren Verbindungen der Kleinhirnrinde und deren Beziehungen zu Pons und Medulla oblongata. Arb. a. d. Neurol. Inst. a. d. Wiener Univ. Bd. 23, S. 74.

——. 1922. Weitere Untersuchungen über die inneren Verbindungen der Kleinhirnrinde. Arb. a. d. Neurol. Inst. a. d. Wiener Univ., Bd. 24, S. 77.

SCHAFFER, K. 1915. Gibt es eine cerebello-olivare Bahn? Zeitschr. f. d. ges. Neurol. u. Psychiat., Bd. 30, S. 70.

SCHRÖDER, A. H., AND KIRSCHBAUM, W. 1928. Ueber eigenartige degenerative Erkrankungen des Zentralnervensystems mit vorwiegender Beteiligung des olivocerebellaren Systems. Zeitschr. f. d. ges. Neurol. u. Psychiat., Bd. 114, S. 681. Also Deutsche Zeitschr. f. Nervenh., Bd. 102, S. 129.

SCHWARTZ, L. 1916. Untersuchungen über die Helwegsche Dreikantenbahn. Arb. a. d. neurol. Inst. a. d. Wien. Univ. (Obersteiner's), Bd. 21, S. 325.

SHERRINGTON, C. S. 1898. Decerebrate rigidity and reflex coördination of movements. J. Physiol., vol. 22, p. 319.

——. 1906. The integrative action of the nervous system. C. Scribner's Sons, New York.

STRONG, O. S.   1929.   Unsolved problems suggested by cerebellar connections and cerebellar histology.   The Cerebellum, VIth Research Publ. of Assoc. for Research in Nerv. and Ment. Dis., p. 1.   Williams and Wilkins Co., Baltimore.

THOMAS, A., AND DURUPT, A.   1914.   Les localisations cérébelleuses.   Vigot, Paris.

TILNEY, F.   1919.   The functional significance and principal syndrome of the cerebellum.   Neurol. Bull., vol. 2, p. 289.

——.   1923.   Genesis of cerebellar function.   Arch. Neurol. and Psychiat., vol. 9, p. 138.

——.   1927.   The chief intracerebellar and precerebellar nuclei.   Brain, vol. 50, p. 275.

TILNEY, F., AND PIKE, F. H.   1925.   Muscular coördination experimentally studied in its relation to the cerebellum.   Arch. Neurol. and Psychiat., vol. 13, p. 289.

VAN VALKENBURG, C. T.   1912.   Algemeine klinische lokalisatie in het zenuwstelsen.   Wolters, Groningen.

——.   1913.   Bijdrag tot de kennis eener localisatie in de menschelijke kleine hersenen.   Nederl. tijdschr. v. geneesk., Heft 1, S. 6.

VINCENZONI, G.   1908.   Recherches experimentales sur les localisations fonctionnelles dans le cervelet de la brebis.   Arch. ital. de biol., vol. 49, p. 385.

WEISENBURG, T. H.   1927.   Cerebellar localization and its symptomology.   Brain, vol. 50, p. 357.

——.   1929.   Cerebellar localization and symptomatology.   The cerebellum.   VIth Research Publ. of Assoc. for Research in Nerv. and Ment. Dis., p. 497.   Williams and Wilkins Co., Baltimore.

WERTHAM, F. J., AND LYMAN, R. S.   1929.   Disturbances of voluntary rhythmic movements in cerebellar disease (arrhythmiokinesis).   The Cerebellum, VIth Research Publ. of Assoc. for Research in Nerv. and Ment. Dis., p. 520.   Williams and Wilkins Co., Baltimore.

CHAPTER VIII

THE MESENCEPHALON AND THE DIENCEPHALON

The mesencephalic and diencephalic centers are sufficiently closely related to make a joint consideration of them of considerable advantage. Yet in certain fundamental respects, as will be seen, they are distinctly different from each other.

Both regions contain all the constituents of the embryonic neural tube: alar and basal portions, a floor plate, and a roof plate. The alar and basal parts are separated, as in the medulla oblongata region, by the sulcus limitans. However, in the diencephalic region the sulcus limitans swings far ventralward and disappears near the preoptic recess in front of the optic chiasma. In earlier chapters it was stated that the functions of the alar plates are largely sensory and correlative, *i.e.* they are on the receptive side of the arc, while those of the basal plates are chiefly motor and coördinative and are concerned with the effective side of the arc. The deviation ventralward of the sulcus limitans is an indication of the fact that the sensory, correlative centers increase very considerably in passing rostralward (fig. 423) much more proportionately than do the effectory, coördinative areas. The telencephalon, including part of the preoptic recess, must be regarded as a continuation of the supralimitary sensory correlation area.

The more dorsal portions of the midbrain, situated above the sulcus limitans, are largely centers for the correlation of optic impulses with exteroceptive impulses from the face and trunk, which reach these centers by way of secondary trigeminal and spino-mesencephalic paths. In lower vertebrates secondary tracts from lateral-line areas reach mesencephalic centers for synapse with other secondary tracts. In higher vertebrates, beginning with land amphibians, the lateral-line centers have disappeared. In a sense their places are taken by cochlear centers, and mesencephalic areas concerned with the correlation of auditory with other impulses appear. In all vertebrate types below mammals, these regions of the midbrain, the tectal and subtectal areas, are the main centers of termination of the ascending secondary sensory paths such as the spino-mesencephalic tract, the lateral lemniscus, the secondary trigeminal tracts, and, to a considerable extent, the optic tracts. From such tectal and subtectal areas arises a system of tecto-thalamic paths increasing in complexity, size, and number with the gradual differentiation of the secondary ascending sensory paths on the one hand, and the diencephalic centers on the other. In higher reptiles and mammals the subtectal auditory center of lower forms, which is a forerunner of the inferior colliculus, gradually assumes a more dorsal position and becomes a tectal center. The secondary ascending tracts from the spinal cord and from the trigeminal and cochlear centers are much larger in most mammalian forms

865

but the percentage of such fibers which terminate in the tectal areas is greatly diminished, while the number which passes directly to diencephalic areas is enormously increased, this condition becoming progressively more evident from lower to higher mammalian forms. With the gradual increase of direct lemnisci connections to the diencephalon there is a gradual decrease of the tecto-thalamic tracts in mammals. This indicates that phylogenetically the midbrain becomes progressively of much less importance as a way station to thalamic and, after a synapse in the thalamus, to cortical centers. However, it retains, in mammals,

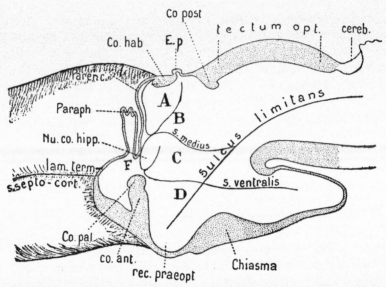

Fig. 423. The ventricular fissures of the midbrain and diencephalon of Axolotl. C. J. Herrick.

A, epithalamus; B, dorsal thalamus; C, ventral thalamus; co.ant., commissura anterior; co.pal., commissura pallii; D, hypothalamus; F, foramen of Monro; Nu.co.hipp., nucleus commissurae hippocampi; Paraph., paraphysis (between this and the parencephalon is the velum transversum); Parenc., parencephalon (saccus dorsalis or pulvinar epiphyseos); S.septo-cort., sulcus septo-corticalis of the telencephalon.

its reflex functions. Thus in higher primates its superior colliculus is a light reflex center and a place of synapse for efferent paths to motor centers mediating visual reflexes by way of thalamic optic centers; its inferior colliculus is an auditory reflex center.

Below the aqueduct lie the efferent centers of the mesencephalon. Much of the area is occupied by fibers of passage coursing to and from the higher centers, in certain cases with, and in other cases without, synaptic relations with midbrain areas. Among the nuclear masses of the region must be mentioned the motor nuclei of the oculomotor and trochlear nerves, situated at the levels of the superior and inferior colliculi respectively. These have been discussed in a previous chapter. In lower vertebrates scattered cells of the mesencephalic reticular nuclear group occupy much of the field below the motor nuclei; in higher vertebrates many of these scattered groups have been organized into a more or less compact nuclear mass, the red nucleus.   In mammals the red nucleus and the substantia nigra are conspicuous nuclear groups in the more ventral portions of the midbrain.   Other nuclear groups, as for example the interpeduncular nucleus and the nucleus peduncularis transversus, will be discussed under the account of the various regions.   No generalizations can characterize adequately this region of the midbrain, but it may be said that, on the whole, its nuclear masses represent way stations in efferent pathways from cortical centers (in mammals), the striatum, the epithalamic and subthalamic (or ventral thalamic) regions of the diencephalon, the tectum, and the cerebellum to efferent centers of the brain stem and spinal cord.   Thus, to a considerable extent, the ventral part of the midbrain develops with the development of higher centers and their efferent pathways, and is more highly specialized in mammalian forms than in those below mammals.   To some extent this ventral part of the midbrain subserves midbrain reflexes and, in higher forms, at least one of its special centers, the red nucleus, discharges to the dorsal thalamus.   In mammals still another portion of the midbrain is present, known as the basis pedunculi, which includes the substantia nigra and the cortico-pontine, cortico-bulbar, and cortico-spinal tracts in their course through the midbrain or mesencephalon.   The forerunners of this region are present at least as far down as reptiles.

The diencephalon is divisible in all vertebrates, with the possible exception of certain cyclostomes, into four major regions: epithalamus, dorsal thalamus, ventral or subthalamus, and hypothalamus (fig. 423).   The epithalamic centers, largely olfacto-somatic correlation centers, are the least variable of the group, for, with the exception of the epiphysis, they remain much the same throughout the vertebrate series from cyclostomes to man.   The dorsal thalamus is the great receptive center of the diencephalon.   It develops on the one hand with the development of the ascending lemnisci systems and, in forms below mammals, with the tectum, and, on the other hand, with the striatum and the cerebral cortex (where present).   It is a place of synapse for all exteroceptive and proprioceptive impulses to the mammalian cortex.   Its degree of development in any form is a very satisfactory index of the degree of development of striatal or cortical centers, or both.   In addition to these functions the dorsal thalamus also represents an end station for ascending impulses which are relayed from the dorsal thalamus to the efferent centers of the ventral thalamus and to the tectum, thus making possible thalamic reflexes, although the major discharge path for thalamic reflexes appears to be by way of the striatum.   It is this dorsal portion of the diencephalon which develops most during the course of phylogeny.

The ventral thalamus or subthalamus is an efferent center; receiving impulses most particularly from the striatum (via ansa lenticularis) and to some extent from the mammalian cortex, and discharging to lower motor centers.   It, too, develops during phylogeny although not to so great an extent as does the dorsal thalamus.

The hypothalamus, while represented in all vertebrate types, varies greatly in development in the different forms.   Among lower vertebrates it reaches its greatest development in teleosts, where it is a visceral center of great importance.

In tailless amphibians the hypothalamus is small, a condition associated with their terrestrial mode of life. In reptiles there is some increase in differentiation and in mammals the hypothalamus again reaches a high degree of development, although different in type and in certain respects motivated by factors different from those operating in teleosts.

THE RELATIONS IN AMPHIOXUS

A brief discussion of the nervous system of Amphioxus is to be found in the first part of Chapter II of this text. The bibliographic references for this form are found in connection with that chapter. Only certain pertinent facts will be reviewed here, facts concerning the brain of Amphioxus which can be related to structural characteristics of the diencephalon and mesencephalon of higher forms.

It is not possible to determine with certainty the limits of the midbrain in Amphioxus since neither optic nerves nor eye muscles are present. The ventriculus dorsalis, which lies immediately behind the infundibular region, apparently is in part a ventriculus mesencephali, although it has been designated the ventriculus quartus by *Hatschek* ('92) and others. The dorsal nerve entering it probably corresponds to the nervus ophthalmicus trigemini (nervus mesencephalicus, see *Tretjakoff*, '09; also page 872 of this text), but this homology is not beyond question. The cells of Joseph probably are not light perceptive cells, according to the experiments of *Parker* ('08). It may be stated that the absence of pigment alone, which observers have regarded as evidence of an inability to perceive light, cannot be regarded as necessarily indicating such an inability, since eyes lacking in pigment are present in roundworms (*Ariëns Kappers*). Whether these cells may mark the position of the future tectum (phylogenetically speaking) is very uncertain.

It is quite certain that the so-called infundibular region of *von Kupffer* ('06) belongs, together with the region in front of it, to the prosencephalon. This prosencephalon represents in a very primitive way the anterior brain vesicle, an undifferentiated diencephalon and a telencephalon medium of craniotes. This region has a wall several cells thick and in this wall certain areas are identifiable. Ventral to the widest part of the ventriculus dorsalis is the infundibular organ, which is probably the primitive homologue of the specialized epithelium of the saccus vasculosus as seen in the diencephalon of gnathostome fishes. In Amphioxus it is characterized by the knob-shaped thickening on the hairs of the sense cells. This infundibular region obviously belongs to the primitive diencephalon and, according to *Boeke* ('14), it receives and gives rise to fiber fascicles.

In front of the infundibular region enters the nervus terminalis, its region of entrance marking approximately the preoptic and postoptic recesses of vertebrates, since in vertebrates, but not in Amphioxus, an eye develops in this region. In front of the entrance of the nervus terminalis, at the front end of the nervous system, are pigment cells which, according to *Parker's* experiments, are not light perceptive. They do not mark the position of an intracerebral eye for they are not to be regarded as a retinal anlage. At most they might be regarded as a lamina pigmentosa retinae. The further differentiation of the anterior neuropore and lobus parolfactorius impar belongs to the telencephalon medium, and will be considered very briefly in Chapter IX, on page 1242. It may be said in conclusion that a midbrain cannot be identified with certainty in Amphioxus,

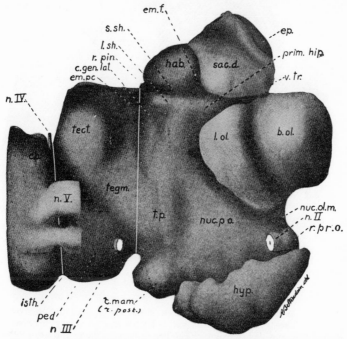

FIG. 424. Lateral view of the mesencephalon, diencephalon, and telencephalon of Ichthyomyzon. *Herrick* and *Obenchain.*
The white line marks the rostral border of the mesencephalon. *b.ol.*, bulbus olfactorius; *cb.*, cerebellum; *c.gen.lat.*, corpus geniculatum laterale; *c.mam.(r.post.)*, recessus posterior corporis mamillaris; *em.f.*, eminentia fimbriae; *em.pc.*, eminentia postcommissuralis; *ep.*, epiphysis; *hab.*, habenula; *hyp.*, hypophysis; *isth.*, isthmus; *l.ol.*, lobus olfactorius; *l.sh.*, lobus subhabenularis; *nuc.ol.m.*, nucleus olfactorius medialis; *ped.*, pedunculus cerebri; *prim.hip.*, primordium hippocampi; *s.sh.*, sulcus subhabenularis; *sac.d.*, saccus dorsalis; *r.pin.*, recessus pinealis; *r.pr.o.*, recessus preopticus; *t.p.*, tuberculum posterius; *tect.*, tectum opticum; *tegm.*, tegmentum; *v.tr.*, velum transversum.

and that, although a diencephalic area is present in this animal, it is not as yet demarked from such portions of the telencephalon as find representation in these forms.

THE MESENCEPHALON AND DIENCEPHALON OF CYCLOSTOMES

In cyclostomes, as compared with Amphioxus, the development of paired eyes and paired olfactory nerves is productive of new relationships. In these forms the mesencephalon appears as a distinct area while the prosencephalon is divisible into two sections: a caudal one, the diencephalon, and a paired and largely olfactory brain, the telencephalon (l. ol. and b. ol. of fig. 424).

In both the petromyzonts and the myxinoids, and particularly in the latter (*Holm*, '01; *Johnston*, '02 and '12; *Holmgren*, '19; *Jansen*, '30, and others), considerable compression has occurred which has affected the primitive relation-

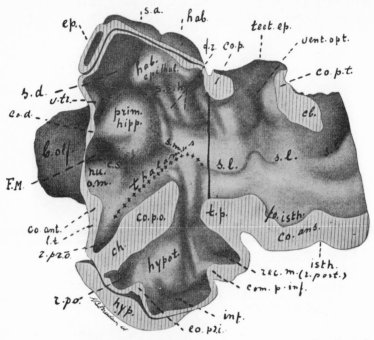

Fig. 425. A view of the inner surface of the wax reconstruction shown in figure 424. The transverse black line indicates the boundary between the mesencephalon and diencephalon. The line of crosses (under the word "thalamus") forms the hypothetical continuation of the sulcus limitans (*s.l.*) within the diencephalon, according to the interpretation of *Herrick* and *Obenchain*. *b.olf.*, bulbus olfactorius; *cb.*, cerebellum; *c.s.*, corpus striatum; *ch.*, chiasma; *co.ant.*, commissura anterior; *co.d.*, commissura dorsalis; *co.p.*, commissura posterior; *co.p.o.*, commissura postoptica (sometimes termed supraoptica); *co.pr.i.*, commissura preinfundibularis; *co.p.t.*, commissura posttectalis; *ep.*, epiphysis; *F.M.*, foramen Monroi; *f.r.*, fasciculus retroflexus; *hab.*, habenula; *hyp.*, hypophysis; *hypot.*, hypothalamus; *l.t.*, lamina terminalis; *nu.o.m.*, nucleus olfactorius medialis; *prim.hipp.*, primordium hippocampi; *r.p.o.*, recessus postopticus; *r.pr.o.*, recessus preopticus; *rec.m.(r.post)*, recessus mamillaris or posterior; *s.d.*, saccus dorsalis; *s.l.*, sulcus limitans; *s.m.*, sulcus medius; *s.s.h.*, lobus subhabenularis; *t.p.*, tuberculum posterius; *tect.ep.*, the ependymal roof of the optic ventricle; *v.tr.*, velum transversum.

ships.   This change in relations is more evident in the myxinoids, where a regression has taken place, since, with the great reduction of the optic nerve and the absence of eye muscle nerves, many centers of primary importance are lacking.

THE MESENCEPHALON AND DIENCEPHALON OF PETROMYZONTS

While the mesencephalon and diencephalon of Petromyzon present relations of fundamental importance, the fronto-caudal compression must be taken into account and all relations, therefore, must not be regarded as primitive.   The mesencephalon, which is the less influenced by this compression, extends dorsally from about the decussation of the trochlear nerve to the pineal recess. It extends ventrally from the isthmus into the recessus mamillaris (r. mam., r. post.). In general structure it resembles the rest of the brain stem more closely than does the diencephalon. A clearly defined sulcus limitans divides it into dorsal or alar and ventral or basal portions. Of these the portion above the sulcus limitans, which includes tectal and certain subtectal centers, is much larger than the basal portion. Reference is made here to figures 424 and 425.

The optic tectum is still partly ependymal in character, but it shows a surprising degree of lamination (fig. 426) in view of the organization exhibited by other parts of the brain (*Huber* and *Crosby*, '34). Internal to a narrow stratum zonale is the stratum opticum, the fibers of which either terminate among scattered intercalate neurons or in greater part turn into the underlying stratum fibrosum et griseum superficiale to come into synaptic relations with its neurons. This last mentioned stratum consists of entering fiber fascicles of optic and other systems interspersed with cells not showing definite lamination. Among such neurons are so-called horizontal and vertical cells. The horizontal cells, which are also present among the fascicles of the stratum opticum, have both neuraxes and dendrites spread out horizontally and it is probable that they serve as correlation cells. The dendrites of the vertical cells extend toward the surface, while their neuraxes come into synaptic relations with cells of origin for efferent systems. Within the tectum of these animals there is correlation of optic impulses with those from the cervical cord and bulbar centers by way of a spino-mesencephalic tract and a bulbar lemniscus (with acoustico-lateral and other secondary fibers, p. 442), which distribute in part to tegmental and in part to tectal regions. The beginning of thalamo-tectal connections is heralded by the appearance of a few fascicles to the stratum fibrosum et griseum superficiale, but these are not numerous. Internal to the stratum fibrosum et griseum superficiale is the stratum griseum centrale (or profundum), which receives afferent impulses through the stratum fibrosum et griseum superficiale, either directly by way of dendrites, which it sends into that stratum, or through the intermediation of cells of the stratum. The neuraxes of neurons constituting the stratum griseum centrale form the major efferent tracts of the optic tectum, which run in part among the cells of the stratum but in part converge beneath it to form the stratum fibrosum (album) centrale or profundum. Chief among such efferent systems are tecto-bulbar fibers which course ventralward from their origin in the optic tectum, undergo a partial decussation in the commissura ansulata near the base of the midbrain, and then turn caudalward along the base of the medulla oblongata. They terminate particularly around reticular elements, from which impulses are relayed to motor nuclei of the brain stem and cord. The much smaller tecto-lobar tract runs along the base of the midbrain and then swings obliquely forward to the lobi inferiores (*Johnston*, '02) or to neighboring areas of the ventral thalamus or hypothalamus. The significance of this tract is not understood as yet. Internal to the stratum fibrosum centrale is the stratum griseum periventriculare, an area of deeply stained rather closely packed neurons continuous with the underlying mesencephalic periventricular gray. Fascicles coursing in part within the stratum griseum centrale and in part lying ventral to it constitute the stratum fibrosum periventriculare, as far as represented here. These fascicles convey impulses from diencephalic regions, from the torus semicircularis, and possibly from other regions. Two major commissures are related to the optic tectum of petromyzonts. The commissura transversa (a post- or supra-optic decussation) interconnects the optic tecta of the two sides, although it may have other connections also, such as collaterals to the anterior hypothalamic gray (*Ariëns Kappers*). The very peculiar course of this commissure, ventrocephalad through the diencephalon to its decussation in the chiasmal ridge, is said (*Ariëns Kappers*, '21) to suggest its relation in some peculiar neurobiotactic way to the optic stalk. The commissura tecti is divided into a caudal part, the commissura posttectalis, and a cephalic part, the commissura posterior (fig. 427A), by the intervening ependymal roof of the tectum. The caudal course of the fibers of the posterior commissure, which extend to the caudal end of the midbrain, gives

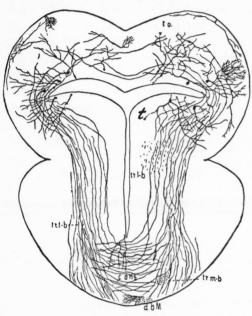

FIG. 426. A cross section through the caudal end of the mesencephalon of Petromyzon. *Johnston.*

c. ans., commissura ansulata; *d.b.M.*, the decussation of Meynert's bundle; *t.*, regio tegmentalis mesencephali; *t.o.*, tectum opticum; *tr.m.b.*, tractus mamillo-bulbaris; *tr.t.b.*, tractus tecto-bulbaris.

this commissure a horseshoe shape. Whether the peculiar courses of the tectal commissures are due to the stimulative effect of other bundles crossing at the same level, or to other factors, is not known.

A primordial pretectal nucleus, with relations to the commissura pretectalis and to descending paths, is present along the front end of the tectum. The subtectal portions [1] of the mesencephalon above the sulcus limitans are large and include a primordial torus semicircularis with the usual connections. In general the subtectal areas receive, as does the tectum, fibers of the commissura transversa and bundles from the secondary ascending systems — the fasciculus longitudinalis lateralis or bulbar lemniscus and the tractus spino-mesencephalicus.

[1] It is of phylogenetic interest that *Tretjakoff* ('09), in the larva of Petromyzon (Ammocoetes), found a small, apparently sensory nerve entering the midbrain near its anterior border. He termed this dorsal nerve, nervus mesencephalicus. It does not appear to be constant and its peripheral relations are not well understood, but it seems possible (*Ariëns Kappers*, '21) that one is dealing here with a portion of the nervus ophthalmicus profundus which has not been displaced caudalward but which has retained its primitive relations with the midbrain. It is possible that it is comparable with a part of the second septal nerve of Amphioxus.

The large reticular elements (p. 648) and the motor nuclei of the oculomotor and of the trochlear nerves (see pp. 524 to 527), which make up the most important constituents of the mesencephalic regions ventral to the sulcus limitans, have been described previously. Nearly all other cells of the basal

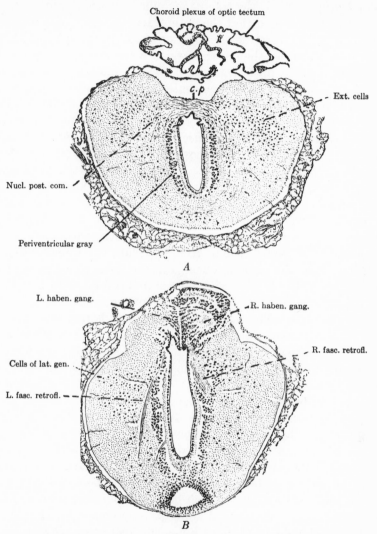

Fig. 427. *A*. A cross section through the region of the commissura posterior in Petromyzon marinus.
B. A cross section directed slightly caudal of the diencephalon of Petromyzon marinus.

region are smaller than the motor or reticular elements and have a primitive position, most of them being situated in the periventricular gray near the ependyma (fig. 427A). Occasionally peripheral cell groups are found attracted to their new positions through the neurobiotactic effect of peripheral fiber systems. Among such may be mentioned the nucleus (or ganglion) interpeduncularis, which lies at the base of the midbrain near the oculomotor roots. This gray mass is the nucleus of termination for the decussated fibers of the fasciculus retroflexus or the tractus habenulo-peduncularis. Through this area passes a descending fiber system arising from the recessus mamillaris and running toward the medulla oblongata. This is the tractus mamillo-bulbaris (tr. m. b., fig. 426).

In general it may be said that the optic tracts and the commissural systems are very important factors in the organization of the mesencephalic regions dorsal to the sulcus limitans and that in this region a correlation occurs between the impulses carried by the optic tracts and those passing over other secondary "vital" paths. Thus this region is a center for vital correlations, *i.e.* those for general sensibility. The faculty of perceiving images (the epicritic or gnostic faculty of vision), if present at all, is certainly poorly developed in these forms. The optic functions in these animals are limited to primitive photostatic functions concerned with the directing of movements, as are also those of the acoustic system, which is represented in these animals only by the vestibular nerve. The results of these correlations are transmitted to the lower centers by tecto-bulbar paths.

That portion of the mesencephalon ventral to the sulcus limitans consists largely of efferent centers (eye muscle nuclei) and coördinating nuclei — nucleus interpeduncularis and the reticular groups. Thus the dorsal regions of the mesencephalon, as of the medulla oblongata, are areas concerned with sensory correlations; the ventral regions with efferent and coördinating impulses.

The diencephalon in Petromyzon falls into epithalamic, thalamic, and hypothalamic portions. The thalamus undoubtedly is represented by a dorsal thalamus and a ventral thalamus, although the line of division between these two portions cannot be drawn with certainty since as yet there is an insufficient knowledge of the fiber connections of the region. The epithalamic centers will be considered first.

Between the habenula and the small velum transversum the roof of the third ventricle is formed by a saccus dorsalis or parencephalon. Since the septum transversum (fig. 423, the border of the forebrain) is scarcely definable in the adult cyclostomes (is represented, according to *Sterzi*, by a small sac), the frontal part of the parencephalon lies for the most part directly behind the choroid roof of the telencephalon. Attached to the parencephalon is the epiphyseal stalk (figs. 424 and 425) which becomes continuous with the ventricle behind the habenula, its ependymal lining passing over into the higher cells of the subcommissural organ from which Reissner's fiber arises (*Dendy*, '06 and '07). From this epiphyseal stalk there are two outgrowths, both of which are sense organs. Of these the superior, which is derived from the right side, is called the pineal organ, the inferior the parapineal organ. In the adult animal the pineal organ lies between the lateral eyes, directly beneath the skin, which is devoid of pigment. So also is the upper wall of the pineal organ itself, which is called the membrana pellucida. In Petromyzon marinus the membrane consists of several layers and has the form of a plano-convex lens (*Studnička*, '05). The cells of the lower wall, the retina, are of two sorts: supporting cells and neuroepithelial cells.   The former contain a white calcareous pigment.   The knob-like ends of the neuroepithelial cells often extend into the lumen of the pineal organ where they seem to come into relation with the cells of the membrana pellucida.   The lower parts of these cells terminate in fibers, the course of which is not well understood.   Beneath the neuroepithelial cells, parallel to the pineal organ, cells closely resembling ganglion cells are to be seen.   The neuraxes of these latter cells pass to the right habenula.   The parapineal organ, lying underneath the pineal organ and slightly in front of it, although less specialized, shows considerable similarity in structure to that of the pineal organ.   Its membrana pellucida consists of a single layer of cells and its retina has no white pigment, but otherwise has the same structure as does the retina of the pineal organ.   Its fiber connections, if present at all, are not sufficiently well known.

The epithalamic nuclei, the habenulae, were regarded by *Dendy* ('06) as connected with the pineal and parapineal organs by means of fiber bundles.   This observer, who studied a New Zealand species of Petromyzon (Geotria australis), found a connection between the parapineal organ and the smaller left habenular nucleus.   It is generally recognized that the right habenular nucleus is the larger of the two (fig. 427B), covering in certain cases the entire dorsal thalamus, but there is not general agreement regarding the termination of the tracts just mentioned within these masses.   According to *Tretjakoff* ('09a) they merely traverse the nuclei and end in a dorsal segment of the forebrain, on the side of their origin.   *Nils Holmgren* (see p. 922) traced similar fibers to the tectum in animals other than cyclostomes.   It is evident that the matter requires further investigation.

The habenulae receive fibers from almost all parts of the telencephalon. Those from lateral and dorsal segments of the lobus olfactorius are known as the tractus olfacto-habenularis (see fig. 535 tr. o. h.).   Bundles from the nucleus olfactorius medialis (nu. o. m., fig. 425) and the region of the preoptic recess (the preoptic area) comprise the tractus olfacto-habenularis medialis.   These tracts lie side by side before their entrance into the habenula through the stria medullaris.   In part the fibers are crossed in the habenular commissure and in part they are homolateral, but the majority end in the larger, right habenula. Accompanying the tracts mentioned above is the commissura superior telencephali, which by certain observers has been regarded erroneously as the homologue of the reptilian commissura pallii posterior.   The commissura superior telencephali consists of fibers which arise in the forebrain area of one side of the brain and terminate in a corresponding area on the other side (*Schilling*, '07; *Tretjakoff*, '09a; *Johnston*, '02).   In their course they accompany the dorso-lateral and medial olfacto-habenular tracts in the stria medullaris, and cross with bundles from these tracts in the habenular commissure.   Efferent fibers leave the habenula by way of the tractus habenulo-peduncularis (the fasciculus retroflexus of Meynert).   The larger part of the bundle originates from the right habenula.   Figure 427B shows the course of the tract.   Its decussation at the base of the midbrain, where it terminates in the nucleus interpeduncularis, is indicated in figure 426.   The anterior part of the habenula lies within the ventricle, and near its free end, below the taenia thalami, is a small eminence (the eminentia fimbriae of *Herrick* and *Obenchain*, '13).   This has fibers from the stria medullaris and small neurons.

Little that is entirely satisfactory is known regarding the nuclear structure of the thalamus in petromyzonts.   The sulcus limitans extends into the caudal part of the region but is interrupted there so that even its primitive position cannot be followed with certainty through the midthalamus region.   *Herrick* and *Obenchain* ('13, see fig. 425 also) have carried this forward tentatively to meet the sulcus medius of their terminology (part of the sulcus hypothalamicus of *Johnston*, '12).   The sulcus medius extends from the cephalic end of the thalamus forward into the hemisphere, where it forms the under boundary of their lobus subhippocampalis (see p. 1240), running forward in this position to the foramen.   A branch given off the more caudal end of the sulcus medius extends ventralward into the preoptic recess and probably represents the cephalic termination of the sulcus limitans.

The habenula is separated from the underlying structures by a sulcus subhabenularis (fig. 425), a deep semilunar sulcus on the left side which is broken into parts on the right side by the large habenulo-peduncular fascicles and their associated gray.   Ventral to the sulcus subhabenularis, approximately halfway between that and the sulcus limitans, another longitudinal sulcus, parallel to the sulcus limitans, divides the ventricular face of the diencephalon — the sulcus intermedius (*Herrick* and *Obenchain*, '13).   The greater part of the area between the sulcus subhabenularis and the sulcus intermedius is occupied by an eminence named the lobus subhabenularis (see fig. 425, labeled s. s. h.) by *Herrick* and *Obenchain*.   These observers have delimited the lobe cephalically by a transverse sulcus which they termed the sulcus thalamicus 2.   The sulcus thalamicus 3, present on the right side, divides the subhabenular lobe into cephalic and caudal parts.   The sulcus thalamicus 3 is the sulcus medius of *Johnston;* the part immediately cephalic to this he found associated with the stria medullaris and with the eminentia thalami, the caudal part he related to the habenulo-peduncular tract.   This caudal part extends to a marked ventricular recess which passes up into relation with the pineal recess and which has been termed, largely on topographic grounds, the recessus metathalamicus (*Herrick* and *Obenchain*).   Between the sulcus intermedius dorsally, and the caudal end of the sulcus medius and the cephalic end of the sulcus limitans ventrally, is an eminence termed the lobus medius thalami (*Herrick* and *Obenchain*).   This eminence is delimited cephalically by the eminentia thalami and its bounding sulcus thalamicus 2, and is continued caudally into the tegmentum of the midbrain dorsal to the sulcus limitans.   The lobus medius is continuous dorsocaudally with the recessus metathalamicus which occupies the region caudal to the lobus subhabenularis.   In the region between the cephalic end of the sulcus limitans and the caudal end of the sulcus medius, the lobus medius becomes continuous with the lobus ventralis which extends ventralward from that position toward the hypothalamus.   In front of the sulcus thalamicus 2, and behind the sulcus thalamicus 1 (or sulcus limitans hippocampi of *Johnston*, '12), is an eminence, the eminentia thalami (*Herrick*, '10 ; *Johnston*, '12 ; *Herrick* and *Obenchain*, '13, and others). This extends dorsalward to the eminentia fimbriae and ventralward to the sulcus medius. It is largely an intercalated nucleus in the course of the olfacto-habenular tract. It is probable that it is interconnected by short fibers with the lobus ventralis. The connections of the lobus medius are practically unknown. So far as evidence is available at present, the lobus medius does not receive any forebrain fibers and apparently is related in no direct way to the olfactory system. A few optic tract fibers terminate in a small group of cells which have shifted peripheralward under the neurobiotactic influence of the optic tract. These cells probably are to be regarded as a primitive lateral geniculate nucleus (*Herrick* and *Obenchain*, '13, for Ichthyomyzon ; *Holmgren*, '19, for Petromyzon), possibly the forerunner of the pars ventralis of mammals.

The lobus ventralis is larger than the lobus medius of the thalamus and has connections with the telencephalon by the tractus olfacto-thalamicus (et hypothalamicus) and the tractus thalamo-olfactorius. This latter bundle carries impulses from this ventral thalamic portion and the hypothalamus to the forebrain. According to *Johnston* ('02) this tract, the function of which is as yet unknown, terminates, after decussation in the decussatio postoptica, in the dorsomedial wall of the telencephalon.

The interpretation of the areas above described in terms of higher vertebrate patterns must be deferred until the fiber connections of the region are known more thoroughly. It appears probable, as *Herrick* and *Obenchain* have implied, that the lobus medius may correspond in a general way to the dorsal thalamus. Probably the recessus metathalamicus also belongs to this dorsal portion. The lobus ventralis, then, is the forerunner of the ventral thalamus and it is probable that the eminentia thalami also belongs in part to the ventral thalamus. The lobus subhabenularis probably, and the taenia fimbriae quite certainly, are epithalamic structures.

In general in Petromyzon, where the thalamus proper, and particularly its dorsal portion, is very small, the principal connections of the diencephalon are olfactory in character, their nuclei of termination being the epithalamic and hypothalamic regions. The hypothalamus is a conducting center with discharge paths to efferent centers of the bulb. The arcs thus formed are probably concerned in relating olfactory impulses to the feeding reflexes. In these animals, then, the diencephalon differs markedly from the mesencephalic centers, which are somatic correlation centers concerned with the regulation of body movements such as posture.

The hypothalamus, which will be considered next, while not so highly developed as in other fishes, consists of a number of areas more or less continuous with each other. Behind the optic chiasma is the recessus postopticus (fig. 425, r. p. o.), which is bounded caudally by the commissura preinfundibularis (fig. 425, co. pr. i.). Then follows the infundibular region (inf.). The posterior end of this latter region is devoid of the neuroepithelium characteristic of the area in plagiostomes, teleosts, and ganoids, and consequently does not form a real saccus vasculosus. The recessus hypophyseus, or cerebral part of the hypophysis, is very distinct. The remainder of the hypophysis is also of ectodermal origin. The pars intermedius arises from the mouth, where it makes its appearance as the hypophyseal furrow (Rathke's pouch of higher vertebrates). The nasal fold in front of the hypophyseal fold, which is the origin of the vestibule of the hypophysis, retains its fold-like form in Petromyzon and is continuous with the medial olfactory placode (*Woerdeman*, '14). The origin of the lobuli laterales is uncertain. Probably they are lateral outgrowths of the pars intermedius. Behind the recessus hypophyseus and separated from it by the commissura postinfundibularis is the recessus posterior (fig. 425, rec. m. (r. post.) or recessus mamillaris).

In cyclostomes the hypothalamus is the principal center for the coördination of olfactory impulses. The major fiber tract appears to be the tractus olfactohypothalamicus, which spreads out throughout most of the extent of the hypothalamus. Another tract probably arising in the nucleus preopticus extends into the infundibular region and apparently distributes to the hypophysis. This is the tractus thalamo-preoptico-infundibularis because it arises from the preoptic area and because no true saccus vasculosus with its specialized epithelium is present (*Dammerman*, '10). The hypothalamus also receives fibers from tectal centers through the tractus tecto-lobaris, which was mentioned in the account of the midbrain (see p. 871). It is possible that this tract is concerned in the correlation of olfactory and optic impulses. The hypothalamus receives ascending fibers from the cerebellum, or at least from the vestibular and lateral-line areas of the medulla oblongata with which the cerebellar plate is related. Finally the infundibular regions of the two sides are united by fibers crossing in the commissura preinfundibularis (between the recessus postopticus and the infundibulum) and the commissura postinfundibularis (between the infundibulum and the recessus posterior; fig. 425, co. pr. i; com. p. inf.).

From the above account it is evident that the hypothalamic region in cyclostomes contains important coördinating centers concerned with the interrelation of olfactory impulses with other sensory impulses. The discharge to efferent centers suggests that the hypothalamus is concerned with visceral functions, since its main tracts discharge to visceral centers of the medulla oblongata. Special mention may be ·made of the tractus lobo-bulbaris and its neighboring tract on the ventral side, the tractus mamillo-peduncularis. The latter tract arises from the region immediately surrounding the ventral recess. Both tracts run caudalward along the nucleus interpeduncularis to the base of the medulla oblongata. They can be traced as far back as the level of the vagus. By means of reticular elements impulses carried by them are transmitted to the spinal cord.

THE MESENCEPHALON AND DIENCEPHALON OF MYXINOIDS

The location of the major subdivisions of the myxinoid brain and the boundaries between such subdivisions are still matters of serious dispute among neurologists. The following brief survey of the present status of the knowledge of mesencephalic and diencephalic centers in these brains is intended to present the problems involved in a study of them, and is little more than a review of the results obtained by various observers, and most particularly by *Holmgren* ('19), *Conel* ('29), and *Jansen* ('30).

Conel studied the embryonic development of the brain of Bdellostoma stouti and found that the diencephalon develops from the third and the mesencephalon from the fourth pair of lobes.   In his 1929 paper this observer discussed the probable presence of a small cerebellum at the cephalic end of the rhomben-cephalon, although he left the matter for further study.   Later results apparently

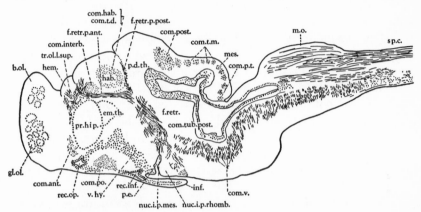

Fig. 428.   A sagittal section through the brain of Myxine glutinosa in which the extent of midbrain and diencephalon are shown according to the interpretation of *Jansen*.   (Redrawn.)

b.ol., bulbus olfactorius; *com.ant.*, commissura anterior; *com.hab.*, commissura habe-nularis; *com. interb.*, commissura interbulbaris; *com.po.*, commissura postoptica; *com.post.*, commissura posterior; *com.p.t.*, commissura posterior tecti; *com.t.d.*, commissura tecti diencephali; *com.t.m.*, commissura tecti mesencephali; *com.v.*, commissura ventralis; *f.retr.p.ant.*, pars anterior of the fasciculus retroflexus; *f.retr.p.post.*, pars posterior of the fasciculus retroflexus; *gl.ol.*, glomeruli olfactorii; *hem.*, hemisphere; *inf.*, infundi-bulum; *mes.*, mesencephalon; *m.o.*, medulla oblongata; *nuc.i.p.mes.*, nucleus interpe-duncularis pars mesencephalica; *nuc.i.p.rhomb.*, nucleus interpeduncularis pars rhomben-cephalica; *p.e.*, plica encephali; *rec.inf.*, recessus infundibuli; *rec.op.*, recessus preopticus; *sp.c.*, spinal cord; *tr.ol.l.sup.*, tractus olfactorius lateralis superficialis; *v.hy.*, ventriculus hypothalamicus.

led him to question its presence, since he stated that probably Bdellostoma stouti has no cerebellum.   For the details of the development of this brain refer-ence is made to *Conel's* paper and particularly to the figures of his models.   In general his results appear to substantiate those of *Jansen*.   (See *Conel*, '29, '31).

In his account of the brain of Myxine glutinosa, *Jansen* ('30; see fig. 428) described the midbrain in that cyclostome as "more or less wedge-shaped with a rounded, bilobated dorsal surface and a narrow base which is restricted to the bottom of the plica encephali."   In the absence of a trochlear nerve in this animal, he established the dorsocaudal boundary as the isthmic fissure and the cephalic end of the commissura ventralis of the rhombencephalon as the ventro-caudal termination of the mesencephalon.   Much of this region belongs to the cerebellum according to certain earlier writers (*G. Retzius*, '93; *Sanders*, '94, and others) and particularly according to the interpretation of *Holmgren* ('19).   Other workers, among whom may be mentioned *Holm* ('01) and *Edinger* ('06), have considered the region as belonging to the midbrain. *Holmgren* regarded the nucleus interpeduncularis as mesencephalic but presented a number of reasons for his conclusion that the rest of the area is cerebellar in character; among the reasons may be mentioned his recognition of various commissural systems, one of which he interpreted as a decussatio veli, another as a cerebellar commissure, and a third group as bundles similar to those crossing in the roof region of the cerebellum in various forms. He identified certain fiber systems, such as tecto-cerebellar and cerebello-tectal and bulbo-cerebellar and cerebello-bulbar tracts. He called attention to the relations of the region with trigeminal, acoustic, and vagus fibers and thought that the ventricle in general outline resembles that of the cerebellar region in sharks. Finally he emphasized, what is undoubtedly a fact, that the area does not look like the mesencephalon typical of most vertebrate forms, and thought that its cells were the forerunners of typical Purkinje cells. It may be added that neither does it look like typical cerebellum and that its cells are not sufficiently differentiated, but that they might be the anlagen of many types of specialized neurons of the central nervous system. None of the evidence presented by *Holmgren* is fully convincing of cerebellar structure, but much the same must be said of the evidence presented to establish it as mesencephalon. The optic tract is usually regarded as the criterion for the presence of an optic tectum, but in Myxine the optic nerves, although always present according to both *Holmgren* and *Jansen*, are exceedingly small and *Jansen* was unable to trace them to the region which he regarded as the optic tectum, although he thought that they might possibly reach that area in company with postoptic commissure fibers. *Jansen* described a medial longitudinal fasciculus which, in its general position in relation to the ventricle, corresponds to this fasciculus in other forms if the area be regarded as mesencephalic. Its position in the medulla oblongata and cord suggests its homology with the medial longitudinal fasciculus of higher vertebrates. However, the crucial connections of the eye muscle nuclei and vestibular apparatus are lacking in correspondence with the great reduction of the eyes and the absence of eye muscles and of the acoustico-lateral apparatus in these forms. The distributions of many of the tracts described by *Jansen*, as was the case with those described by *Holmgren*, cannot be regarded as implying necessarily that the area is mesencephalic; their interpretation is biased by the interpretation of the region, since the areas from which they arise or end frequently in phylogeny are connected with both mesencephalic and cerebellar centers. However, this does not apply to all the bundles described by *Jansen*. The distribution of the postoptic system to the region he regarded as tectum is a fact of very great significance in determining homologies since this connection is a characteristic one for the mesencephalon of many vertebrates but has never, within our knowledge, been carried to the cerebellum. It would seem premature to attempt to reach any final conclusions in the matter although the balance of evidence is considerably in favor of the interpretation of *Jansen* and, within certain limits, of that of his predecessors, *Holm* ('01), *Edinger* ('06), *Röthig* and *Ariëns Kappers* ('14), and others.

Jansen was unable to delimit any nuclear masses in the midbrain of his terminology other than certain reticular groups, such as the nucleus reticularis mesencephali, an accumulation of cells related to the posterior commissure (nucleus commissurae posterioris), and the pars mesencephalica of nucleus interpeduncularis.   According to this observer, the nucleus reticularis mesencephali is represented by certain large, multipolar cells, motor in type, among which are a few giant cells giving rise to Müller's fibers.   Neurons from the fronto-dorsal part of the nucleus send out dendrites which radiate among the bundles of the posterior commissure.   The neuraxes enter the fasciculus longitudinalis medialis.   *Holmgren* ('19) and *Jansen* ('30) recognized a mesencephalic nucleus interpeduncularis.   *Jansen* (fig. 428) divided the nucleus interpeduncularis into a pars mesencephalica and a pars rhombencephalica, of which the former part is a midbrain structure.   In order to understand the relations of these parts of the interpeduncular nucleus it is necessary to know something of the habenulo-peduncular tract (or tractus retroflexus).   This bundle, made up of both fine and coarse components (see fig. 428), swings ventralward and slightly caudal-ward from the habenular region of the diencephalon in order to decussate in the ventral part of the midbrain in what is termed its dorsal decussation.   It then runs lateralward and ventralward and then gradually turns medialward during its caudal course to decussate a second time near the ventral surface in what *Jansen* termed its ventral decussation.   The tractus habenulo-peduncularis encircles the nucleus interpeduncularis, the pars mesencephalica lying partly in front of the tract, partly scattered among its fascicles or ventral to them, and partly caudal to its dorsal decussation in the triangular space made by the separation of the two arms of decussating fibers.   The pars rhombencephalica is surrounded by the fasciculus retroflexus and is separated from the ventral surface for a part of its extent by the caudomedially running fibers of the two fasciculi and by their ventral decussation.   After this ventral crossing, the terminal bundles swing around the rhombencephalic part of the nucleus, making an unknown number of coils of finer fibers before breaking up among its cells.   The cell bodies of the pars rhombencephalica are spindle-shaped and may be either bipolar or, more rarely, unipolar.   The more centrally located cells are the smaller ; those toward the periphery of the nucleus the larger.   The neuraxes either fray out into the tegmental region of the midbrain as a tractus inter-pedunculo-tegmentalis or pass caudalward in the medulla oblongata as a tractus interpedunculo-bulbaris (*Jansen*).   The neurons of the pars mesencephalica of the interpeduncular nucleus are large and multipolar in outline.   They contrib-ute to the dense neuropil which *Jansen* described as occupying the triangle dorsal to the pars rhombencephalica of the interpeduncular nucleus and ventral and ventromedial to the fasciculi interpedunculares at their dorsal crossing and in their ventrolateral course beyond that decussation.   This region, according to the observer quoted above, also receives fibers of the bounding tracts and the ventral commissure.

The remainder of the midbrain, for lack of specific differentiation, *Jansen* ('30) grouped into : (1) a zone of ventral gray which surrounds the ventricle ; (2) a zone of fiber bundles which carries many large fiber tracts interspersed with rows of cells of various types ; (3) a molecular zone which carries largely bulbo-tectal and supraoptic (or postoptic) commissural connections.   A few cells are present here.   *Jansen* described the central gray as consisting of smaller cells surrounded by a layer of larger cells, which send their dendrites peripheralward, interlacing with the fiber bundles.   The cells in the fiber tract layer are either bipolar or multipolar and frequently their long, little branched neuraxes extend out at right angles to the brain surface.   Curious unipolar cells near the surface, in the outer part of the molecular layer, send a dendritic process centralward.   Here, as elsewhere in the myxinoid brain, many mossy processes radiate in all directions. The main fiber bundles of this region (*Jansen*) are (1) the tractus tecto-bulbaris et spinalis, associated with which is the tractus tecto-tegmentalis, (2) the tractus tecto-thalamicus, (3) the fasciculus longitudinalis medialis, and (4) a group of commissures — the commissura posterior, the commissura tecti mesencephali, and the commissura tuberculi posterioris.

The tractus tecto-bulbaris et spinalis was traced from a region dorsal to the posterior commissure ventralward and ultimately, after a rather round-about course, spinalward through the tegmentum (where a part of the fibers decussate in the ventral commissure forming a tractus tecto-bulbaris cruciatus) to the medulla oblongata where the bundle passes caudalward along the ventral surface.   The tecto-thalamic tract is composed of the ascending branches of bifurcating fibers which join the bulbar lemniscus and run with it to the dorsal thalamus.   The descending branch runs spinalward.   The medial longitudinal fasciculus (see p. 880) in Myxine, according to *Jansen's* interpretation, appears to be composed largely of processes of reticular cells of the mesencephalon and medulla oblongata.   The commissura posterior carries coarse fibers originating from neuraxes of cells lateral to the ventricle.   These neuraxes, after decussation, join the medial longitudinal fasciculus.   Other components, made up chiefly of finer fibers, interconnect adjoining (probably tectal) areas and carry crossed fibers probably to such efferent systems as the tecto-bulbar and tecto-thalamic tracts and perhaps also some crossed fibers of the ascending lemniscus system (see *Holmgren* and *Jansen*).   The commissura tecti mesencephali (or commissurae ; fig. 428) of *Jansen*, regarded by *Holmgren* as a cerebellar commissural system, is composed of a series of decussating fibers, the origins or terminations of which are not well known.   *Holmgren* believed that through this system certain fascicles of the lemniscus reached the contralateral dorsal part of the region.   It undoubtedly carries commissural fibers between neighboring areas.   The commissura tuberculi posterioris (commissura ansulata) carries fibers related to the tegmentum and to hypothalamic areas, together with certain crossed fascicles of the tractus thalamo-bulbaris.   It crosses in the tegmental region, sometimes between the bundles of the tractus habenulo-peduncularis.

The disagreement among various observers as to the location of the mesencephalon in myxinoids of course raises similar questions as to the boundaries of the diencephalon, the crux of the discussion centering around the recognition of the posterior commissure.   *Holmgren* thought this commissure crossed through the habenular bodies and he and others as well have regarded the diencephalic region, with the exception of the epithalamic and hypothalamic centers, as buried from the surface between the two hemispheres. *Jansen's* interpretation of crossing fibers caudal to the habenula as posterior commissure fibers places the boundary of the diencephalon caudal to the limits set for it by other observers. The limits as set by *Jansen* are as follows: cephalically — "by a line which follows the anterior surface of the habenula curves along the posterior aspect of the primordium hippocampi, and reaches the ventral surface immediately in front of (or behind?) the postoptic commissure." A curved line, with the convexity forward, joining the epiphyseal recess dorsally (sulcus dimesencephalicus) and the plica encephali ventrally constitutes the caudal diencephalic boundary. The region may be subdivided into epithalamic, hypothalamic, and thalamic portions. Reference is made here to figure 428.

The epithalamic region contains no epiphysis in myxinoids. An habenular body (fig. 428) is present, and this consists of two portions, a dorsal nucleus composed of multipolar cells and a ventrolateral nucleus consisting of bipolar neurons. *Holmgren* ('19) regarded the habenula as representative of both the medial habenular and the subhabenular nuclei of other forms. The habenulae are fused to form a single body macroscopically, but microscopic study shows that there are right and left habenulae. They are asymmetrical, the right being larger than the left. According to *Jansen* ('30), the incoming connections to the habenula come from the hemisphere, the area basalis, and the primordium hippocampi by way of olfacto-habenular, medial olfacto-habenular, and cortico-habenular tracts respectively. Fibers from the olfactory bulb (*Holmgren* and *Jansen*) and the lateral olfactory tract (deep and superficial portions; *Jansen*) also cross in the so-called interbulbar commissure which occupies much of the cephalic part of the habenular body. Other incoming connections to the habenula, according to *Jansen*, are fibers from the eminentia thalami (the tractus eminentia-habenularis) and from the pars dorsalis thalami (the commissura tecti diencephali). To the tractus habenulo-peduncularis, to which reference has been made earlier and which supplies not only the nucleus interpeduncularis but probably also, to some extent, the tegmental region behind it (*Jansen*), must be added the tractus habenulo-tubercularis to the nucleus tuberculi posterioris and the tractus habenulo-thalamicus to the pars ventralis thalami.

In the thalamus proper, *Holmgren* recognized a nucleus centralis thalami, comparable to the eminentia thalami of *Jansen*, and a nucleus lateralis thalami homologous to the pars ventralis thalami of the latter observer. The nuclei centrales or eminentiae thalami of the two sides are fused in the midline, forming thus a centrally located mass of cells which lies ventral to the habenula (and caudal to the primordium hippocampi). Lateral to the central nucleus (eminentia thalami) is the nucleus lateralis thalami, first recognized and described by *Holmgren*, and later described under the name of pars ventralis by *Jansen*. Cephalically this portion is in close relation to the eminentia thalami. Having in certain planes the appearance of being a caudal continuation of the lateral nucleus or the pars ventralis thalami, but distinguishable through the smaller size and closer arrangement of the cells, is the nucleus tuberculi posterioris of *Jansen* (Lateralkern or Geniculatum of *Edinger*, '06, and *Holmgren* '19), its name serving to indicate its probable homology with the similarly designated nucleus of Necturus (*Herrick*, '25; see bibliography for amphibians). This homology is discussed at length in *Jansen's* paper, page 489. The pars dorsalis thalami of *Jansen's* terminology lies dorsal to the pars ventralis in the region commonly known as the dorsal lobe and has been regarded as tectal in character by other students of the myxinoid brain. *Jansen* subdivided the region secondarily into three relatively indistinct nuclear masses, the nucleus dorsomedialis, the nucleus dorsolateralis, and the nucleus profundus.

With regard to the fiber connections of the myxinoid thalamus much remains to be learned. The nucleus centralis is said by *Holmgren* to be connected with the dorsal part of the hypothalamus and to receive terminal fibers of the tractus spino-bulbo-thalamicus. *Jansen* carried fibers from the nucleus (his eminentia thalami) to the pars ventralis thalami and to the nucleus tuberculi posterioris, in company with habenulo-thalamic and habenulo-tubercular tracts. Other bundles passed to the habenula. The pars dorsalis thalami of *Jansen*, the tectum mesencephali of *Holmgren* and others, has been shown by the latter observer to be connected with its neighbor of the other side through a commissural system (commissura posterior of *Holmgren*, commissura tecti diencephali of *Jansen*), to receive fibers from the commissura ventralis (tractus thalamo-hypothalamicus rectus et cruciatus and tractus thalamo-bulbaris cruciatus, portions of the postoptic system of *Jansen*) and to discharge impulses to the hypothalamus (tractus tecto-lobaris of *Holmgren*) and to the medulla oblongata. This latter system carries also ascending fibers, forming thus the tractus tecto-bulbaris et bulbo-tectalis of *Holmgren* — the tractus thalamo-bulbaris pars dorsalis of *Jansen*. *Jansen* also described connections with the tegmentum of the midbrain, with the tectal area of his nomenclature (tractus tecto-thalamicus) and forward to the area basalis (tractus thalamo-frontalis). From the forebrain region *Holmgren* carries a strio-thalamic tract into the diencephalic region. This tract falls into several divisions of which the tractus cortico-thalamicus at least (in part, the tractus olfacto-thalamicus rectus of *Jansen*) ends in the region under consideration. The nucleus lateralis thalami or the pars ventralis thalami of *Jansen*, by whichever name it is designated, receives many fibers of the ventral or postoptic commissure system. Incoming impulses reach it from the telencephalon by the olfacto-thalamic and strio-thalamic tracts of *Jansen*, and it discharges to the hypothalamus and to peduncular and tegmental areas by a series of fiber bundles.

THE MESENCEPHALON AND DIENCEPHALON IN PLAGIOSTOMES

THE GROSS RELATIONS

An inspection of their gross structure alone indicates that the mesencephalic and diencephalic centers are much more highly developed in the plagiostomes than in the cyclostomes. A brief account of the morphologic relations of these areas in the former animals will precede the description of their microscopic structure.

The roof of the mesencephalon, the tectum (figs. 429 and 430), is more massive in plagiostomes than it is in cyclostomes and no longer boasts a thin ependymal portion. In the smaller plagiostomes it is partly covered, and, in the larger plagiostomes, practically completely covered by the lobus anterior of the cerebellum, which in most cases extends to the caudal poles of the habenular nuclei (fig. 429). Externally it is separated from the tegmental portion of the midbrain by a furrow, which may be termed the sulcus tecto-tegmentalis (figs. 431 and 433, s. t. tegm., figs. 434 and 435, s. t. t.). In the midline a depression divides the tectum into two lateral portions, forming thus the corpora bigemina (figs. 430 to 434).

The ventricle, which is very large in these animals, spreads out beneath the tectum. In the caudal part of its floor, on either side, are two protuberances which appear to correspond to the positions of the oculomotor and trochlear nuclei. Where the tectum joins the tegmentum the wall is very thick and bulges out more or less into the ventricle, thus forming a sort of torus semicircularis (figs. 433 and 434; t. semic.) on either side. Such a torus (under which lies the nucleus tegmentalis medialis) is not a so clearly defined, separate structure as is that found in the ganoids or teleosts (see page 914).

Usually the sulcus limitans is well developed in the mesencephalon; it is less clear in the diencephalon where it turns down toward the preoptic recess. The fissura media (see figs. 431, 433, 434), or the sulcus medius, of the ventricle is not very deep in the caudal part of the mesencephalon but increases in depth orally where it goes over into the aditus ad infundibulum. The roof of the midbrain extends farther frontalward than its base, overlaps the commissura posterior, and projects over the diencephalon to the level of the habenulae.

The caudal limit of the diencephalon on the dorsal side is the commissura posterior. Between this commissure and the habenular bodies is the epiphyseal stalk terminating in a small vesicle, the epiphysis, which has lost the characteristics of a pineal eye and is merely glandular in structure. Where the epiphyseal stalk joins the brain the ependyma of its posterior wall becomes continuous with the large ependymal cells of the subcommissural organ from which Reissner's fiber originates (*Nicholls;* see Chapter II, page 167, for a description of this fiber). This fiber passes caudalward through the ventricles and the central canal of the cord to become attached to a mass of mesenchymatous tissue at the end of this canal.

Along the wall of the third ventricle of the plagiostome brain a fissure, the sulcus subhabenularis, separates the epithalamus from the thalamus proper; the sulcus medius, virtually or actually a branch of the sulcus limitans (figs. 429, 436, 438, 439), marks the line between the dorsal thalamus and the ventral thalamus. The ventricular ependyma is well developed near the sulcus medius and in general has an unusually rich capillary supply. It probably contributes to the secretion of the cerebrospinal fluid (see discussion, page 46). The sulcus thalamo-hypothalamicus internus (fig. 440, s. t. hyp. int.) separates the ventral thalamus

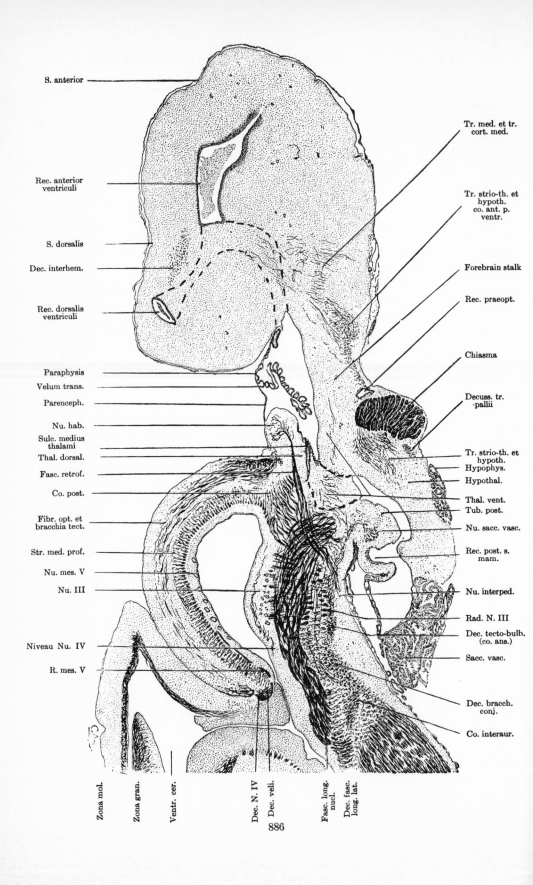

S. anterior

Rec. anterior
ventriculi

S. dorsalis

Dec. interhem.

Rec. dorsalis
ventriculi

Paraphysis
Velum trans.
Parenceph.

Nu. hab.
Sulc. medius
thalami
Thal. dorsal.

Fasc. retrof.

Co. post.

Fibr. opt. et
bracchia tect.

Str. med. prof.

Nu. mes. V

Nu. III

Niveau Nu. IV

R. mes. V

Tr. med. et tr.
cort. med.

Tr. strio-th. et
hypoth.
co. ant. p.
ventr.

Forebrain stalk

Rec. praeopt.

Chiasma

Decuss. tr.
pallii

Tr. strio-th. et
hypoth.
Hypophys.
Hypothal.

Thal. vent.
Tub. post.

Nu. sacc. vasc.

Rec. post. s.
mam.

Nu. interped.

Rad. N. III
Dec. tecto-bulb.
(co. ans.)
Sacc. vasc.

Dec. bracch.
conj.

Co. interaur.

Zona mol.
Zona gran.
Ventr. cer.
Dec. N. IV
Dec. veli.
Fasc. long.
nucl.
Dec. fasc.
long. lat.

886

from the hypothalamus.   The hypothalamus in these forms, as in cyclostomes, is the largest subdivision of the diencephalon.   It begins orally in the region of the preoptic recess.   Behind this recess is the optic chiasm and then a small postoptic recess which is not so distinct as in petromyzonts (r. postopt., fig. 438). The commissura preinfundibularis separates the postoptic recess from the infundibulum.   The infundibulum is much deeper in plagiostomes than in cyclostomes, and extending out from it are bilateral recesses surrounded by a massive nervous wall.   These are the lobi inferiores (figs. 433–435, l. inf., fig. 440, r. l. i.). The basal plate is thin and shows caudally two enlargements — the brain portion of the hypophysis (figs. 433 and 434, hyp.) and behind that the saccus vasculosus.   This saccus vasculosus (figs. 429 to 431, 441) is a highly vascularized sense organ which extends far caudalward.   The dorsal wall of this organ passes over into the posterior wall of the recessus posterior (recessus mamillaris), the most caudal portion of the hypothalamus (fig. 429).

THE FINER STRUCTURE OF THE PLAGIOSTOME MESENCEPHALON

A study of the microscopic structure of the mesencephalon and diencephalon in plagiostomes indicates that these areas are much better developed than the corresponding regions in cyclostomes.   The midbrain falls into the usual tectal and tegmental portions.   The tectum may be divided into a stratum medullare externum, a stratum cellulare externum, a stratum medullare internum, and a stratum cellulare internum.   The stratum medullare externum, lying at the periphery, is formed by bundles of the tractus opticus and the brachium tecti. Scattered among the fibers are horizontal, intercalary cells, described by *Houser* ('01) for plagiostomes and similar to those observed in cyclostomes.   The stratum cellulare externum, according to *Sterzi* ('05), has a zona externa and a zona interna.   Of these, the former contains small cells which receive incoming impulses from the external medullary layer and discharge them to the cells of the zona interna.   These latter cells are larger and they have relatively long dendrites, some of which extend toward the periphery to come into synaptic relation with the external medullary layer.   Their neuraxes pass to the stratum

---

Fig. 429.   A paramedian section through the brain of Scyllium canicula.

Br. tect., brachium tecti; *Chiasma*, chiasma opticum; *Com.ant.p.vent.*, commissura anterior pars ventralis; *Co.interaur.*, commissura interauricularis; *Co.post.*, commissura posterior; *Dec.brach.conj.*, decussation of the brachium conjunctivum; *Dec.fasc.long.lat.*, decussation of the fasciculus longitudinalis lateralis; *Dec. interhem.*, decussatio interhemispherica; *Dec.N.IV*, decussation of the nervus trochlearis; *Dec.tecto-.bulb.* (*co.ans.*), decussatio tractus tecto-bulbaris (commissura ansulata); *Fasc.long.med.*, fasciculus longitudinalis medialis; *Fasc.retrof.*, fasciculus retroflexus; *Fibr.op.*, fibrae opticum; *Hypophys.*, hypophysis; *Hypothal.*, hypothalamus; *Niveau nu.IV*, region of nucleus trochlearis; *Nu.hab.*, nucleus habenularis; *Nu.interped.*, nucleus interpeduncularis; *Nu.mes.V*, nucleus of the mesencephalic root of the trigeminal; *Nu.III*, nucleus oculomotorius; *Parenceph.*, parencephalon; *Paraphysis*, paraphysis; *R.mes.V*, mesencephalic root of the trigeminal; *Rad.N.III*, root fibers of nervus oculomotorius; *Rec. anterior ventriculi*, recessus anterior ventriculi; *Rec.post.s.mam.*, recessus posterior or mamillaris; *Rec. preop.*, recessus preopticus; *S.anterior*, sulcus anterior; *S.dorsalis*, sulcus dorsalis; *Sacc.vasc.*, saccus vasculosus; *Str.med.prof.*, stratum medullare profundum; *Sulc.medius thalami*, sulcus medius thalami; *Thal.dorsal*, dorsal thalamus; *Thal.vent.*, ventral thalamus; *Tr.cort.med.*, tractus corticalis medialis; *Tr.med.*, tractus medianus; *Tr.str.thal.et hypoth.*, tractus striothalamicus et hypothalamicus; *Tub.post.*, tuberculum posterius; *velum trans.*, velum transversum; *Ventr.cer.*, ventriculum cerebelli; *Forebrain stalk*, forebrain stalk; *Zona gran.*, zona granulosa; *Zona mol.*, zona molecularis.

medullare internum through which they enter the tecto-bulbar tracts. It is to be noted that the important outgoing paths of the tectum arise from this layer. Below the internal medullary stratum lies the stratum cellulare internum,

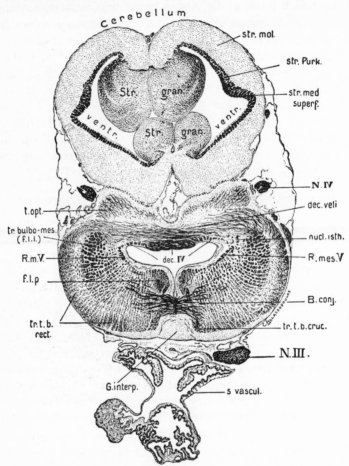

Fig. 430. A cross section through the more caudal end of the mesencephalon, through the cerebellum and through the saccus vasculosus of Acanthias vulgaris.

B.conj., brachium conjunctivum; *dec.veli*, decussatio veli; *dec.IV*, decussation of trochlear nerve; *f.l.p.*, fasciculus longitudinalis medialis; *N.IV*, nervus trochlearis; *g.interp.*, nucleus interpeduncularis; *nucl.isth.*, nucleus isthmi; *s.vascul.*, saccus vasculosus; *str.gran.*, stratum granulosum; *str.med.superf.*, stratum medullaris superficialis; *str.mol.*, stratum moleculare; *str.Purk.*, stratum of *Purkinje* cells; *R.mes.V*, mesencephalic root of the trigeminal; *tr.bulbo-mes.(f.l.l.)*, tractus bulbo-mesencephalicus (fasciculus longitudinalis lateralis); *tr.t.b.cruc.*, tractus tecto-bulbaris cruciatus; *tr.t.b.rect.*, tractus tecto-bulbaris rectus; *ventr.*, ventricle.

a band of gray containing various cell types. Among these may be mentioned small correlation cells, the dendrites of which branch out in the stratum medullare internum, while the neuraxes enter the lamina commissuralis tecti (fig. 432). Other neurons of similar type and with neuraxes probably distributed in the same way have their cell bodies in this layer but send their dendrites into the optic tract layer. Finally, forming conspicuous elements of the stratum cellulare internum, are the cell bodies of the nucleus of the mesencephalic root of the trigeminal (compare figs. 159 and 238). If the terminology sometimes used for higher

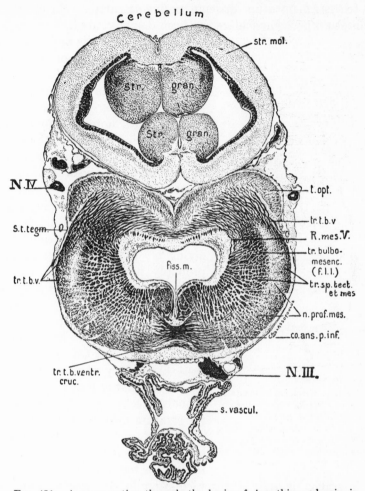

Fig. 431. A cross section through the brain of Acanthias vulgaris, in front of figure 430.

co.ans.p.inf., commissura ansulata pars inferior; f.l.l., fasciculus longi-tudinalis lateralis; fiss.m., fissura media; N.IV, nucleus trochlearis; n.prof. mes., nucleus profundus mesencephali; R.mes.V, mesencephalic root of the trigeminal nerve; s.t.tegm., sulcus tecto-tegmentalis; s.vascul., saccus vascu-losus; str.gran., stratum granulare; str.mol., stratum moleculare; tr.bulbo-mesenc., tractus bulbo-mesencephalicus; t.opt., tectum opticum; tr.sp.tect.et mes., tractus spino-tectalis et mesencephalicus; tr.t.b.v., tractus tecto-bul-baris ventralis; tr.t.b.ventr.cruc., tractus tecto-bulbaris ventralis cruciatus.

fishes, reptiles, and birds (Huber and Crosby, '33, '34; bibliography, page 1218) is applied here, the external medullary layer of plagiostomes includes the stratum opticum of teleosts (with possibly certain additional fibers); the zona externa, with cells and processes and regions of synapse, is the stratum fibrosum et griseum superficiale of teleosts; the zona interna of plagiostomes is the stratum griseum centrale of teleosts; the stratum medullare internum of plagiostomes is the stratum album centrale of teleosts; and the scattered cells internal to this, together with the cells of the mesencephalic root of the trigeminal in plagiostomes, form the teleostean stratum griseum periventriculare. No clearly developed stratum fibrosum periventriculare has been demonstrated.

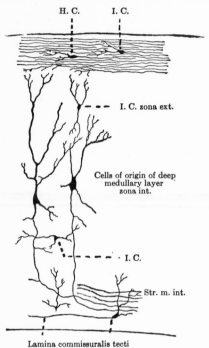

FIG. 432. Certain histologic elements in the optic tectum of a shark. (Built up from the work of Sterzi and Houser.)

Optic tract fibers at outer edge; *H.C.*, horizontal cells; *I.C.*, intercalary cells; *str. m.int.*, stratum medullare internum; *zona ext.*, zona externa; *zona int.*, zona interna.

The optic tract is probably the most important afferent tract of the tectum. It is a pathway for the visual impulses, and such visual impulses, in addition to their ordinary function, play an important rôle, in conjunction with impulses from other centers, in establishing static functions of the body, as is evident from the numerous connections of the midbrain with various gravistatic centers. After a total decussation near the region of the preoptic recess (fig. 436), the optic tract passes dorsocaudalward along the lateral wall of the diencephalon, (fig. 438) giving off in its course collaterals, though probably not stem fibers, to the nucleus geniculatus lateralis. Before the tract reaches the tectum it divides into two branches, a smaller medial and a larger lateral branch, and these branches, with fibers of the commissura transversa, the brachium tecti (secondary fibers connecting the nucleus geniculatus lateralis and the tectum, probably tecto-thalamic in large part), form the stratum medullare externum.

Secondary tracts from the acoustic and lateral-line centers of the medulla oblongata reach the tectum by the fasciculus longitudinalis lateralis (lemniscus acustico-lateralis or tractus octavo-mesencephalicus; *Wallenberg*, '07). Neuraxes, or at all events collaterals of neuraxes, of cells of the nucleus of the descending or spinal root of the trigeminal, or from the dorsal horn gray, after decussation, ascend as the tractus spino- et bulbo-mesencephalicus to tegmental and tectal centers. The tectum, then, is a center for the correlation of optic with other exteroceptive impulses. The resultant discharge occurs over final common paths which are represented chiefly in the tecto-bulbar systems and in the fiber tracts to the eye muscle nuclei. It is of interest that tecto-bulbar tracts are present not only in animals born blind, but even in blind species (see *Charlton's* work on teleosts). This is an indication of the importance of the non-optic components to the tectum.

In the tecto-bulbar tracts two systems can be distinguished, a smaller dorsal and a larger ventral system. Both arise from the large cells of the zona

interna (fig. 432) and both contain homolateral and contralateral bundles
which run caudalward to the medulla oblongata. The dorsal tecto-bulbar

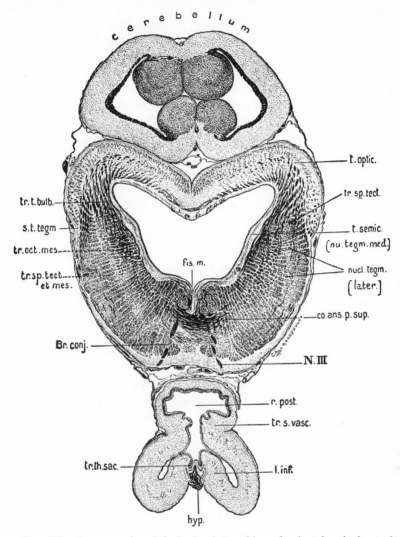

FIG. 433. A cross section of the brain of Acanthias vulgaris, taken in front of
that in figure 431.

Br.conj., brachium conjunctivum; *co.ans.p.sup.*, commissura ansulata pars superior; *fis.m.*, fissura media; *hyp.*, hypophysis; *l.inf.*, lobus inferior; *N.III*,
nervus oculomotorius; *nucl.tegm.(later.)*, nucleus tegmentalis lateralis; *nu.tegm.
med.*, nucleus tegmentalis medialis; *r.post.*, recessus posterior; *s.t.tegm.*, sulcus
tecto-tegmentalis; *t.optic.*, tectum opticum; *t.semic.*, torus semicircularis; *tr.oct.
mes.*, tractus octavo-mesencephalicus; *tr.s.vasc.*, tractus saccus-vasculosis; *tr.sp.
tect.et mes.*, tractus spino-tectalis et-mesencephalicus; *tr.t.bulb.*, tractus tecto-bulbaris; *tr.th.sac.*, tractus thalamo-saccularis.

tract runs near the ventricle (tr. t. b. p. do., fig. 434). As it approaches the
midline it undergoes a partial decussation at the rostral level of the oculomotor
nucleus (co. ans. p. sup., fig. 433). Some of the crossed fibers terminate in rela-

tion to this nucleus, but the majority of such fibers, together with the uncrossed component, run caudalward in company with the medial longitudinal fasciculus. Fibers from the extreme frontal and extreme caudal parts of the tectum appear to constitute the uncrossed portion, and fibers from the middle regions the crossed portion, of the ventral tecto-bulbar tract. Such crossed fibers have their decussation a little behind that of the dorsal tecto-bulbar system and then run caudalward along the nucleus interpeduncularis, medial to the direct ventral tecto-bulbar tract (tr. t. b. rect., fig. 430). At the level of the oculomotor nucleus a few bundles of both crossed and uncrossed fibers bend dorsally in order to enter this nucleus. However, the great majority run farther caudalward, the crossed fibers terminating before the uncrossed ones, which latter can be traced to the middle of the vagus region.

Whether or not fibers from the tectum pass to the lobi inferiores of the hypothalamus in plagiostomes is at present uncertain. Such bundles appear to come from the caudal part of the tectum, but it has not been definitely established as yet that they are tectal rather than tegmental in origin. A component of the tractus mesencephalo-cerebellaris, which will be considered in relation to the tegmentum, arises from the tectum. It is possible that this is the forerunner of the tractus tecto-cerebellaris of teleosts (p. 911).

The commissural systems of the midbrain roof are much better developed in plagiostomes than in cyclostomes, for the lamina commissuralis tecti (figs. 434, 439, 440) extends without interruption over its whole length from the decussation of the trochlear nerve to the commissura posterior. The fibers of the commissura posterior in part originate from the tectum, and, in part, appear to have their origin in pretectal cells or in the nucleus geniculatus lateralis. However, the greater number of the fibers of this commissure seem to take origin in a group of cells lying in front of and lateral to the oculomotor nucleus. Fibers, after crossing in the posterior commissure, run caudalward to the medulla oblongata (in company with the tractus pretecto-bulbaris) from cells near the frontal end of the tectum. Whereas, in petromyzonts most of the neuron groups of the mesencephalic region below the tectum are arranged as periventricular gray with interneuronal connections established at the periphery, in plagiostomes the cell groups have dispersed throughout the brain wall under the influence of various fiber systems.

The nuclei of the oculomotor and trochlear nerves and the reticular cell groups have been discussed in a previous chapter (Chapter VI, pages 534 to 536). The oculomotor nuclear groups are related to the tectum by crossed and uncrossed bundles running with the tecto-bulbar systems. The major connection of the reticular elements of the midbrain base is the tractus cerebello-mesencephalicus et diencephalicus or the brachium conjunctivum. Probably this arises from the cerebellar cortex and subcerebellar nuclei (p. 724). It swings ventromedialward and forward to cross ventral to the fasciculus longitudinalis medialis at a level caudal to the commissura ansulata (B. conj., figs. 429 and 430). Certain small bundles are sent directly to the oculomotor nucleus. However, the majority of the fibers terminate in the hypothalamus and the

ventral thalamus and upon the reticular cells in the lower part of the mesencephalon.

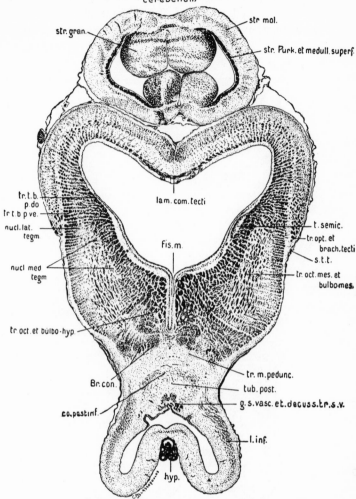

FIG. 434.   A cross section through the brain of Acanthias vulgaris in front
of the plane of figure 432.

Br.con., brachium conjunctivum; *brach.tecti*, brachium tecti; *co.post.inf.*,
commissura postinfundibularis; *fis.m.*, fissura media; *g.s.vasc.et. decuss.tr.sv.*,
ganglion saccus vasculosus and decussation of its tract; *hyp.*, hypophysis;
l.inf., lobus inferior; *lam.com.tecti*, lamina of the commissura tecti; *nucl.lat.
tegm.*, nucleus lateralis tegmenti; *nucl.med.tegm.*, nucleus medialis tegmenti;
s.t.t., sulcus tecto-tegmentalis; *str.gran.*, stratum granulare; *str.mol.*, stratum moleculare; *str.Purk.et medull.superf.*, stratum of *Purkinje* cells and
superficial medullary layer; *t.semic.*, torus semicircularis; *tr.m.pedunc.*,
tractus mamillo-peduncularis; *tr.opt.*, tractus opticus; *tr.oct.et bulbo-hyp.*,
tractus octavo- et bulbo-hypothalamicus; *tr.oct.mes.et bulbo-mes.*, tractus
octavo-mesencephalicus et bulbo-mesencephalicus; *tr.t.b.p.do.*, tractus tecto-
bulbaris pars dorsalis; *tr.t.b.p.ve.*, tractus tecto-bulbaris pars ventralis.

Among the most interesting of the midbrain centers is a group of large cells
lateral to the velum medullare anterius and traversed by fibers of the commissura
veli.   This group of cells constitutes the nucleus isthmi, which was described

first in sharks by *Johnston* ('05).   This nucleus is situated far dorsally near the lateral corner of the aqueduct, from which it is separated by the root of the trochlear nerve and by the mesencephalic root of the trigeminal nerve.   It is a frontal continuation of the acoustico-lateral area of the medulla oblongata and receives

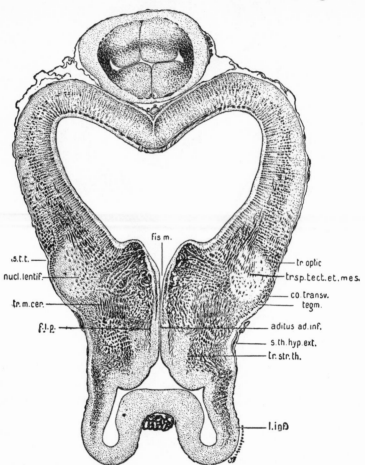

FIG. 435.   A cross section rostral to the plane of figure 433, in the place where the fissura media (*fis.m.*) passes over into the entrance to the infundibulum (*aditus ad infundibuli*).

   aditus ad.inf., aditus ad infundibuli; *co.transv.*, commissura postoptica (or transversa); *f.l.p.*, fasciculus longitudinalis medialis; *fis.m.*, fissura media; *l.inf.*, lobus inferior; *nucl.lentif.*, nucleus lentiformis; *s.th.hyp.ext.*, sulcus thalamo-hypothalamicus externus; *s.t.t.*, sulcus tecto-tegmentalis; *tegm.*, tegmentum; *tr.m.cer.*, tractus mesencephalo-cerebellaris; *tr.optic.*, tractus opticus; *tr.sp.tect.et mes.*, tractus spino-tectalis et mesencephalicus; *tr.str.th.*, tractus strio-thalamicus.

fibers of the fasciculus longitudinalis lateralis (the acoustico-lateral lemniscus of certain observers).   Frontally it is connected with the tectum and the tegmentum, thus serving as a correlation center for acoustico-lateral and optic impulses.

   Other nuclear groups within the mesencephalon receive secondary acoustico-lateral fibers (tr. bulbo-mesenc. (f. l. l.), fig. 431).   Among such is the nucleus profundus mesencephali. This nucleus — if so scattered a group of cells may be designated by this term — lies in the ventral part of the midbrain (fig. 431, n. prof. mes.). Processes of its cells extend dorsalward, indicating its relation to the other tegmental areas of the midbrain (fig. 433, nu. tegm.). Two cell groups — nucleus tegmentalis medialis and nucleus tegmentalis lateralis — lie farther frontalward. Of these, the medial receives the acoustico-lateral fibers. The tractus spino- et bulbo-mesencephalicus from the spinal trigeminal nucleus terminates in part in the lateral tegmental nucleus and in the region cephalic to it, the so-called nucleus lentiformis. In part it distributes to the tectum as spino- and bulbo-tectal fibers (tr. sp. tect., fig. 433). Thus quite evidently within the plagiostome brain there are two distinct areas in the tegmental part of the midbrain (and adjacent caudal portions of the diencephalon): a medial, somewhat more caudal area, receiving secondary tracts concerned with orientation in space and equilibrium, and a lateral and more frontal area, constituting the end station of the ascending sensory systems of the head and neck (*Wallenberg*, '07). The termination of these fibers so near the photostatic and gravistatic centers (as represented in the tectum) probably explains the intimate correlation of these impulses in movements of the animal.

The tractus spino- et bulbo-mesencephalicus (et tectalis) must not be confused with medial lemniscus fibers or with secondary trigeminal tracts from the chief sensory nucleus of higher forms which are concerned with epicritic sensibility. These plagiostome tracts carry vital or protopathic sensations. They carry pain, temperature, general tactile sensation, possibly some primitive muscle sense, which latter certainly is represented in the nucleus of the mesencephalic root of the trigeminal. These sensations, correlated with sensations of equilibrium brought over secondary acoustico-lateral paths, make the tectum and the adjacent tegmental areas correlation centers, concerned in bringing into relation such vital sensations with the directive sense of light (photostatic sense) carried by the optic tract. The midbrain, then, has an important part in regulating movements and posture.

The tegmentum, as well as the tectum, is connected with the cerebellum by a tractus mesencephalo-cerebellaris (fig. 435, tr. m. cer.). This tract arises in the frontomedian part of the tegmentum and in the tectum. In its course caudalward the tract runs between the lateral longitudinal bundle or acoustico-lateral lemniscus and the medial longitudinal fasciculus.

An important tegmental nucleus is the nucleus interpeduncularis which, though larger than its homologue in petromyzonts, retains approximately the same position at the base of the midbrain (fig. 430, G. interp.). It receives the tractus habenulo-peduncularis (fasciculus retroflexus of Meynert).

THE FINER STRUCTURE OF THE PLAGIOSTOME DIENCEPHALON

The consideration of the diencephalic centers may be begun by an account of the epithalamic centers. It will be remembered that the epiphysis is glandular in character in plagiostomes and has lost all characteristics of a pineal eye. Nevertheless, there is a difference in the size of the two habenulae of the

epithalamus in these animals as there was in cyclostomes, with this outstanding difference, that the left habenular nuclear mass is larger in the former and
the right in the latter animals (compare figures 427B and 436). The habenular
nuclei are connected with the olfactory areas of the forebrain by way of a series
of secondary tracts. The tractus cortico-habenularis lateralis emerges from the
ventrolateral segment of the telencephalon, while the tractus olfacto-habenularis
medialis arises from the parolfactory or septal areas (*Johnston's* nucleus olfacto-

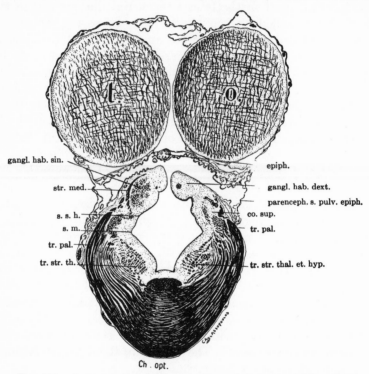

FIG. 436.   A cross section through the diencephalon of Acanthias vulgaris.
co.sup., commissura superior telencephali; *epiph.*, epiphysis; *gangl.hab.*
dext., right habenular nucleus; *gangl.hab.sin.*, left habenular nucleus;
parenceph.s.pulv.epiph., parencephalon or pulvinar epiphyseos; *s.m.*, sulcus
medius thalami (note the extent of the dorsal thalamus between *s.m.* and
s.s.h.); *s.s.h.*, sulcus subhabenularis; *tr.pal.*, tractus pallii; *tr.str.th.*, tractus
strio-thalamicus; *tr.str.thal.et hyp.*, tractus strio-thalamicus et hypothalamicus.

rius medialis), supplemented by bundles from the region of the preoptic recess
(tractus olfacto-habenularis medialis posterior, *Johnston*, '11).   Other fibers
originate from the forebrain mantle, the primordium hippocampi of American
authors.   These are usually termed the tractus cortico-habenularis although it
might be preferable to call them the tractus olfacto-habenularis dorsalis since
they are the homologue of the tract of that name in Petromyzon, rather than
of the cortico-habenular tract of higher animals.   *Johnston* traced fibers from
the thalamus to the habenula — a tractus thalamo-habenularis.   Most of the
fibers — and particularly those of olfacto-habenular components — end in the
left habenular nuclear mass.   This implies that fibers from the right side of the

forebrain cross to a great extent before their termination.   This crossing occurs
in the commissura habenularum or commissura superior, which, as in petromyzonts, contains both decussating and commissural fibers.   The true commissural
fibers arise in the caudal portion of the telencephalic mantle on one side and
terminate in the corresponding area on the other side.   These commissural fibers
constitute what usually is termed the commissura superior telencephali.   This is
unmyelinated; the other fibers entering the habenular commissure are myelinated.   It is striking that the decussating myelinated fibers always surround the
unmyelinated fibers of the commissura superior telencephali (fig. 437), thus forming
a thin sheath of medullated
fibers around a thick bundle
of naked neuraxes.   This
relation is often found where
myelinated fibers join unmyelinated fibers; thus it has
been found in the habenulo-
peduncular   tract   (*Ariëns
Kappers*) and in the toro-tec-
tal fibers of teleosts (*Kudo*),
which are surrounded by the
medullated   fibers   of   the
lamina commissuralis tecti.
The position of the myelinated bundles at the pe-
riphery of the unmyelinated
tracts probably is attributable to the same causes that
produce myelinated fibers
(Chapter I, Neurobiotaxis).
The   commissura   superior

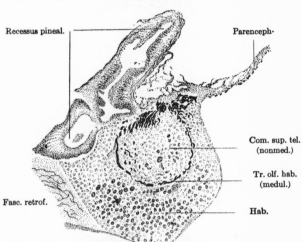

Fig. 437.   A sagittal section through the habenular nuclei of
Scyllium canicula to demonstrate the unmedullated commissura
superior telencephali.
Com.sup.tel., commissura superior telencephali (unmedullated);
Fasc.retrof., fasciculus retroflexus; *Hab.*, habenula; *Parenceph.*,
parencephalon; *Recessus pineal.*, recessus pinealis; *Tr.olf.hab.*,
tractus olfacto-habenularis.

telencephali is the commissura pallii posterior of certain authors.   The homologizing of this commissure with the commissura pallii posterior of reptiles
apparently is incorrect, since this latter commissure derives its fibers from the
archipallium.   Moreover, a true commissura superior telencephali, arising and
ending in the secondary olfactory areas, is present in some reptiles.   The circuitous
course taken by this commissure is somewhat surprising.   Instead of crossing in
the telencephalon it follows the olfacto-habenular tract through the stria medullaris to the habenula, and, after crossing, reaches the opposite side by a similar
route.   Its course may be due to the neurobiotactic influence of the stimula-
tively related olfacto-habenular tract.
     The chief efferent system of the habenula, the habenulo-peduncular tract,
or fasciculus retroflexus of Meynert, is larger and contains more myelinated
fibers on the left than on the right side, corresponding to the difference in size
of the two habenulae (figs. 438, 439, and 440).   It passes ventrocaudalward
through the diencephalon, occupying, during this course, a position close to

the ventricular wall. The tract terminates after decussation in the nucleus interpeduncularis. From there the impulses are transmitted to the visceral motor nuclei of the medulla oblongata. From the subhabenular, rather than the habenular, region arises a fiber bundle, the tractus habenulo-thalamicus. The components of this tract partly surround those of the tractus habenulo-pedun-

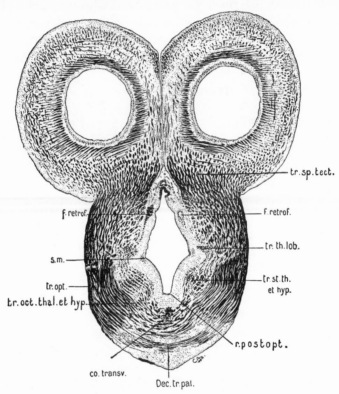

Fig. 438. A cross section through the posthabenular diencephalic region of Acanthias vulgaris. Note the unmedullated appearance of the right fasciculus retroflexus.

co.transv., commissura transversa (commissura postoptica or supra-optica dorsalis); *Dec.tr.pal.*, decussatio tractus pallii; *f.retrof.*, fasciculus retroflexus; *r.postopt.*, recessus postopticus; *s.m.*, sulcus medius; *tr.oct.thal.et hyp.*, tractus octavo-thalamicus et hypothalamicus; *tr.opt.*, tractus opticus; *tr.sp.tect.*, tractus spino-tectalis; *tr.st.th.et hyp.*, tractus strio-thalamicus et hypothalamicus; *tr.th.lob.*, tractus thalamo-lobaris.

cularis. The termination of the tractus habenulo-thalamicus has not as yet been determined.

The dorsal part of the thalamus is still very small; much smaller than the part immediately beneath, the ventral thalamus. These relations are indicated particularly in figure 429, but also in figures 436 and 438. The relative size of the two areas is in harmony with the fact that the dorsal thalamus sends relatively few fibers to the telencephalon as compared with the number of such fibers in higher forms. *Johnston* ('11) believed that he could follow fibers from the lateral geniculate nucleus, and possibly from pretectal and tectal areas, to the somatic area (pars striatalis of the hemisphere). A connection forward from the latter two areas is highly improbable and that postulated from the lateral geniculate nucleus at least requires further proof. He also found ascending fibers from other parts of the dorsal thalamus. Following *Johnston, Herrick* ('22) diagrammed connections from the lateral geniculate and dorsal thalamus to the striatal region. Collaterals, but probably not stem fibers, of the optic tract reach a differentiated portion which is to be regarded as a primitive lateral geniculate nucleus. The tractus spino- et bulbo-mesencephalicus from the spinal nucleus of the trigeminal reaches a differentiated posterior part of the dorsal thalamus which has been termed the lenticular nucleus. The majority of these ascending systems end, however, in the tectal and subtectal regions in plagiostomes.

The ventral thalamus and hypothalamus receive the greater number of telencephalon fibers passing to diencephalic areas, with the exception of those described for epithalamic centers. Many of these bundles run in the tractus strio-thalamicus et hypothalamicus (figs. 429, 436, 438 to 440), which consists of a large uncrossed portion and a smaller crossed portion, decussating in the commissura anterior. The majority of the fibers originate in the ventrolateral part of the telencephalon (Chapter IX), but a part of them arise from septal regions. Medium-sized cells in the ventral thalamic and hypothalamic areas mark the terminations of fibers of this bundle, but are not organized into clearly distinct nuclei. These cells comprise the nucleus strati grisei described by *Houser* ('01, p. 139) as forming a broad zone (about "one-fourth the thickness of the entire thalamus.") The neurons constituting this nuclear group were described as polygonal in outline with an eccentric, lightly stained nucleus and with dendrites radiating out in all directions from the cell body, while the terminal fascicles of the strio-thalamic tract were seen to enter the nucleus in bundles which later broke up in synaptic relation with the cells. The neurons of the nucleus strati grisei (according to *Houser*) send their neuraxes into the thalamo-tectal tract. The term nucleus diffusus is applied to the more caudal of certain nuclear groups which lie chiefly along the lateral wall of the lobi inferiores but extend upward into the ventral thalamus itself. Farther frontally a special group of such neurons receives the name of nucleus interpeduncularis. Other fiber connections with the forebrain areas are provided for by the tractus pallii, which carries ascending and descending fibers, partly homolateral and partly contralateral, between the primordium hippocampi, and the hypothalamic areas. A tractus medianus also connects the hypothalamus with the telencephalon; according to certain observers, with the area superficialis basalis (*Ariëns Kappers*, '21, earlier edition of present text); according to others, with the primordium hippocampi. In his 1911 paper, *Johnston* regarded this path as the homologue of the fornix of higher animals. This tract is discussed further on page 1265. Afferent connections with caudal areas are provided through fibers of the spino- et octavo-hypothalamic systems.

The efferent tracts of the plagiostome, as of the cyclostome diencephalon, arise chiefly in the lobus inferior and the recessus posterior (or mamillaris), forming the tractus lobo-bulbaris and the tractus mamillo-peduncularis. These tracts can be traced to the most caudal regions of the medulla oblongata where they probably come into relation with the visceral efferent nuclei of the region, particularly those of the trigeminal and facial nerves. A tractus lobo-cerebellaris passes directly from the hypothalamus to the cerebellum.

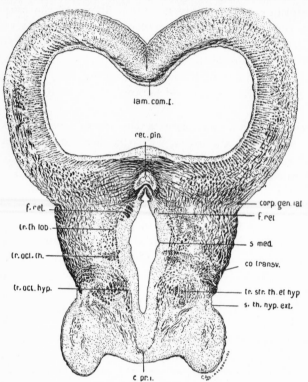

FIG. 439.   A cross section caudal to that of figure 425.

c.pr.i., commissura preinfundibularis; *co.transv.*, commissura transversa (commissura postoptica or supraoptica dorsalis); *corp. gen.lat.*, corpus geniculatum laterale; *f.ret.*, fasciculus retroflexus; *lam.com.t.*, lamina commissurae tecti; *rec.pin.*, recessus pinealis; *s.med.*, sulcus medius thalami; *s.th.hyp.ext.*, sulcus thalamo-hypothalamicus externus; *tr.oct.hyp.*, tractus octavo-hypothalamicus; *tr.oct.th.*, tractus octavo-thalamicus; *tr.str.th.et hyp.*, tractus strio-thalamicus et hypothalamicus; *tr.th.lob.*, tractus thalamo-lobaris.

Fibers from the diencephalon to the telencephalon originate largely in the ventral part of the diencephalic region, near the juncture of the hypothalamus and the base of the midbrain. The ascending character of this bundle, which constitutes the tractus pallii, has been demonstrated by *Wallenberg* ('07). The bundle keeps constantly to the lateral side in the region where the lobi inferiores join the ventral thalamus. Running forward in this position, it decussates directly behind the level of the optic chiasm (fig. 438, Dec. tr. pal.), then passes through the dorsal ridge of the forebrain peduncle immediately ventral to the stria medullaris and distributes to the caudal part of the forebrain mantle. It yet remains to be proved that this tract, as has been thought, carries gustatory sensibility to the forebrain.

Other ascending fibers, probably similar to those to be described for teleosts, appear to connect the hypothalamic and septal areas.

A number of commissures cross in the lower part of the diencephalon. Of these the commissura postoptica, sometimes termed the commissura transversa (co. transv., figs. 438–440), which crosses immediately behind the optic chiasma (fig. 438), is the largest. This commissure passes along the lateral surface of the diencephalon to tectal and tegmental centers with which it is functionally related (p. 890). Two other commissures — commissura preinfundibularis and commissura postinfundibularis — belong to the hypothalamus proper. The commissura preinfundibularis (fig. 439, c. pr. i.) consists of medullated, dorsally running fibers, the origin and termination of which are not sufficiently known as yet. It is possible that this commissure carries those fibers of the tractus octavo- et cerebello-hypothalamicus which cross at a frontal level. The commissura postinfundibularis appears to be more nearly a true

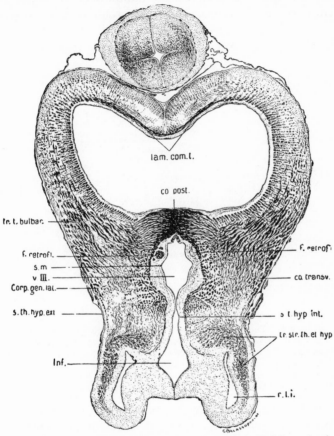

Fig. 440. A cross section through the brain of Acanthias vulgaris, at the level of the commissura posterior (co.post.).

co.post., commissura posterior; co.trans., commissura transversa (commissura postoptica or supraoptica dorsalis); corp.ger.lat., corpus geniculatum laterale; f.retrofl., fasciculus retroflexus; inf. infundibulum; lam.com.t., lamina commissuralis tecti; r.l.i., recessus lateralis inferior; s.m., sulcus medius thalami; s.t.hyp.ext., sulcus thalamico-hypothalamicus externus; s.th.hyp.int., sulcus thalamico-hypothalamicus internus; tr.str.th.et hyp., tractus strio-thalamicus et hypothalamicus.

commissure. It lies in the anterior part of the tuberculum posterius and connects the gray centers of the caudal part of the inferior lobe (fig. 434, co. post. inf.).

Somewhat caudal and ventral to the level of these commissures there is a smaller, unmedullated fiber decussation which is approximately at the level of the nuclei of the tractus sacci vasculosi (Ariëns Kappers). This decussation, which is termed the decussatio postinfundibularis inferior, is to be differentiated from the commissura postinfundibularis (*Dammerman*, '10) since it does not carry commissural fibers but merely crossed fibers of the tractus sacci vasculosi, an apparently well-developed unmedullated tract formed of the processes of cells of the saccus vasculosus (fig. 2). The wall of the saccus vasculosus consists of cubic or cylindric cells which have sense hairs with knob-shaped terminations turned toward the lumen of the sac. Between these cells are smaller, secretory elements. The neuraxes of these neurosensory cells run in the wall of the sac, forming an evident fiber layer. Frontalward they form a fascicle of fibers.

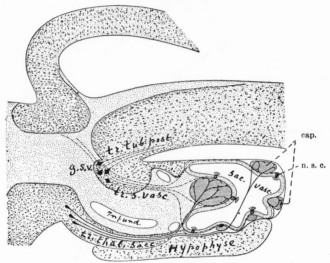

FIG. 441. The connections of the saccus vasculosus in the shark. A schematic representation by *Dammerman* (compare also figure 429). *cap.*, capillaries; *g.s.v.*, nucleus sacci vasculosi; *hypophyse*, hypophysis; *infund.*, infundibulum; *n.s.c.*, neurosensory cells; *sac.vasc.*, saccus vasculosus; *tr.s.vasc.*, tractus sacci vasculosi; *tr.thal.sacc.*, tractus thalamo-saccularis; *tr.tub.post.*, tractus tubero-posterius.

In the region where the wall of the sac passes over into that of the posterior recess this fiber fascicle enters the gray substance of the tuberculum posterius as a well-circumscribed little bundle which ascends to the level of the decussatio postinfundibularis inferior. After decussating, the majority of the fibers terminate around the polygonal cells of the nucleus sacci vasculosi. According to *Dammerman* ('10), some of these fibers run past this nucleus and, strengthened by processes from the cells of the nucleus, continue their course frontalward and dorsalward toward the central gray of the dorsal thalamus. Such bundles form the tractus sacco-thalamicus. From the nucleus sacci vasculosi arises another fiber system, the tractus tubero-posterior, an independent tract which passes caudalward from the nucleus sacci vasculosi through the tuberculum posterius. The termination of this tract is at present unknown (fig. 441).

The blood vessels of the saccus, to the great number of which that structure owes its name, possess an afferent tract — the tractus thalamo-saccularis. This originates in the frontal part of the dorsal thalamus (the so-called nucleus anterior thalami), passes caudalward along the ventricle near the sulcus medius, and then turns downward to terminate in the caudal part of the lobi inferiores. The tract may contain some ascending fibers but consists chiefly of descending fibers (*Wallenberg*, '07). Consequently it is not to be regarded as the homologue of the mammillo-thalamic tract of mammals. However, it is possible that the mammalian tract is influenced in its development by the presence of the more primitive thalamo-lobar bundle. In more caudal regions the upper part of the thalamus is connected with the lobi inferiores by fibers as is the case in teleosts. In plagiostomes these are not organized into distinct bundles.

As yet no experiments have made clear the specific functions of the saccus vasculosus. However, the fact that the sense-hairs of its neurosensory epithelium protrude into the ventricular cavity of the saccus suggests that it is concerned with perceptions related to the ventricular fluid (as *Johnston* suggested in 1906). Such an explanation is in accord with the presence of a rich blood supply and an innervation of the vessels effected by the thalamo-saccular tract (see *Dammerman's* account, page 902). The fact that this organ occurs in Amphioxus and in fishes (with the exception of cyclostomes) suggests that its function is associated with the water life of these animals, probably related to the estimation of varying conditions of pressure (*Ariëns Kappers*, '21).

THE MESENCEPHALON AND DIENCEPHALON OF GANOIDS AND TELEOSTS

The structure of the mesencephalon and diencephalon of ganoids and teleosts differs greatly from that of the corresponding areas in plagiostomes. Moreover, there are wide differences in pattern among the various teleosts, while the variation among plagiostomes is relatively slight. Such differences are evident both in the external morphology and the internal structure. In the following account only brief mention can be made of the most outstanding features of the diencephalic and mesencephalic regions in ganoids and teleosts. For details the original papers must be consulted.

THE CYTOLOGIC STRUCTURE AND STRATIFICATION OF THE OPTIC TECTUM

The usual divisions of the mesencephalon, the tectum and the tegmentum, are present in ganoids and teleosts. Important differences are to be found in the optic tecta of various animals. In all teleosts it is a completely nervous structure frontally. In animals having a small valvula (for example, in Monopterus and Lophius) the whole roof is formed of nervous tissue, but in forms such as Gadus, Arius (fig. 375), and particularly Mormyrus, the two halves of the tectum, especially caudally, are partly or entirely separated. The intermediate space is bridged over by an ependymal membrane, an inward fold of which is attached to the edge of the valvula (fig. 370, Megalops cyprinoides). Blind fishes are said to have relatively small optic tecta (Trypauchen, *Franz*, '12), the histologic differences manifesting themselves in a reduced number of cells in layers receiving optic tract fibers in other fishes.

The cytoarchitecture of the tectal region in teleosts shows a considerable advance over that in plagiostomes. Among the observers who have studied the cytoarchitecture of the tectal centers of the teleosts, particular mention may be made of *Fusari* ('87), *P. Ramón* ('90 and '99), *Mirto* ('95), *van Gehuchten* ('94), *Neumayer* ('95), *Catois* ('01), and *Ramón y Cajal* ('11).   By these observers the tectum has been divided into various layers, for example, *Stieda* recognized five layers, *van Gehuchten* described six, and *Fusari* and *Neumayer* identified seven. *Ramón y Cajal* (following *Ramón*) mentioned ten zones or strata beginning with the ventricular surface and counting toward the outer surface of the tectum.   The grouping used in the following account has been chosen because it fits into the description of the tectal layers as seen in other vertebrates (*Huber* and *Crosby*, '34) and because it is based on a functional interpretation of the layers.   The

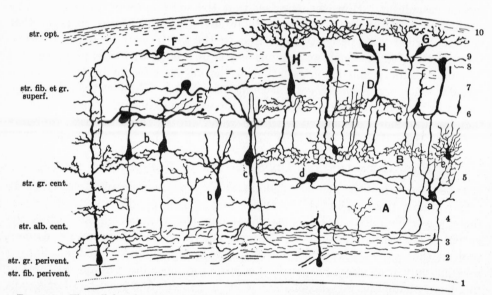

Fig. 442.   The cellular elements of the optic tectum of Barbus fluviatilis.   *Ramón* and *Ramón y Cajal*.   The numbers 1–10 are the layers according to the numbering of Ramón and Ramón y Cajal. *str.alb.cent.*, stratum album centrale; *str.fib.et gr.superf.*, stratum fibrosum et griseum superficiale; *str. fib.perivent.*, stratum fibrosum periventriculare (with adjoining gray); *str.gr.cent.*, stratum griseum centrale; *str.gr.perivent.*, stratum griseum periventriculare; *str.opt.*, stratum opticum.

references in parentheses refer to the numbers used by *Pedro Ramón* and by *Ramón y Cajal*.   Reference is made here to figure 442.

1. A stratum opticum (zone 10 of *Ramón* and *Ramón y Cajal*). This carries optic tract fibers as they pass close to the superficial surface of the tectum. The individual fibers in part turn away from the stratum opticum and enter the next stratum where they break up in relation with the dendrites of more deeply situated neurons.

2. A stratum fibrosum et griseum superficiale (zones 9 to approximately 6 of *Ramón* and *Ramón y Cajal;* the latter zone is divided, functionally considered, into two parts, see stratum 3 of this terminology).   This second zone is made up of alternate layers of fibers and of cells.   The fibrous layers represent in part positions of afferent tracts, in part regions of synapse.   This zone, which receives terminal fibers of the optic stratum, constitutes a main receptive layer of

the tectum. Here enter the spino-tectal and bulbo-tectal (or mesencephalic) tracts and, in part at least, the brachium tecti (the thalamo-tectal portion of it).

3. A stratum griseum centrale (zones 5 and 4 of *Ramón* and *Ramón y Cajal*). This layer contains the cells of origin for the larger efferent tracts of the tectum. In teleosts, such as the carp, it may be divided into four secondary strata, of which the deepest is a gray band, zone 4 of *Ramón* and *Ramón y Cajal*, while the other substrata are the deep, median, and superficial parts of zone 5 of these authors; toward the periphery, zone 5 is not definitely delimited. Characteristic of zone 5 is its median layer, which is composed of the terminal branchings of the dendrites and neuraxes of more superficially placed cells which here come into relation with axon processes or their collaterals arising from the more deeply situated cells. Both superficial and deep to this layer lie the large cells which give rise to efferent fiber tracts, although the majority of such cells lie deep to the layer of synapsis. It would appear that layer 5 as described by *Ramón* and *Ramón y Cajal* is divisible into an upper portion, largely receptive and correlative, and a deeper portion, the cells of which are distinctly efferent in character; facts which explain the apparent hesitancy in delimiting stratum 2 of this account, since, when functionally considered, a part of zone 5 of *Ramón* and *Ramón y Cajal* in reality belongs to zone 6 of these authors.

4. A stratum album centrale (zone 3 of *Ramón* and *Ramón y Cajal*). This is made up of efferent fibers from the tectum, including tecto- or mesencephalo-cerebellar, tecto-oculomotor, tecto-bulbar, and probably tecto-thalamic paths. Here also course fasciculi of the lamina commissuralis tecti, which provide a commissural connection between the two halves of the optic tectum, decussating efferent paths, and fibers terminating in the contralateral torus longitudinalis (*Kudo*, '23).

5. A stratum griseum periventriculare (zone 2, *Ramón* and *Ramón y Cajal*). This layer consists of cells which receive fibers of the periventricular system and in part send their dendrites out into the stratum fibrosum et griseum superficiale to come into synaptic relation with incoming paths. Their neuraxes enter the stratum album centrale, so that they constitute efferent neurons.

6. A stratum fibrosum periventriculare. This was not recognized as a separate zone by *Ramón* and *Ramón y Cajal*. It appears to be absent in certain teleosts and indistinct in others. Where represented at all it carries periventricular fibers.

The zone 1 of *Ramón* and *Ramón y Cajal* is the ventricular ependyma which is not regarded here as a tectal layer. It is well developed in teleosts, sending its fuzzy processes out toward the periphery as in other vertebrates.

In most ganoids (with the exception of Acipenser, *Kudo*, '23) and in teleosts the medial part of the tectal gray extends into the ventricle as a paired torus longitudinalis (figs. 447 and 448 and 455 to 458). In various teleosts, but not in Esox (*Kudo*, '23), this torus is thicker at the rostral end where it joins the commissura posterior (fig. 456).[2] In its structure and relations the torus longi-

---

[2] This region is termed the eminentia thalami by *Holmgren* ('20). It must be distinguished from the eminentia ventralis thalami of *Herrick* ('10, see page 963).

tudinalis shows an interesting resemblance to the granular ingrowths of the cerebellum found in plagiostomes. It consists, as does the cerebellar structure, of granule cells which form bilateral eminences in the ventricle; the neuraxes of these enter the superficial fiber layers of the tectum, just as the granule cells in the cerebellum send their neuraxes to the molecular layer (*Kudo*, '23a). Moreover, the torus longitudinalis, like the eminentia granularis of the cerebellum, arises through the development of granule cells in relation with more specialized layers. Among other connections this mesencephalic structure receives cerebello-toral fibers. The volume of the torus longitudinalis is not always parallel to that of the tectum (as for example in Orthagoriscus, Balistes, or Trachinus). It is strongly developed in Reniceps and is very small in blind fishes (Trypauchen and Amblyopsis spelaeus, *Franz*, 12). In such animals as Arius, where the two halves of the tectum are drawn apart, the torus longitudinalis is divided into two portions (fig. 375).

THE FIBER CONNECTIONS OF THE OPTIC TECTUM INCLUDING THE OPTIC TRACT AND TECTO-BULBAR CONNECTIONS

A consideration of the fiber connections of the teleostean tectum may well begin with a description of the optic nerve. In blind fishes, such as Amblyopsis

FIG. 443. Size relations between the eye and the tectum of Cyclopterus lumpus.

Olfactory nerve
Forebrain
Optic tectum

spelaeus and Trypauchen, the optic nerves have rarely if ever been traced from the eye to the brain (*Ramsay*, '01; *Eigenmann*, '04; *Franz*, '12; *Charlton*, '33); in others, such as Siluris glanis, these nerves are small; in still others, as for example Cyclopterus and Leuciscus (figs. 443, 444), the eyes and the optic nerves are very large. In the flat fishes the optic nerve has a peculiar tape-like form which, according to *Gegenbauer*, is also found in the herring and in scomberoids.

The crossing of the optic nerve, which is always a total decussation in fishes, takes place in different ways and at different levels. In most teleosts there is no intermingling of the fibers, the bundles from the right eye passing entirely underneath those from the left eye. In the herring one optic nerve passes through a hole in the other nerve. The decussation does not always occur in the ventral part of the diencephalon, but may be found far forward, sometimes even in front of the forebrain (Gadus morrhua, Orthagoriscus). Such forms furnish favorable material for a study of the supraoptic commissural systems.

The following account of the optic tract is based on the relations in the brain of the cod where its course and connections are very clear. The absence of the left eye in an available series and the consequent atrophy of the right optic tract (figs. 449 to 451) made it much easier to distinguish the optic fibers (*Ariëns Kappers*). In the cod, soon after its decussation under the forebrain, the optic tract (figs. 549 to 553) gives off a small bundle which enters the dorsofrontal portion of the diencephalon. This is the fasciculus medialis nervi optici which has been described by a number of observers, including *Bellonci* ('88), *Ariëns Kappers* ('06), *Franz* ('12), and *Jansen* ('29). By these observers this tract is regarded as terminating in the optic tectum. In its course it accompanies the commissura minor of *C. L.*

Herrick ('91), and probably is to be regarded as an aberrant bundle of the optic tract. According to *Ariëns Kappers* ('21, p. 1293, and also footnote, p. 815), *Lubsen* was unable to trace it to the optic tectum and believed that it may terminate in the region immediately caudal to the nucleus anterior thalami of the fish. *Jansen's* study of the cod material mentioned above (where the specimen was blind in one eye) appears to confirm the tectal connection of this fasciculus medialis nervi optici. The main or marginal optic tract runs dorsocaudalward along the external wall of the diencephalon (possibly giving off

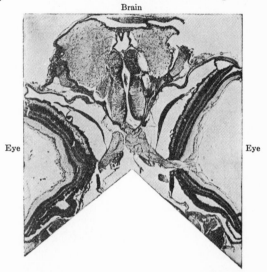

Brain

Eye   Eye

FIG. 444. The course of the optic nerve fibers from the retina to the optic chiasma in Leuciscus rutilus. *van der Horst.*

during the early part of its course some fibers to the ventral thalamus, *Lubsen, Ariëns Kappers*, '21, page 1293). As it reaches the level of the lateral geniculate nucleus it gives off fibers (or possibly collaterals, since *Bellonci*, '88, was of the opinion that only collaterals of optic fibers reach thalamic areas in fishes) to the lateral geniculate nucleus (fig. 451B). The structure and size of this nucleus vary in the different teleosts (*Franz*, '12, also fig. 454). The optic fibers which supply this nucleus were believed by *Zeeman* and *Lubsen* (*Ariëns Kappers*, '21, page 1292) to originate in the posterior quadrants of the retina. Compared to the tectal ending of the optic nerves, the connection to the lateral geniculate nucleus is very small. Before entering the tectum the marginal optic tract divides into two parts. The medial optic tract (tr. opt. med., fig. 451 on the left) runs caudalward along the dorsomedial edge of the tectum while the tractus opticus lateralis or ventralis (fig. 451 on the left) passes along the ventrolateral edge of this area. Both divisions of this tract either enter the outer part of the tectum, the stratum opticum, from which fibers turn into the stratum fibrosum et griseum superficiale, or certain of the fibers swing directly into this superficial receptive layer. This marginal optic tract has been recognized by most students of the region, among whom may be mentioned *Bellonci* ('88), *Krause* ('98), *Franz* ('12), *Wallenberg* ('13), *Jansen* ('29), and *Meader* ('34).

By a separate extirpation of retinal quadrants *Lubsen* and *Zeeman* [3] demonstrated that the ending of the optic nerve within the tectum occurs in such a manner that the frontal part of the retina is projected upon the caudal part of the contralateral tectum and the caudal part of the retina upon the frontal part of the contralateral tectum. Moreover, the ventral part of the retina is projected upon the dorsal part and the dorsal part of the retina upon the ventral part of the contralateral tectum.

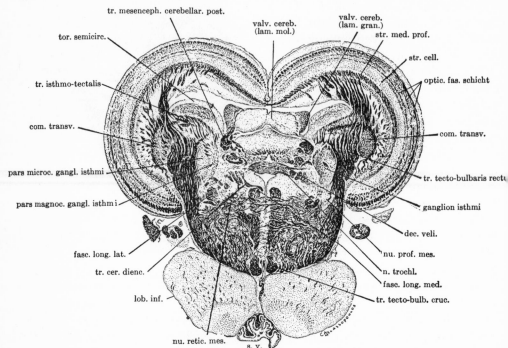

FIG. 445.   A cross section through the more caudal part of the midbrain of Perca fluviatilis.
com.trans., commissura transversa; *dec.veli*, decussatio veli; *fasc.long.lat.*, fasciculus longitudinalis lateralis; *fasc.long.med.*, fasciculus longitudinalis medialis; *lob.inf.*, inferior lobe; *n.trochl.*, nervus trochlearis; *nu.prof.mes.*, nucleus profundus mesencephali; *nu.retic.mes.*, nucleus reticularis mesencephali; *pars magnoc. gangl. isthmi*, pars magnocellularis of the nucleus isthmi; *pars microc.gangl.isthmi*, pars microcellularis of the nucleus isthmi; *str.alb.cent.*, stratum album centrale; *str.fib.et gris.cent.*, stratum fibrosum et griseum centrale; *str.opt.*, stratum opticum; *tor.semicirc.*, torus semicircularis; *tr.cer.dienc.*, tractus cerebello-diencephalicus; *tr.isthmo-tectalis*, tractus isthmo-tectalis; *tr.mesenceph.-cerebellar.post.*, tractus mesencephalo-cerebellaris posterior; *tr.tecto-bulb.cruc.*, tractus tecto-bulbaris cruciatus; tractus tecto-bulbaris rectus.

Still other bundles have been regarded as parts of the optic tract system of teleosts. Among these may be mentioned the fasciculus dorsomedialis of *Jansen* ('29), the tractus recesso-opticus, the tractus preoptico-opticus posterior and the tractus olfactorius lateralis optici of *Holmgren* ('20), the fibrae tectales n. optici of *Bellonci* ('88) and *Krause* ('98), and the tractus isthmo-opticus of *Franz* ('12).   Later work has not in all cases confirmed the relation of the fiber bundles to the optic tract system.   These tracts will be considered briefly.

[3] Over de projectie van het netvlies op het tectum opticum bij een beenvisch.   Nederl. Tijds. v. Geneesk., v. 2, p. 1258 (reviewed by *Ariëns Kappers*, '21, pp. 1292, 1293).

The fasciculus dorsomedialis of *Jansen* ('29) in all probability is the fasciculus of the optic tract traced in the goldfish by *Wallenberg* ('13) to a nucleus lateral to the nucleus fasciculi longitudinalis dorsalis.   *Jansen* traced his fasciculus dorsomedialis to the tegmentum of the midbrain, but his material was unfavorable for the determination of its precise ending.   *Meader* ('34) likewise was unable to trace it with certainty to its ending.

The tractus olfactorius lateralis optici was described by *Holmgren* ('20) in Osmerus as composed of fibers which pass from the olfactory bulb caudally in the lateral olfactory tract and enter the optic nerve, passing peripheralward in this nerve.   Fibers from the medial olfactory tract into the optic nerve have been described in Callionymus by *Holmgren* ('20) and *Kudo* ('23) and in several other teleosts by the latter observer, who used for these fibers the name of tractus olfactorio-opticus.   *Kudo* appears to have been uncertain with regard to the ultimate termination of these fibers, that is, as to whether they actually accompanied the nerve and passed peripheralward or whether they left it to pursue a course caudalward.

The tractus recesso-opticus and tractus preoptico-opticus posterior (*Holmgren*, '20), the latter of which tracts is the homologue of the tractus preoptico-opticus of *Jansen*, represent a bundle from the preoptic nucleus to the optic nerve.   At least in part these tracts represent afferent fibers to the retina according to *Holmgren* and *Jansen*.   *Charlton* ('33) believed that the remnant of the optic tract left in Typhlichthys and Troglichthys represents this tract.   *Meader* ('34) could not find them in Holocentrus.

No basal optic root such as is present in the amphibians, reptiles, birds, and mammals has been demonstrated in ganoids and teleosts.   Various suggestions have been made regarding the homology of certain fascicles with the basal root but none of the tracts suggested have as yet been shown to have the necessary relations.

The fibrae tectalis of the optic nerve were described, though not so named, by *Bellonci* ('88) as a little fascicle of optic tract fibers accompanying the tractus opticus dorsalis into the tectum and appear to have been regarded by him as afferent with respect to that center.   *Krause* ('98) identified them, but from experimental material prepared by both Marchi and Weigert methods reached the conclusion that the direction of conduction was tecto-optic.   *Jansen* ('29) suggested that the fibers in question are components of the postoptic system and *Meader* ('34) interpreted them as a ventral intertectal commissure.

The tractus isthmo-opticus of *Franz* ('12), which has been of much interest to observers, is strongly suspected of being not isthmo-optic but isthmo-tectal and possibly pretectal instead.   *Franz* believed that this path might afford an efferent path from the tectum to the retina, but *Kudo* ('23) found that fibers extending forward from the nucleus isthmi entered the tectum, and in certain fishes the pretectal nucleus, affording isthmo-tectal or possibly tecto-isthmal connections.   These were not present in blind fishes, a nucleus isthmi also being lacking (*Charlton*, '33).   A tractus isthmo-tectalis (figs. 445 and 446) was found by *Ariëns Kappers* ('21).

Both optic roots are accompanied by fibers which connect the nucleus geniculatus lateralis and the optic tectum through fascicles constituting the brachium tecti. In the material studied such fibers stand out clearly as a distinct black bundle against a background of atrophied optic fibers. The brachium divides into two parts, a smaller dorsal and a larger lateral part, which accompany the

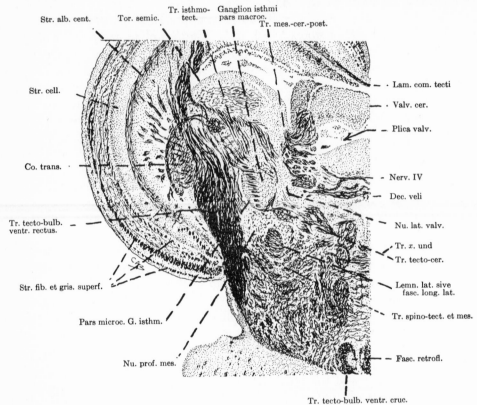

FIG. 446. A drawing of a midbrain level several sections in front of the plane of figure 429. Perca fluviatilis.

Co.trans., commissura transversa; *Dec.veli*, decussatio veli; *Fasc.long.lat.*, fasciculus longitudinalis lateralis; *Fasc.retrofl.*, fasciculus retroflexus; *Lam.com.tecti*, lamina commissuralis tecti; *Lem.lat.*, acoustico-lateral lemnisci; *Nerv.IV*, nervus trochlearis; *Nu.lat.valv.*, nucleus lateralis valvulae; *Nu. prof.mes.*, nucleus profundus mesencephali; *Ganglion isthmi pars macroc.*, pars macrocellularis of the nucleus isthmi; *Pars microc.g.isthmi*, pars microcellularis of the nucleus isthmi; *Plica valv.*, plica valvulae; *Str.alb.cent.*, stratum album centrale; *Str.fib.et gris.superf.*, stratum fibrosum et griseum superficiale; *Tor.semic.*, Torus semicircularis; *Tr.isthmo-tect.*, tractus isthmo-tectalis; *Tr.mes.cer. post.*, tractus mesencephalo-cerebellaris posterior; *Tr.tecto-bulb.vent.rectus*, tractus tecto-bulbaris ventralis rectus; *Tr.tecto-cer.*, tractus tecto-cerebellaris; *Tr.x*, tractus x; *Valv.cer.*, valvulae cerebelli.

corresponding optic tract divisions. The fibers of the brachium tecti are visible even in the most caudal part of the tectum (fig. 457, on the right). They usually lie somewhat deeper than the optic tract fibers, entering the stratum fibrosum et griseum superficiale, although some to the superficial tectal regions have been described by *Franz* ('12) and *Radl* ('15). A brachium anterius tecti has been seen by *Kudo* ('23) and *Shanklin* ('35). The optic tectum receives fibers of the commissura minor (*Herrick*) which ends in its frontal part (fig. 450).

Connections from the pretectal nucleus and probably from the dorsal thalamic nuclei, other than the lateral geniculate nucleus, pass to the tectum. Such bundles may carry fibers which are efferent as well as afferent with respect to this conduction. From the brain stem and the upper part of the spinal cord the tectum receives impulses over bulbo-tectal and spino-tectal (and mesencephalic) fasciculi. The fasciculi so labeled in figures 457 and 458 (*Ariëns Kappers*, '21) are believed to be largely tecto-spinal, since they emerge from the efferent tectal layer, and are only in small part afferent to the tectum (*Huber* and *Crosby*; *Burr*, '28, and *Woodburne*, '35, bibliography, p. 1239). The bulbo-tectal fibers arise chiefly in the contralateral nucleus of the descending root of the trigeminal. Collaterals from the fasciculus longitudinalis lateralis and bundles, largely periventricular from the torus semicircularis, pass to the tectum. *Tuge* ('34; J. Comp. Neurol., vol. 60) described cerebello-tectal fibers.

The efferent and commissural systems of the teleost tectum are well developed. Prominent among such efferent paths is the tractus mesencephalo-cerebellaris anterior or tractus tecto-cerebellaris (figs. 446 to 448, 457, 458). The direction of conduction of this path was established by the experimental work of *Franz* ('12), who found that the path degenerated when the midbrain roof was destroyed. The path passes out of the stratum album centrale (deep medullary layer) of the rostral part of the tectum and curves backward, ventral to the tractus mesencephalo-cerebellaris posterior. In its course it appears to be joined by fibers which arise (or end) in the nucleus lateralis valvulae and ultimately enters the cerebellum. This tract is often termed the tecto-cerebellar tract, but the name should be qualified in some fashion, for this bundle is not the tecto-cerebellar tract of avian, reptilian, and mammalian forms, which leaves the tectum from its caudal end, is joined by fibers from the torus semicircularis, and passes to the cerebellum, in large part after a decussation in the cerebellar commissure. It has been shown that a second tecto-cerebellar system comparable to the avian and reptilian systems is present in teleosts (*Pearson* '33, Dissertation).

Major efferent tracts of the tectum are found in the tecto-bulbar system, which is divisible into a dorsal tecto-bulbar and a ventral tecto-bulbar (and tecto-spinal) tract. Both have their origin in the efferent cell layers (the stratum griseum centrale and probably the stratum griseum periventriculare) of the tectum and pass through the tectum and out of it in the stratum album centrale. The dorsal tecto-bulbar tract courses ventromedially around the periventricular gray to the region below the ventricle near the medial longitudinal fasciculus, where a part of the bundle decussates at a level just in front of the dorsal oculomotor nucleus. Certain of the fibers (tecto-oculomotor fibers) end in the oculomotor gray. The greater number do not decussate, however, but accompanied by crossed fibers, run caudalward in company with the medial longitudinal fasciculus.

The ventral tecto-bulbar tract consists of a larger homolateral and a smaller contralateral portion. The homolateral part, the tractus tecto-bulbaris ventralis rectus (cf. fig. 446) arises, to some extent, from the most frontal segment of the tectum and, to a greater extent, from its caudal segment. It can be traced to the caudal end of the medulla oblongata (fig. 445, tr. tecto-bulbaris rectus,

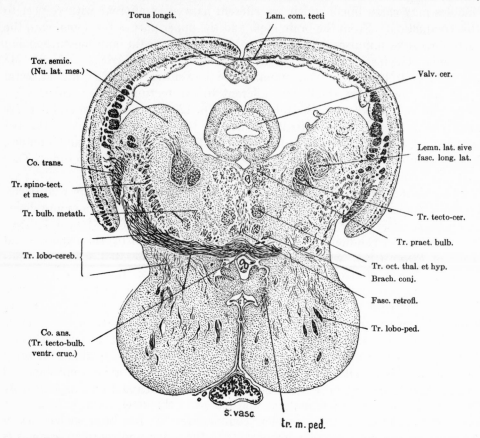

Fig. 447. A section through the commissura ansulata (*co.ans.*) and the tori semicirculares of the cod (Gadus morrhua).

Brach.conj., brachium conjunctivum; *Co.ans.*(*tr.tecto-bulb.ventr.cruc.*), commissura ansulata (tractus tecto-bulbaris ventralis cruciatus); *fasc.long.lat.*, fasciculus longitudinalis lateralis; *Fasc.retrofl.*, fasciculus retroflexus; *Lam.com.tecti*, lamina commissuralis tecti; *S.vasc.*, saccus vasculosus; *Torus.longit.*, torus longitudinalis; *Tor.semicirc.*(*Nu.lat.mes.*), torus semicircularis (nucleus lateralis mesencephali); *Tr.bulb.metath.*, tractus bulbo-metathalamicus; *Tr.lobo-cereb.*, tractus lobo-cerebellaris; *Tr.m.ped.*, tractus mamillo-peduncularis; *Tr.oct.thal.et hyp.*, tractus octavo-thalamicus et hypothalamicus; *Tr.praet.bulb.*, tractus pretecto-bulbaris; *Tr.spino-tect.et mes.*, tractus spino-tectalis et mesencephalicus; *Tr. tecto-cer.*, tractus tecto-cerebellaris or cerebello-mesencephalicus anterior; *Valv.cer.*, valvula cerebelli.

compare with this fig. 248, Tect. bulb. tract). Certain bundles which accompany it may run even farther caudalward, constituting a tecto-spinal tract (*Burr*, '28). The tractus tecto-bulbaris ventralis cruciatus originates from the central portion of the tectum and, after its decussation, divides into medial and lateral portions. The decussation takes place in the commissura ansulata of *Haller* ('98). This commissure lies in front of and beneath the ventral oculomotor nucleus to which the tract sends some fibers. The larger part of the tractus tecto-bulbaris ventralis cruciatus courses caudalward along the base of the medulla oblongata, but terminates in ventral reticular cells of the area before reaching the level of the glossopharyngeus. The relative size of the tracts appears to vary in different fishes. Thus in Orthagoriscus *Burr* ('28) was unable to identify with certainty a dorsal tecto-bulbar tract, but found a well-developed ventral tecto-bulbar system and a related tecto-spinal tract.

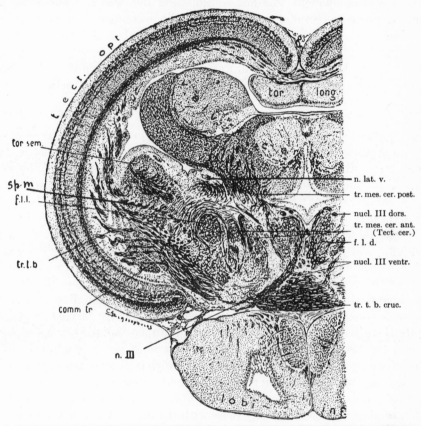

Fig. 448. The tractus mesencephalo-cerebellaris posterior and the tractus mesencephalo-cerebellaris anterior (sometimes known as tractus tecto-cerebellaris) described for Idus idus by van der Horst.

Comm.tr., commissura transversa; *f.l.l.*, fasciculus longitudinalis lateralis; *n.III*, nervus oculomotorius; *nucl.III dors.*, nucleus oculomotorius dorsalis; *nucl.III vent.*, nucleus oculomotorius ventralis; *tect.opt.*, tectum opticum; *tor.sem.*, torus semicircularis; *tr.mes.cer.ant.*, tractus mesencephalo-cerebellaris anterior; *tr.mes.cer.post.* tractus mesencephalo-cerebellaris posterior; *tr.t.b.*, tractus tecto-bulbaris; *tr.t.b.cruc.*, tractus tecto-bulbaris cruciatus.

From a neurobiotactic standpoint it is not surprising that the two halves of the tectum which receive so many simultaneous impulses should develop strong commissural connections, as do many bilateral sensory correlation centers. Largely such connections form the lamina commissuralis tecti (figs. 446, 447) which is deep in the tectum, with its cells of origin near the ventricular wall. Since the tectum is predominantly a correlation center, this well-developed commissural system, which interrelates the impulses reaching the two sides, is of

great functional importance.   Possibly some of the crossing fibers are efferent
to the tectum.   The posterior commissure also carries intertectal or crossed
tecto-pretectal fibers (see p. 919).   *Franz* ('12) carried fibers of the commissura
horizontalis (figs. 450 to 451, 456 to 459) to the midbrain roof.   Their failure
to degenerate after destruction of this mesencephalic region led him to believe
that the tectal component was not commissural but was a decussating path,
probably of pretecto-tectal character.   A bundle accompanying the optic tract
fibers in normal eyed fishes, but not degenerating when the tract is cut, has
been recognized by *Krause* ('98), *Wallenberg* ('13), and *Jansen* ('29).   Recently
Charlton ('33) in his study of the brains of blind fishes interpreted this tract as
a commissural system, terming it the commissura superficialis tecti.

THE TORUS SEMICIRCULARIS AND THE NUCLEUS LATERALIS VALVULAE

In plagiostomes the subtectal segment of the regio tegmentalis corresponding
to the torus semicircularis, that is the nucleus tegmentalis medialis, is distinguishable from other nuclear masses at the base of the tectum (figs. 433 and 434,
t. semic).   In bony fishes the gray substance of the torus semicircularis forms
a clearly defined body (figs. 445 to 448), the form and size of which varies in
different teleosts with the degree of development of the vestibular and particularly of the lateral-line system.   This gray mass attains its greatest size in
Mormyrus.   The position of the torus semicircularis is influenced by the development of the valvula cerebelli.   If this is slightly developed as in Monopterus,
the tori of the two sides lie close to each other.   However, generally they are
widely separated by a large valvula (as in Cyprinoids, cod, Perca; fig. 445).
Such a wide separation has caused the nucleus frequently termed the nucleus
tegmentalis medialis in sharks to be termed the nucleus lateralis mesencephali
in teleosts (fig. 447, Nu. lat. mes.).   This latter must not be confused with the
nucleus lateralis mesencephali of plagiostomes which is likewise present in teleosts,
extending from the basal, frontal portion of the torus semicircularis to the nucleus
lentiformis.   It is identified by the typical fiber connections of the region.

A large valvula cerebelli usually fuses with the region which lies medial to the
tori semicirculares.   In this region, which gives rise to the large tractus mesencephalo-cerebellaris posterior (fig. 445), is the "Uebergangsganglion" of Stieda,
or the nucleus lateralis valvulae of *Herrick* ('05; fig. 446, Nu. lat. valv., also
shown but unlabeled in fig. 448).   The size of this nucleus varies, as does that
of the valvula cerebelli, with the degree of development of the acoustico-lateral
projection system.

The commissura transversa runs for the greater part of its course in the zonal
layer of the torus semicircularis (figs. 445, 446, 447).   It probably sends fibers to
the nucleus isthmi and to the tectum, reaching this latter through a thin little
tegmento-tectal bundle.   In teleosts the fasciculus longitudinalis lateralis or
acoustico-lateral lemniscus (figs. 445 and 446) terminates in the torus semicircularis and the nucleus isthmi but sends no fibers, as in plagiostomes, to the
tectum.   Consequently the differentiation between the gravistatic centers (the
tori semicirculares) and the photostatic center (the tectum) is more pronounced

in bony fishes than in sharks.   In some fishes (for example Monopterus, *van der Horst*, '17) the tori of the two sides are connected by a commissure, commissura tegmentalis posterior.   In several teleosts, *Kudo* ('23) found an intratoral connection passing through the commissura posterior.

The nucleus lateralis valvulae and the torus semicircularis are connected with the cerebellum by way of a tractus mesencephalo-cerebellaris posterior (or tractus tegmento-cerebellaris), which arches downward and caudalward from

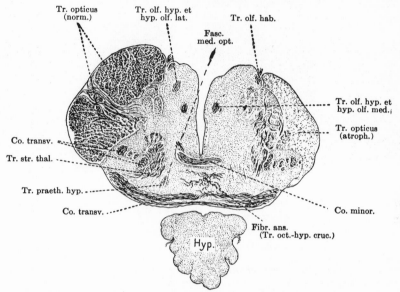

FIG. 449.   A cross section through the postoptic commissures in the diencephalon of a cod, the left eye of which was atrophied.   Note the degeneration of the right optic tract and the absence of the fasciculus opticus medialis on the right side.

Co.minor, commissura minor of C. L. Herrick; *Co.transv.*, commissura transversa; *Fasc.med.opt.*, fasciculus opticus medialis; *Fibr.ans.*(*Tr.oct.hyp.cruc.*), fibrae ansulatae (tractus octavo-hypothalamicus cruciatus); *Hyp.*, hypophysis; *Tr.olf.hab.*, tractus olfacto-habenularis; *Tr.praeth.hyp.*, tractus praethalamo-hypothalamicus; *Tr.olf.hyp.et hyp.olf.lat.*, tractus olfacto-hypothalamicus et hypothalamo-olfactorius lateralis; *Tr.olf.hyp.et hyp.olf.med.*, tractus olfacto-hypothalamicus et hypothalamo-olfactorius medialis; *Tr.opticus*(*norm.*), normal optic tract; *Tr.opticus*(*atroph.*), atrophied optic tract; *Tr.str.thal.*, tractus strio-thalamicus.

these centers to reach the cerebellum.   Sometimes, as in Gadus, this tract comes into close relation with the tractus mesencephalo-cerebellaris anterior or tecto-cerebellaris from the tectum (and from the nucleus lateralis valvulae) to the cerebellum at the place where the valvula joins the tegmentum of the mid-brain, so that the combined bundles pass through the valvula to the corpus cerebelli.   In Arius, Idus, and Perca (and perhaps in other fishes) the bundles do not combine; the anterior mesencephalo-cerebellar tract passes by a caudal course to the cerebellum while the posterior bundle enters by way of the valvula cerebelli (figs. 445, 446, and 448).   The hypertrophy of the tractus mesencephalo-cerebellaris posterior or tegmento-cerebellaris (fig. 448) in animals with a large lateral-line system suggests a correlation in function between this fiber tract and the acoustico-lateral system.   This is in contrast to the development of the tractus mesencephalo-cerebellaris anterior, which is largest in those animals having a well-developed optic system and probably carries gravistatic and photostatic impulses to the cerebellum.

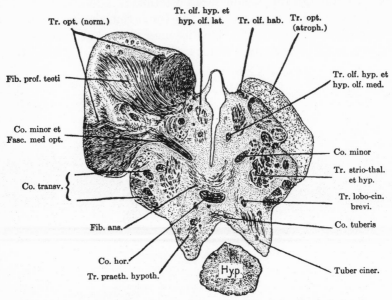

FIG. 450. A cross section through the rostral part of the diencephalon (somewhat caudal to figure 449).

Co.hor., commissura horizontalis; *Co.minor*, commissura minor; *Co.transv.*, commissura transversa; *Co.tuberis*, commissura tuberis; *Fasc.med.opt.*, fasciculus opticus medialis; *Fib.ans.*, fibrae ansulatae; *Fib.prof.tecti*, fibrae profundae tecti; *Hyp.*, hypophysis; *Tr.lobo-cin.brevi.*, tractus lobo-cinereus brevis; *Tr.olf.hab.*, tractus olfacto-habenularis; *Tr.olf.hyp.et hyp.olf.lat.*, tractus olfacto-hypothalamicus et hypothalamo-olfactorius lateralis; *Tr.olf.hyp.et hyp.olf.med.*, tractus olfacto-hypothalamicus et hypothalamo-olfactorius medialis; *Tr.opt.(atroph.)*, atrophied optic tract; *Tr.opt.(norm.)*, normal optic tract; *Tr.praeth.hypoth.*, tractus praethalamo-hypothalamicus; *Tr.strio-thal.et hyp.*, tractus strio-thalamicus et hypothalamicus; *Tuber ciner.*, tuber cinereum.

CERTAIN OTHER FIBER PATHS AND NUCLEI OF THE MESENCEPHALIC TEGMENTUM. NUCLEUS ISTHMI

The fiber connections are understood somewhat better for the teleost and ganoid tegmentum than for the tegmentum of plagiostomes. Many observers have contributed to our knowledge of them, among whom may be mentioned *Johnston* ('01 and '11), *Ariëns Kappers* ('06 and '07), *Franz* ('12), *Holmgren* ('20), *Hocke Hoogenboom* ('29), and others. Passing through the midbrain tegmentum from the dorsal region of the diencephalon (the habenulae) are habenulo-peduncular tracts, which are of about equal size on both sides and which terminate in the nucleus interpeduncularis. Lateral and dorsal to this nucleus are the longitudinal paths of the midbrain base and the decussations.

Prominent among these latter is the decussation of the brachium conjunctivum. After their origin in the cerebellum and subcerebellar gray, the fibers of this bundle run ventromedialward near the ventricle and cross the midline in the midbrain region under the fasciculus longitudinalis medialis (fig. 375). They terminate in part within the substantia reticularis of the midbrain where scattered groups of large cells suggest the future nucleus ruber.   The remainder of the tract — and the larger part — ends in the hypothalamus.   In the cod the brachium conjunctivum is accompanied by the tractus cerebello- et octavo-motorius anterior which enters the fasciculus longitudinalis medialis and so reaches the oculomotor nucleus.   This part of the mesencephalon is traversed also by fibers arising from the nucleus gustatorius anterior or superior and running to the hypothalamus (see Chapter III), thus correlating gustatory and olfactory impulses (*Herrick*, '05; see also *Barnard*, '35).   Accompanied by other fibers they end in the posterior segment of the lobus inferior, terminating on the cells of origin of the tractus lobo-bulbaris (*Ariëns Kappers*, '21), the efferent tract of the coördination region of the hypothalamus.

A consideration of the tegmental centers of the mesencephalon makes it evident that, while certain nuclei remain relatively the same, others show great variations in the different teleosts.   Thus the nucleus interpeduncularis with its associated fasciculus retroflexus has similar features in all teleosts, while the nucleus isthmi is different in nearly every order of this class.   This latter is small in the cod, much larger in Callionymus, and very highly developed in the perch (fig. 443).   In these latter fishes it appears as a large, semilunar cell group surrounded by smaller elements, situated at a level in front of the trochlear nerve, and partly embedded in the gray substance of the torus semicircularis.   It is made up of parvocellular and magnocellular portions in those fishes in which the nucleus is particularly well developed, as for example in the perch, but such parts may be indistinguishable in other teleosts.   Thus in Orthagoriscus, although the nucleus isthmi is rather large, *Burr* was unable to recognize definite parvocellular and magnocellular portions.   The gray masses (figs. 445 and 446, *nu. prof. mes.*), corresponding to the nucleus profundus mesencephali of plagio-stomes and, like this nucleus, fused dorsally and frontally with the gray substance of the torus semicircularis, show great variation in size and form in different teleosts.   Large cells in the region ventral and ventrolateral to the medial longitudinal fasciculus, constituting a nucleus reticularis mesencephali (see Chapter VI, p. 652), are the forerunners in part of the red nucleus of higher forms and are so considered by various observers (*Franz*, '12, and *Holmgren*, '20, for example).

Dorsally the nucleus isthmi forms a correlation center between photostatic and gravistatic impulses.   This nucleus receives collaterals, and possibly stem fibers, from the fasciculus longitudinalis lateralis, which arises from the acoustico-lateral region of the medulla oblongata.   It also receives another ascending bundle from the medulla oblongata, *Mayser's* ('81) bundle (fig. 446, tr. *x*), the origin of which is as yet uncertain.   The nucleus isthmi is interconnected with the tectum by isthmo-tectal and tecto-isthmal tracts.   The tractus isthmo-tectalis, which might also be termed the tractus isthmo-pretectalis, has been identified by various observers (*Franz*, '12; *Holmgren*, '20; *Kudo*, '23).   This tract originates in the nucleus isthmi and follows a ventrally convex curve

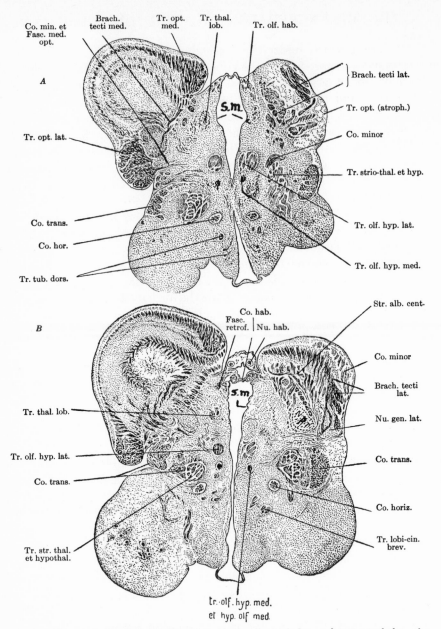

FIG. 451, *A* and *B*. Cross sections through the diencephalon and mesencephalon of a cod, the left eye of which was atrophied.

Brach.tecti lat., brachium tecti lateralis; *Brach.tecti med.*, brachium tecti medialis; *Co.hab.*, commissura habenularum; *Co.hor.*, commissura horizontalis; *Co.minor*, commissura minor; *Co.trans.*, commissura transversa; *Fasc.med.opt.*, fasciculus opticus medialis; *Fasc. retrof.*, fasciculus retroflexus; *Nu.gen.lat.*, nucleus geniculatus lateralis; *Nu.hab.*, nucleus habenularis; *Str.alb.cent.*, stratum album centrale; *Tr.hyp.olf.med.*, tractus hypothalamico-olfactorius medialis; *Tr.lobi.cin.brev.*, tractus lobo-cinereus brevis; *Tr.olf.hab.*, tractus olfacto-habenularis; *Tr.olf.hyp.lat.*, tractus olfacto-hypothalamicus lateralis; *Tr.olf.hyp. med.*, tractus olfacto-hypothalamicus medialis; *Tr.opt.(atroph.)*, atrophied optic tract; *Tr.opt.lat.*, tractus opticus lateralis; *Tr.opt.med.*, tractus opticus medialis; *Tr.strio-thal.et hyp.*, tractus strio-thalamicus et hypothalamicus; *Tr.thal.lob.*, tractus thalamo-lobaris; *Tr.tub.dors.*, tractus tuberis dorsali.

about the torus semicircularis in order to enter the superficial layer of the frontal end of the tectum and the pretectal nucleus.   *Kudo* has identified this tract in Clupea, Cyprinidae, Syngnathidae, Osphromeneus and Pleuronectidae with the exception of Solea and Callionymus.   In some fishes (Megalops, Gasterosteus, Mugil, and others) as in birds, the tract appears to enter the lateral optic tract. This is the reason that *Franz* termed it the tractus isthmo-opticus.   However, *Kudo* believed that it only accompanied the tract for a distance and then terminated in the tectum.   The tractus tecto-isthmicus (tractus isthmo-tectalis of *Ariëns Kappers*, '21, fig. 430; see also fig. 446 of present text) is believed to conduct impulses from the tectum to the nucleus isthmi (*Huber* and *Crosby*). *Franz* has described it as originating as two bundles of fibers from the middle part of the tectum, then coursing through the lateral border of the torus, and finally forming a capsule about the nucleus, similar to that found in frogs.

COMMISSURA POSTERIOR

Another commissure, the commissura posterior, lies at the line between the mesencephalon and the diencephalon.   It belongs to this region of transition. In all bony fishes (fig. 456) this commissure consists of two parts, a dorsal and a ventral.   There exists a difference of opinion with regard to the connections of the dorsal part in fishes.   *Ariëns Kappers* ('07 and '21) believed that it is a commissural connection for the lateral geniculate nuclei in Amia and in Pleuronectidae.   Observers working with other fishes (*Hocke Hoogenboom*, '29, for Polyodon) have regarded it as commissural for pretectal nuclei; still others have considered that it might carry also tecto-pretectal connections. The ventral part carries crossed fibers of the medial longitudinal fasciculus from reticular cells near the oculomotor nucleus, which have been termed the nucleus commissurae posterioris (*Ariëns Kappers*).   Probably they are the homologue of the nucleus interstitialis of higher forms.

CERTAIN SECRETORY REGIONS OF THE DIENCEPHALON

The roof of the third ventricle in front of the habenula is formed in fishes by a modified choroid plexus, the parencephalon.   In higher vertebrates such telae choroidae with their accompanying capillary plexuses grow into the ventricles, but in lower vertebrates they may become very large, sac-like structures which bulge out from the surface.   Such protrusions have been described previously in the choroid membrane of the diencephalon and medulla oblongata in Petromyzon (p. 874).   In higher fishes they are most conspicuous in the diencephalic regions, the parencephalon even in sharks (fig. 436) and ganoids (*Hocke Hoogenboom*, '29) having laterally extending sacs.   In some fishes these sacs reach an enormous size, as in Lepidosteus (fig. 452) and in Amia where dorsal and lateral sacs are present.   The large dorsal outgrowth on which the epiphyseal stalk rests extends frontalward over a large part of the forebrain, covering the paraphysis.   The lateral outgrowths (*a* and *b*) are larger, but otherwise correspond to those of Acanthias reproduced in figure 436.   In Lepidosteus and in Amia (*Kingsbury*, '97; *Ariëns Kappers*, '07; *Brookover*, '10) they extend frontally along the forebrain and caudally along the midbrain and medulla oblongata to the vagal region. Their epithelium and vessels receive a rich sympathetic innervation (*Brookover*). The epithelium of the posterior sac differs in structure, the cells of the exterior plate being higher than those of the interior plate, as *Kingsbury* noted. By staining in Altmann's dye it can be demonstrated that the cells have a great number of granules and show an active secretion. In younger animals *Brookover* demonstrated cilia on this epithelium. Between the dorsal outgrowth (*D*) and the upper lateral outgrowth, there is a knot of glandular tubes (*XX*) of the paraphysis.

It is not possible at present to explain exactly why this thin ventricular wall should be so strongly developed in bony ganoids. Similar outgrowths have been

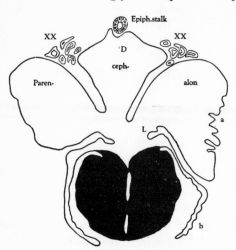

FIG. 452. The marked development of the roof membrane of the diencephalon (the parencephalon) in Lepidosteus.

described for a crossopterygian, Polypterus, by *Waldschmidt*. The choroid plexus of higher forms serves a double function. It both secretes the ventricular or cerebro-spinal fluid and acts as a membrane permitting it to pass through to the subarachnoid spaces. In mammals the amount of this excretion is very large compared with the very small excretion present in fishes which have no subarachnoid spaces. Thus the protrusion of the choroid membranes in lower vertebrates probably is due to the accumulation of cerebro-spinal fluid. Apparently the production of the ventricular fluid precedes phylogenetically the development of the perimedullary spaces and cavities. This is a confirmation of

the results obtained by *Weed* ('17; see bibliography, p. 132) in his study of the development of the cerebro-spinal spaces. This investigator found indications of the secretion of cerebro-spinal fluid within the neural tube in very young pig embryos while its excretion into the forming perimedullary spaces could not be observed until the pig embryo had reached a 14 mm. length.

In some teleosts (Phoxinus) the pineal body appears to be slightly affected by light and influences color change (*von Fritsch*, '12). However, in most teleosts the pineal organ has only a glandular structure in which but few rudimentary sense cells are found (*Studnička*, '05; *Tilney* and *Warren*, '19). The parapineal organ has entirely disappeared in the adult animals. However, in Amia, *Kingsbury* ('97) could demonstrate a small trace of a parapineal organ which was connected with the left habenular ganglion. (The fiber connections are discussed under the account of the habenula, page 922.)

In the thalamus of certain bony fishes (fig. 453), near the sulcus medius, there is a pronounced growth of the ventricular ependyma which is here devoid of cilia. Underlying this epithelium is a rich capillary plexus. The general character of this epithelium and its rich blood supply suggest strongly that it is secretory in function and that it is concerned with the production of the cerebro-spinal fluid. Similar epithelium is found near the sulcus medius in various higher vertebrates (*Charlton*, '28, and others; see page 971).   This secretory ependyma must not be confused with the high cylindrical ependymal cells which in nearly all animals (*Studnička*) are found under the posterior commissure and constitute the so-called sub-commissural organ (*Niels* and *Bauer-Jokl*), from which *Reissner's* fiber arises (see pp. 167 and 179).

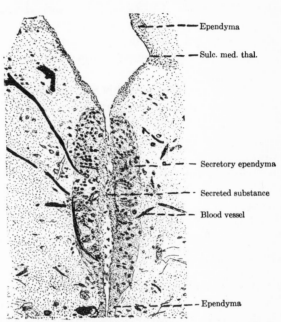

The hypophysis in teleosts varies greatly in form and size. The most peculiar form is found in Lophius where the cerebral part of the hypophyseal stalk extends frontalward for a great distance in order to reach the hypophyseal gland, which in these animals is located in front of the forebrain. This is due to the peculiar position of the mouth in these animals.   In other teleosts, such as Esox and Orthagoriscus, the cerebral part of the hypophysis is short but frequently branches, particularly inside of the pars intermedia, where it forms solid cords of

FIG. 453.   Richly vascularized secretory ependyma in the thalamus of a fish (Monopterus).   *Ariëns Kappers*.

cells.   This affords an example of the intimate relation of the two parts (*Stendell*, '14; *Burr*, '28).   The principal part of the hypophysis consists of solid cords of cells rather than of the tubuli characteristic of this region in sharks.

NUCLEAR CENTERS OF THE DIENCEPHALON AND THE DIENCEPHALIC-MESENCEPHALIC TRANSITION REGION

The diencephalon may be divided into the three typical portions; epithalamus, hypothalamus, and thalamus proper.   This last region is divided by the sulcus medius into dorsal and ventral portions, of which the latter is the larger.

In the epithalamus, in addition to the pineal organ (and any traces of the parapineal organ), are a part of the posterior commissure (the dividing line between the diencephalon and the mesencephalon passing through this) and the habenula with its associated fiber tracts.   The pineal organ and posterior commissure have been discussed.   It yet remains to describe briefly the habenula. This paired gray mass is much smaller in teleosts than in plagiostomes.   In many teleosts (Tinca, Zoarces, Reniceps, and others; *Holmgren*, '20), although not in ganoids, it is symmetrical on the two sides. However, *Gierse* ('04, see *Shanklin*) in Cyclothone, *Shanklin* ('35) in Bathypterois and *Holmgren* ('18, '18b, '20) in Osmerus, Clupea, and Salmo salar found asymmetry, the right habenular nucleus being larger than the left, and in Salmo *Holmgren* traced fibers from the parapineal organ to the smaller left nuclear mass. In Belone, Perca, Gadus, and certain other fishes, this observer found the left habenula somewhat larger than the right. *Goldstein* ('05) and *Ariëns Kappers* ('06) described two habenular nuclei in ganoids and teleosts, comparable presumably to the lateral and medial habenular nuclei of higher forms. *Holmgren* described only a single nucleus, apparently comparable to the medial habenular nucleus (see fig. 451B).

The habenulae receive fibers from various parts of the forebrain. The major components of the stria medullaris in teleosts (as in plagiostomes) are the tractus olfacto-habenularis medialis and the tractus olfacto-habenularis lateralis, which together constitute the stria medullaris. The first of these two tracts derives its fibers, most of which are unmedullated, from the cells of the preoptic recess and particularly from the ventromedial septal or parolfactory segment of the forebrain. The majority of them terminate in the contralateral habenular nucleus, crossing in the habenular commissure (see tr. olf. hab., figs. 449 to 451A).

The tractus olfacto-habenularis lateralis originates from the tuberculum taeniae ; that is, from the ventrolateral segment of the hemisphere. These fibers cross before terminating. In most animals these fibers are unmyelinated but in certain fishes (as for example Thynnus) they have medullary sheaths. Certain of these fibers appear to form a commissural system, the commissura superior telencephali, which connects the so-called tuberculum taenia of one side with that of the other. However, in teleosts on the whole, where the olfactory apparatus (and indeed the whole forebrain) is not very highly developed, such commissural fibers are far less numerous than in plagiostomes. Probably part of the tractus olfacto-habenularis lateralis corresponds to the so-called tractus cortico-habenularis lateralis of the selachians (p. 896).

In ganoids the habenula receives fibers from the epiphysis (*Johnston*, '01). According to *Holmgren* ('20) there is a considerable difference in the distribution of the fiber bundle from the epiphysis in different teleosts. He traced fibers arising from bipolar neurons in the epiphyseal wall toward the tectum and, in certain cases, into the beginning of the medial longitudinal fasciculus.

The efferent fibers from the habenula run mainly in two bundles, the tractus habenulo-thalamicus (which may be the superior commissure connection of *Holmgren*), and the tractus habenulo-peduncularis or fasciculus retroflexus (figs. 456 to 458), which ends, after crossing, in the interpeduncular nucleus. This latter tract often is surrounded, as in Arius, by myelinated fibers arising from the subhabenular region, which also terminate at the base of the midbrain. The habenular nuclei, and consequently the habenulo-peduncular tracts, do not show marked differences in size on the two sides of the brain in most teleosts.

The sulcus medius of *Herrick* (fig. 423), *Ariëns Kappers* ('21), and *Brickner* ('29) appears to separate the dorsal from the ventral thalamus on the ventricular wall. This sulcus may be seen in figure 451.

It is not possible to decide with surety whether certain thalamic nuclei should be relegated to the dorsal or to the ventral thalamus.   Consequently no sharp division between these regions has been made in the present account.   In general to the dorsal thalamus and the thalamo-mesencephalic transition region of teleosts (and of ganoids so far as the groups have been recognized) may be delegated : the posthabenular region (including the inner segment of the dorsal thalamus of *Brickner*, '29) ; the nuclei pretectalis, corticalis, and intermedius ; the nucleus anterior or corpus glomerulosum pars anterior ; functionally, if not morphologically, the corpus glomerulosum pars rotunda or nucleus rotundus, and the nucleus geniculatus lateralis.

To the ventral thalamus may be delegated the nucleus dorsalis thalami of *Goldstein* or the nucleus tegmenti motorius ventralis, the nucleus prerotundus, the nucleus subrotundus (the classification of the nucleus suprarotundus is uncertain), and probably the nucleus posterior thalami.   The nucleus ruber tegmenti of *Goldstein* is mesencephalic.

The region ventral to the habenular nucleus, and caudal to it in both ganoids and teleosts, is the subhabenular or posthabenular region (*Goldstein*, '05 ; *Sheldon*, '12 ; *Hocke Hoogenboom*, '29, and others) or the eminentia thalami (*Holmgren*, '20). In the ganoid Polyodon (*Hocke Hoogenboom*, '29) there is no special nuclear differentiation, but such differentiation is present in teleosts and will receive brief consideration now.   This region (*Holmgren*, '20) is separated from the habenular nuclei by a deep subhabenular sulcus which extends caudalward under the posterior commissure, while its ventral boundary is formed by the sulcus hypothalamicus (sulcus medius of *Herrick*).   *Holmgren* ('20) found the eminentia thalami in Osmerus divisible on the ventricular side into three secondary portions indicated by horizontal sulci and he ('20, pp. 235–238) presented evidence for the homologizing of this region in bony fishes and petromyzonts (as analyzed by *Johnston*, see p. 876) but stated that : "Ein Unterschied liegt aber insofern vor, dass diese Bildungen bei den Knochenfischen horizontal liegen, während sie bei den Neunaugen vertikal sind."   *Brickner* ('29) termed the major portion at least of the "posthabenuläre Zwischenhirngebiet" of *Goldstein* and the eminentia thalami of *Holmgren*, the inner segment of the thalamus, agreeing with *Ariëns Kappers* (see *Brickner*, p. 240) that its connections indicate it to be representative of either the anterior or medial nucleus of the thalamus (*Ariëns Kappers*, '06, nucleus anterior thalami ; *Ariëns Kappers*, '21, as in fig. 459, nucleus anterior thalami dorsalis).   A small area, undifferentiated in character, dorsal to the subhabenular sulcus but ventral to the habenula was described by *Brickner* as the subhabenular area.   He carried his nucleus tegmenti motorius dorsalis medialward over the inner segment ; this may represent the nucleus of the posterior commissure as labeled by *Burr* ('28) with the eminentia medialis of the latter observer falling within the inner segment of *Brickner*, but with regard to these latter homologies there is some uncertainty.   *Charlton* ('33) identified the inner segment as described by *Brickner* (fig. 455A).   It is the pars dorsalis thalami of *Jeener* ('30) and *Shanklin* ('35).

Dorsolateral to the inner segment of teleosts is a group of nuclei which in reality represent a transition between the adjoining areas, for sometimes they are grouped as the pretectal part of the dorsal thalamus; sometimes they are regarded as mesencephalic. A nucleus pretectalis has been described by many observers (*Catois*, '01; *Goldstein*, '05; *Franz*, '12; *Holmgren*, '20; *Ariëns Kappers*, '21; *Burr*, '28; *Charlton*, '33; *Shanklin*, '35) but the limits imposed vary with the observer. The pretectal nucleus of *Catois*, *Goldstein*, and *Holmgren* is more inclusive than that of many observers and involves much, at least, of the nucleus tegmenti motorius dorsalis of *Brickner* ('29). *Catois* ('01) described it as consisting of stellate or oval neurons, 20–30μ in size, scattered in arrangement and intermingled with fiber bundles. *Goldstein* found two cell types in the nucleus and *Holmgren* noted smaller neurons in the caudal part extending medialward into the eminentia thalami. This suggests the overlap of *Brickner's* inner segment by his nucleus tegmenti motorius dorsalis and this medial extension may represent the nucleus of the posterior commissure as labeled by *Burr* ('28, fig. 9), although these homologies are uncertain. There is a tendency to restrict the name to a group of multipolar cells, with a few intermingled smaller neurons, lying at the base of the tectum (fig. 455A, *Burr*, '23; *Charlton*, '33; *Shanklin*, '35). This is the corpus geniculatum posterius pars lateralis of *Meader* ('34). A pretectal nucleus has been described for Amia by *Ariëns Kappers*. Cells representative of the region have been seen in Polyodon by *Hocke Hoogenboom* ('28).

The nucleus corticalis (fig. 455) of *Fritsch* ('78), *Ariëns Kappers* ('06), and *Holmgren* ('20) is represented by a thin plate formed of cells, similar to those in the nucleus pretectalis, lying along the border of the tectum lateral to this latter nucleus. Between the nucleus pretectalis and the corpus glomerulosum pars anterior (or nucleus anterior) is the nucleus intermedius of *Goldstein* ('05) and *Holmgren* ('20). Such cells, which constitute the corpus geniculatum posterius pars ventralis of *Meader* ('34) either form a relatively independent mass or may fuse with the corpus glomerulosum pars anterior (or nucleus anterior), as in Osmerus.

The lateral geniculate nucleus is present in ganoids (Amia, *Ariëns Kappers*, '07; Polyodon, *Hocke Hoogenboom*, '29) in a simple form but reaches a considerable degree of development in certain teleosts, where it occupies a position near the lateral wall of the brain in transverse sections of the diencephalon passing through the habenular nuclei. In many teleosts (as Trigla and Pleuronectidae) the nucleus has a laminated structure (fig. 454) such as is found frequently in sensory nuclei. In others (as Gadus) it is less well developed. In fishes living near the bottom of streams (as Ameiurus, Centronotus, and Lophius) it is said to be difficult to identify the nucleus (*Franz*, '12). However, *Charlton* ('33) found it in the blind fishes studied by him (as did *Shanklin*, '35, in the nearly blind Bathypterois) and pointed out that its presence in these forms suggests that it may have other functions as well as those concerned with direct optic impulses. In Orthagoriscus (*Burr*, '28) the lateral geniculate nucleus consists of three portions. This is the corpus geniculatum ipsum of *Meader* ('34), who recognized also a corpus geniculatum posterius, with a pars lateralis (nucleus pretectalis), a pars ventralis (nucleus intermedius) and a pars dorsalis.

The cell mass designated as the nucleus anterior in teleosts by *Franz* ('12),

Holmgren ('20), and others (not present in Polyodon ; Hocke Hoogenboom) was labeled the nucleus rotundus by *Jansen* ('29) and considered a part of that nucleus by *Burr* ('28). However, it is not the nucleus rotundus of *Sheldon* ('12) nor the corpus glomerulosum of *Franz* ('12). It belongs to the rotundus complex of *Holmgren* ('20) although it is not the nucleus rotundus (or better, pseudorotundus) of that observer. The nucleus anterior (corpus glomerulosum pars anterior) may be a relatively conspicuous element of the dorsal thalamus or it may be much less evident or almost entirely absent. Between the two extremes there are various degrees of development. *Franz* ('12) pointed out that the nucleus has a vicarious relation to a larger nuclear mass, the corpus glomerulosum pars rotunda,

situated more ventrally in the thalamus of higher teleosts, being small when the latter nucleus is highly developed and vice versa. *Holmgren* ('20) was in agreement with this interpretation of *Franz* ('12), and *Burr* ('28) and *Brickner* ('29) considered the nucleus anterior and the corpus glomerulosum of *Franz* portions of a single nuclear mass, to which *Burr* gave the name of the nucleus rotundus, while *Brickner* (following the suggestion of *Ariëns Kappers*) termed it the corpus glomerulosum,

FIG. 454. Different forms of the lateral geniculate nucleus of bony fishes. *Franz.*
1, Anguilla; *2*, Clupea; *3*, Trutta; *4*, Carassius; *5*, Exocoetus; *6*, Caraux; *7*, Scomber; *8*, Scorpaena; *9*, Agonus; *10*, Trigla; *11*, Pleuronectes; *12*, Cyclopterus.

applying the terms pars anterior and pars rotunda to the two portions. Where characteristically developed the corpus glomerulosum pars rotunda (fig. 455B) is a conspicuous nuclear mass situated in the more ventral regions of the thalamus. It has a round or oval basal portion which may be prolonged to a greater or less extent in the direction of, and, in some cases at least, into direct continuity with, the nucleus anterior, thus giving the whole mass the appearance of an inverted comma or a sort of comet shape. The main mass of the nucleus is surrounded by a medullated capsule and includes within it, as fibers of passage, a medullated fiber tract, the commissura horizontalis (figs. 457, 458). The round elements peculiar to this nucleus were mistaken formerly for large cells. However, *Franz* demonstrated that they are telodendria which terminate in a glomerular type of synapse. The actual cell bodies of this nucleus are relatively small and lie at the periphery of the nuclear mass (*Goldstein*, '05). Physostomes lack a corpus glomerulosum in the sense of *Franz*, that is they do not have a nucleus with the peculiar glomerular terminations which are so notable a feature in the thalami of certain other teleosts. However, Physostomes have a well-developed nucleus anterior, which shows histologically a structure comparable to that of the

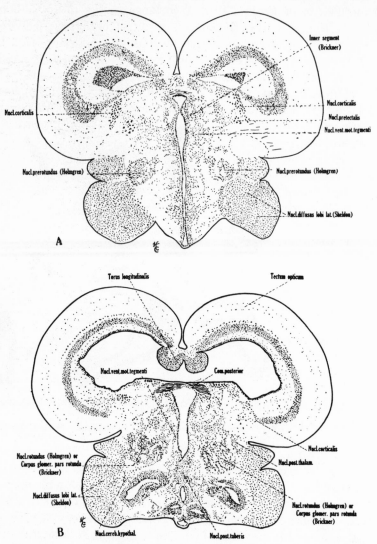

FIG. 455. *A.* Cross section through the diencephalon and tectum of the sunfish (Eupomotis gibbosus) at the level of nucleus prerotundus of Holmgren.
B. Cross section through the diencephalon and tectum of the sunfish (Eupomotis gibbosus) at anterior end of nucleus rotundus or better pseudorotundus of Holmgren. *Huber* and *Crosby.*

corpus glomerulosum pars rotunda or nucleus rotundus where present. This led Franz to suppose that the latter nucleus has developed by a caudoventral shifting of the nucleus anterior. In substantiation of this is the earlier quoted fact that the corpus glomerulosum pars rotunda, in many fishes at least, runs forward into relation with the nucleus anterior, forming a continuous nuclear mass. Moreover, the thalamo-lobar and rotundo-lobar tracts have homologous relations in the different forms.   Reference is made here to figure 455.

The nucleus rotundus described by *Sheldon* ('12) in the carp has been said by *Holmgren* to have nothing to do with the nucleus rotundus of *Fritsch* ('78) or the corpus glomerulosum of *Franz* but to be represented in the lateral part of the nucleus prerotundus of *Holmgren* and others, while the medial part of this nucleus prerotundus of *Holmgren* represents the nucleus prerotundus of *Sheldon*.   As further evidence of this *Holmgren* pointed out that *Sheldon's* nucleus rotundus does not show the relations to the commissura horizontalis or tractus thalamo-mamillaris (or rotundo-lobaris) typical of the nucleus rotundus of *Fritsch* (or the corpus glomerulosum of *Franz*).   The rotundus complex of *Holmgren*, then, includes the nucleus prerotundus, the nucleus rotundus, and the nucleus subrotundus of *Sheldon*, this latter observer having in turn followed the description of this complex in Gadus and Lophius as given by *Ariëns Kappers* ('06).   *Holmgren* divided his nucleus prerotundus into a lateral part, comparable to the *Sheldon* nucleus rotundus (termed nucleus pseudorotundus or rotundus) and a medial part, the nucleus prerotundus of *Sheldon* which extends medialward to fuse ultimately, as does its fellow of the opposite side, into a midline nuclear mass (presumably the ganglion interpedunculare of certain observers).   The nucleus prerotundus of *Holmgren* (fig. 455A) quite evidently is the nucleus ventralis of *Goldstein*, probably the nucleus ventralis hypothalami and the nucleus peduncularis pars medialis (as seen in Amia by *Ariëns Kappers*, '06; see also *Holmgren*, '20), and includes at least the nucleus prerotundus of *Brickner*.   A nucleus subrotundus, rather large celled and without myelinated capsule, has been described by *Ariëns Kappers* ('06), *Sheldon* ('12), *Holmgren* ('20), and *Shanklin* ('35).   It occupies a position beneath the remainder of the rotundus complex.   According to *Holmgren* it has an almost constant position in teleosts "medial und dorsal unmittelbar an dem Ependym des hinteren Astes vom Ventriculus lateralis hypothalami."   The nucleus subrotundus was regarded by *Holmgren* ('20) and others as part of the hypothalamus.   The present writers should consider it as possibly part of the ventral thalamus.   Lateral to the lateral part of the nucleus prerotundus (or nucleus pseudorotundus) and medial to the lateral lobes of the hypothalamus lies the nucleus posterior thalami of *Goldstein*, *Sheldon*, and *Holmgren* (fig. 455B), presumably the nucleus peduncularis thalami pars lateralis of *Ariëns Kappers* ('06) and possibly the nucleus paraentopeduncularis of *Brickner* ('29).   In Osmerus (*Holmgren*, '20) this nucleus has relatively small, closely grouped cells. He found the nucleus in relation with the nucleus anterior (as it is in certain available trout material) through the intermediation of somewhat more scattered cells.   The nucleus has a relatively considerable caudoventral extent—from planes through the nucleus anterior to well toward the caudal end of the diencephalon — but maintains similar relations throughout.

A nucleus suprarotundus, showing variable degrees of development in different teleosts, has been identified by *Sheldon* ('12) and *Holmgren* ('20), and is seen in the available trout material.   It is connected slightly with the nucleus posterior thalami but extends forward to the eminentia thalami and caudalward to the region of the nucleus ruber of *Goldstein* (nucleus lateralis thalami of *Holmgren*).

Ventral to the sulcus medius *Goldstein* ('05) described a nucleus dorsalis thalami which has been reidentified by *Brickner* ('29) and apparently by *Charlton* ('33). *Brickner* termed it the nucleus tegmenti motorius ventralis and redivided it into a pars dorsalis, which at more frontal levels extends dorsalward toward the habenula, and a pars ventralis (fig. 455B); it is the (pars) ventralis thalami of *Jeener* ('30) and *Shanklin* ('35).

The mass of large cells caudal to the nucleus posterior and extending upward in a crescent-shaped line toward the ventricular wall is largely mesencephalic and falls within the nucleus ruber tegmenti of *Goldstein* and probably is the nucleus tegmentalis thalami of *Ariëns Kappers* and the nucleus lateralis thalami of *Holmgren*.

Among the hypothalamic (and preoptic) centers may be mentioned the following nuclear groups: nucleus preopticus magnocellularis, nucleus tuberis lateralis, nucleus posterior thalami, nucleus tuberis anterior, nucleus tuberis posterior, nucleus tuberis ventralis, corpus mamillare, ganglion sacci vasculosi, nucleus diffusus lobi inferioris and nucleus cerebellaris hypothalami.

The nucleus preopticus magnocellularis consists of large, polygonal cells appearing in the preoptic region close to the ventricle (figs. 545, 551 to 553, 558, Chapter IX) and is richly provided with blood vessels. In Anguilla in particular, the cells are enormous (*van der Horst,* '17). This cell group may extend relatively far dorsalward and caudalward. The caudal part probably constitutes the nucleus tuberis ventralis. The lateral hypothalamic nucleus (nucleus tuberis lateralis) is to be regarded as merely a ventrocaudal extension of the nucleus preopticus magnocellularis. It consists of cells of similar type but slightly smaller and is located at the base of the hypothalamus. The area has visceral functions (discussion, p. 937). Lateralward, in the region directly behind the commissura transversa, a mass of smaller cells appears. This is the nucleus tuberis anterior or nucleus anterior hypothalami, which, particularly in Periophthalmus, is very large. In Osmerus *Holmgren* ('20) found it composed of small cells grouped in "islands." The hypothalamic nuclei thus far described all lie in front of the infundibulum. However, the nucleus tuberis posterior (fig. 455) lies caudal to it. This nucleus, which *Sheldon* ('12) and *Holmgren* have described, may acquire a great size (*e.g.* Periophthalmus). The nuclei of the two sides fuse with each other in the midline. The two nuclei occupy a position near the place where the base of the midbrain lies against the infundibulum. Beneath the nucleus tuberis posterior, and also behind the infundibulum near the mammillary recess, lies the ganglion or nucleus sacci vasculosi. This nucleus was described by *Ariëns Kappers* ('06, '21) and recently for the ganoid Polyodon by *Hocke Hoogenboom* ('29). It seems probable that it is the corpus mamillare of *Goldstein* ('05), *Sheldon* ('12), *Holmgren* ('20), and *Burr* ('28). *Ariëns Kappers* ('07) described lateral swellings of gray substance directly over the attachment of the lobi inferiores as the tori laterales. *Holmgren* ('20) spoke of the nucleus diffusus tori lateralis as "ein dorsaler abgetrennter Teil des Nucleus diffusus." Yet to be mentioned is the nucleus cerebellosus hypothalami (fig. 455), a band of fairly large, scattered cells along the inner border of the inferior lateral lobes, ventrolateral to the nucleus rotundus, then to the nucleus posterior thalami and (still farther caudal) to the nucleus subrotundus. Often it is very poorly differentiated. The inferior lobe consists of scattered cells which constitute the nucleus diffusus lobi inferioris (fig 455B).

THE FIBER CONNECTIONS OF THE THALAMO-MESENCEPHALIC TRANSITIONAL REGION AND THE DORSAL THALAMUS

The connections of the eminentia thalami or posthabenular region do not appear to be understood fully. *Sheldon* ('12) described an habenulo-posthabenular tract in the carp, but *Holmgren* found a connection in the contralateral direction between these areas in *Osmerus*. Tecto-eminentia (tractus tecto-eminentialis) fibers arising from the stratum griseum centrale (layer 5 of *Cajal; Holmgren,* '20) were traced to the posthabenular region and through the periventricular system. The tractus eminentia-tectalis passes to the tectum. In addition, *Holmgren* carried collaterals of the optic fibers, tractus optico-eminentialis, to this region. The preoptic regions were shown to be interrelated by afferent and efferent paths with the posthabenular region (*Sheldon,* '12). The region is pierced by many fibers of passage, such as habenulo-peduncular, habenulo-diencephalic, and stria medullaris fibers, and it is thought that the first of these tracts may receive fibers from this region. Optic fibers (*Shanklin,* '35), fibers of the commissura transversa (*Brickner,* '29), and connections with the tectum, and with the corpus glomerulosum pars rotunda (*Shanklin*) and with the cerebellum (*Brickner, Shanklin*) have been described to the nucleus dorsalis motorius tegmenti.

The nucleus pretectalis (and probably the nucleus corticalis) receives optic fibers (largely collaterals). It gets impulses through its dendrites from the tectum, the corpus glomerulosum pars anterior, and the lateral geniculate nucleus. The tractus spino-tectalis (et mesencephalicus) sends a few fibers to the nucleus pretectalis and the nucleus lentiformis (*Ariëns Kappers,* '21), thus introducing into the transition zone between the diencephalon and mesencephalon, bundles carrying general sensibility, temperature and pain (that is, vital sensibility). The commissura minor (*C. L. Herrick,* '91) passes through, and probably has some synaptic connections with, the nucleus pretectalis (fig. 450). The nucleus corticalis is thought to receive collaterals of optic tract fibers and to have connections with the nucleus pretectalis and the tectum.

The following efferent connections of the nucleus pretectalis are those commonly recognized :

a. Fibers (possibly interpretectal) through the commissura posterior (*Catois,* '01 ; *Holmgren,* '20 ; *Hocke Hoogenboom,* '29, *Shanklin,* '35, and others).

b. Pretecto-tectal connections. These were described by *Radl* ('15). They are present in forms other than fishes. *Holmgren* ('20) was not able to establish this connection, although he could trace dendrites of pretectal cells into the tectum.

c. Pretecto-cerebellar tract. This bundle passes to the cerebellum, following quite closely the course of the anterior mesencephalo-cerebellar tract.

d. Pretecto-bulbar tract. This tract, described by *Haller* ('98) as a rostro-ventral association fascicle and later as a pretecto-spinal or bulbar tract by

Goldstein ('05), *Holmgren* ('20), and *Ariëns Kappers* ('21), consists of fibers from the nucleus pretectalis and the nucleus corticalis. The fibers run ventromedial-ward and, after a partial decussation in the midline near the nucleus interstitialis of the medial longitudinal fasciculus, turn caudalward in company with this latter fasciculus. According to *Holmgren* ('20), this bundle gives off a tractus pretecto-lateralis as it passes into relation with the fasciculus longitudinalis lateralis, but

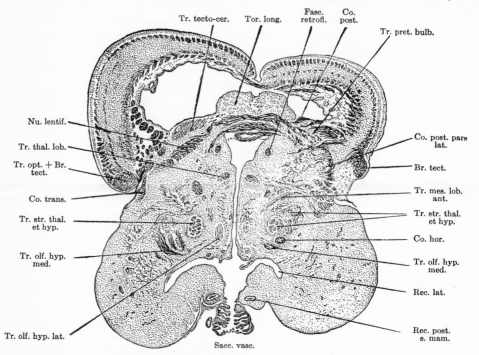

Fig. 456. A cross section through the commissura posterior of a cod with an atrophied left eye. Note the atrophy of the optic tectum on the right side.

Br.tect., brachium tecti; *Co.hor.*, commissura horizontalis; *Co.post.*, commissura posterior; *Co. post.pars lat.*, commissura posterior pars lateralis; *Co.trans.*, commissura transversa; *Fasc.retrofl.*, fasciculus retroflexus; *Nu.lentif.*, nucleus lentiformis; *Rec.lat.*, recessus lateralis; *Rec.post.s.mam.*, recessus posterior of sulcus mamillaris; *Sacc. vasc.*, saccus vasculosis; *Tor.long.*, torus longitudinalis; *Tr.mes.lob.ant.*, tractus mesencephalo-lobaris anterior; *Tr.olf.hyp.lat.*, tractus olfacto-hypothalamicus lateralis; *Tr.olf.hyp.med.*, tractus olfacto-hypothalamicus medialis; *Tr.opt.*, tractus opticus; *Tr.pret.bulb.*, tractus pretecto-bulbaris; *Tr.str.thal.et hyp.*, tractus strio-thalamicus et hypothalamicus; *Tr.tecto-cer.*, tractus tecto-cerebellaris; *Tr.thal.lob.*, tractus thalamo-lobaris.

this observer did not trace the tract to its destination. *Charlton* ('33) carried it to the motor trigeminal nucleus. Another tract (the tractus pretecto-spino-thalamicus) has been mentioned by *Holmgren* but no adequate description appears to be available at present. (For the tractus pretecto-bulbaris see figures 456 and 458.)

The nucleus anterior thalami and its posterior continuation, the corpus glomerulosum pars rotunda, are said to receive impulses by the commissura horizontalis of *Fritsch* (*Catois*, '01 ; *Holmgren*, '20 ; figs. 450, 451, 456 to 458). *Franz* found the nucleus pierced by fibers of this commissure. The nucleus anterior receives fibers from the commissura minor (*C. L. Herrick*, '91), as shown by *Franz* ('12) and *Holmgren* ('20). *Franz* ('12) and *Holmgren* ('20) found the nucleus related to a thalamo-mammillary or thalamo-lobar (figs. 456 and 457) or thalamo-hypothalamic (*Shanklin*, '35) tract.   Dendrites of pretectal neurons reach it. *Franz* and *Holmgren* traced neuraxes of its neurons in a tectalward direction in the commissura horizontalis.   The caudal part of the nuclear complex also has connections with the hypothalamus through the tractus rotundo-lobaris (fig. 458).

The lateral geniculate nucleus receives collaterals of optic tract fibers, also dendrites from the pretectal nucleus.   *Holmgren* ('20) traced neuraxes of lateral geniculate neurons, constituting a tractus geniculo-tectalis, to the tectum.   Such geniculo-tectal connections belong to the fasciculo geniculado-lobaris of *Ramón y Cajal* and the dorsal and ventral brachia tecti of *Shanklin* ('35; see *Ariëns Kappers*, '06, '21, and *Kudo*, '23).   *Goldstein* ('05, like *Burr* '23) regarded the commissura minor (*C. L. Herrick*, '91), about which there has been considerable difference of opinion, as an intergeniculate commissure, although he was uncertain that all fibers were of this type, while *Holmgren* regarded these commissural fibers as fibers of passage on their way to the tectum, with which interpretation *Charlton* ('33) and *Shanklin* ('35) agreed.   Intergeniculate fibers, in close relation with the optic tract and the optic connections to the nucleus were described by *Holmgren* for Callionymus lyra.   These constitute the commissura intergeniculata ventralis of *Meader* ('34), and correspond probably to the fascicles from the commissura transversa described by *Burr* and *Shanklin*.   The teleost lateral geniculate nucleus is said to be connected with surrounding nuclei, such as the (nucleus) corpus glomerulosum pars anterior and the nucleus tegmenti motorius dorsalis, and with the cerebellum.

THE FIBER CONNECTIONS OF THE VENTRAL THALAMIC AND HYPOTHALAMIC REGIONS

a. Connections with Telencephalic Areas.   The nucleus prerotundus of the ventral thalamus of teleostean forms is found to receive fascicles from the tractus strio-thalamicus lateralis.   It contributes fibers to the postoptic commissure, the commissura transversa.   In addition to these connections the nucleus prerotundus sends fibers to the mammillary body and also sends a large, unmedullated tract dorsalward and forward, at first lateral and then medial to the strio-thalamic system, to reach the eminentia thalami or posthabenular region (*Holmgren*, '20).   The nucleus suprarotundus is believed to have efferent fibers passing caudalward but their termination is not known (tractus suprarotundo-spinalis or tectalis of *Holmgren*, '20).

The hypothalamic areas receive a greater proportion of telencephalic fibers than does the epithalamus.   In the cod three descending tracts can be demonstrated.   These are the tractus olfacto-hypothalamicus medialis, the tractus olfacto-hypothalamicus lateralis, and the tractus strio-thalamicus et hypothalamicus.   The bundle first mentioned is connected with the ventromedial or septal portion, and the second with the lateral segment of the telencephalon, while the third connects with more intermediate regions, that is, with striatal and epistriatal centers.   Of these the tractus olfacto-hypothalamicus medialis is the smallest. It is myelinated and, in its course through the diencephalon (fig. 451A), runs ventral to the tractus olfacto-hypothalamicus lateralis. Its descending fibers originate from the pars supracommissuralis septi (figs. 552 and 553) and end in the lobi inferiores (figs. 449, 450, 451, and 456) in front of the termination of the tractus olfacto-hypothalamicus lateralis. This system is very constant throughout vertebrates, for it probably represents the septal portion of the fornix

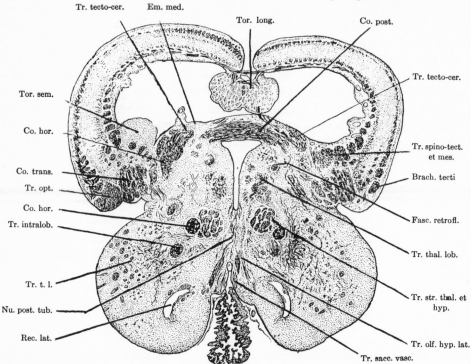

FIG. 457. A cross section through the brain of a cod, having an atrophied left eye.

Brach.tecti, brachium tecti; *Co.hor.*, commissura horizontalis; *Co.post.*, commissura posterior; *Co.trans.*, commissura transversa; *Em.med.*, eminentia medialis; *Fasc.retrofl.*, fasciculus retroflexus; *Nu.post.tub.*, nucleus posterior tuberis; *Rec.lat.*, recessus lateralis; *Sacc.vasc.*, saccus vasculosis; *Tor. long.*, torus longitudinalis; *Tor.sem.*, torus semicircularis; *Tr.olf.hyp.lat.*, tractus olfacto-hypothalamicus lateralis; *Tr.intralob.*, tractus intralobaris; *Tr.opt.*, tractus opticus; *Tr.sacc.vasc.*, tractus sacci vasculosi; *Tr.spino-tect.et mes.*, tractus spino-tectalis et mesencephalicus; *Tr.str.thal.et hyp.*, tractus strio-thalamicus et hypothalamicus; *Tr.t.l.*, tractus tecto-lobaris; *Tr.tecto-cer.*, tractus tecto-cerebellaris.

system as found in higher forms. In many teleosts it is accompanied by direct olfactory fibers which originate in the formatio bulbaris (*Kudo*, '23). The tractus olfacto-hypothalamicus medialis is believed to have associated with it the tractus hypothalamo-olfactorius medialis. To both these bundles the term medial forebrain bundle is sometimes applied. This ascending tract arises from the nucleus tuberis posterior. Part of its fibers decussate in the diencephalon, others in the commissura anterior. By means of this tract impulses are transmitted to the precommissural (septal) parts of the forebrain from postinfundibular regions (*Sheldon*, '12).

The other two tracts, the lateral olfacto-hypothalamic and the strio-hypothalamic, in many teleosts, although not in Gadus, have a joint course. Both contain descending and ascending fibers. The descending fibers (figs. 450, 451, 456 to 459) originate in the paleopallium, the epistriatum, and the striatum, and end, after a partial decussation in the commissura anterior, the nucleus entopeduncularis, the corpus glomerulosum pars rotunda, and the most caudal part of the hypothalamus, the tuber posterior, where they come into synaptic relation with cells of origin of the medial longitudinal fasciculus (*Sheldon*, '12), through which bundle impulses from the olfactory (and possibly also non-olfactory) centers of the telencephalon are transmitted to the efferent centers of the medulla oblongata and the spinal cord. Similar hypothalamic connections are maintained by the basal olfactory tract of higher vertebrates.

As yet it has not been possible to determine the type of impulses carried over these tracts from hypothalamic to telencephalic centers. Possibly they provide for the transmission of gustatory impulses forward, for the work of *Herrick* ('05) indicates that the tertiary gustatory tract of his account arises in the frontal gustatory nucleus (v. G. K., fig. 147) and terminates in the lobi inferiores.

The hypothalamus in these higher fishes is obviously a correlation center for olfactory, gustatory, and other types of sensory impulses. From this region tracts pass to the efferent centers of the medulla oblongata. The hypothalamus (perhaps the ventral thalamus as well) are important correlation centers in the paths involved in feeding. In this they are in contrast to the dorsal thalamus and the midbrain centers, which are concerned in the correlation of exteroceptive and proprioceptive sensations and in the establishment of photostatic and gravistatic impulses.

b. Connections with the Dorsal Thalamus. In addition to the longer conduction pathways, the diencephalon in these fishes contains a great number of fibrae propriae, which are of much interest. Those establishing dorsoventral and ventrodorsal connections will be considered first. These serve largely to relate ventral thalamic and hypothalamic areas with the dorsal thalamus and the midbrain. Among such dorsoventral connections may be mentioned the tractus thalamo-lobaris or mamillaris, mentioned before (page 931). This originates in part in the nucleus anterior but includes both ascending and descending fibers (*Wallenberg*, '07; *Holmgren*, '20). The ascending fibers arise from the large cells of the mammillary recess and lobi inferiores hypothalamici and are considered by *Holmgren* ('20) the equivalent of the mammillo-thalamic or Vicq d'Azyr bundle of mammals. Such an homology needs confirmation. The descending fibers reach these regions from the nucleus anterior thalami, and also join the commissura horizontalis which they accompany in both directions. Another tract providing for dorsoventral connections is the tractus mesencephalo-lobaris or lobo-mesencephalicus (*Holmgren*, '20). This arises at a caudal level of the lobi inferiores and runs dorsofrontalward, losing itself in or near the posterior commissure (fig. 456, tr. mes. lob. ant). The caudal part of the tract may even reach the tectum, constituting thus a so-called tractus lobo-tectalis.

The tracts mentioned above must not be confused with the tractus tuberodorsalis of *Goldstein* ('05; fig. 451A), which has a very peculiar course. *Holm-*

gren studied this bundle very carefully and termed it the tractus tubero-mesen-cephalicus.   Beginning — or ending — in the frontomedial part of the hypothal-amus (tuber cinereum) near the ventricle, its fibers curve lateralward and then ascend along the periphery of the thalamus.   They terminate in the dorsal part of this latter area, probably in the eminentia thalami or nucleus lentiformis (*Ariëns Kappers*, '21).   This bundle varies considerably in its development in different animals.   *Holmgren* ('20) found it well developed in Callionymus; less well developed in Osmerus.   In Callionymus *Holmgren* believed that it did not end in the dorsal thalamus but continued on into the torus semicircularis. He thought that some of it might cross in the posterior commissure.   A study of certain other fishes (*Ariëns Kappers*) showed that it is largest in Thynnus, very large in Cyprinus, smaller in Gadus, and completely lacking in Monopterus.

A fourth connection between the thalamic and hypothalamic regions is medi-ated by the tractus geniculo-hypothalamicus of *Franz* ('12), who thought that the fibers arose in the lateral geniculate nucleus and then ran backward and down-ward.   An attempt to follow these fibers in certain fishes, including Pleuronec-tidae, in which, of the group studied, they were the best developed, was not entirely successful.   In the preparation available the tract appeared to pass by the geniculate nucleus rather than arise from it and suggested that the fibers in ques-tion are branches of the posterior commissure (*Ariëns Kappers*).   *Holmgren* thought that the tract arises from the subhabenular portion of the (preoptic) peri-ventricular gray.   *Shanklin* ('35) related the tract to the lateral geniculate nucleus.

In addition to the dorsoventral correlation tracts in this region there are inter-nuncial fibers concerned in interrelating various parts of the preoptic and hypo-thalamic areas.   Fibers arising in the preoptic nuclei pass back to the tuber cinereum region.   Of such bundles the best known is the so-called tractus pre-thalamo-hypothalamicus.   This tract has its origin in the nucleus preopticus magnocellularis (figs. 449, 450, 545, 552, 553, 558).   If the optic chiasma occupies its usual position under the diencephalon, this unmyelinated bundle passes over it and hence was called the fasciculus supraopticus by *Röthig* ('11), who identified it in most classes of vertebrates.   Caudally the tract, after being joined by fibers from the ventral hypothalamic nuclei (especially large in Belone), passes into the hypophysis and the saccus (*Sheldon;* tractus praethalamo-saccularis and trac-tus praethalamo-hypophysis).   These tracts are visceral in function since they terminate around the blood vessels of the saccus and hypophysis.   *Holmgren* also saw these fibers ending around the cells of the hypophysis.   Such bundles are very evident in Lota, the cod, and the eel, where the nucleus preopticus magnocellularis is highly developed.

Another tract belonging to the frontal region of the tuber cinereum is the trac-tus intralobaris (fig. 457, tr. intralob.).   This arises from the tuber cinereum and ends in the caudal part of the lobi inferiores.   Another short connection relating hypothalamic and ventral thalamic centers is the tractus rotundo-lobaris (or lobo-rotundus; fig. 458).   This originates, at least in part, from the cells of the lobi inferiores and recessus mamillaris and enters the myelinated capsule of the nucleus rotundus (fig. 458, tr. rot. lob.).   In addition to these larger, more definite tracts there are many short, internuncial fibers connecting various diencephalic centers.   For a further account of these, reference is made to the paper of *Holmgren* ('20).   The details of these finer connections are too complicated to fall within the scope of the present description.

c. Interrelating Commissural Systems.   The commissures of the diencephalon are numerous.   However, many of them merely have their decussations here, their origin and termination being largely if not wholly in mesencephalic regions.   They belong, then, no more to the hypothalamic and ventral thalamic regions than to other portions of the brain.   Among such commissures may be mentioned the commissura minor, the commissura transversa, and the commissura horizontalis.

The commissura minor apparently accompanies the fasciculus medialis of the optic nerve to the frontal part of the tectum (*Ariëns Kappers*, '06, '21 ; *Charlton*, '33 ; p. 931).   The commissura transversa, which is much larger than the commissura minor, decussates ventral to it.   This commissura transversa interconnects the caudal portions of the torus semicircularis and the tectum — and perhaps nucleus isthmi — of one side with the corresponding areas of the other side (figs. 449 to 451 and 456 to 459).   It is surprising that this commissural connection associated with the most caudal portions of the mesencephalon should cross at the most frontal level of the diencephalon.   Whether this is due to a functional relation between the postchiasmatic region of the hypothalamus and the torus semicircularis is not certain but probable, since both have secondary acoustico-lateral fibers from the medulla oblongata, the torus receiving the tractus octavo-mesencephalicus, the tuber anterius, the tractus octavo-hypothalamicus.   The static function of the postchiasmatic region is further proved by the origin of a tract — the tractus lobo-cerebellaris — from the frontal part of the hypothalamus (in Periophthalmus) to the cerebellum (fig. 447).

Crossing at a level immediately caudal but not so far ventral as the commissura transversa is the commissura horizontalis of *Fritsch* ('78 ; figs. 450, 451A, 456 to 459).   Primitively this bundle follows a horizontal course, but in higher fishes, after passing through the nucleus rotundus or corpus glomerulosum pars rotunda (fig. 458) where it is joined by fibers of the tractus rotundo-pretectalis, it curves dorsalward and frontalward, ascending toward the frontal tectal region.   In the latter part of its course it is accompanied by fibers of the tecto-cerebellar tract (fig. 458 on the right).   Both the origin and termination of this tract are to be sought in the frontal part of the midbrain roof and in the nucleus pretectalis, both of which lie at a considerable distance oral to the corpus glomerulosum pars rotunda, at about the upper level of the decussation.   Thus the commissura horizontalis forms a double arch.   This course is to be explained from the fact that the corpus glomerulosum pars rotunda in which the commissure is embedded originally occupied a position farther frontalward and dorsalward (page 925).   As a consequence of the backward shifting of this nuclear mass, a corresponding shifting of the limbs of the horizontal commissure crossing in the pretectal area occurred.   *Franz* ('12) was of the opinion that commissura horizontalis contributed fibers to the corpus glomerulosum pars rotunda. It is probable that if present these are collateral rather than stem fibers, since the tract does not appear to diminish in size in its course through the nucleus.

Ventral to the horizontal commissure is the commissura subhorizontalis, observed by *Haller* ('98) and *Holmgren* ('20) in Callionymus. This bundle does not enter the nucleus rotundus, but, after a caudal course, spreads out lateral to

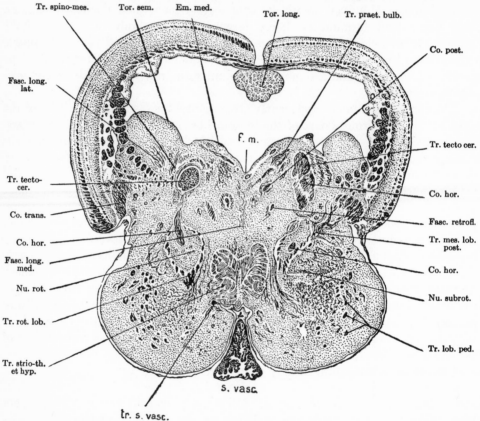

Fig. 458. A cross section through the midbrain and diencephalon of the cod, caudal to the plane of figure 457 and in front of figure 445.

Co.hor., commissura horizontalis; *Co.post.*, commissura posterior; *Co.trans.*, commissura transversa; *Em.med.*, eminentia medialis; *Fasc.long.lat.*, fasciculus longitudinalis lateralis; *Fasc.long.med.*, fasciculus longitudinalis medialis; *Fasc.retrofl.* fasciculus retroflexus; *Nu.rot.*, nucleus rotundus; *nu.subrot.*, nucleus subrotundus; *S.vasc.*, saccus vasculosus; *Tor.long.*, torus longitudinalis; *Tor.sem.*, torus semicircularis; *Tr.lob.ped.*, tractus lobo-peduncularis; *Tr.mes.lob.post.*, tractus mesencephalolobaris posterior; *Tr.praet.bulb.*, tractus pretecto-bulbaris; *Tr.rot.lob.*, tractus rotundo-lobaris; *Tr.s.vasc.*, tractus sacci vasculosi; *Tr.spino-mes.*, tractus spino-mesencephalicus; *Tr.strio-th.et hyp.*, tractus strio-thalamicus et hypothalamicus; *Tr.tecto-cer.*, tractus tecto-cerebellaris.

this nucleus and terminates (and arises) in the lobi inferiores. This system appears to be closely related in function to the pre- and postinfundibular commissures. The preinfundibular commissure (or commissura tuberis, fig. 450, co. tuberis.) connects the lateral parts of the hypothalamus. The somewhat larger postinfundibular commissure establishes similar connections behind the infundibulum. This latter commissure is not so large as in plagiostomes. In this postinfundibular commissure run neuraxes of cells of the saccus vasculosus or infundibular sense organ.

d. *The Saccus Vasculosus, with its Connections.*   Johnston ('01, in ganoids) and *Boeke* ('01, in teleosts) gave the first correct descriptions of the cellular structure of the saccus vasculosus.   *Dammerman* ('10) published a detailed account of the fiber connections of the region.   This latter observer found that among teleosts the saccus was best developed in sea fishes, less developed in fishes living in fresh water, and least developed in those making their homes in shallow water.

The epithelium of the inner lining of the saccus (fig. 2B) is composed of supporting cells and neurosensory cells, the ventricular surfaces of which are ciliated.   The neuraxes emerging from these latter cells form the tractus sacci vasculosi, which passes through the ridge connecting the infundibulum with the recessus posterior.   Immediately behind the ridge the fibers cross and then separate into three or four bundles.   Of these bundles the lateral ones run toward the nucleus sacci vasculosi while the two medial tracts, sometimes united into a single unpaired bundle, enter the frontal part of the tuberculum posterius.   They pass through this tuberculum and probably end in the dorsal part of the thalamus (*Dammerman's* tractus sacco-thalamicus).   In Gadus, this system forms the greater part and, in trout, the smaller part of the bundle.   These fibers are accompanied sometimes by secondary fibers from the nucleus sacci vasculosi (fig. 441).

Generally the lateral fibers to the nucleus sacci vasculosi are more numerous than the medial fibers.   Such lateral fibers do not cross in all teleosts (*Dammerman*, '10), although they are thought to do so in some.   From the nucleus sacci vasculosi a secondary tract emerges and passes through the tuberculum posterius into the base of the midbrain.   It probably extends as far as the beginning of the medulla oblongata and corresponds to the tractus tubero-posterius of *Goldstein* ('05).   Visceral fibers to the saccus from the nucleus magnocellularis preopticus[4] and the lateral and ventral hypothalamic nuclei (the thalamo-saccular part of the tractus prethalamo-hypothalamicus) have been described (p. 934).

The saccus, as in plagiostomes, probably is concerned in the perception of intracerebral liquid pressure.   Thus it may be used by the animal in determining depth, this perception being transmitted as changes in pressure.   In this connection it is of interest that certain teleosts are provided with an apparatus connected with the swimming bladder which is greatly influenced by pressure, and the central end of which (Weber's organ) lies above the saccus (*Ariëns Kappers*, '21).

e. *Connections with the Lower Centers.*   The ventral thalamus and especially the hypothalamus constitute the most important correlation areas of the diencephalon in these higher fishes, and consequently require, on the efferent side of the arc, relatively well developed discharge paths to lower centers.   The materials for such correlative and effective functions are provided by the connections typical of these regions, as may be seen from the following brief review.

---

[4] The position of the nucleus preopticus magnocellularis at the frontal end of the sulcus limitans suggests a possible visceral efferent function.   According to *Holmgren* ('18a and '20) this is the region of termination of the nervus terminalis, the sensory fibers of which, according to *Brookover* ('10), are accompanied by preganglionic fibers to the frontal blood vessels.

Thus connections with olfactory centers of the forebrain and gustatory regions of the medulla oblongata indicate that they are primarily concerned in the mediating of feeding reactions.   These are aided by the correlation of the olfactory and gustatory fibers with those from the saccus, for most fishes, in their search for food, are limited to certain depths of water.   Such correlations are aided further by the impulses received from the cerebellum and discharged to it (tractus lobo-cerebellaris).   It is to be expected, then, that these ventral portions will have

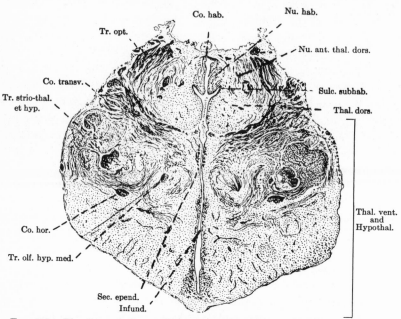

FIG. 459.   The diencephalon of Monopterus javanensis.   *van der Horst*.   Note the limited development of the dorsal thalamus in contrast to that of the ventral thalamus and hypothalamus.

Co.hab., commissura habenularum; *Co.hor.*, commissura horizontalis; *Hypothal.*, hypothalamus; *Infund.*, infundibulum; *Nu.hab.*, nucleus habenulae; *Sec.epend.*, secretory ependyma; *Sulc.subhab.*, sulcus subhabenularis; *Thal.dors.*, dorsal thalamus; *Thal.vent.*, ventral thalamus; *Tr.olf.hyp.med.*, tractus olfacto-hypothalamicus medialis; *Tr.opt.*, tractus opticus.

important connections with the efferent nuclei of the branchial nerves.   Indeed, the importance of the midbrain as a center concerned with bodily movements and posture is equaled by that of the ventral diencephalon as a region concerned with body nutrition.   Two of such paths to efferent centers may be mentioned: they are the tractus lobo- and mamillo-peduncularis and the centrifugal portion of the X bundle of Mayser ('81).   The lobo- and mamillo-peduncular fibers have their origin in the caudal segments of the lobi inferiores, the recessus mamillaris (fig. 447).   They run caudalward parallel to the nucleus interpeduncularis and can be traced through the base of the midbrain and the medulla oblongata to the most caudal part of the vagus region.   The centrifugal part of Mayser's bundle X originates from the lateral segments of the hypothalamus.   It runs caudalward dorsomedial to the lateral bundle of the tract and supplies the motor nuclei of the trigeminal and facial nerves (*Wallenberg*, '07).

The static functions of the hypothalamus are evident not only through its fiber relations to the saccus vasculosus but also through its connections, afferent and efferent, with the cerebellum.   It receives crossed fibers of the brachium conjunctivum which terminate in the lateral wall of the lobus inferior, and it discharges impulses from the anterior part of the hypothalamus to the cerebellum by way of the tractus lobo-cerebellaris.   This part of the hypothalamus, which is particularly distinct in Periophthalmus, receives, among other fibers, the termination of the octavo-hypothalamic tract (fig. 447, Tr. oct. thal. et hyp.).

THE MESENCEPHALIC AND DIENCEPHALIC CENTERS IN AMPHIBIANS

The following account of tailed amphibians is based particularly on the descriptions of these regions in Necturus and Amblystoma by *Herrick* ('17, '25, '30, '33) and in various urodeles by *Röthig* ('23, '24, '27).   In the account of the tailless forms the studies of *Bellonci* ('88), *Gaupp* ('89), *Ariëns Kappers* and *Hammer* ('18), *Ariëns Kappers* ('21), *Larsell* ('23 and '31), and *Röthig* ('23, '26, and '27) have been utilized especially, and checked on the series of frog brain available in the collection of the Laboratory of Comparative Neurology at the University of Michigan.

THE TECTAL AND SUBTECTAL NUCLEAR CENTERS IN THE TAILED AMPHIBIANS

The morphologic and histologic characteristics of the brain of Necturus indicate, according to *Herrick* ('17), that it is primitive even if in certain respects degenerate in type. The walls of the mesencephalon and diencephalon are relatively thin and the ventricles are very greatly dilated (fig. 461).

FIG. 460.   A dorsal view of the brain of Rana mugiens.

The midbrain portion—arbitrarily divided from the diencephalon by a line drawn from a point rostral to the posterior commissure (or through it) to a level immediately behind the posterior tuber — has the usual tectal and peduncular or tegmental portions.   The posterior boundary of the mesencephalon, established dorsally by the decussatio veli (which includes the crossing of the trochlear nerve), is indicated laterally by the fissura isthmi and caudoventrally by the fovea isthmi. The floor of the midbrain in these amphibians is relatively very much shorter rostro-caudally than is the roof.   The tectal portion of the mesencephalon cannot be sharply delimited from the tegmental portions in ordinary preparations. However, the neurons are more closely packed in the tectal than in the tegmental regions and this permits the drawing of an approximate line of separation between the two areas.

The tectum in Necturus (figs. 461 and 462) has several rather indistinct layers. At the surface of the tectum is a relatively wide band, consisting to a considerable extent at least of medullated fibers, which is termed the stratum album.   Internal to this are the cellular layers of the tectum, collectively termed the stratum

griseum.   At the line between these two layers of fibers and cells is a band of
tangential fibers, largely unmyelinated, which constitutes the tractus tecto-
peduncularis profundus (fig. 462) of *Herrick* ('17), a connection between the
tectal and peduncular or tegmental regions.   It is to be noted, then, that in these
forms the efferent fibers are external to the cell layer, homologous to the stratum
griseum centrale and stratum griseum periventriculare of reptiles (*Huber* and

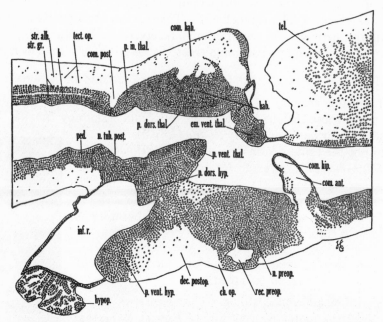

Fig. 461.   Drawing of a toluidin blue preparation, sagittally cut, of the brain
of Necturus, showing the positions of various areas of the mesencephalon and
the diencephalon.   *Huber* and *Crosby*.

b, layer of fibers, largely unmedullated, separating the stratum griseum into
inner and outer layers; *ch.op.*, chiasma opticum; *com.ant.*, commissura anterior;
com.hab., commissura habenularum; *com.post.*, commissura posterior; *dec.
postop.*, decussatio postoptica; *em.vent.thal.*, eminentia ventralis thalami;
hab., habenula; *hypop.*, hypophysis; *inf.r.*, extension of IIIrd ventricle into
infundibular region; *n.preop.*, nucleus preopticus; *n.tub.post.*, nucleus tuberis
posterior; *p.dors.hyp.*, pars dorsalis hypothalami; *p.dors.thal.*, pars dorsalis
thalami; *p.in.thal.*, pars intercalaris thalami; *p.vent.hyp.*, pars ventralis hypothalami; *p.vent.thal.*, pars ventralis thalami; *ped.*, peduncle (Herrick); *rec.
preop.*, recessus preopticus; *str.alb.*, stratum album; *str.gr.*, stratum griseum;
tect.op., tectum opticum; *tel.*, telencephalon.

Crosby, '33, '34).   Internal to this is an outer gray layer separated from a similar
inner layer by a band of unmyelinated tangential fibers (fig. 461), probably dendrites for the most part, which also extend between tectal and tegmental areas.
In Necturus these two gray layers apparently consist of neurons of similar type.
Internal to the inner layer and next to the ventricle is the stratum ependymale,
which contains some scattered neurons among the ependymal cells.   The ependymal elements thicken up below the posterior commissure to form the subcommissural organ of *Dendy* and *Nicholls* ('10), from which Reissner's fiber takes origin
(fig. 462, *S*).   A somewhat similar region of thickened ependyma was observed

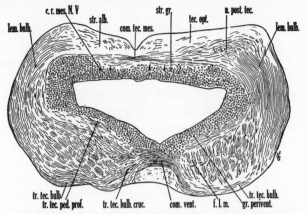

FIG. 462A. Drawing to illustrate certain paths in the tectal region of Necturus made from a transverse series prepared by the pyridin silver method. *Huber* and *Crosby.*

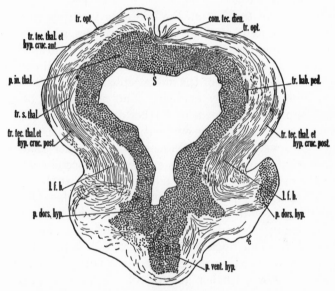

FIG. 462B. Drawing of a transverse section, cephalic to figure 462A, to show certain fiber tracts in the region. *Huber* and *Crosby.*

c.r.mes.N.V., cells of the mesencephalic root of the trigeminal nerve; *com.tec.dien.,* commissura tecti diencephali; *com.tec.mes.,* commissura tecti mesencephali; *com.vent.,* commissura ventralis; *f.l.m.,* fasciculus longitudinalis medialis; *gr.perivent.,* griseum periventriculare; *lem. bulb.,* lemniscus bulbaris; *l.f.b.,* lateral forebrain bundle; *n.post.tec.,* nucleus posterior tecti; *p.dors.hyp.,* pars dorsalis hypothalami; *p.in. thal.,* pars intercalaris thalami; *str.alb.,* stratum album; *str.gr.,* stratum griseum; *tec.opt.,* tectum opticum; *tr.hab.ped.,* tractus habenulopeduncularis; *tr.opt.,* tractus opticus; *tr.s.thal.,* tractus spino-thalamicus; *tr.tec.bulb.,* tractus tecto-bulbaris; *tr.tec.bulb.cruc.,* tractus tecto-bulbaris cruciatus; *tr.tec.ped.prof.,* tractus tecto-peduncularis profundus; *tr.tec.thal. et hyp.cruc.ant.,* tractus tecto-thalamicus et hypothalamicus cruciatus anterior; *tr.tec.thal. et hyp.cruc.post.,* tractus tecto-thalamicus et hypothalamicus cruciatus posterior. (*S,* see p. 940.)

at the posterior end of the tectum by *Herrick,* at the level of which lies a dorso-medial group of cells of the mesencephalic root of the trigeminal nerve.

The histologic characters of certain of the tectal cells are figured in the *Herrick* paper, to which reference is made here for those interested in details of the cytoarchitectonic structure.   One of the typical neurons of the region (*Herrick,* '17, in figs. 22, 23) has its cell body in the stratum griseum and sends its dendrites into the stratum album.   Such dendrites may spread out for great distances in the tectum, sometimes throughout the whole dorsoventral extent, and thus, as *Herrick* pointed out, come into intimate relation with various functional systems.   The neuraxis ordinarily arises from one of the larger dendrites.   Soon after its origin it acquires a myelin sheath and becomes a constituent of some efferent tract. The arrangement of the tectal gray suggests that in these forms there has not been as yet a differentiation of a layer chiefly receptive in character such as is found in the stratum fibrosum et griseum superficiale of both teleosts and reptiles (see discussion, p. 944).

At the caudal end of the tectum the midbrain ventricle widens out into the recessus posterior.   In figure 462 the wall of this recess, which is composed of an area of closely packed neurons that are present in both Necturus and Amblystoma, has been termed the nucleus posterior tecti (or inferior colliculus).   More dorsally in the wall lies the nucleus of the mesencephalic root of the trigeminal nerve (fig. 462); root fibers of this are evident.   This nucleus has been discussed for amphibians in Chapter V and needs no further description at this time.   Ventral to the nucleus posterior tecti is the eminentia subcerebellaris tegmenti (fig. 462), which belongs, however, to the rhombencephalon rather than to the mesencephalon.   Immediately dorsal to this eminentia subcerebellaris tegmenti, behind the nucleus posterior tecti and, in adult Necturus, at the angle between the midbrain and the cerebellum, is the secondary visceral nucleus (*Herrick,* '17).   This occupies a position in the posterior wall of the posterior recess in larval Amblystoma.   A homologous secondary visceral nucleus has been identified in the frog by *Larsell* ('23).   This nucleus in larval stages is behind the sulcus separating the midbrain from the isthmus region and so is not to be regarded as a mesencephalic structure.   For a further account of this nucleus page 366 should be consulted.

THE TECTAL AND SUBTECTAL NUCLEAR CENTERS IN TAILLESS AMPHIBIANS

A comparison of the midbrain regions of a tailless amphibian (such as Rana mugiens) with corresponding regions in Necturus emphasizes certain interesting variations in the amphibian pattern.   The optic tectal portion is relatively large in the frog compared with that in Necturus.   However, it still retains much of a primitive character when the area in the frog is compared with the area in higher forms, for its surface is covered by a wide stratum album and the stratum griseum suggests in position the embryonic central gray.   However, this stratum griseum can be further subdivided into several layers separated by narrow fiber bands.   *Pedro Ramón* ('96) studied the finer structure of the tectum in the frog and the results of this work are illustrated in figure 463.   It will be seen that internal to the stratum album is the principal cell layer, the homologue, probably, of the outer layer of the stratum griseum in Necturus. In the frog this is separated from the underlying granular layers by a medullated band of fibers, the stratum medullare profundum. This is more superficial in frogs than in bony fishes and consists very largely of efferent fibers. It is said to contain some afferent bundles, the spino- and bulbo-tectal tracts of the frog (*Ariëns Kappers*). The inner granular zone (probably for the most part homologous with the inner part of the stratum griseum in Necturus) can be subdivided in the frog into three more or less distinct portions — an outer cellular (granular) layer, a middle cellular (granular) layer, and an inner cellular (granular) layer — by narrow plexiform bands. The arrangement in the frog in spite of this layering is not so different fundamentally from that in Necturus, for in both animals the cells of the various layers send their major dendrites toward the periphery to arborize in the stratum album, the shorter dendrites form the plexiform layers, and the neuraxes are given off the major dendrites rather than from the cell bodies of the neurons. Such neuraxes from certain of the more deeply situated granular cells in the frog ascend to the optic fiber layer and appear to join it. Their termination is

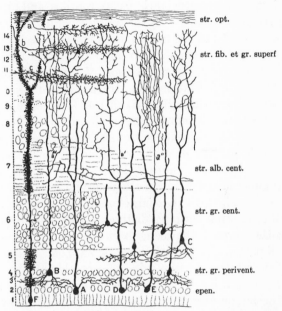

FIG. 463. The cytoarchitectonic structure of the tectum opticum of the frog. *P. Ramon.*
epen., ependyma; *str.alb.cent.*, stratum album centrale; *str.fib.et gr.superf.*, stratum fibrosum et griseum superficiale; *str.gr.cent.*, stratum griseum centrale; *str.gr.perivent.*, stratum griseum periventriculare; *str.opt.*, stratum opticum.

not known. It is possible that they are comparable to the fibrae tectales nervi optici of certain vertebrates (as for example, reptiles), which are sometimes regarded as passing to the retina. Neuraxes of the cells of the middle and deeper tectal layers pass toward the surface and break up into collaterals near the optic tract layer. Still other neuraxes, arising in the inner and middle layer, enter the stratum album centrale (or stratum medullare).

Examination of the optic tectum in the frog (*Huber* and *Crosby*, '33, '33a, '34) material leads one to think that the pattern described above resembles that of fishes on the one hand and of reptiles and birds on the other hand, more especially in that the main efferent pathways which, functionally considered, homologize with the pathways constituting the stratum album centrale of fishes and reptiles, but which in urodeles lie superficial to the main cell layer, the stratum griseum centrale, in frogs, as in fishes and birds, lie deep to this layer. This apparent transposition of the main efferent pathways is explainable on the supposition that the urodele optic tectum represents, phylogenetically considered, a less developed center. In urodeles it is composed essentially of a central gray layer and of a peripheral white layer, of which the superficial portion consists of optic and other afferent (and efferent) tectal paths while the deeper portion is composed chiefly of efferent paths. In the frog a certain proportion of cells have migrated peripheral-ward, in response to neurobiotactic influences, so that internal to the stratum opticum a layer of gray and white appears corresponding to the stratum fibrosum et griseum superficiale of fishes, reptiles, and birds, and, internal to this, a stratum griseum centrale. In the more generalized reptiles (*Huber* and *Crosby*, '33), as represented in the turtles, with the increase in the importance of the tectum as a sensory correlation center, a greater migration of cells toward the surface occurs, evidenced by a stratification of alternate gray and white layers and a more definite delimitation of a stratum griseum centrale. As a result of this migration the stratum griseum centrale (the neurons of which send their neuraxes into the stratum album centrale, the main efferent fiber layer) is separated by the stratum album centrale from a deeper layer, the stratum griseum periventiculare, which remains near the ventricle but more or less distinctly separated from it by a plexiform fibrous layer, the stratum fibrosum periventriculare. This peripheral migration of the neurons of the stratum griseum centrale causes their neuraxes, which to a large extent arise from dendrites, to turn toward the ventricles, often forming distinct loops, and to pass to the border of the tectum, either through the deeper part of stratum griseum centrale or through the stratum album centrale, which in reptiles appears as a definite efferent fiber layer situated between the stratum griseum centrale and the stratum griseum periventriculare. In certain lizards a further step in the development occurs with the entrance of the major number of the neuraxes of the nerve cells of the stratum griseum centrale almost directly into the stratum album centrale. The cells adjacent to the ventricular ependyma in all cases send their neuraxes into the efferent layer. The above discussion is based on a comparison of the accounts of the amphibian tectum with the results of investigations of the cellular structure and arrangement and the fiber connections of the reptilian tectum by *Huber* and *Crosby* ('33, '33a, '34). On this basis there may be recognized in frogs, as in reptiles: (1) a stratum opticum overlaid by a primordial stratum zonale, (2) a stratum fibrosum et griseum superficiale, (3) a stratum griseum centrale, (4) a stratum album centrale, and (5 and 6) a stratum griseum periventriculare intermingled with a stratum fibrosum periventriculare.

The nucleus posterior tecti (or inferior collicular region, fig. 462), identified in Necturus chiefly through its fiber connections, appears in the frog as a strongly developed ventricular eminence on either side of the brain, which often is termed, as in other lower animals, the torus semicircularis. The tori of the two sides are separated frontally, but caudally they join in the midline (fig. 464). This fusion, which occurs first in amphibians, is of considerable importance morphologically, for it separates the ventricle in this region into two portions, an optic ventricle and an aqueduct. The union of the tori semicirculares is a further step toward the formation of the inferior colliculi as these occur in higher forms.

The tori semicirculares develop at the place of union of the tegmentum and the tectum. They consist of small cells with a very considerable number of large cells scattered among them. Their relation to the tectum is indicated by the continuation within them of certain of the tectal layers. The periventricular

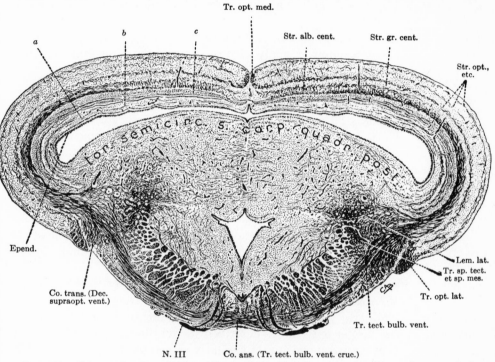

Fig. 464. Cross section through the midbrain of Rana mugiens (catesbyana). *a, b, c,* gray layers of the stratum griseum periventriculare; *Co.ans.(Tr.tect.bulb.vent.cruc.),* commissura ansulata (tractus tecto-bulbaris ventralis cruciatus); *Co.trans.(Dec.supraopt.vent.),* commissura transversa (decussatio supraoptica ventralis); *Epend.,* ependyma; *Lem.lat.,* lemniscus lateralis; *N.III,* nervus oculomotorius; *Str.alb.cent.,* stratum album centrale; *Str.gr.cent.,* stratum griseum centrale; *Str.opt.,etc.,* tractus opticus and other afferent tectal tracts; *Tr.opt.lat.,* tractus opticus lateralis; *Tr.opt.med.,* tractus opticus medialis; *Tr.sp.tect.et sp.mes.,* tractus spino-tectalis et spino-mesencephalicus; *Tr.tect.bulb.vent.,* tractus tecto-bulbaris ventralis.

layers of the tectum continue over the ventricular side of the tori. Associated fiber paths (acoustico-optic in character) permit an indirect correlation of the optic impulses reaching the tectum with the acoustic impulses distributed to the tori semicirculares.

A piriform-shaped nuclear mass in the isthmus region of the frog, crowded caudally against the subcerebellar region but, from connections and development essentially a midbrain structure, was termed by *Gaupp* ('89) the ganglion isthmi and recognized by him as the homologue of the corpus posterius of *Bellonci* ('88) and the nucleus magnus of *Stieda* ('75). The nucleus isthmi (fig. 164 and fig. 379) has been identified by other observers since *Gaupp's* work appeared and has been studied in particular by *Larsell* ('23) with regard to its structure and fiber connections.   It is very easily identified in frog material, since its cortex-like band of deeply staining cells, surrounding a medulla of scattered cells and fibers, is open only at the dorsomedial corner, where it is filled by thin fibers of cortical cells, and at the hilus which is situated ventrolaterally and through which fiber bundles pass.   The secondary visceral nucleus lies against the caudal and ventral end of the nucleus isthmi, but the position is purely topographic ; the two do not appear to be connected by fiber bundles and do not receive similar fibers.   The nucleus profundus mesencephali of fishes is also present in frogs (*Ariëns Kappers* and *Hammer*, '18 ; *Ariëns Kappers*, '21), as a diffuse mass of cells medial to the lateral lemniscus and continuous dorsally with the gray of the torus semicircularis.

MAJOR FIBER CONNECTIONS OF THE TECTAL AND SUBTECTAL REGIONS IN AMPHIBIANS

(a) *Optic System*.   Three optic bundles have been recognized in various amphibians.   Thus, in the frog, *Wlassek* ('93) identified, behind the optic chiasma, (1) a superficial or marginal optic bundle which follows the surface of the diencephalon dorsocaudalward to its termination in the stratum album of the tectum, (2) an axial bundle which runs more deeply, passing through both the nucleus anterior superior corporis geniculati thalami of *Bellonci* ('88) and the corpus geniculatum thalami of *Gaupp* ('89) on its way to the tectum, and finally (3) a basal optic bundle which passes caudalward to a nucleus in the base of the midbrain just in front of the level of the oculomotor nerve and undoubtedly comparable to the nucleus of the basal optic root of reptiles.   The three optic bundles were identified in substantially the same relations in Necturus by *Herrick* ('17, '33 ; figs. 462A and B), who, however, was unable to trace the axial bundle to its termination.   He ('33) described an anterior accessory optic tract, the homologue of the deeper optic fibers described for reptiles, as part of this axillary system.   That it corresponds to the similarly named tract in mammals needs demonstration.   This observer ('17) found that the basal optic root (posterior accessory tract; *Herrick*, '33) in these forms does not terminate directly in a nucleus but in a region of neuropil in the midbrain wall which is his area lateralis tegmenti (see page 953).   An outstanding difference in the two forms is to be found in the structure of the optic nerve itself, which in Necturus has retained its embryonic character, the space inside being continuous with the third ventricle ; here the optic nerve is entirely unmedullated.   In Necturus the part of the tectum receiving optic tract fibers via the marginal optic tract was regarded by *Herrick* ('17) as the true optic tectum or superior colliculus.   This involves the dorsomedial part of the tectum but does not extend to its caudal end.   A study of the optic tract and centers in Amblystoma and frog led *Herrick* ('25) to much the same conclusions which he had reached earlier in the study of Necturus material.   He believed that the tract terminates in the optic tectum.   The basal optic root was carried by *Herrick* to the nucleus ectomamillaris, which he found to lie deep within the motor tegmentum in the urodele and which is a correlation center for various impulses, including, in addition to optic impulses, gustatory and olfactory impulses.   In the frog the nucleus is better differentiated from the general tegmental area and apparently is dominated more completely by optic impulses; it is really, then, a nucleus of the basal optic root. The diencephalic optic centers will be considered later (p. 959).

(b) *Secondary Ascending Tracts.* Vying in importance with the optic tracts to the tectum are the secondary ascending tracts from the cord and the medulla oblongata to this area. The spino-tectal and associated spino-thalamic tracts, described by *Herrick* in both Amblystoma ('14) and Necturus ('17, '30) as spinal lemniscus, arise largely heterolaterally in spinal cord regions, cross in the ventral decussation, and swing frontalward with other ascending systems. They pass through the medulla oblongata in company with the spino-cerebellar tract and in large part intermingled with it (figs. 377 and 378). At the level of the motor root of the trigeminal nerve, between the bulbo-tectal tract and this root, at the upper levels of the medulla oblongata, the spino-tectal and spino-cerebellar bundles swing lateralward, and the latter bundle separates off and enters the cerebellum. In the isthmus region the spino-tectal tract turns sharply dorsalward and occupies a position dorsomedial to the acoustico-lateral lemniscus and ventral to the mesencephalic root of the trigeminal nerve, and farther forward lateral to the tractus tecto-peduncularis posterior. The tract runs forward in this position, some of the bundles terminating in the caudal part of the pars dorsalis thalami but the majority of them ending in the lateral and caudal part of the tectum, to which region the name of colliculus inferior (*Herrick*, '17, or nucleus posterior, *Herrick*, '30) has been applied (fig. 462).

The acoustico-lateral lemniscus (*Herrick*, '17), from the contralateral acoustico-lateral areas (page 464), lies external to the spino-tectal tract. It runs forward through the stratum album centrale, distributing chiefly to the caudal and lateral parts of the tectum but sending some fibers to the optic portion of that area and others forward to the pars dorsalis thalami. Its distribution is similar then, in these forms, to that of the spino-tectal tract. Recently (1930) *Herrick* has applied to the acoustico-lateral lemniscus, which is obviously the homologue of the fasciculus longitudinalis lateralis of fishes, the name of bulbar lemniscus, because he believed that while its cells lie in the acoustico-lateral area of the medulla oblongata they are permitted to pick up impulses from various centers so that the fibers of this bulbar lemniscus carry various types of sensory impulses. Reference is made here to figures 376 to 378.

The origin of the bulbo-tectal tract is not definitely known as yet for Necturus, although in Amblystoma *Herrick* ('14, '17) believed it to arise in part from the contralateral gray associated with the spinal tract of the trigeminal and the fasciculus solitarius. In his 1930 paper *Herrick* has designated the tract the lateral bulbo-tectal tract or the primordial lateral lemniscus. He was unable to trace it to its origin; until such has been done the question as to whether or not it is a forerunner of the mammalian lateral lemniscus must remain unsettled. The lateral bulbo-tectal tract is associated with a system of descending fibers, the tractus tecto-spinalis posterior (*Herrick*, '30). The termination of this bulbo-tectal tract is in the nucleus posterior tecti, which nucleus gives rise, according to *Herrick*, to fibers of the supraoptic or postoptic system (bundles of the tractus tecto-thalamicus et hypothalamicus cruciatus posterior) and probably has a connection with the nuclei of the oculomotor nerves through the tractus tecto-peduncularis posterior, which swings ventralward and then forward from the nucleus.   The lateral bulbo-tectal tract is illustrated in figures 376 and 377.

The above account indicates that in tailed amphibians, as represented by Necturus, only the dorsal and medial tectal regions are under the direct influence of the optic tract.   The caudal and lateral parts of the area particularly, but other tectal regions as well, including those receiving optic impulses, receive secondary acoustico-lateral and spino-tectal fibers.   The bulbo-tectal tract is apparently confined in its midbrain distribution to the nucleus posterior tecti. In the rhombencephalon region immediately caudal to the mesencephalon is the secondary visceral nucleus, which receives the ascending secondary gustatory fibers (gustatory lemniscus, Herrick).

In adult frogs the lateral-line centers have disappeared and a cochlear nucleus has made its appearance within the medulla oblongata.   From this nucleus crossed and certain uncrossed secondary fibers ascend along the lateral wall of the rhombencephalon and distribute to the torus semicircularis and to some extent, as in plagiostomes and lower amphibians, to the optic tectum.   Collaterals and perhaps stem fibers are given off to the nucleus isthmi.   From this nucleus, isthmo-tectal fibers, partly crossed in the velum medullare anterius and partly uncrossed, run to the caudal regions of the tectum (Larsell, '23).

Spino-tectal or -mesencephalic (figs. 376 to 378) fascicles, homologous with those described for Necturus, reach the lower lateral parts of the torus semicircularis and extend forward to the frontal part of the tectum in the frog.   They are accompanied by contralateral, ascending trigemino-mesencephalic (bulbo-tectal) fibers from the gray about the spinal root of the trigeminal nerve, which likewise terminate in the torus semicircularis and the frontal tectal areas.   Ariëns Kappers and Hammer ('18) and Ariëns Kappers ('21) regarded this bundle as entering the deep medullary layer of the optic tectum, that is, the stratum album centrale.   Accompanying the bundle so described are fascicles which enter the more superficial receptive portions of the optic tectum and it is suggested (Huber and Crosby), although the matter requires experimental proof, that the fibers described as related to the superficial layers are bulbo- (and spino-) tectal, while those continuous with the stratum album centrale are tecto-spinal, corresponding to the tecto-spinal systems described for Necturus by Herrick ('33).   Both the spino-tectal and bulbo-tectal systems are thought to send forward fibers to the posterior end of the dorsal thalamus.

The tori semicirculares of the frog receive, in addition to the lateral lemniscus and spino- and bulbo-mesencephalic tracts, connections from the nucleus isthmi and contralateral torus semicircularis by means of the commissura transversa (figs. 464 and 467) and interconnections with the optic tectum through internuclear fibers.   An uncrossed connection between this area and the nucleus isthmi has not been definitely established in frogs.

(c) Descending Tectal Paths.   The efferent impulses leave the tectal regions in amphibians by a number of fiber systems.   Among these is the tecto-bulbar system (figs. 462 and 464), which in frogs consists of dorsal and ventral divisions similar to those in fishes.   The dorsal tecto-bulbar carries a considerable number of crossed fibers which decussate at a level in front of the crossing of the ventral tecto-bulbar tract.   A majority of the fibers of the dorsal bundle appear to terminate in or near the nuclei of the oculomotor and trochlear nerves.   Certain bundles run caudalward in company with the medial longitudinal fasciculus.

The ventral tecto-bulbar paths originate from the whole roof of the midbrain in the frog but more particularly from its middle and caudal portions.   They descend along the periphery of the mesencephalon.   Part of the fibers cross, the decussation occurring in the commissura ansulata (fig. 464) at the level of emergence of the oculomotor nerve.   The caudal extent of the tract has not as yet been ascertained.   There appears to be no reason to expect its relations to be other than those of the homologous tracts in fishes.   It is relatively safe to assume its termination around efferent centers, including reticular nuclei, of the medulla oblongata.

In larval Amblystoma ('14) and in Necturus ('17) *Herrick* described and figured a tractus tecto-bulbaris rectus et cruciatus.   He found the tract, which is myelinated, arising from all parts of the tectum but particularly from the more caudal and lateral portions (that is, from inferior collicular regions).   The greater portion of the fibers decussates in the ventral commissure (fig. 462), consequently behind the midbrain.   These, associated with uncrossed fibers, accumulate along the ventrolateral margin of the brain wall and then continue back through the medulla oblongata, some even reaching the spinal cord.   The tractus tecto-bulbaris rectus et cruciatus is in all probability the tractus tecto-bulbaris ventralis of the frog and various other vertebrates.

Another fiber system in Necturus (*Herrick*, '17), the tractus tecto-peduncularis, probably includes, among other systems, the tractus tecto-bulbaris dorsalis of the frog and of other forms.   The tecto-peduncular tract is divisible into superficial, intermediate, and deep portions.   The superficial portion, associated with all parts of the tectum, lies at the periphery of the tectum, swings ventro-medialward behind the emergence of the oculomotor, and distributes to homolateral and contralateral tegmental areas — including the oculomotor nuclei and the nuclei of the posterior commissure.   Other fibers join the medial longitudinal fasciculi of the same and opposite sides and ascend and descend to motor centers.   The intermediate tecto-tegmental tract interconnects the tectum and underlying tegmental regions.   The fibers are mainly unmyelinated and apparently uncrossed and were regarded by *Herrick* as formed mostly by dendrites of tegmental and tectal cells, thus making them partly afferent to the tectum.   The deep tecto-peduncular system is largely unmedullated and runs downward and forward to the region of the oculomotor and trochlear nuclei.   The bundles are crossed in part and in part terminate on the same side.   Reference is made here to figure 462.

Röthig ('27) described, as descending paths from the tectum of Cryptobranchus, a tractus tecto-bulbaris dorsomedialis, of which he considered the tractus tecto-bulbaris profundus of *Herrick* a part, and a tractus tecto-bulbaris ventrolateralis, which included, according to *Röthig*, a part of the tractus tecto-peduncularis superficialis of *Herrick*. The partial homology at least of the two latter tracts appears probable but the tractus tecto-bulbaris dorsomedialis, according to *Röthig*, decussates (at least in Cryptobranchus) in the more caudal part of the commissura tuberculi posterioris (commissura ansulata), while the tractus tecto-bulbaris profundus as described in Necturus by *Herrick* ('17) crosses in the ventral tegmental decussation.

(d) *Supraoptic Commissure System; Tectal Components*. The supraoptic commissural system is associated with tectal and subtectal areas. It also has connections with thalamic and hypothalamic regions. A brief résumé of its various components, in so far as they have been determined in amphibians, will be found under the account of the diencephalon. However, reference must be made to those parts which are primarily tectal in character.

In the frog that portion of the system called the commissura transversa in lower forms (fig. 464), and the ventral part of the ventral supraoptic decussation or Gudden's commissure in higher forms, interconnects the tori semicirculares of the two sides and has connections with the nucleus isthmi. Undoubtedly further tectal connections, and hypothalamic connections as well, are present in this form, although to our knowledge they have not been demonstrated as yet.

The supraoptic system, as described by *Herrick* ('17, '33) for the tailed amphibians, in part is tectal in character. That portion concerned with the tectum forms the tractus tecto-thalamicus et hypothalamicus cruciatus (figs. 462 and 466). This tract was identified in Siren and Salamandra by *Röthig* ('24 and '27) and in Proteus by *Kreht* ('31). It consists of an anterior and a posterior part. The anterior portion appears to connect the optic tectum (*Herrick*, '33; or all the tectum, *Röthig*, '24) with the contralateral thalamic areas, the lateral hypothalamic areas, and adjacent tegmental regions as far back as the tuberculum posterius. It may carry some intertectal fibers. Those associated with the thalamus appear to be unmedullated; the remainder are relatively heavily medullated. The posterior division is probably the homologue of the commissura transversa of fishes and frogs, for it connects with caudal and lateral portions of the tectum which receive acoustico-lateral and spino-tectal fibers (the inferior collicular region or nucleus posterior tecti of *Herrick*). Both myelinated and unmyelinated fibers are described and they are joined by a similar fiber bundle from the nucleus posterior tecti. The fibers are regarded by *Herrick* as mainly efferent with respect to the tectum, although a few incoming bundles suggest that a part of the system is commissural. A large portion of the tract terminates either in the pars ventralis thalami and the nucleus of the postoptic commissure of both sides or, after decussation in the more rostral part of the chiasma ridge, in the contralateral parts of the dorsal thalamus, the dorsal part of the hypothalamus, and the nucleus of the tuberculum posterius (*Herrick*). The pars anterior of the tractus tecto-thalamicus et hypothalamicus cruciatus is described as accompanying the marginal optic tract from the tectum to near the optic chiasm, where it separates off in order to cross behind that tract as the most anterior component of the supraoptic complex. The posterior division also crosses in the anterior part of the chiasmal ridge.   Its course is "parallel with the optic tract, but farther caudal and at a somewhat deeper level" (*Herrick*, '17).

(*e*) *Tecto-habenular and Tecto-cerebellar Connections.*   Tecto-habenular fibers are present in both tailed and tailless amphibians.   A crossed component has been described for the latter under the name of tractus tecto-habenularis cruciatus. Both tracts contain both myelinated and unmyelinated fibers.   The crossed tract decussates in the commissura tecti.   Terminal fibers to the pars inter-calata thalami, with collaterals to the commissure, suggest the presence of some habenulo-tectal fibers (*Herrick*, '17) in the bundles.   *Röthig* ('24 and '27) found tecto-habenular fibers in Necturus although he was unable to identify them with certainty in some other urodeles.

Between the tectum and the optic thalamic center in the frog are fibers which interconnect the two areas, the lateral tecto-thalamic tract (the primitive peduncle of the superior colliculus).   In Necturus a connection between the optic tectum and the dorsal part, and to a less extent the ventral part, of the thalamus has its chief connection (*Herrick*, '33) with the nucleus sensitivus (see page 959). It has been termed the tractus tecto-thalamicus rectus (*Herrick*, '17, and *Röthig*, '24 and '27) in various urodeles.

Tecto-cerebellar connections are present in the frog.   They are probably also present in the tailless amphibians (*Herrick*, '14 and '17), although apparently as diffuse fascicles.   In the frog a tecto-isthmal tract (*Gaupp*, '89; *Larsell*, '23) runs from the deeper layers of the optic tectum to the dorsomedial tip of the nucleus isthmi, which it enters.

From regions of the epiphysis to the end of the tectum there is a series of crossing fibers in the dorsal brain wall.   Most anterior of these is the commissura tecti diencephali (*Gaupp*, '89; *Herrick*, '17), which is partly commissural for ad-jacent regions and carries crossed tecto-habenular fascicles (*Herrick*, '17) and fibers of the tractus tecto-thalamicus rectus (*Herrick*, '33), and immediately caudal to this the posterior commissure.   This latter, which is at the rostral end of the midbrain, carries in various amphibians, including Necturus (*Herrick*) and the frog (University of Michigan preparations), crossed fibers from the nucleus of the commissure (recognized also by *Röthig*, '27, in Cryptobranchus and Nec-turus) to the contralateral fasciculus longitudinalis medialis, intertectal fibers, and tectal fibers to the medial longitudinal fasciculus and apparently to the nu-cleus of the oculomotor nerve.   In various urodeles *Röthig* ('27) traced lateral fascicles of the commissure into the fiber region of the subtectum.   In the salamander *Röthig* ('24 and '27) described an unmedullated and, in Spelerpes fuscus, a medullated thalamo-commissural path.   Behind this posterior com-missure, illustrated in figures 461, 462B, and 465, is a continuous band of decussating fibers (fig. 462A; the commissura tecti-mesencephali of *Herrick*, '17, and *Röthig*, '27).   Certain of these appear to be commissural, others crossed tecto-tegmental in character.

Before leaving the consideration of the dorsal part of the mesencephalon, it is necessary to consider briefly the connections of the nucleus isthmi.   A num-ber of the connections have been mentioned elsewhere in this account and may be summarized as follows: Fibers to this nucleus, perhaps collaterals only, from the acoustico-lateral lemniscus have been described by various observers. *Bellonci* ('88), *Gaupp* ('89), *Ariëns Kappers* ('21), and *Larsell* ('23) have found fibers of the commissura transversa associated with this nuclear mass. Tecto-isthmal, homolateral and contralateral, isthmo-tectal (*Gaupp*, '89; *Ariëns Kappers*, '21; *Larsell*, '23), and quadrigemino-tectal bundles are also present. In addition to the above-mentioned connections, which have been described previously,

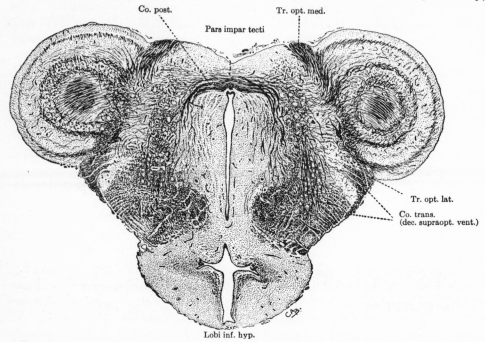

Co. post. Tr. opt. med.

Pars impar tecti

Tr. opt. lat.

Co. trans.
(dec. supraopt. vent.)

Lobi inf. hyp.

Fig. 465. A cross section through the most frontal portion of the midbrain of Rana mugiens (catesbyana). *Co.post.*, commissura posterior; *Co.trans.* (*dec.supraopt.vent.*), commissura transversa (decussatio supraoptica ventralis); *Lobi inf.hyp.*, lobi inferiores hypothalami; *Pars impar tecti*, pars impar tecti; *Tr.opt.lat.*, tractus opticus lateralis; *Tr.opt.med.*, tractus opticus medialis.

three others may be added. The first of these is the tractus isthmo-thalamicus of *Larsell* ('23), described as arising from the medullary portion of the nucleus and swinging forward to the thalamus where it terminates, at least in part. This tract may be the homologue of the isthmo-pretectal system of fishes. It is extremely doubtful in our opinion that this carries efferent retinal fibers (as *Larsell* suggested). That portion of the nucleus isthmi which is believed to serve such a function in birds (*Wallenberg*, '98A) is not represented in the nucleus isthmi thus far described for the frog. For similar reasons it is improbable that optic fibers reach this area as *Gaupp* had supposed. *Bellonci, Ariëns Kappers,* and *Larsell* were unable to substantiate such optic connections. Commissural fibers associated with the nucleus isthmi cross in the commissura isthmi and the decussatio veli. The commissura isthmi enters (and leaves) the dorsomedial tip of the nucleus isthmi. The crossing takes place in the anterior medullary velum and the commissure consists of interisthmal fibers. The decussatio veli receives fibers from the caudal portion of the nucleus isthmi. These, joined after crossing by homolateral fibers, pass forward to the tectum.

THE MESENCEPHALIC TEGMENTAL CENTERS AND THEIR CONNECTIONS

The ventral portion of the mesencephalic area in Necturus has a layer of periventricular gray, the stratum griseum, surrounded peripherally by a stratum album. The cell bodies lie in the gray layer and the dendrites, on the whole less twisted than those of the tectum, extend out into the white layer, giving off in their course, at the border between the two layers, tangentially running dendrites which break up into finer branches among the neuraxes in the region. Some of the most ventral tegmental cells send dendrites to the interpeduncular nucleus. Occasionally cell bodies of neurons are found scattered among the fascicles of motor tracts with dendrites spread out between the fiber bundles. Certain cell masses have been designated as nuclear groups in this region by *Herrick* ('17, '25) and others; these are the nucleus of the tuberculum posterius, the nucleus ectomamillaris or nucleus of the basal optic root, the interpeduncular nucleus, the nuclei of the oculomotor and the trochlear nerves, and the nucleus of the posterior commissure. The nuclei of the oculomotor and trochlear nerves have been described in Chapter V and need not receive further consideration at this time.

The nucleus of the tuberculum posterius (fig. 461) of urodele amphibians lies dorsal and in front of the bend in the brain floor known as the tuberculum posterius, formed at the place where the rostral end of the midbrain floor turns ventralward to the hypothalamus. The nucleus of the tuberculum posterius receives impulses from various efferent systems. It has many small neurons (*Herrick*, '33), but its characteristic neurons ('17, '33) are large, efferent in type, and have richly branched dendrites. *Herrick* ('17) has emphasized in particular the great spread of the dendrites of this nucleus. Some were traced to the pars dorsalis thalami and pars intercalaris, others to the hypothalamic regions as far forward as the caudal end of the supraoptic or postoptic commissure, where they come into relation with the nucleus of the tractus pallii and with various efferent fiber systems such as the forebrain bundles, postoptic commissure components from tectal areas, and thalamo-peduncular and posterior commissure systems. Thus this nucleus is a highly important correlation center for efferent impulses. Closely related to this nucleus, in fact included in part in the eminence formed by it, are the larger, more dorsally placed cells constituting the nuclei of the posterior commissure and the medial longitudinal fasciculus. Lateral to the tuberculum posterius *Herrick* ('17) identified a superficial neuropil area as the area lateralis tegmenti. This has become his nucleus ectomamillaris of urodeles (*Herrick*, '25). To this region were traced dendrites of the nucleus of the tuberculum posterius, neuraxes from the medial forebrain bundle, from hypothalamic areas and pars intercalaris diencephali. This observer stated that there are indications, not entirely substantiated, that fibers entering it from behind come from the visceral sensory nuclei. It receives the unmyelinated fibers of the basal optic root. A nucleus of the basal optic root (or as certain observers prefer to call it, the nucleus opticus tegmenti) has been known and figured for a long time in amphibians, or at least in the frog (*Bellonci*, '88; *Gaupp*, '89; *Wlassak*, '93; *Herrick*, '25), although it has not been recognized always as a recipient of optic tract fibers.

The nucleus interpeduncularis extends from the tuberculum posterius caudalward through the midbrain and for a considerable distance into the medulla oblongata.   The midbrain part of the nucleus is not so well developed as its more caudal portions.   The distribution of dendritic branches of the neurons of the central gray to this nucleus has been mentioned previously.   Habenulo-peduncular fibers, supplemented by fibers from the nucleus, course through the interpeduncular nucleus into medulla oblongata regions.   Nervus terminalis fibers to this nucleus were described by *McKibben* ('11) for Necturus and mammillopeduncular fibers by *Herrick* ('17).   *Kreht* ('31) has described bulbo-interpeduncular fibers in Proteus which apparently correspond to a ventral interpedunculobulbar tract traced by *Herrick* ('30) from bulbar centers of the medulla to the interpeduncular gray.   The dorsal interpedunculo-bulbar tract mentioned by this last observer does not appear to have been found as yet in other amphibians.

A nucleus interpeduncularis and its associated habenulo-peduncular tract are present also in the frog (*Ariëns Kappers* and *Hammer*, '18; *Ariëns Kappers*, '21, and others); in fact it is constant in vertebrates from cyclostomes on, although in higher vertebrates it does not extend so far caudalward.   A connection of the nervus terminalis with this region in the frog has not been observed.

The isthmus region behind the fovea isthmi, termed by *Herrick* ('17) the eminentia subcerebellaris tegmenti, is intimately connected with the tectum, which overlaps it, and with the tegmentum of the midbrain, and sends impulses forward to the ventromedial nucleus of the oculomotor nerve by way of the tractus tegmento-interpeduncularis.   This observer identified also, at the side of the gray matter of the eminentia subcerebellaris, a group of neurons of very considerable size which gives rise to a tegmento-bulbar tract to the reticular formation of the medulla oblongata.

Certain major connections of the tegmental or peduncular region of the midbrain as identified by *Herrick* ('17, '30, '33) and *Kreht* ('30, '31) may be summarized here.   The region receives fibers of the lateral forebrain bundle (tractus strio-thalamicus et tegmentalis) and, in its ventral portion, an olfacto-tegmental component of the medial forebrain bundle.   Between the nucleus of the tuberculum posterior and the eminentia subcerebellaris are five dorsal fascicles which interconnect these areas, although some fibers may extend even farther.   Since they are in synaptic relation orally with terminal fibers of the lateral forebrain bundle, such tegmental fasciculi undoubtedly are a part of chain paths from the forebrain to the efferent centers of the medulla oblongata.   Farther ventrally other bundles, the ventral tegmental fascicles, interconnect the tegmentum with the regions behind it, the eminentia subcerebellaris, and with more caudal portions of the medulla oblongata.   These ventral fasciculi include the medial longitudinal fasciculus, which arises from its nucleus and the adjacent nucleus of the tuberculum posterius.   These bundles are joined by others in their course so that the complex becomes a well-developed bundle as it runs caudalward. It terminates largely around neurons of the subcerebellar eminence and in the reticular gray of the medulla oblongata. Fibers of the fasciculus decussate at various levels, in the commissure of the tuberculum posterius, and in front of and behind the fovea isthmi. In the description of figure 462, the approximate positions of the dorsal and ventral tegmental fasciculi are given.

Associated with these other ventral tegmental fascicles is an unmedullated bundle which appears to arise in the subcerebellar eminence. Its fascicles run forward just in front of the brachium conjunctivum at the line between the gray and white strata, then run medialward and ventralward into the dendritic plexus of the interpeduncular nucleus and forward in this position. According to *Herrick*, who identified and described this tract, the fibers appear to terminate in what he regarded as the Edinger-Westphal nucleus, although their direction of conduction is uncertain.

The ventral portions of the midbrain contain a very rich system of crossing fibers, termed collectively in Necturus (*Herrick*, '17) and in Cryptobranchus japonicus (*Röthig*, '27, fig. 5), the commissure of the tuberculum posterius. In this commissure are certain bundles which merely cross the midline and others which are truly commissural, since they connect like areas. As summarized by *Herrick* these include, in addition to commissural hypothalamic bundles, the superficial and deep tecto-peduncular tracts, the medial longitudinal fasciculus, a few fibers of the habenulo-peduncular tract, some crossed fascicles of the mammillo-peduncular tract, and a descending path from the ventral part of the thalamus to the tegmental region (the deep portion of the tractus thalamo-peduncularis profundus).

Another component of this commissure, earlier described by *McKibben* ('11) and confirmed by *Herrick* ('14), consists of crossed fibers of the nervus terminalis. These occupy a position near the ventral brain wall from their point of entrance along the under border of the olfactory bulb until the level of the commissura tuberculi posterioris. Certain fibers of the nerve cross in this commissure, others in the supraoptic system, and still others in the anterior commissure. They terminate in relation to the interpeduncular nucleus (*McKibben*, '11).

Many bundles which usually cross in the ventral and caudal parts of the midbrain in various urodeles decussate, according to *Herrick* ('17) and *Röthig* ('27), in the ventral tegmental decussation, which is situated behind the fovea isthmi and consequently in the rhombencephalon. This includes the crossing fascicles of descending tecto-bulbar (fig. 462) and tecto-peduncular systems and the ascending tegmento-interpeduncular tract. To this decussation the unmyelinated bundles of the brachium conjunctivum were traced.

GENERAL RELATIONS OF THE DIENCEPHALON

As was stated previously, the caudal boundary of the diencephalon is indicated dorsally by the posterior commissure. The most posterior part of the diencephalic roof is occupied in urodeles by a commissural system, the commissura tecti diencephali of *Gaupp* ('89). It is associated in Necturus with the pars intercalaris thalami of *Herrick*. In front of this commissure lies the pineal stalk with the attached pineal gland and the pineal recess and then the habenula with its habenular commissure. In front of the habenula the roof of the ventricle is membranous. The oral limits of the diencephalic segment are not so easily determined. *Johnston* ('09) considered that the boundary between the telencephalon and diencephalon lies, in the embryo, in a plane indicated dorsally by the velum transversum and ventrally by the optic chiasm, but there is not general agreement as to the exact position of such a boundary in the adult brain. In the adult frog the velum transversum develops into the plexus choroideus medius, bordering frontally the small parencephalon or dorsal sack. Accordingly, in the adult frog the hind wall of the plexus choroideus medius forms the dorsofrontal limit of the diencephalon (*Ariëns Kappers*). Rostrally the floor of the diencephalon has at least part of the chiasmal ridge, containing the optic and supraoptic decussations. Caudal to this region the floor is occupied by the infundibular portion with its attached hypophysis. The boundary between the diencephalon and mesencephalon falls at the rostral border of the angle where the hypothalamic region passes over into the tegmental region of the midbrain. This has been termed in certain amphibians the tuberculum posterius (*Herrick*, '17). For the positions of the above mentioned areas, figure 461 should be consulted.

Epithalamic, thalamic, and hypothalamic portions have been described as in other forms. The thalamic portion is divided secondarily into dorsal and ventral portions by the sulcus medius. Before entering upon the detailed account of these regions some mention should be made of the subdivisions of the diencephalic area as presented by *Bergquist* ('32) in his series of studies on this region in various fishes and amphibians. In this study he combined the developmental history of the region with its phylogenetic relations and divided the diencephalon into a pars frontalis, a pars medialis, and a pars caudalis thalami; a pars tuberalis posterior (usually considered mesencephalic); a pars dorsalis, a pars ventralis, and a pars caudalis hypothalami; and a pars synencephali. Included in the paper are a series of tables which homologize his areas with those described by others and to these tables the reader is referred.

THE EPITHALAMUS AND ITS CONNECTIONS

The epithalamus, in certain urodeles at least, contains, in addition to structures usually recognized in vertebrates (the habenula, the pineal stalk, and the associated structures), a relatively very large posthabenular region to which *Gaupp* ('89) applied the name of pars intercalaris. In Necturus the habenular portion is separated from the underlying dorsal thalamus by the subhabenular sulcus, the pars intercalaris by the sulcus dorsalis. In some amphibians a single sulcus is present.

The pars intercalaris is associated with the fibers of the commissura tecti diencephali (fig. 442B), under which is a forward continuation of the subcommissural organ, which extends almost to the pineal recess. In the frog the posterior wall of the pineal recess represents *Gaupp's* pars intercalaris diencephali and fuses with the commissura posterior and the pars impar tecti. Other connections of the pars intercalaris diencephali are collaterals of fibers of passage — optic, postoptic, and tecto-habenular systems (*Herrick*, '33), the tractus preoptico-intercalaris, and a part of the tractus thalamo-peduncularis dorsalis.   The last two tracts have been identified and studied by *Herrick* ('17 and '33) in Necturus. The tractus preoptico-intercalaris is a small, unmedullated bundle passing from

the very large preoptic area of these forms backward and upward through the stratum album to its apparent termination in the pars intercalaris. The tractus thalamo-peduncularis dorsalis, to be described in connection with the dorsal thalamus, carries also fibers from the pars intercalaris, which follow a more superficial course downward and caudalward at the line between mesencephalon and diencephalon and terminate in the area lateralis tegmenti (see page 953).   Certain bundles run across the thalamus, where they receive additions from both dorsal and ventral portions.   Other fibers from the pars intercalaris form a component of the fasciculus retroflexus, which passes to the tuberculum posterius.   *Herrick* ('33) suggested a possible relation between this area and the pretectal nucleus of other forms but this requires further verification.

The pineal organs of amphibians are paired structures embryologically (*Cameron*, '02–'03) but soon become reduced

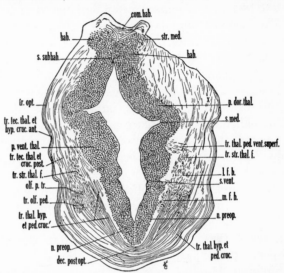

FIG. 466. A drawing illustrating the major subdivisions and certain of the fiber tracts in the diencephalic regions of Necturus. The terminology and descriptions of *Herrick* ('17, '33) have been employed.   Pyridin silver preparation. *Huber* and *Crosby*.

com.hab., commissura habenularum; *dec.postopt.*, decussatio postoptica; *hab.*, habenula; *l.f.b.*, lateral forebrain bundle; *m.f.b.*, medial forebrain bundle; *n.preop.*, nucleus preopticus; *olf.p.tr.*, olfactory projection tract; *p.dors.thal.*, pars dorsalis thalami; *p.vent.thal.*, pars ventralis thalami; *s.med.*, sulcus medius; *s.subhab.*, sulcus subhabenularis; *s.vent.*, sulcus ventralis; *str.med.*, stria medullaris; *tr.olf.ped.*, tractus olfacto-peduncularis; *tr.opt.*, tractus opticus; *tr.str.thal.f.*, tractus thalamo-frontalis (p. 962); *tr.tec.thal.et hyp.cruc.ant.*, tractus tecto-thalamicus et hypothalamicus cruciatus anterior; *tr.tec.thal.et hyp.cruc.post.*, tractus tecto-thalamicus et hypothalamicus cruciatus posterior; *tr.thal.hyp.et ped.cruc.*, tractus thalamo-hypothalamicus (et peduncularis) cruciatus; *tr.thal.hyp.et ped.cruc'.*, tractus thalamo-hypothalamicus et peduncularis cruciatus (after crossing); *tr.thal.ped.vent. superf.*, tractus thalamo-peduncularis ventralis superficialis.

to a single cavity surrounded by a wall in which *Studnička* ('05) and *Holmgren* ('18) found rod-like neurosensory cells. Similar cells, and neurons as well, have been observed in the epiphyseal stalk.   According to *Holmgren*, the tractus pinealis, strengthened by fibers from the epiphyseal stalk, runs to the posterior commissure and to the tectum. *Kingsbury* ('95) and *Herrick* ('17) described a parietal nerve in Necturus, the latter observer recognizing a rostral root which he traced to the region cephalic to the habenular commissure, a middle root which passed to the region caudal to this commissure, and a caudal root cutting through the fibers of the commissura tecti diencephali. All three roots united and joined the habenulo-peduncular tract. *Röthig* ('24) found this nerve only in Siren lacertina. *Kreht* ('30) recognized it in Cryptobranchus.

The habenulae (figs. 461, 466) are well developed and show differentiation into two nuclear masses, often designated as dorsal and ventral habenular nuclei. The incoming impulses to these nuclear masses pass over tracts, most of which converge into the stria medullaris (fig. 466) which passes to the habenular region, where it terminates in part either before or after decussation. It carries also certain fibers of passage for this region. Its components will now be discussed briefly. First to be mentioned is the tractus bulbo-bulbaris (*Röthig*, '26; *Kreht*, '30) regarded by *Röthig* as connecting one olfactory bulb with the other through the habenular commissure but as having relations also with the habenular centers and the lateral olfactory area. This interbulbar connection was recognized by *Snessarew* ('08), *Benedetti* ('27), *Kreht* ('30), and *Herrick* ('33). The last-mentioned observer, however, believed that the major connections of this system arise from the anterior olfactory area and synapse in the habenular region of both sides and in the olfactory area of the opposite side, constituting primarily a tertiary olfactory path. *Herrick* termed the bundle the tractus olfacto-habenularis anterior (figs. 561, 563). Fibers from the medial basal region of the hemisphere, particularly from the preoptic area, and running medial and lateral to the forebrain bundles to reach the stria medullaris, constitute, respectively, the medial and lateral olfacto-habenular tracts of *Herrick* ('10, '17, '33; fig. 564) and the medial olfacto-habenular tract of *Ariëns Kappers* ('21), who prefers to reserve the term of lateral olfacto-habenular tract for the lateral cortico-habenular tract of the Herrick terminology. *Röthig* ('11), studying Necturus and Siren lacertina, *Benzon* ('26), considering Cryptobranchus, and *Kreht* ('30), studying Cryptobranchus, reached the conclusion that the lateral olfacto-habenular tract arises from the medial forebrain bundle. *Herrick* ('33) thought that a few fibers of the system may have such origin. From the septal regions of the hemisphere (and the bed nucleus of the commissure) arises a septo-habenular tract, which has accompanying strio-habenular fibers (*Herrick*, '33; probably the tractus habenulo-striatus of *Ariëns Kappers*, '21). From the olfactory centers of the lateral hemisphere wall two other tracts enter the stria medullaris — an amygdalo-habenular tract (fig. 564) from the amygdaloid area (*Herrick*, '33) and a lateral cortico-habenular tract (*Herrick*, '10, '17, and elsewhere; *Kreht*, '30, '31) from the primordial piriform lobe (fig. 564). This latter tract is the homologue of the lateral olfacto-habenular tract of *Ariëns Kappers* ('21), who prefers to reserve the term "cortico-" for fibers of the stria medullaris arising from the hippocampus and passing to the stria by the medial cortico-habenular tract (*Herrick*, '10, '17, and elsewhere; *Benzon*, '26; *Kreht*, '30, '31). There is considerable evidence that the term commissura superior telencephali is appropriately applied to the lateral cortico-habenular tract referred to above, since, as *van Gehuchten* ('97) showed for the salamander and as others have found since for various amphibians, this tract carries commissural fibers from one hemisphere to the other.

That certain fibers of this system end directly or by collaterals in the habenular regions (both before and after decussation) appears probable. The stria medullaris ends partly in the homolateral and partly in the contralateral habenular nuclear mass (the decussation occurring in the habenular commissure) in addition to carrying commissural fibers. As it passes along the most frontal part of the dorsal thalamus it provides collaterals and possibly stem fibers to the thalamic area; these constitute the tractus olfacto-thalamicus (Herrick, '33). A thalamo-habenular tract is provided by scattered fibers which pass along the dorsal thalamus to the habenula. Another afferent connection of the habenula, the tecto-habenular tract (p. 951), received consideration earlier.

The major efferent systems of the habenulae, so far as observed, are (1) the tractus habenulo-thalamicus, which Herrick ('17) regarded as ending in the frontal part of the ventral thalamus but described as a diffuse connection with the dorsal thalamus later ('33), and (2) the tractus habenulo-peduncularis (Herrick, '17; Ariëns Kappers, '21; Röthig, '26; Kreht, '30), which arises from both habenular nuclei and follows a course relatively typical for the tract in vertebrates to the interpeduncular nucleus. According to Herrick ('33, not '17) it decussates in Necturus. In this animal (Herrick, '17; figs. 462 and 466) it runs for a long distance in relation with the interpeduncular nucleus, distributing to it throughout its extent in both the mesencephalon and the rhombencephalon. It is important to mention that the habenulo-peduncular tracts are of equal size on both sides as the habenulae are symmetrical in amphibians.

THE DORSAL THALAMIC NUCLEI AND THEIR CONNECTIONS

The dorsal thalamus of amphibians is delimited from the ventral thalamus by the sulcus medius of Herrick ('17 and elsewhere) and is proportionately smaller and less differentiated in tailed than in tailless amphibians. In a recent paper this last mentioned observer, following the analysis of the anuran diencephalon as given by Röthig ('23), divided the dorsal thalamus of Necturus into anterior, middle, and posterior areas. Slightly ventral and in front of the oral end of the dorsal thalamus is the eminentia thalami (fig. 461) and immediately caudal to this eminentia, in the anterior part of the dorsal thalamus, is the nucleus of Bellonci (Herrick, '33; pars optica thalami, Herrick, '17; x, fig. 466), which had been described by Bellonci ('88) in the frog under the name of the nucleus anterior superior corporis geniculati as a region of differentiated neuropil in the general stratum album of the area. In Amblystoma Herrick ('25) identified a nucleus geniculatus lateralis and recently ('33) he applied the name of geniculate neuropil to a portion of the middle area of the dorsal thalamus, caudal to the nucleus of Bellonci although broadly connected with it, since he believed it to be in a general way, although not in a precise way, comparable to the lateral geniculate complex of higher amphibians.

Two other differentiated portions are recognized in the dorsal thalamus of Necturus (Herrick, '33). The more frontal of these, a nucleus sensitivus within the middle division of the dorsal thalamus, was considered the forerunner in a general way of the lateral and medial thalamic nuclei of higher forms, because it receives terminal fibers of the spinal and bulbar lemnisci systems and is connected with the forebrain. The other thalamic center is located in the posterior area of the dorsal thalamus of Necturus and consists of a region of differentiated neuropil receiving homolateral and contralateral tectal fibers as well as impulses from the lemnisci systems. In Amblystoma and Rana, *Herrick* ('25) identified a pretectal nucleus.

As was stated earlier, *Röthig* ('23) divided the dorsal thalamus of Anura into anterior, medial, and posterior parts. He redivided the first mentioned division

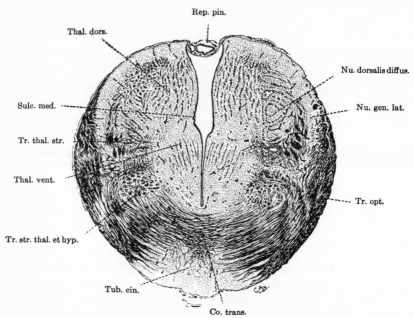

FIG. 467. A cross section through the diencephalon of Rana mugiens.
Co.trans., commissura transversa; *Nu.dorsalis diffus.*, nucleus dorsalis diffusus; *Nu. gen.lat.*, nucleus geniculatus lateralis; *Sulc.med.*, sulcus medius thalami; *Thal.dors.*, dorsal thalamus; *Thal.vent.*, ventral thalamus; *Tr.opt.*, tractus opticus; *Tr.str.thal.et hyp.*, tractus strio-thalamicus et hypothalamicus; *Tr.thal.str.*, tractus thalamo-striatalis.

into dorsal, intermediate, and lateral areas. It appears probable, although not entirely certain, that the dorsal area of Röthig represents the nucleus of Bellonci, while the intermediate area, and possibly part of the lateral, belongs to the nucleus dorsalis diffusus of *Ariëns Kappers* and *Hammer* ('18; fig. 467). These latter observers called the region under the habenula the nucleus anterior thalami (fig. 468). The corpus geniculatum of *Gaupp* ('89), buried between the superficial and deep layers of the stratum album of the dorsal thalamus, is relatively easily recognized in the frog (fig. 467, Nu. gen. lat.). *Herrick* ('25) believed that he was able to recognize an anterior and a posterior portion of the lateral geniculate nucleus in the frog and that from the latter he could trace projection fibers to the forebrain. This suggests that this posterior portion of the lateral geniculate nucleus is comparable to the dorsal part of the nuclear complex in higher forms.

Mention has been made in the foregoing paragraphs of certain connections of the nuclear areas of the amphibian dorsal thalamus. For convenience the general connections are summarized here. In Amblystoma and the frog, *Herrick* ('25) found the nucleus of Bellonci to have not only optic connections but also connections with the lateral habenulo-peduncular tract and with the dorsal thalamus and to discharge to the peduncular regions of the midbrain. In Necturus the same observer found the connections of this area to be of various types, consisting of collaterals of the stria medullaris (the tractus olfacto-thalamicus, page 959) and impulses from the hippocampus by way of the medial cortico-habenular tract and the deep ventral thalamo-peduncular tract, in addition to fibers of the postoptic and optic systems. He suggested, on the basis of these connections, a general homology of this area with the nucleus dorsomedialis anterior of reptiles.

The optic tract connections appear to be fairly widespread within the dorsal thalamus of amphibians. They pass specifically to the lateral geniculate nucleus (or the geniculate neuropil in Necturus) as well as to the nucleus of Bellonci. *Herrick* ('25) stated that much of the dorsal thalamus of amphibians is under the influence of optic tract fibers. *Röthig* ('24 and '26) carried optic tract fibers to the dorsal and lateral parts of the anterior division or area of the dorsal thalamus in Cryptobranchus and in Rana.

To the dorsal portion of the thalamus in tailed amphibians, to the regions of neuropil in the middle and posterior areas (see page 959), extend the spino-thalamic tract and the acoustico-lateral fibers or the bulbar lemniscus system (*Herrick*, '17, '33; *Kreht*, '30, '31). Certain spino-thalamic and bulbo-thalamic fascicles have been traced to the nucleus dorsalis diffusus in the frog (*Ariëns Kappers*, '21). Into the dorsal thalamus of tailed amphibians and of the frog enter somewhat scattered bundles from the optic tectum. Such an uncrossed component (a tractus tecto-thalamicus rectus, p. 951) was described in lower amphibians by *Herrick* ('17, '33) and by *Kreht* ('31). This is the forerunner of the richer tecto-thalamic systems found in reptiles and birds. It contains particularly tecto-geniculate fascicles which, in the frog, pass as a partly differentiable bundle to the anterior part of the lateral geniculate nucleus. It is probable that the posterior part of the geniculate complex, recognized by *Herrick*, has geniculo-tectal fibers, though this demands documentation. *Röthig* described a tractus thalamo-mesencephalicus posterior to the pars posterior of the dorsal thalamus. Crossed tecto-thalamic and hypothalamic fibers and perhaps other postoptic fibers bring impulses to the dorsal thalamus of amphibians (see the account of this system on page 950). *Kreht* ('31) described strio-thalamic fibers to the more caudal part of the dorsal thalamus in Proteus. From the dorsal region of the thalamus in the frog ascending thalamo-cortical (or thalamo-striatal) fibers can be traced (*Rubaschkin*, '03). A comparable thalamo-frontal tract has been described (*Herrick*, '17; *Kreht*, '31). Herrick recognized a myelinated posterior portion from the regions of termination of the lemnisci systems, comparable to the previously mentioned thalamo-striatal path, and an unmyelinated but larger anterior bundle previously described by *Kingsbury* ('95), which arises from the middle part of the thalamus.   The thalamo-striatal tract of the frog (fig. 467)— or its homologue, the thalamo-frontal tract of Necturus (fig. 466A) — is a component of the lateral forebrain bundle.   From the evidence on hand at present it appears probable that the first projection of neothalamic impulses on the telencephalon occurs in amphibians.   At least such projection fibers have not been demonstrated with certainty for fishes.   The lateral forebrain bundle of amphibians is discussed in Chapter IX, page 1309.

Other efferent paths of the dorsal thalamus, as described for Necturus, are the tractus thalamo-hypothalamicus (et peduncularis) cruciatus, the tractus thalamo-peduncularis dorsalis, and the tractus dorsoventralis thalami.   The first of these tracts, the tractus thalamo-hypothalamicus (et peduncularis) cruciatus (fig. 466), is a component of the supraoptic commissure system, one bundle of which, the tractus tecto-thalamicus et hypothalamicus cruciatus, was described under the account of the optic tectum (p. 950).   The tractus thalamo-hypothalamicus (et peduncularis) cruciatus consists of medullated and unmedullated fibers.   Its fibers arise in the pars dorsalis thalami, swing ventralward outside of the lateral forebrain bundle, and cross in the postoptic decussation.   The medullated bundles remain as a more or less dense fiber mass which crosses in the dorsal part of the ridge, above and behind the crossing of the posterior part of the tecto-thalamic and hypothalamic component.   After the decussation they terminate in the ventral thalamus and the peduncular regions of the midbrain.   Some of the bundles of the crossed thalamo-peduncular component, which pass more caudalward, belong to the dorsal tegmental system and have been traced to the region of emergence of the trigeminal nerve in Amblystoma (*Herrick*, '14, the thalamo-bulbar tract).   The thalamo-hypothalamic component of the tractus thalamo-hypothalamicus (et peduncularis) cruciatus connects the dorsal thalamus of one side with the dorsal hypothalamic areas and the oral (but not the caudal) end of the ventral hypothalamic areas of the other side.   For details of the course of these various components reference is made to the *Herrick* papers ('14, '17, etc.).

The tractus dorsoventralis thalami consists of neuraxes of neurons in the dorsal thalamus which accompany the tractus thalamo-peduncularis dorsalis and terminate in the ventral thalamus in Necturus.   The latter tract consists of a deep and a superficial bundle.   The deep portion (tractus thalamo-peduncularis dorsalis profundus, *Herrick*, '17), consisting of a few myelinated and more unmyelinated fibers, accompanies the habenulo-peduncular tract ventralward to the region of the tuberculum posterius and areas farther caudalward.   A small unmyelinated bundle (tractus thalamo-peduncularis dorsalis superficialis, *Herrick*) follows a more superficial course downward and backward, sending fibers to the pars ventralis thalami, the pars dorsalis hypothalami and the tuberculum posterius.

Röthig ('26, see fig. 32) described and figured three descending bundles from the dorsal thalamus of Rana : a tractus thalamo-peduncularis anterior from the pars anterior, a tractus thalamo-peduncularis medialis from the pars medialis, and a tractus thalamo-peduncularis posterior from the pars posterior of the thalamus.   The account of this observer is too brief to permit of establishing any close homologies between these fiber tracts and those described by *Herrick*. It seems probable, as *Röthig* ('26, p. 55) also stated, referring to *Ariëns Kappers* and *Hammer* ('18) and *Ariëns Kappers* ('21), that the thalamo-lobar tract from the dorsal and frontal part of the thalamus (probably from the nucleus anterior of *Ariëns Kappers*) to the most caudal and ventral part of the diencephalon is the homologue of the tractus thalamo-peduncularis anterior of *Röthig*.

THE VENTRAL THALAMIC AND HYPOTHALAMIC NUCLEI AND THEIR CONNECTIONS

Because of certain similarities of connections the pars ventralis thalami and the hypothalamus will be considered together. The pars ventralis thalami (figs. 461, 466 to 468) does not show any high degree of differentiation in amphibian forms. An eminentia thalami (*Herrick*, '17, '33; *Ariëns Kappers* and *Hammer*, '18, and others; fig. 461) is present which lies at the region of transition between the primordium hippocampi and the ventral thalamus, its neurons being in synaptic relation with tracts of the region (the stria medullaris, the tractus cortico-thalamicus medialis, and the hippocampal commissure) and its neuraxes passing to the ventral thalamus and the stria medullaris (*Herrick*, '33). *Huber* and *Crosby* regard this area as probably homologous with the reptilian area anterior ventralis (as did *Herrick*, '33, but not '17). The name, nucleus of the tractus olfacto-habenularis medialis, has been applied to cells intercalated in the course of the fascicles of this tract, as was mentioned by *Herrick* ('33), who stated that "these neurons establish functional connections with various other regions and evidently they serve as a correlation center for diverse physiological systems."

The main mass of the ventral thalamus (the subthalamus of *Herrick*, '33) in urodeles has neurons, the widely branching dendrites of which put the region into relation with many areas — with the telencephalon by lateral forebrain fibers, with the dorsal thalamus by dorsoventral correlation bundles, with the tectum by components of the postoptic systems, with the nucleus of the tuberculum posterius, and with the hypothalamus. It represents a correlation center on the efferent side of the arc, with discharge to efferent centers through thalamo-peduncular fascicles. The above account follows particularly *Herrick* ('33). Probably an essentially similar pattern with possibly more differentiation occurs in the pars ventralis thalami of the frog, but the details of structure in this region are not known to the writers at present. In frogs (*Ariëns Kappers*, '21) a nucleus entopeduncularis posterior and a nucleus juxtapeduncularis are found in this region which are clusters of cells associated with the lateral forebrain bundle, analogous with the nuclei entopedunculares of other vertebrate types.

The hypothalamus, further subdivided by *Herrick* into a pars dorsalis and a pars ventralis (fig. 462), lies behind the large preoptic nucleus and below and partly separated from the pars ventralis thalami by the sulcus ventralis (fig. 466). The dorsal part of the hypothalamus in Necturus, secondarily divided into dorsal and ventral lobes (*Herrick*, '33), is the "Haubenwulst" as described by *Gaupp* ('89) in the frog, representing that portion of the area related to the nucleus of the tuberculum posterius caudally and the pars ventralis thalami

orally.   It represents a primordial mammillary body (*Herrick*, '34).   The pars
ventralis hypothalami comprises the most ventral part of the diencephalon and
includes the postoptic decussation, the infundibular or posterior lobes, and the
so-called saccus vasculosus (in Necturus, or pars nervosa of the hypophysis,
Herrick, '34), together with certain less differentiated areas.   The walls, but not
the floor and the roof, of the infundibulum consist of nervous tissue but are thin.
The saccus vasculosus, which occupies the most caudal part of the infundibular

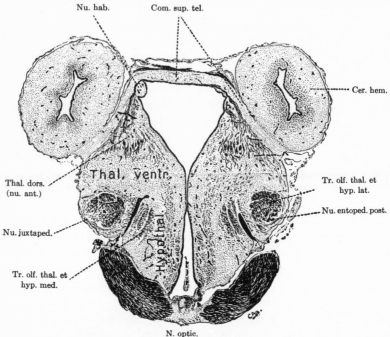

Fig. 468.   A cross section through the anterior part of the diencephalon of Rana
mugiens, in front of the plane of figure 468.
   Cer.hem., cerebral hemispheres; *Com.sup.tel.*, commissura superior telencephali;
Hypothal., hypothalamus; *N.optic.*, nervus opticus; *Nu.entoped.post.*, nucleus entopeduncularis posterior; *Nu.juxtaped.*, nucleus juxtapeduncularis; *Thal.dors.(nu.ant.)*;
dorsal thalamus (nucleus anterior); *Thal.ventr.*, ventral thalamus; *Tr.olf.thal.et hyp.
lat.*, tractus olfacto-thalamicus et hypothalamicus lateralis; *Tr.olf.thal.et hyp.med.*,
tractus olfacto-thalamicus et hypothalamicus medialis.

wall, receives unmedullated nerve fibers from this wall.   The pars ventralis
thalami and the pars ventralis hypothalami are continuous near the posterior
end of the thalamic area.   The above account is based on the description and
figures of urodeles by *Herrick* ('17, '33, '34).   In the frog the lobi laterales are
relatively small but the gray is well developed in the ventral wall of these lobes,
in particular, and in the tuber cinereum region.   The hypophysis in amphibians,
as in other vertebrates, is attached to the infundibular stalk.   According to
Stendell ('14) the pars intermedia secretes into the blood vessels with which
it is richly provided.
   Outstanding among the connections to the hypothalamic and ventral thalamic
regions are the lateral forebrain bundle, the tractus olfacto-peduncularis, the

olfactory projection tract, the medial forebrain bundle, the fasciculus preopticus, the postoptic commissural systems (the tractus tecto-thalamicus et hypo-thalamicus cruciatus, page 950, the tractus thalamo-hypothalamicus et pedun-cularis cruciatus, page 962), the tractus tecto-thalamicus rectus (page 951), the tractus thalamo-peduncularis ventralis, the tractus dorsoventralis thalami (page 962), and the tractus hypophyseus, the mammillo-thalamic and mammillo-peduncular tracts, the tractus infundibularis ascendens, and certain other bundles. Many of these have been described elsewhere in this text and need not receive further consideration here. The others will now be described briefly.

The efferent part of the lateral forebrain bundle (tractus strio-thalamicus of Anura, *Herrick*, '10) arises from the paleostriatal portion of the forebrain. The path undergoes a partial crossing in the anterior commissure; in the frog it is myelinated. On reaching the thalamic areas in the frog it enters the eminentia fascicularis of *Gaupp* ('89). It terminates partly in the ventral thalamic areas, particularly in the nucleus entopeduncularis of the frog, has a slight distribution to the hypothalamus, and swings back into the basal part of the midbrain region (*Ariëns Kappers*, '21). *Herrick* ('17) has traced fibers of this system in larval Amblystoma to the upper end of the medulla oblongata. In this latter form he found the fibers, which he termed the tractus strio-thala-micus et tegmentalis, to be partly unmedullated. This observer has given various descriptions of the system, among which may be mentioned the very recent accounts ('33, '34), where the bundle, designated as the tractus strio-tegmentalis et peduncularis, is traced not only from striatal regions but also from the "ventral and dorsal parts of the lateral sector of the anterior olfactory nucleus and rostral part of the primordium piriforme," thus including certain dorsally arising fibers which probably represent *Röthig's* pars corticalis of the lateral forebrain system. This tractus strio-tegmentalis et peduncularis distrib-utes to "pars ventralis thalami, nucleus of the tuberculum posterius and motor tegmentum" (*Herrick*, '34).

Another tract with the lateral forebrain bundle in the frog (*Herrick*, '10) and in urodeles (*Herrick*, '17) is compared by *Herrick* to a tract recognized by *Johnston* ('02) in ganoids and termed by him the tractus pallii; however, it is uncertain whether this tract of ganoids is homologous with the tractus pallii of amphibians (*Johnston*, '23). This tract provides a connection between the posterolateral wall of the hemispheres and the hypothalamus behind the level of the postoptic decussation, in which some of the bundles cross. The area in the hypothalamus with which these fibers are associated had been termed the nucleus tractus pallii by *Herrick* ('17). This tract is thought to carry impulses in both directions and probably includes the tractus hypothalamo-olfactorius lateralis of certain observers (*Ariëns Kappers*, '21). It was termed the dorsal olfactory projection tract by *Herrick* in 1921 and the olfactory projec-tion tract by him in 1933 and 1934 (see figs. 466 and 563).

A partially medullated tract from the primordial head of the caudate nucleus and adjacent gray, the tractus olfacto-peduncularis of *Herrick* ('27 and later; figs. 466, 563), probably the strio-hypothalamic tract of *Röthig* ('24 and his pars striatica of the lateral forebrain bundle, '11) and of *Kreht* ('30) takes a position ventromedial to the lateral forebrain bundle and runs caudalward, undergoing a partial decussation in the anterior commissure.   Part of its fibers run to the pars dorsalis of the hypothalamus with medial forebrain fascicles.

The medial forebrain bundle (figs. 466, 563, 564; also *Herrick*, '34) carries impulses from the anterior olfactory nucleus to the dorsal hypothalamus and from the parolfactory or septal region and primordium hippocampi, to the ventral hypothalamic areas and, to some extent, to the basal regions of the mesencephalon.   In Necturus, at least, this tract is largely unmyelinated. In amphibians in general it swings down from its origin to a position ventromedial to the lateral forebrain bundle and accompanies this tract to the diencephalon, carrying fibers partly crossed in the anterior commissure.   Ascending fibers to hemispheric areas are found also in this bundle.

The fasciculus preopticus is a tract described first by *Röthig* ('11).   This medullated bundle is believed to arise in the cells of the preoptic nucleus, decussate in the chiasmal ridge, and pass into the hypothalamus.   Descending bundles from the most ventral portions of the diencephalon to the medulla oblongata are believed to supply an efferent system comparable to the tractus lobo-bulbaris of fishes (*Ariëns Kappers*, '21).   According to *Herrick* ('17), *Ariëns Kappers* ('21), and *Larsell* ('31) there are certain fascicles interconnecting the hypothalamus and the cerebellum.   Part of such bundles were found to enter the secondary gustatory center in the isthmus region (*Herrick*, '30, and *Larsell*, '31), and *Herrick* ('30) appears to have reached the conclusion that none of them are cerebellar.

RÉSUMÉ

It may be said then, that within the amphibian midbrain the optic tectal regions are less highly developed than in fishes, but the differentiation of the cochlear centers has begun, at least in tailless amphibians.   Within the diencephalon, the epithalamus shows little change as compared with that of fishes, the dorsal thalamus has increased in relative size and presents definite telencephalic connections, while the hypothalamus is relatively reduced.   From the ventral and cephalic portions of the anterior preoptic area — the periventricular region and the pars magnocellularis — accumulate bundles which, after a partial decussation in the chiasmal ridge, can be followed caudalward as the tractus hypophyseus, into the massive part of the ventral hypothalamus, where they are augmented by fibers from the ventral hypothalamic region.   These fibers pass caudalward along the sides and floor of the infundibular recess into the pars nervosa of the hypophysis (or so-called saccus vasculosus of Necturus) to end among its cells.   According to *Herrick* ('34) they do not enter other portions of the hypophysis in Necturus, although they may do so in the frog and in Amblystoma.   The direction of conduction is not known.

According to *Herrick* ('34) an uncrossed thalamo-mammillary and an only partly decussating mammillo-thalamic path interconnect the dorsal thalamus with the pars ventralis hypothalami, while short internuclear fibers interrelate the pars dorsalis hypothalami with the region caudal to it.   The tractus infundibularis ascendens of *Herrick* ('34) passes forward as dorsal and ventral bundles from the caudal portion of the pars ventralis hypothalami to terminate in the pars dorsalis hypothalami along the lateral wall of the recessus infundibuli. Nervus terminalis (*McKibben*, '11, and *Herrick*, '33) fibers also reach ventral hypothalamic areas.

THE MESENCEPHALIC AND DIENCEPHALIC CENTERS IN REPTILES

THE GROSS RELATIONS.   INTERNALLY SECRETING PORTIONS

In reptiles a very marked advance is to be noted in the development of both mesencephalic and diencephalic centers as compared with that of homologous regions in amphibians.   Among reptiles there are very considerable differences

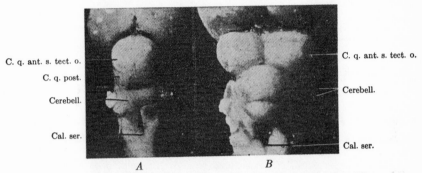

C. q. ant. s. tect. o.

C. q. post.

Cerebell.

Cal. ser.

C. q. ant. s. tect. o.

Cerebell.

Cal. ser.

A   *B*

Fig. 469.   Dorsal view of brain of a snake (*A*) and a crocodile (*B*).

in various regions depending in part upon the development of certain sensory systems, in part upon the phylogenetic history and relationships of the form under consideration, in part upon still other, less recognized factors.

The midbrain region in reptiles has essentially the limits set for it in the frog. Tectal (with related subtectal) and tegmental regions are present as in these latter forms.   The relations of the tectal to the subtectal portions, as these can be demonstrated by gross inspection, vary in the different reptiles.   Thus in crocodiles the relations resemble those of frogs (compare figs. 460 and 469).   The tori semicirculares are still entirely covered by the tectum.   They bulge out from the caudolateral tectal wall into the ventricle, their posterior portions being fused with each other while their frontal portions are still widely separated.   In turtles the size is proportionately equal to that of frogs.   Crocodiles, on the contrary, have very large tori semicirculares which, however, do not have a caudal enlargement visible from the surface as do snakes and lizards.   In crocodiles the optic ventricle resembles that of Rana, the paired optic ventricles becoming continuous with a ventriculus impar tecti mesencephali.   The midbrain roof of snakes (Eunectes, Boa, Python) shows externally four protuberances ; the corpora quadrigemina posteriora are visible here at the surface.   This may be due largely to the reduction of the optic tectum in these forms.   In the lizard, Chameleon, the corpora posteriora are visible on the external surface of the brain ; in Varanus only a very small part of this region can be seen from the outside, for it is covered not only by the optic tectum in front but also by the cerebellum behind.

Caudal and lateral to each corpus posterius or torus semicircularis is a nucleus isthmi which in many reptiles, in contrast to lower vertebrates, is visible macroscopically, since it forms a protuberance at the level of the velum anticum cerebelli, directly in front of the trochlear nerve (fig. 470). It is larger in alligators and crocodiles than in turtles, and largest of all in chameleons, where it has

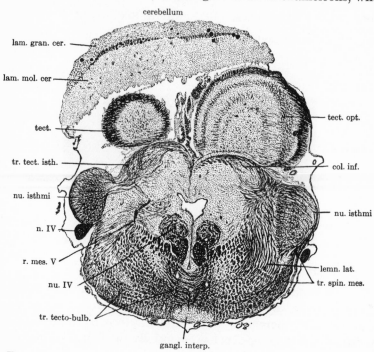

FIG. 470. A transverse section through the isthmus region in the Chameleon. Note the marked development of the nucleus isthmi and the trochlear nucleus. (*de Lange;* slightly modified as to nomenclature.)

col.inf., inferior colliculus; *gangl.interp.*, nucleus interpeduncularis; *lam.gran. cer.*, lamina granularis cerebelli; *lam.mol.cer.*, lamina molecularis cerebelli; *lemn. lat.*, lemniscus lateralis; *n.IV*, trochlear nerve; *nu.isthmi*, nucleus isthmi; *nu.IV*, nucleus trochléaris; *r.mes.V*, mesencephalic root of the trigeminal nerve; *tect. opt.*, tectum opticum; *tr.spin.mes.*, tractus spino-mesencephalicus; *tr.tecto-bulb.*, tractus tecto-bulbaris; *tr.tect.isth.*, tractus tecto-isthmi.

nearly the same size as the corpus posterius. In some other lizards and snakes it is small.

In all reptiles, with the exception of certain snakes, the roof and side walls of the diencephalon are covered by the hemispheres of the forebrain. If these latter are removed, immediately behind the velum transversum is the dorsal sac, saccus dorsalis or parencephalon, which is very well developed in certain reptiles. On this sac lies the pineal gland or epiphysis (fig. 454) which is connected to the brain by the pineal or epiphyseal stalk in the region behind the commissura habenularum, where the third ventricle becomes continuous with the pineal recess. In crocodiles (*Sörensen,* '93; *Reese,* '10) an epiphysis is not present.

In addition to the epiphysis, several reptiles have a parietal eye or at least a rudiment of it. In turtles, crocodiles, and snakes it is lacking, but it is present in most lizards, as the work of *de Graaf* ('86) indicated and that of *Baldwin Spencer* ('86) confirmed. The shape of the parietal eye is different in different animals, varying from the pear-shaped form characteristic of Anolis to the flat organ found in Anguis. Its position in the skull is marked by a hole covered by connective tissue and epithelium. The lens, which is embedded here, is usually transparent, but in some animals con-

tains pigment cells. In nearly all cases the organ is provided with a pigmented retina (as illustrated in fig. 471). Earlier *de Graaf* ('86) described several layers in this retina. In the retina, *Dendy* ('10), to whom we owe important publications on this subject, distinguished neurosensory cells (the ends of which are turned toward the corpus vitreum), radial supporting elements, pigment cells, and, underneath these, a layer of ganglion cells. This pigment, under the influence of light, shifts toward the front (*Nowikoff*, '07) as in the ordinary eye. The nerve bundle arises from the ganglion cells. It attains its greatest size during larval development, but gradually decreases in size. Thus reduced it persists during later life in some

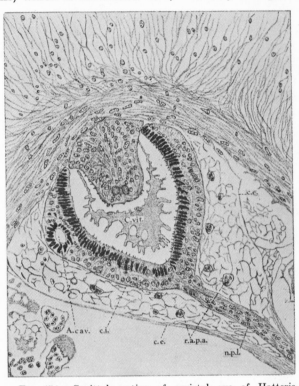

FIG. 471. Sagittal section of parietal eye of Hatteria. *Dendy;* redrawn in single color.
A.cav., accessory cavity; *c.i.,* internal capsule; *c.e.,* external capsule; *c.vit.,* corpus vitreum; *n.p.l.,* pineal nerve; *r.a.p.a.,* anterior branch of pineal artery.

species, as for example in Hatteria. In other forms it disappears gradually after embryonic life as *Studnička* ('05) proved was the case with Lacerta. In Iguana, according to *Klinckowström* ('93), the main nerve is connected with the right habenula; however, a second parietal nerve connects with the left habenula. In Sphenodon this nerve ends in the neighborhood of the left nuclear mass. According to *Dendy,* the right habenula only receives fibers from the parapineal organ. Undoubtedly the work of *Klinckowström* indicates the paired relation of the pineal and parapineal organs and, if the observations of this worker are correct, it suggests that the organ on either side may develop into a parietal eye. Such a condition appears very probable if the relations in cyclostomes are taken into account. It is surprising that as yet no connections with the tectum, such as

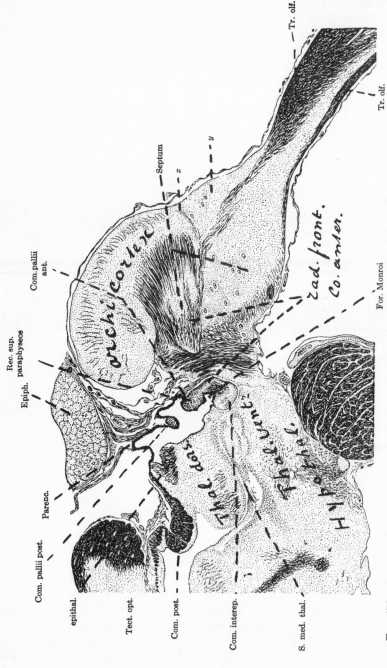

Fig. 472. A paramedian, sagittal section through the diencephalon and the telencephalon of Varanus salvator. *Co.anter.*, commissura anterior; *Com.interep.*, commissura interepithalamica; *Com.pallii ant.*, commissura pallii anterior; *Com.pallii post.*, commissura pallii posterior; *Com.post.*, commissura posterior; *Epiph.*, epiphysis; *epithal.*, epithalamus; *For.Monroi*, foramen of Monro; *Hypothal.*, hypothalamus; *Parenc.*, parencephalon; *Rec.sup.paraphyseos*, paraphyseal superior recess; *rad.front.*, frontal radiations; *S.med.thal.*, sulcus medius thalami; *Tect.opt.*, tectum opticum; *Thal.dors.*, dorsal thalamus; *Thal.vent.*, ventral thalamus; *Tr.olf.*, tractus olfactorius; *x*, anterior boundary of the archicortex; *y*, cortex over the head of the striatum.

970

have been described for fishes, have been observed. For further accounts of the structure and relation of the parietal eye, reference is made to the original papers of *Studnička* ('05) and to *Tilney and Warren's* ('19) paper.

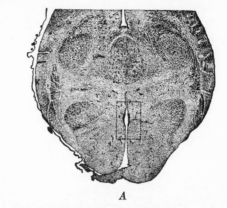

Other gross relations of the diencephalon are relatively simple. The habenular nuclei are small. The dorsal thalamus extends farther frontalward than in amphibians and much farther than in fishes, reaching almost as far forward as the eminentia ventralis thalami of the ventral thalamus, which forms the posterior wall of the interventricular foramen of Monro (compare figures 423, 429, and 472). The dorsal thalamus is separated from the ventral thalamus by a sulcus, the sulcus medius thalami, which appears to anastomose caudally with the sulcus limitans, as is the case in cyclostomes and selachians. The dorsal thalamus, particularly in turtles and crocodiles, shows a contralateral fusion which sometimes extends well forward (crocodiles) and sometimes is confined to the more caudal portion of the region (turtle, Testudo). Ventral to this region of fusion, for a certain distance, the ventricular ependyma in the ventral thalamus is taller than usual and sometimes is folded. This specialized ependyma can be followed caudally where it extends into the hypothalamus below the tuberculum posterius. The cells in this specialized portion have lost their ciliary processes. Usually they are covered by a precipi-

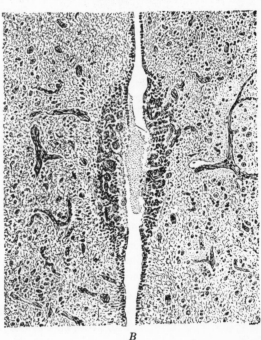

FIG. 473, *A* and *B*. *A*, drawing of a cell preparation of the diencephalon of Crocodilus porosus as a key drawing for figure 476 *B*. The area outlined by dotted lines is shown at a higher magnification in figure 476 *B*.

B, the highly vascularized and more particularly secretory portion of the diencephalic ependyma of Crocodilus porosus.

tate and they overlie a rich capillary plexus. They have the appearance of being secretory in character and are probably comparable to the secretory ependyma described for fishes (*Ariëns Kappers; Charlton*, '28). The degree of development of this modified ependyma varies in different reptiles.

The above account applies specifically to Crocodilus porosus (fig. 473). Essentially similar relations exist in Varanus (*Frederikse*, '31), and Alligator mississippiensis (where there is not such clear evidence of a folding, *Huber* and *Crosby*). In Chelone midas the area is larger, although apparently not so clearly secretory in character; in snakes it is said to be absent (*Ariëns Kappers*). Possibly the recessus geniculi described in Hatteria by *Gisi* ('07) and *Dendy* ('99 and '10) is the homologue of this area, but a study of the developmental stages of Crocodilus porosus suggests that more probably it is represented in the recessus prenuclearis thalami of *Dendy*, which at somewhat more frontal levels, below the nuclei rotundi, extends into the gray substance of the diencephalon.

While the dorsal thalamus of reptiles shows a great advance over that of frogs, the ventral thalamus and hypothalamus show much less advance, and, in the case of the latter area may show an actual decrease in proportional size although not in nuclear differentiation. The hypothalamic areas are continuous forward with the telencephalic preoptic areas, which in turn extend forward, as in amphibians, under the anterior commissure. The thin-walled postoptic recess in certain reptiles extends forward under the chiasm and sometimes even in front of it. In turtles and crocodiles this sac is flat and has a broad, low ventricle. In Varanus the sac is pointed and the ventricle is narrow. Caudally this recess fuses with a somewhat larger cavity which in turtles and lizards remains unpaired but in crocodiles presents lateral enlargements of which the wall is thicker at the base, as in frogs. In snakes, which have no subchiasmatic continuation of the postoptic recess, the caudal part of the hypothalamus is much larger than in other reptiles and its lobi laterales have walls so thick that they resemble the lobi inferiores of teleosts. There is no saccus vasculosus in reptiles.

The cerebral part of the hypophysis usually is short in reptiles with a slightly widened end where it joins the pars intermedia. This latter region is believed to pour its secretion into the third ventricle, while that from the oral part enters the blood (*Stendell*, '14). The hypophysis is particularly well developed in snakes.

In the following consideration of the microscopic structure of the various mesencephalic and diencephalic centers, beginning with the optic tectum, the nuclear pattern for each center is considered first and then the fiber connections are listed. To avoid repeating descriptions of fiber bundles they are described in connection with their major nuclei of origin or termination or, in certain cases, as major fiber groups, and cross references indicate where such descriptions may be found.

THE CELL STRUCTURE AND FIBER CONNECTIONS OF THE OPTIC TECTUM

The optic tectum, with the associated dorsal thalamus, provides for the centers of higher correlation within the reptilian brain. It is an important way station for most impulses passing forward to the dorsal thalamus, and its high grade of functional activity is indicated structurally by an elaborate arrangement of layers. It has been the subject of a relatively large amount of intensive work. *Ramón's* ('96) observations enabled him to describe and figure fourteen layers (including the ependyma) in the optic tectum. His work has formed the basis of later studies, and, because of its importance, a brief résumé of his results, as previously summarized by *Huber* and *Crosby* ('33), is here presented.

Ramón recognized and described the following layers in the optic tectum:

1. An epithelial zone consisting of ependymal elements with processes radiating toward the surface of the tectum.

2. A molecular zone composed chiefly of dendritic processes from cells of the overlying zones (3 and 5) but containing also a few thin, medullated nerve fibers and a certain number of scattered nerve cells.

3. A cellular zone composed of two or three rows of cells of three distinct types: (a) a piriform or pyramidal type with basilar dendrites ramifying in the adjoining zones (2 and 4), apical dendrites extending toward the periphery and giving off side branches at the various cell levels, and a neuraxis which enters the peripheral fiber zone, giving off collaterals in its course; (b) a cell similar to that just described except that its neuraxis is given off from a dendrite in the region of zone 9, forms a distinct crook or arch, and runs ventricleward until zone 6 is reached, which it enters; (c) a cell, the neuraxis of which is given off at the bifurcation of the apical dendrite in layer 7, courses peripheralward for a short distance, and then turns back to break up within zone 7 into a series of terminal branches.

4. A molecular zone containing a dendritic plexus and certain myelinated fibers.

5. A cellular zone composed of three to five cell layers separated by fiber bands. Cells of the three types described in zone 3 occur here.

6. A molecular zone formed chiefly of myelinated fibers. A small number of neurons are found here; of these the giant ganglion cells send out dendrites which spread widely in their course toward the periphery. Other cells found here and known as "células empenachadas" or plumed cells have an elongated, more or less cylindric body, from which numerous dendrites are given off. Occasionally such a dendritic branch runs horizontally, giving off in its course oblique branches toward the periphery. These and the preceding cells also occur in zone 7. The fibers in zone 6 show various arrangements, being sagittally arranged in the inside of the layer, obliquely in the middle portion, and tangentially in the external and inferior portion. The layer delimits along its inner border relatively clearly but along its outer border fascicles of fibers are given off which extend outward at least as far as the arborizations of the incoming optic nerve fibers. This layer contributes to the posterior commissure and, in the more lateral portion of the layer, two bundles of fibers are given off, an inner which forms a partial decussation under the floor of the fourth ventricle in the region of the oculomotor, and an external portion which swings farther lateralward. Both bundles later assume a horizontal direction. Certain of the fibers of zone 6 appear to connect with the inferior colliculus. *Ramón* found the following cells contributing fibers to this layer: the "célula en cajado," the large triangular cells, the conical or pyramidal cells of both the 8th and 9th zones, and the so-called "células empenachadas" or plumed cells of both the 6th and 7th zones.

7. A zone containing many irregularly distributed neurons. It is divided into three portions — (a) a deep portion containing numerous cells of varying

types, particularly the plumed cells (células empenachadas) and the "célula en cajado," which were found also in zone 6; (b) a middle strata consisting of

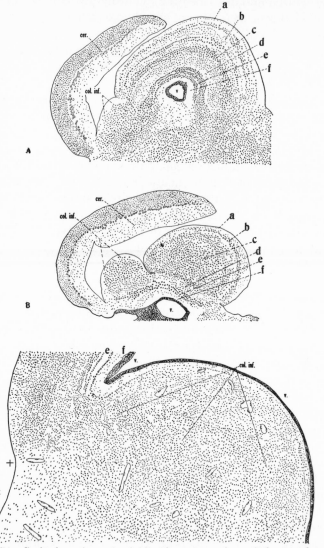

FIG. 474. Sagittal sections of toluidin-blue preparations of the tectal region. *Huber* and *Crosby*. *A* and *B*, Anolis carolinensis; *C*, Alligator mississippiensis; + marks intercollicular sulcus.

a, stratum opticum; *b*, stratum fibrosum et griseum superficiale; *c*, stratum griseum centrale; *d*, stratum album centrale; *e*, stratum griseum periventriculare; *f*, stratum fibrosum periventriculare; *cer.*, cerebellum; *col.inf.*, colliculus inferior; *v.*, ventricle.

irregular groups of cells, many of them representing a special type "célula en cajado," which gives off a rich plexus toward the periphery from the dendritic branches of which arise hooked neuraxes running ventricleward to enter the central fiber zone (zone 6); (c) a peripheral zone containing scattered cells of several types and among these the special type of "célula en cajado" (described in zone 3) with a peripherally directed axis cylinder, and a conical or fusiform type with a neuraxis extending ventralward toward the 6th zone while the dendrites extend into the formation of the peripheral plexuses.

8. A cellular zone, composed of 2 or 3 irregular rows of cells better differentiated in the lateral proximal region than in the medial region, where they are more or less intermingled with the external layer of zone 7. The periph-

erally directed dendrites of such cells ramify in the peripheral plexuses, the centrally directed dendrites in the 7th zone. The neuraxes give off side branches in their course through the 7th into the 6th zone. At the level of the 8th zone there may be observed fine, irregularly oriented fascicles, which possibly belong, at least in part, to the fasciculo óptico-commissural of *Ramón* (see page 1003).

9. A molecular zone which contains a few scattered cells and in which the deepest of the optic fibers arborize. There is present a rich dendritic plexus.

10. A narrow, irregular cellular zone containing 2 distinct cell types: (*a*) a small cell with peripherally extending, richly branching dendrites and a centrally directed neuraxis breaking up into many fine branches in the 7th zone, and (*b*) a cell with horizontally arranged dendrites and a neuraxis running horizontally for some distance and appearing to turn centralward with destination uncertain.

11. A molecular zone characterized particularly by the presence of a very rich terminal arborization of optic fibers, the finer branches presenting

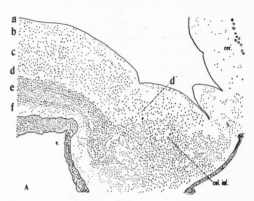

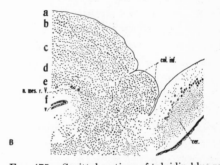

Fig. 475. Sagittal sections of toluidin-blue preparations of the tectal region. *Huber* and *Crosby.* A, Chrysemys marginata; B, Thamnophis sirtalis.

a, stratum opticum; *b*, stratum fibrosum et griseum superficiale; *c*, stratum griseum centrale; *d*, stratum album centrale; *e*, stratum griseum periventriculare; *f*, stratum fibrosum periventriculare; *cer.*, cerebellum; *col.inf.*, colliculus inferior; *d'*, extension of stratum album centrale over inferior colliculus; *n.mes.r.V*, nucleus of mesencephalic root of the trigeminal; *v.*, ventricle.

varicosities. The cellular elements in this zone resemble those described for the preceding layer. However, one type of cell has a neuraxis which deserves special mention, since it divides, one branch passing peripheralward while the other passes centralward.

12. A zone formed of an irregular row of small cells intercalated in the interstices of a plexus of medullated fibers, which are continuous with the optic tract. The cells are of two types: (*a*) tangential cells similar to those described for zone

10, with neuraxes breaking up into terminal arborizations in the same zone, and (*b*) neurons showing no definite orientation, with short, bent dendrites and a neuraxis which enters the interior of the tectum.

13. A molecular zone containing only a few scattered cells and optic tract fibers for which it constitutes the most peripheral region of termination. Into this region extend the terminations of the giant ganglion cells of the 6th zone. Irregularly arranged small cells and cells with horizontally coursing dendrites, such as were described in zone 12, occur in small numbers.

14. A zone of optic tract fibers and a considerable number of neuraxes ascending from deeper levels of the tectum. From here the optic fibers run obliquely away from the surface to end in their three levels of termination, namely zones 13, 11, and probably also zone 7. *Ramón's* consideration of the richness and significance of these terminations will be discussed with the consideration of the optic tract.

The fourteen layers or zones thus described by *Ramón* have been identified by various students of the reptilian tectum, among whom may be mentioned *de Lange* ('13), *Huber* and *Crosby* ('26), and *Shanklin* ('30). These zones differ in the clarity with which they may be delimited, according to the reptile under consideration, being most in accord with the scheme of *Ramón* in the various lizards and less clearly so in turtles and snakes. For details of these differences reference is made to figures 474 to 477 and to the account of *Huber* and *Crosby* ('33). These observers, while recognizing the zones of *Ramón* and their importance as an expression of the degree of histologic differentiation of the optic tectum, believed that a regrouping was desirable on the basis not only of cellular character, but with due account of the distribution of fiber connections as known from the literature (*Edinger*, '08; *de Lange*, '13; *Ariëns Kappers*, '21; *Huber* and *Crosby*, '26; *Cairney*, '26; *Shanklin*, '30; *Frederikse*, '31, and others), and as amplified by an intensive study of both medullated and nonmedullated fibers. This regrouping takes into account both morphological and functional factors, simplifies the conception of layer formation, and permits homologies through the vertebrate series. *Huber* and *Crosby* ('33, '33a, '34) divided the optic tectum into six strata, which, beginning at the periphery and passing toward the ventricle, are termed: *a*, stratum opticum; *b*, stratum fibrosum et griseum superficiale; *c*, stratum griseum centrale; *d*, stratum album centrale; *e*, stratum griseum periventriculare; *f*, stratum fibrosum periventriculare.

The stratum opticum is comparable to the zone 14 of *Ramón*. It contains optic tract fibers, which in lizards course at the periphery of the optic tectum, but is separated from the surface by a fiber free layer (and a very few cells) which, in certain regions in reptiles, such as turtles and lizards, constitutes a potential stratum zonale. The optic tract fibers turn down into the underlying stratum fibrosum et griseum superficiale where they terminate at various levels in relation with processes of its neurons and of those of underlying gray layers.

The stratum fibrosum et griseum superficiale is composed of alternate fibrous and cellular layers. In part the fibrous layers carry bundles of incoming fiber tracts, the impulses of which are integrated and reënforced within this stratum.

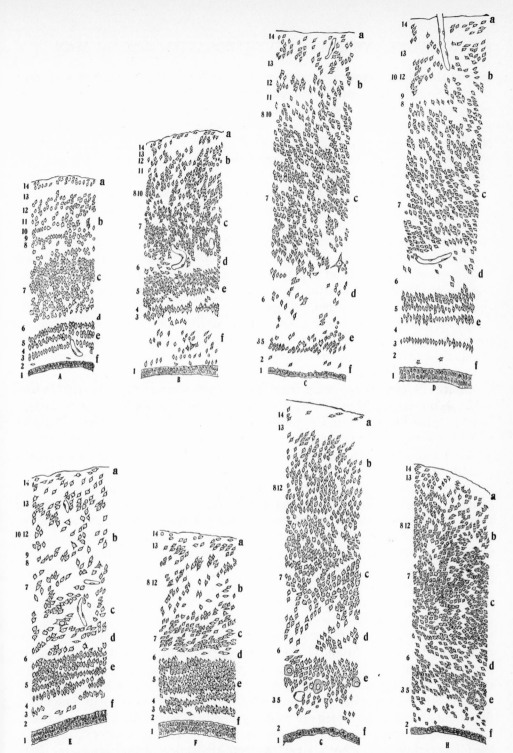

FIG. 476. A series of figures drawn from typical cross sections of toluidin-blue preparations of reptilian optic tecta. *Huber* and *Crosby*. *A*, Anolis carolinensis; *B*, Heloderma suspectum; *C*, Varanus griseus; *D*, Alligator mississippiensis; *E*, Chelhydra serpentina; *F*, young Chelhydra serpentina; *G*, Natrix; *H*, Thamnophis sirtalis.

The numbers designate the respective reptilian optic tectal zones or layers as described by *Ramón*; *a*, stratum opticum; *b*, stratum fibrosum et griseum superficiale; *c*, stratum griseum centrale; *d*, stratum album centrale; *e*, stratum griseum periventriculare; *f*, stratum fibrosum periventriculare.

977

In part the fibrous layers are regions of synapse between the neuraxes of afferent neurons and the dendrites of efferent neurons and incoming fiber tracts. The cell layers consist of the cell bodies of neurons, the dendrites of which synapse in the fibrous layers while the neuraxes, for the greater part, discharge to dendrites of cells of the underlying gray strata. This layer, then, is to be regarded as a receptive and correlative layer, with the possibility of possessing also the function of reënforcing impulses.

The stratum griseum centrale consists of neurons, the neuraxes of which constitute a most important part of the efferent fibers of the tectum. The shorter dendrites of these cells are in synaptic relation with neuraxes entering from overlying layers, the longer dendrites extend out through the stratum fibrosum et griseum superficiale where they come in contact with incoming fiber tracts and with neuraxes of the cells of this latter stratum. Collaterals of the neuraxes of neurons of the stratum griseum centrale turn outward also to discharge around the processes of cells in the more peripheral stratum, and so the stratum probably serves as a reënforcing mechanism, somewhat like that in the cerebellum, as *Ramón* has pointed out. Other neuraxes are said to enter the stratum opticum, forming the fibrae tectalis optici, which are believed by some observers to pass to the retina (*Ramón*).

Many efferent fibers arising from the stratum griseum centrale run for considerable distances within this layer in certain reptiles (as for instance in turtles). Others turn directly into the underlying stratum album centrale. In some reptiles a variable number of them pass directly to the stratum album centrale, while in the lizards practically all of them take this course, this stratum thus constituting the major efferent path of the optic tectum.

The stratum griseum periventriculare, situated internal to the stratum album centrale, varies in size and arrangement in the various reptiles. In certain of them this stratum shows a definite arrangement into layers with intervening fibro-reticular bands, which are largely regions in which synapses occur. Its characteristic neurons send long dendritic branches toward the periphery of the tectum, which synapse in the strata external to the stratum album centrale. The shorter dendrites of the periventricular gray extend toward the ventricle in order to come into relation with entering fibers of the diencephalic and mesencephalic periventricular system. The great majority of the neurons of the periventricular gray contribute neuraxes to the stratum album centrale. In this region lie the cells of origin of the mesencephalic root of the trigeminal nerve (see pp. 391 and 392), which have been identified in a number of reptiles and studied particularly in these forms by *van Valkenburg* ('11) and *Weinberg* ('28).

Between the ventricle and the stratum griseum periventriculare enter thin fibers and fiber fascicles which are made up largely of nonmedullated nerve fibers. The major connections of this area are as follows: The optic tract (page 1001), the fibrae tectales optici (see above), the tecto-thalamic and thalamo-tectal paths (page 1003), the ascending trigemino-tectal fibers (page 390), the lateral lemniscus (page 979), the posterior commissure (page 985), the commissure of the superior colliculi (page 980), the mesencephalic and diencephalic periventricular system (page 978), connections with the inferior colliculus, the spino-mesencephalic and bulbo-mesencephalic tract and collaterals from the lateral lemniscus, intermediate tecto-bulbar and ventral tecto-bulbar tracts, tecto-marginal and nigrotectal tracts, and isthmo-tectal and tecto-isthmal bundles.

Into the optic tectum come fibers from the cord by way of the tractus spino-et bulbo-mesencephalicus (*Ariëns Kappers*, '21) or spino-mesencephalic system

Fig. 477. Representative, typical neurons as found in Golgi preparations of the optic tectum of Pseudoemys elegans, selected and drawn separately with the aid of the camera lucida, combined in a single figure, and arranged with reference to their positions in the respective strata. *Huber* and *Crosby*.

a, stratum opticum; *b*, stratum fibrosum et griseum superficiale; *c*, stratum griseum centrale; *d*, stratum album centrale; *e*, stratum griseum periventriculare; *f*, stratum fibrosum periventriculare.

(*Huber* and *Crosby*, '26, '33). This tract, which ascends in close relation with the more ventral part of the spino-cerebellar system, gradually turns somewhat dorsalward and, at about the transverse level of the chief sensory nucleus of the trigeminal nerve, turns somewhat medialward and forward to be distributed to the optic tectum. Similarly lateral lemniscus fibers and secondary ascending fibers of the trigeminal system reach the tectum. Therefore, the optic tectum constitutes a center of correlation for optic-tactile, optic-auditory, and optic-pain impulses. It is of interest that, in part, these fibers terminate in the caudal portion of the tectum, in the outer edge of the stratum griseum centrale in close proximity to the cells of origin for the tecto-thalamic tract to the nucleus rotundus. Probably in part they enter the stratum fibrosum et griseum superficiale. Certain fascicles of these secondary ascending systems swing forward toward the dorsal part of the diencephalon, where it has been suggested that they reach the lentiform nucleus and the nucleus rotundus, but the evidence for such a connection is not fully convincing.

A commissura colliculi superioris (fig. 482A) is present in tectal regions. The tectum is connected with efferent centers by a series of tecto-bulbar tracts, the homolateral and the contralateral dorsal, intermediate, and ventral tecto-bulbar paths. Various observers (*Edinger, '08; de Lange, '13; Ariëns Kappers, '21; Huber* and *Crosby, '26* and *'33; Shanklin, '30; Frederikse, '31,* and others) have studied these systems in reptiles. The dorsal tecto-bulbar fibers appear to arise from homolateral and, in part, from contralateral tectal gray, the amount of fibers which cross in the commissura colliculi superioris varying with the reptile considered. The fibers leave the tectum through the stratum album centrale and swing ventralward and somewhat medialward. Part of the fibers join the medial longitudinal fasciculus of the same side; others pass to the fasciculus of the opposite side. Reference should be made to figure 481.

The tractus tecto-bulbaris intermedius (fig. 481), leaving the stratum album centrale, swings ventralward and then caudalward through the lower part of the tegmental region and the medulla oblongata, distributing during its course. Accompanying these longer fibers from the tectum are tecto-tegmental bundles, and crossed and uncrossed tecto-rubral fascicles, the crossing occurring in the dorsal tegmental decussation. Part of the fibers of the intermediate tecto-bulbar tract are believed to cross within the tectum, at least in certain reptiles.

A partial decussation of the ventral tecto-bulbar tracts (fig. 481) occurs in the ventral midbrain region. The extent to which a decussation in the tectum occurs is uncertain. After the ventral decussation the crossed and uncrossed ventral tecto-bulbar paths proceed caudalward, gradually diminishing in size.

Just internal to the ventral tecto-bulbar system is a bundle of fascicles which reaches the dorsomedial border of the nuclear group termed here the substantia nigra, constituting a tecto-nigral path. Nigro-tectal fibers swing dorsalward from the dorsal pole of the nucleus to enter the stratum fibrosum et griseum superficiale of the tectum.

The tectum is connected with the cerebellum by means of a small, crossed and still smaller, uncrossed fascicle, the direction of conduction being tecto-cerebellar. A few more superficially running fibers may constitute a cerebello-tectal path, but this needs further consideration. The tecto-cerebellar connections have been seen in a number of reptiles (*Huber* and *Crosby, '26* and *'33; Shanklin, '30,* and *Weston, '33,* Dissertation; also fig. 478).

Running in close proximity to the tecto-cerebellar system are the tecto-isthmal and isthmo-tectal tracts. The former bundle, which is the larger, extends downward, then caudalward and slightly lateralward to reach the nucleus isthmi.   The isthmo-tectal fascicle, which is smaller and less easily identified, lies superficial to the bundle just described and enters the more superficial part of

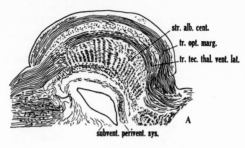

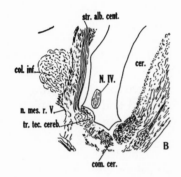

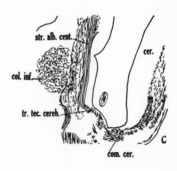

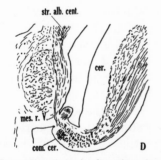

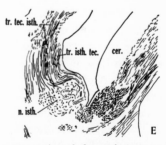

FIG. 478.   *A*, sagittal section of a pyridin-silver preparation of the optic tectum of *Sternotherus odoratus*; *B, C, D*, and *E*, sagittal sections of Weigert preparations of the tecto-cerebellar region of *Chrysemys marginata.*   *Huber* and *Crosby.*
cer., cerebellum; *col.inf.*, colliculus inferior; *com.cer.*, commissura cerebelli; *mes.r.V*, mesencephalic root of the trigeminal; *N.IV*, nervus trochlearis; *n.isth.*, nucleus isthmi; *n.mes.r.V*, nucleus of mesencephalic root of the trigeminal; *str.alb.cent.*, stratum album centrale; *subvent.perivent.sys.*, subventricular periventricular system; *tr.isth.tec.*, tractus isthmo-tectalis; *tr.opt.marg.*, tractus opticus marginalis; *tr.tec.cereb.*, tractus tecto-cerebellaris; *tr.tec.isth.*, tractus tecto-isthmalis; *tr.tec.thal.vent.lat.*, tractus tecto-thalamicus ventro-lateralis.

the tectum.   The tracts as here described have been seen by various students of reptilian brains (*Ariëns Kappers*, '21; *Shanklin*, '30, and others) and the foregoing account agrees in essentials with that of *Larsell* ('23, see bibliography for amphibians) for the frog.   These paths are illustrated in figure 478.

THE CELL STRUCTURE AND FIBER CONNECTIONS OF THE TORUS SEMI-CIRCULARIS AND THE NUCLEUS ISTHMI

The gross relations of the tori semicirculares have been described (page 967). Microscopically they consist of a central group of medium-sized cells to which the name of central nucleus may be applied, as in birds, and a periventricular layer of cells, which is continuous with the deeper cell layers of the optic tectum (*Huber* and *Crosby*, '26, also figs. 474–475.)   Along the bundles accompanying such layers occur the internuclear connections with the tectum.   The major fiber connections of the torus semicircularis are the lateral lemniscus and collaterals and perhaps stem fibers of the trigeminal lemniscus, from the frontal trigeminal nucleus as well as from the spinal trigeminal nucleus.   Furthermore, the torus semicircularis is connected with the pars ventralis of the ventral supraoptic decussation and has isthmo-toral connections.

The nucleus isthmi in reptiles is well developed, consisting usually of two cell masses.   In the alligator these are so arranged that there is a large-celled lateral mass and a small-celled medial or dorsomedial cell group.   (According to *Ariëns Kappers*, in some reptiles the nucleus falls into dorsal and ventral subdivisions.) It receives impulses from the lateral lemniscus and from the decussatio supra-optica ventralis pars dorsalis.   A bundle interconnects the torus semicircularis and the nucleus isthmi, running forward and medialward between the large- and small-celled portions of the cell mass and then swinging into the torus semicircularis. The direction of conduction is not known.   Isthmo-tectal and probably tecto-isthmal tracts are present in the alligator, as well as fine interconnections between the two nuclei isthmi, passing through the anterior medullary velum.   The isthmo-tectal tract runs forward and dorsalward to the tectal areas from the upper tip of the nucleus isthmi.   The optic fibers carried to this nucleus by *Bellonci* ('88) are not demonstrable in any material available for study.   It seems probable that it was supraoptic rather than optic fibers which he traced to this region.   A study of turtle material (figs. 479 and 480) shows essentially the same relations and connections as those given for the alligator except that it has not been possible to demonstrate the connection with the ventral supraoptic system.   The connections here described for reptiles agree essentially with those given by *Larsell* ('23) for the frog.

CERTAIN TEGMENTAL AREAS OF THE MESENCEPHALON

Ventral to the nucleus isthmi and medial to the ascending lateral lemniscus is the nucleus mesencephalicus profundus (fig. 480) consisting of a group of medium-sized to small cells, associated with collaterals, if not with stem fibers, of the lateral lemniscus.   It is essentially a nucleus of this lemniscus.

The red nucleus (fig. 480) is a round, conspicuously large-celled nuclear mass near the midline, lateral to the outgoing fibers of the oculomotor nerve.   This cell mass is probably the forerunner of the magnocellular portion of the nucleus in mammals.   In certain species of Varanus (*Ariëns Kappers*, '21) small cells appear to be scattered among the large cells, but these are more probably the homologue of the small cells found in conjunction with reticular groups (*van Hoevell*, '11) than the indication of a parvocellular division of the nucleus, particularly since the connection with the cortex, characteristic of this small-celled portion in mammals (*von Monakow*, '05, '10, and others), is not present in reptiles.

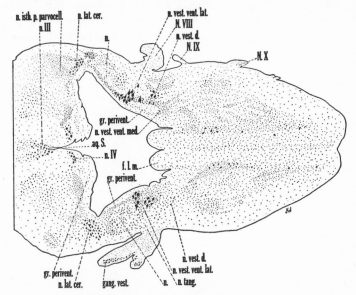

FIG. 479.   Horizontal section passing through the base of the cerebellum and the midbrain of the turtle (Pseudoemys elegans).   Toluidin blue preparation. *Weston.*

aq.S., aqueductus Sylvii; *f.l.m.*, fasciculus longitudinalis medialis; *gang.vest.*, ganglion vestibulare; *gr.perivent.*, griseum periventriculare; *n.* nucleus vestibularis superior of *Beccari*; dorsolateralis of *Weston*; *n.III*, nucleus oculomotorius; *n.IV*, nucleus trochlearis; *N.VIII*, nervus acusticus; *N.IX*, nervus glossopharyngeus; *N.X*, nervus vagus; *n.isth.p.parvocell.*, nucleus isthmii pars parvocellularis; *n.lat.cer.*, nucleus lateralis cerebelli; *n.tang.*, nucleus vestibularis tangentialis; *n.vest.d.*, nucleus vestibularis descendens; *n.vest.vent.lat.*, nucleus vestibularis ventrolateralis; *n.vest.vent.med.*, nucleus vestibularis ventromedialis.

The nucleus ruber is very distinct in turtles, lizards, and crocodiles.   In the Boa constrictor the cells are far less numerous than might be expected, taking into account the connection of this cell mass with the cerebellum.   This connection is mediated by the brachium conjunctivum anterius, or as it is sometimes termed, the tractus cerebello-tegmentalis mesencephali (*Huber* and *Crosby*, '26), a crossed bundle arising in the cerebellum — probably in both cerebellar nuclei (*Weston*, '33) — swinging ventromedialward and forward, crossing under the ventricle, and terminating in the contralateral red nucleus.   Neuraxes of the large cells of the nucleus ruber likewise decussate and pass caudalward, at least as far as the medulla oblongata, constituting a rubro-bulbar and possibly a rubro-spinal path.   Fibers accompanying the tecto-bulbar paths reach the red nucleus; these constitute the tractus tecto-rubralis.

In front of the nucleus ruber and ventral to the more oral portions of the oculo-motor nuclei are the scattered cells of the nucleus of the medial longitudinal fasciculus. These have been figured most clearly by *Ramón* ('97) and by *Beccari* ('23) for Varanus, and are clearly identifiable in Alligator. In general they are reticular in character. *Beccari* ('23) termed the group the interstitial nucleus of the fasciculus longitudinalis medialis because of the relation of the cells to the bundles of the fasciculus. In the lizard *Ariëns Kappers* noted a more medial group of cells contributing fibers to the lower part of the medial longitudinal fasciculus. He termed these the nucleus of Darkschewitsch.

FIG. 480. The nucleus oculomotorius (*N.III*), the nucleus ruber (*N.rub.*), the nucleus profundus mesencephali (*Nu.prof.mesenc.*), and the nucleus isthmi (*nu.isthmi*) in Testudo graeca. *de Lange.*

The nucleus interpeduncularis lies near the midline in the ventral portion of the mesencephalon. It consists of a mass of somewhat scattered cells which receives the terminal fibers of the habenulo-peduncular tract and internuclear connections with the near-lying hypothalamic areas.

Dorsolateral to the nucleus interpeduncularis, along the lateral periphery of the midbrain, is the nucleus of the basal optic root (fig. 481), of which mention has been made in connection with the distribution of optic fibers. In addition to such optic tract fibers, the neurons of this nucleus are in synaptic relation with the dendrites of the ventral interstitial nucleus of the medial longitudinal fasciculus and are thought to be related to the oculomotor nucleus (*Beccari*, '23, Varanus; *Huber* and *Crosby*, '26, Alligator; *Shanklin*, '30, Chameleon; see also fig. 481). Recently *Shanklin* ('33) described this nucleus in Chameleon under the name applied to it in mammals — nucleus opticus tegmenti. This last mentioned

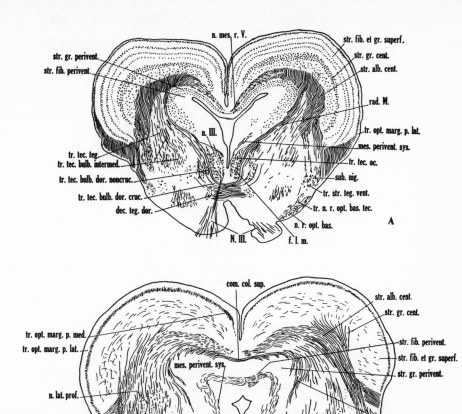

FIG. 481. Cross sections of Weigert preparations; *A*, Anolis carolinensis; *B*, Natrix. *Huber and Crosby.*

dec.teg., decussatio tegmentalis; *dec.teg.dor.*, decussatio tegmentalis dorsalis; *dec.supraopt.vent.p. vent.*, decussatio supraoptica ventralis pars ventralis; *f.l.m.*, fasciculus longitudinalis medialis; *mes.perivent.syst.*, mesencephalic periventricular system; *N.III*, nervus oculomotorius; *n.III*, nucleus of the oculomotor nerve; *n.lat.prof.*, nucleus lateralis profundus mesencephali; *n.r.opt. bas.*, nucleus radicis opticum basalis; *rad.M.*, radiations of *Meynert*; *str.alb.cent.*, stratum album centrale; *str.fib.et gr.superf.*, stratum fibrosum et griseum superficiale; *str.fib.perivent.*, stratum fibrosum periventriculare; *str.gr.cent.*, stratum griseum centrale; *str.gr.perivent.*, stratum griseum periventriculare; *sub.nig.*, substantia nigra; *tr.n.r.opt.bas.tec.*, tractus nuclei radicis opticum basalis ad tectum; *tr.opt.marg.p.lat.*, tractus opticus marginalis pars lateralis; *tr.opt.marg.p.med.*, tractus opticus marginalis pars medialis; *tr.str.teg.vent.*, tractus strio-tegmentalis ventralis; *tr.tec. bulb.dor.*, tractus tecto-bulbaris dorsalis; *tr.tec.bulb.dor.cruc.*, tractus tecto-bulbaris dorsalis cruciatus; *tr.tec.bulb.intermed.*, tractus tecto-bulbaris intermedius; *tr.tec.bulb.dor.noncruc.*, tractus tecto-bulbaris dorsalis noncruciatus; *tr.tec.bulb.vent.*, tractus tecto-bulbaris ventralis; *tr.tec.bulb.vent. cruc.*, tractus tecto-bulbaris ventralis cruciatus; *tr.tec.oc.*, tractus tecto-oculomotorius; *tr.tec.teg.*, tractus tecto-tegmentalis. Associated fibers are indicated with the decussatio supraoptica ventralis pars ventralis.

985

observer also described connections between this nucleus and various tegmental centers — the nucleus geniculatus pretectalis, the nucleus lentiformis mesencephali, the lateral geniculate nucleus — and with the posterior commissure.

A group of cells, entopeduncular in appearance and in their relation to the terminal fibers of the ventral peduncle of the lateral forebrain bundle, occupies a position along the ventrolateral wall of the mesencephalon at the level of the red nucleus. *Beccari* ('23) labeled them "substantio nigra (?)." *Shanklin* ('30) termed this cell complex the nucleus entopeduncularis, a name justified perhaps because the cells develop as interstitial cells of the ventral peduncle of the forebrain bundle, as do certain other subthalamic centers of mammals, since the ventral peduncle of this bundle, in phylogenetic development, becomes the ansa lenticularis of mammals. However, this particular cell group may be differentiated from the remainder of the complex through the position which it occupies and through its tectal connections, which in course and relations are directly comparable to the connections of the substantia nigra as described for the opossum by *Tsai* ('25a) and for carnivores by *Rioch* ('29a). On the basis of these connections and relations, which are particularly clear for certain lizards (Anolis), *Huber* and *Crosby* ('33) have suggested that this nucleus is the reptilian forerunner of a part of the mammalian substantia nigra (see fig. 481A).

THE NUCLEAR PATTERN AND FIBER CONNECTIONS OF CERTAIN PRETECTAL AND SUBPRETECTAL NUCLEAR GROUPS

In the region near the anterior end of the tectum and grading over into the diencephalon are several nuclei, which may be considered as constituting a pretectal group. To what extent they are represented in higher forms and in how far they are diencephalic or mesencephalic is open to question. Under this group will be considered the nuclei of the posterior commissure, the nucleus circularis, the nucleus pretectalis, the nucleus spiriformis, the nucleus lentiformis mesencephali, and the nucleus geniculatus pretectalis of *Beccari*.

The nuclei of the posterior commissure fall into three major groups: a dorsal nucleus, an interstitial nucleus, and a specialized group of such interstitial cells termed by *Beccari* ('23) group *a*. The dorsal nucleus consists of a group of large cells situated at the level of the most anterior part of the tectum directly lateral to the ventricle and medial to the pretectal nucleus. This group, usually designated merely as the nucleus of the posterior commissure, has been identified in various reptiles (in turtles, *de Lange*, '13, and *Ariëns Kappers*, '21; in Varanus, *Beccari*, '23; in Alligator, *Huber* and *Crosby*, '26). Scattered among the fibers of the commissure as these swing downward around the ventricle and thus constituting in part at least the stratum griseum of the region, are the interstitial cells of the posterior commissure, a special group of which constitute group *a*. These latter divisions have been recognized in Varanus and Alligator.

The posterior commissure itself falls into two divisions, a dorsal and a ventral. The latter begins close to the habenular commissure in the alligator and its most laterally directed fibers swing directly out into the dorsal nucleus of the commissure. Some fibers reach the nucleus lentiformis mesencephali and probably the nucleus pretectalis. The most medial fibers arch downward around the ventricle, in part they are synaptic in relation with the associated interstitial nucleus of the commissure and group a, in part they appear to pass directly into the medial longitudinal fasciculus. A few fibers are in relation with a cell group internal to the interstitial nucleus of the posterior commissure which from its outline has been termed the nucleus circularis, but the further connections or homologues of which are at present unknown. The dorsal division of the posterior commissure, the rostral limit of which is just caudal to that of the ventral division, is concerned largely, if not exclusively, in interrelating the optic tecta. The divisions of the posterior commissure are illustrated in figure 482.

Mention has been made of the nucleus pretectalis. This term has been applied to several different cell groups in this region in different vertebrates so that the name has almost lost its significance. As applied here, it is intended to designate an almost round nuclear group (fig. 482) situated in planes through more cephalic levels of the optic tectum, near the periphery and just lateral to the dorsal nucleus of the posterior commissure. It is somewhat caudal to the main mass of the nucleus geniculatus pretectalis and, on the whole, lateral and caudal to the nucleus lentiformis mesencephali. As here employed, the name of nucleus pretectalis accords with the usage of *Edinger* ('99, Tafel III, figs. 1 and 2; '08, Bd. II, p. 158), *de Lange* ('13, fig. 14, and as outlined in Tafel VIII at the conclusion of the paper), *Beccari* ('23, figs. 18, 20, and 25), *Huber* and *Crosby* ('26, fig. 11, '33), and *Cairney* ('26, figs. 32 and 38). *Edinger* ('99 and '08) believed this nucleus to be connected with the nucleus geniculatus lateralis and the nucleus rotundus. Such connections are represented in the alligator by thalamo-tectal and tecto-thalamic paths which send collaterals and perhaps stem fibers to the nucleus pretectalis in their course to tectal centers. The fibers of the supraoptic system have been traced to this nucleus and optic tract fibers reach it. It is interconnected with the tectum by short internuclear fibers (the tractus tecto-pretectalis, *Huber* and *Crosby*, '26). There is indication that the strio-tectal component may also reach this nuclear mass. *Edinger's* ('99, '08) findings in reptiles suggest such a path. Possible connections with the posterior commissure system have been mentioned previously. The nucleus pretectalis is connected by internuclear fibers with the nucleus spiriformis of *Edinger* ('08, Bd. II, p. 158), who identified under this name a cell group in Varanus griseus. A similar group, consisting of rather large cells, is present in Alligator (*Huber* and *Crosby*, '26) dorsomedial to nucleus pretectalis and directly dorsal and somewhat medial to the nucleus dorsalis of the posterior commissure, from which latter nucleus it is not sharply differentiable at all levels. However, since this nuclear group probably is not the homologue of the avian nucleus of this name, the term was abandoned by *Huber* and *Crosby* ('33) and a letter *m* used to designate the group. *Shanklin* ('30) appears to have included it in the cap of cells around his nucleus geniculatus pretectalis, presumably as part of his nucleus lentiformis mesencephali (see page 989). In the reptiles available for study, its differentiation suggests its separation from both of these nuclear masses. It is suggested ten-

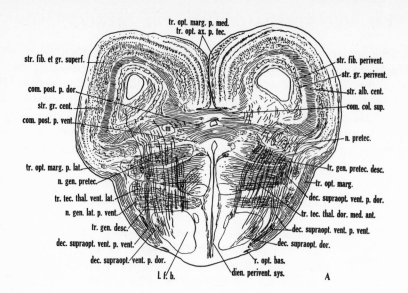

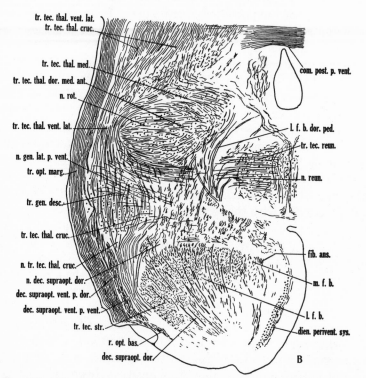

FIG. 482. Cross section of pyridin-silver preparations. *A*, Anolis carolinensis; *B*, Alligator mississippiensis. *Huber* and *Crosby.*

com.col.sup., commissura colliculi superioris; *com.post.p.dor.*, commissura posterior pars dorsalis; *com.post.p.vent.*, commissura posterior pars ventralis; *dec. supraopt.dor.*, decussatio supraoptica dorsalis; *dec.supraopt.vent.p.dor.*, decussatio supraoptica ventralis pars dorsalis; *dec.supraopt.vent.p.vent.*, decussatio supraoptica ventralis pars ventralis; *dien.perivent.sys.*, diencephalic periventricular system; *fib.ans.*, fibrae ansulatae; *l.f.b.*, lateral forebrain bundle; *l.f.b.dor.ped.*, lateral forebrain bundle dorsal peduncle; *m.f.b.*, medial forebrain bundle; *n.dec.*

988

tatively that it is the homologue of the nucleus pretectalis of birds (which is not homologous to the similarly named nucleus in reptiles).

Slightly in front of the nucleus pretectalis (see fig. 482) in Alligator, where the diencephalic centers are going over into the mesencephalon, lies the nucleus lentiformis mesencephali. It lies just medial to the optic tract above the posterior commissure fibers. This nucleus has been described in various reptiles by *de Lange* ('13). It constitutes the nucleus lentiformis of *de Lange* ('13), the nucleo lentiforme del tetto of *Beccari* ('23, see fig. 23) and the nucleus lentiformis mesencephali of *Huber* and *Crosby* ('26; '33), *Cairney* ('26), and *Shanklin* ('30). While all these observers have recognized an homologous nuclear group, the opinions with regard to its exact caudal limits vary; *de Lange* ('13) and *Cairney* ('26) have carried it caudalward to a position which is slightly dorsomedial and also medial to the nucleus pretectalis. In toluidin blue preparations of Alligator the nucleus appears as scattered clusters of neurons with occasional larger, lighter stained cells such as those figured by *de Lange* ('13) in Varanus. The nuclear boundaries are indistinct. The nucleus lentiformis mesencephali is associated with fibers of the ventral tecto-thalamic tract, receives collaterals at least of the dorsal supraoptic decussation, and is interconnected with the tectum by internuclear fibers. Its position is shown in figure 485.

In front of the nucleus lentiformis mesencephali, but definitely in the course of the tectal fibers and so considered as belonging to the pretectal group, although diencephalic nuclei occur at the same level, are the nucleus geniculatus pretectalis and the nucleus posterodorsalis. The name nucleus geniculatus pretectalis is applied here (see fig. 485) to the nucleo geniculato pretectale of *Beccari* ('23), who described this cell group in Varanus, where it is well developed and where the orientation of its cells and their arrangement in a row on either side of a molecular zone gives a structural resemblance to the lateral geniculate nucleus. This nucleus geniculatus pretectalis was seen in the young alligator (*Huber* and *Crosby*, '26) and later ('33), as a better developed nuclear mass, in other reptiles and particularly in certain lizards, such as Anolis. *Cairney* ('26) identified this nuclear group in Sphenodon. The cell group termed the nucleus geniculatus pretectalis by *Shanklin* ('30) does not appear to be an homologous nuclear mass. It is probable that the nucleus geniculatus lateralis pars inferior of his figure 7 (but not of his figure 6) is comparable to the nucleus geniculatus pretectalis of the above

---

supraopt.dor., nucleus decussationis supraopticae dorsalis; *n.gen.lat.p.vent.*, nucleus geniculatus lateralis pars ventralis; *n.gen.pretec.*, nucleus geniculatus pretectalis; *n.pretec.*, nucleus pretectalis; *n.reun.*, nucleus reuniens; *n.rot.*, nucleus rotundus; *n.tr.tec.thal.cruc.*, nucleus tractus tecto-thalamici (et thalamo-tectalis) cruciati; *r.opt.bas.*, radix opticum basalis; *str.alb.cent.*, stratum album centrale; *str.fib.et gr. superf.*, stratum fibrosum et griseum superficiale; *str.fib.perivent.*, stratum fibrosum periventriculare; *str.gr.cent.*, stratum griseum centrale; *str.gr.perivent.*, stratum griseum periventriculare; *tr.gen.desc.*, tractus geniculatus descendens; *tr.gen.pretec.desc.*, tractus geniculatus pretectalis descendens; *tr.opt. ax.p.tec.*, tractus opticus axillaris pars tectalis; *tr.opt.marg.*, tractus opticus marginalis; *tr.opt.marg. p. lat.*, tractus opticus marginalis pars lateralis; *tr.opt.marg.p.med.*, tractus opticus marginalis pars medialis; *tr.tec.reun.*, tractus tecto-reuniens and associated fibers; *tr.tec.str.*, tractus tecto-striatalis et strio-tectalis; *tr.tec.thal.cruc.*, tractus tecto-thalamicus (et thalamo-tectalis) cruciatus; *tr.tec.thal.dor. med.ant.*, tractus tecto-thalamicus et thalamo-tectalis dorsomedialis anterior; *tr.tec.thal.med.*, tractus tecto-thalamicus medialis; *tr.tec.thal.vent.lat.*, tractus tecto-thalamicus et thalamo-tectalis ventrolateralis.

mentioned observers, while his nucleus geniculatus pretectalis belongs to the pretectal complex. The nucleus gives rise to a descending tract, the fasciculus geniculatus pretectalis (*Beccari*, '23; *Huber* and *Crosby*, '26; *Cairney*, '26), which also carries some fibers from the nucleus pretectalis, as various observers have noted. This tract, which is believed to form a descending system, runs ventro-caudalward through the midbrain, but its further course and its termination have not been established as yet. There is some evidence, by no means conclusive, that this nucleus is connected with the tectum by afferent and efferent tracts.

There is a small cell group lateral and ventrolateral to the habenula, which extends caudalward to this latter nucleus into a position close to the midline, where it may form a slight eminence above the posterior commissure. Conceivably this band of cells might be subdivided into two nuclear masses, but for the present it is included under the name, nucleus posterodorsalis (fig. 484). The mass thus designated is present in many reptilian forms, possibly in all of them. It constitutes the nucleus posterodorsalis of *Huber* and *Crosby* ('26 and '33) and is included in the nucleus geniculatus lateralis pars superior of *Shanklin* ('30), although it is probably not the nucleus so designated by *Ramón* ('96) and most certainly is not the nucleus geniculatus lateralis pars dorsalis of *Cairney* ('26), which lies ventral and cephalic to it. It may be included in the region designated the geniculate nucleus by *Warner* ('31, p. 1160, fig. 13). The nucleus receives a special fascicle of optic tract fibers, possibly homologous with the fasciculus dorsomedialis of the tractus opticus of teleosts as described by *Jansen* ('29), but this requires further verification. Tecto-thalamic bundles of the ventral tecto-thalamic tract lie in intimate relation with the cells of this nucleus and probably distribute to them either through stem fibers or collaterals.

The nucleus S of *Beccari* ('23), which is the geniculatum internum of *Bellonci* ('88), Z of *Huber* and *Crosby* ('26), and an unnamed but identified nucleus of *Cairney* ('26), lies near the lateral surface of the midbrain, below the tectum and in intimate relation with the pars ventralis of the ventral supraoptic decussation, to which it contributes and from which it receives fibers. *Beccari* has labeled it "nucleo geniculato mediale (?)" and *Frey* ('33) has so regarded it. *Papez* ('35) has considered it as a forerunner of the nucleus geniculatus medialis pars ventralis of mammals (see also p. 1007).

THE EPITHALAMIC REGIONS OF THE DIENCEPHALON WITH FIBER CONNECTIONS

As has been seen, the reptilian diencephalon contains the usual epithalamic, thalamic, and hypothalamic regions. The epithalamic areas will receive consideration first. The gross relations of this region together with the epiphyseal relations, have been discussed (pp. 968 to 971) and the connections of the posterior commissure, which extends to the line between the mesencephalon and the diencephalon, have been considered. A brief account of the habenula follows. This brain center is divisible into a lateral habenular nucleus and a medial habenular nucleus (see fig. 483 and fig. 484). The lateral habenular nucleus consists of an admixture of small cells and a few larger neurons interspersed among the incoming fibers of the stria medullaris. At first this nucleus occupies a position lateral to the medial habenular nucleus but later is capped by the cells of this latter nucleus. In its more oral part the medial habenular nucleus consists of dorsomedial and ventrolateral portions, which are separated from each other by the lateral habenular nucleus. Gradually the two parts unite, forming a cap over the latter nucleus. As the region of the habenular commissure is approached, the ventromedial part of the medial nucleus swings ventralward and is cut off from the remainder of the nucleus by the commissural fibers. As a whole the medial nucleus consists of medium-sized and relatively deeply staining neurons. The arrangement of the habenular nuclei, described above particularly for Alligator, shows minor variations in the various reptiles. These have been described by so many observers that it appears unnecessary to go into the minor differences. Reference is made here to the papers of *Edinger* ('99 and '08), *de Lange* ('13), and *Cairney* ('26).

The fiber tracts associated with the habenula have been described in various reptiles. There is some difference in opinion as to the nomenclature to be used. A considerable number of observers (*Crosby*, '17; *Hines*, '23; *Huber* and *Crosby*, '26; *Cairney*, '26), in their study of the stria medullaris, use the terminology for the various components emphasized by *Herrick* ('10) in his work on amphibians and reptiles. Other observers follow that used particularly by *Ariëns Kappers* and *Theunissen* ('08) and *Ariëns Kappers* ('21). Both terminologies are based on earlier descriptions in the literature with such additions as appear pertinent. In the following account both names are used wherever homologous tracts are described. A detailed account of the stria medullaris is found on pages 1348 to 1351.

The stria medullaris, the main fiber bundle reaching the habenula, consists of six major divisions. The first of these, the tractus cortico-habenularis medialis (*Herrick*, '10; *Crosby*, '17), or merely the tractus cortico-habenularis (*Ariëns Kappers*, '21), arises mainly from the projection cells of the hippocampal cortex and from the bed nucleus of the hippocampal commissure. It runs caudalward with the fornix bundles and there separates from them to swing dorsocaudally into the stria medullaris (figs. 584 and 585).

The anterior and posterior portions of the tractus cortico-habenularis lateralis in the alligator (figs. 583 to 585, *Crosby*, '17; *Huber* and *Crosby*, '26) appear in certain reptiles to be represented by a single sheet of fibers. They include the tract described for Sphenodon by *Hines* ('23, p. 499c) and by *Cairney* ('26) as the lateral cortico-habenular tract. This tract, together with certain components of the medial cortico-habenular tract of Alligator, constitutes the olfacto-habenular tract of *Ariëns Kappers* and *Theunissen* ('08) and of *Ariëns Kappers* ('21). In the alligator the anterior part arises both from the cortex of the piriform lobe and from the nucleus of the lateral olfactory tract and the nucleus of the diagonal band of Broca, the posterior part from the posterior part of the nucleus of the lateral olfactory tract, the amygdaloid complex, and the overlying cortex. This is probably the amygdalo-hypothalamic component described by *Cairney* ('26) for Sphenodon. In all reptiles it appears to be partly basal and partly cortical in origin. The anterior division runs directly medialward from its origin and then turns dorsalward until the medial regions of the hemisphere are reached and then swings dorsalward into the stria medullaris.

The term, tractus olfacto-habenularis medialis, has been used by *Ariëns Kappers* and others for a sheet of fibers swinging from the ventromedial portions of the telencephalon, particularly the preoptic area, into the stria. Since these fibers swing in part medial to the lateral forebrain bundle and in part lateral to it, *Herrick* ('10) split the system into two bundles in the alligator, a medial olfacto-habenular (fig. 585) and a lateral olfacto-habenular (fig. 585) tract, the former containing only such fibers from the preoptic area as ran medial to the forebrain bundles. Such tracts were recognized in alligator material by *Crosby* ('17) and in Sphenodon by *Cairney* ('26). A tract from the amygdaloid complex to the habenula was termed by *Cairney* the tractus amygdalo-habenularis. It is probably the tractus olfacto-habenularis posterior of *Crosby* ('17). An anterior olfacto-habenular tract, described by *Herrick* ('10) for amphibians, was identified, in Sphenodon, by *Cairney* ('26), who traced it from the tuberculum olfactorium to the stria.

In Sphenodon, *Cairney* was able to divide the stria into three portions on the basis of the degree of medullation of its fibers, since in this form the middle portion of the bundle appears to consist of heavily myelinated fibers bordered medially by thinly myelinated and laterally by unmyelinated fibers. The medial portion contains the septo-habenular (medial cortico-habenular) and medial olfacto-habenular tracts. The lateral portion contains the other bundles described above. The heavily myelinated middle portion contains two components. Fibers of the first component do not belong to the stria but merely accompany it from their origin in the nucleus of the posterior pallial commissure to the level of the nucleus ovalis, around which they bend to enter the medial forebrain bundle on their way to hypothalamic centers. These bundles are accompanied by fibers from the nucleus, which run in the stria medullaris to the habenula. The second component of this middle portion is represented by fine fibers which cut through the basal forebrain bundle and run dorsally then to the stria medullaris. Their origin appears to be uncertain; they are probably the homologue of the tractus transversalis taeniae of *Unger* ('11). The stria medullaris thus formed runs along the dorsomedial surface of the diencephalon to the habenula, where in part it decussates before its termination. As to the exact termination of the various components within the habenular complex there is still grave doubt. *Cairney* stated that his material suggests the termination of the medullated tract in homo- and contralateral nuclei and of the unmedullated in contralateral (and perhaps homolateral) lateral habenular nuclei. The distribution needs experimental verification. However, in many reptiles the so-called lateral cortico-habenular tract consists in large part of commissural fibers interconnecting the lateral areas of the hemispheres. These fibers course through the stria medullaris, decussate in the habenular region in what may be termed the commissura superior telencephali, and then proceed via the contralateral stria medullaris to the opposite lateral hemisphere wall.

Habenulo-tectal fibers accompanying the tecto-thalamic system have been identified in the turtle (*Huber* and *Crosby*, '26 and '33) and in Sphenodon (*Cairney*,

'26).   They cross in part in the commissura tecti diencephali (*Huber* and *Crosby*, '33).   An habenulo-peduncular tract is found in various reptiles (fig. 485; *Edinger*, '99; *Ariëns Kappers*, '21; *Hines*, '23).   It is identifiable in the alligator, but in view of the relations later established for birds, it is our present opinion that the entire path has not been seen as yet in reptiles.   Under the name of funiculus habenulae posterior, *Haller* described an habenulo-thalamic path.   A similar path was described by *Edinger* ('99) as the tractus habenulo-diencephalicus and evidence of such a connection is demonstrable in the turtle material, although not in the alligator material available.   Undoubtedly its absence in this latter form is due to faulty impregnation.   Two so-called habenulo-thalamic paths are mentioned by *Cairney* ('26), the first connecting the habenula with the nucleus dorsomedialis anterior, the other, probably not entirely thalamic, connecting the habenula with the nucleus rotundus.   One is inclined to question whether these may not constitute the homologue of the medial division of the avian habenulo-peduncular tract, which in small part is habenulo-thalamic.   The extent of its connection with the nucleus rotundus requires further investigation.

Ventral to the habenular nucleus is a small subhabenular region consisting anteriorly of the nucleus or regio subhabenularis (*Ariëns Kappers*, '21; *Huber* and *Crosby*, '26) or nucleus magnocellularis (*de Lange*, '13; fig. 488) and posteriorly of a region of somewhat scattered cells, which passes over without a break into the periventricular gray of the mesencephalon and to which the name of nucleus angularis subhabenularis (*Huber* and *Crosby*, '26) has been applied. The significance of this region is at present not clearly understood and it is not possible to say whether these areas are epithalamic or thalamic in character.

THE NUCLEAR MASSES OF THE THALAMUS WITH FIBER CONNECTIONS

The thalamus proper shows a great advance in Reptilia over the corresponding regions in Amphibia, both with respect to nuclear configuration and fiber connections.   In Alligator (*Huber* and *Crosby*, '26) and in Sphenodon (*Cairney*, '26) the dorsal part of the region at the oral end is occupied by three major nuclear masses; nucleus dorsomedialis anterior, nucleus dorsolateralis anterior, and nucleus ovalis.   Of these the nucleus dorsomedialis anterior (figs. 483, 484) is the first to appear, beginning as a small patch of cells just beneath the dorsal surface of the diencephalon.   It increases rapidly in size and soon occupies the dorsomedial part of the thalamic wall above the sulcus medius.   At first it is almost round in outline but gradually becomes irregularly triangular in shape with the increase, on its lateral side, of the nucleus dorsolateralis anterior.   In sections through the habenula and the middle of the nucleus rotundus, the nucleus dorsomedialis anterior is much smaller and soon disappears.   This nucleus consists of medium-sized cells among which are some scattered larger neurons. It is distinct in Sphenodon and Alligator mississippiensis from the nucleus dorsolateralis anterior, with which it is sometimes grouped as the nucleus anterior (*Edinger*, '99; *de Lange*, '11; *Ariëns Kappers*, '21; *Beccari*, '23, and others), both in respect to cell character and fiber connections, for unlike that latter nucleus it receives only a few scattering fibers (probably not direct) from the

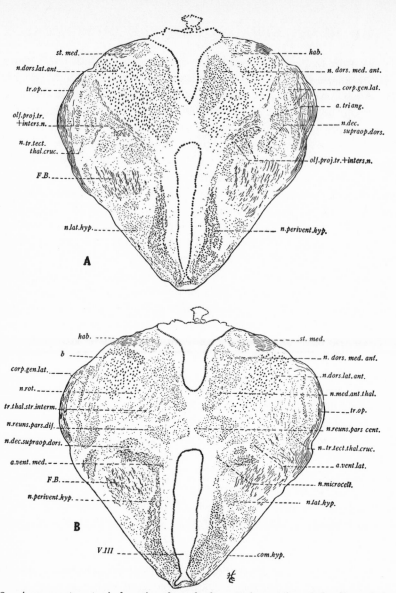

Fig. 483. *A* represents a typical section through the anterior portion of the diencephalon at the level of the greatest development of the nucleus dorsolateralis anterior. The section shows the differentiation between the nucleus dorsomedialis anterior and the nucleus dorsolateralis anterior. Alligator mississippiensis. Toluidin-blue preparation.

B represents a section in the transverse plane through the diencephalon just anterior to the nucleus rotundus. The decrease in size medialward of the nucleus dorsolateralis anterior, as the nucleus rotundus is reached, also the differentiation of the lateral part of the nucleus dorsolateralis anterior, as indicated at *b*, should be noted. Alligator mississippiensis. Toluidin-blue preparations. *Huber* and *Crosby*.

a.triang., area triangularis; *a.vent.lat.*, area ventrolateralis; *a.vent.med.*, area ventromedialis; *com. hyp.*, commissura hypothalami; *corp.gen.lat.*, corpus geniculatum laterale; *F.B.*, forebrain bundle; *hab.*, habenula; *n.dec.supraopt.dors.*, nucleus decussationis supraopticae dorsalis; *n.dors.lat.ant.*, nucleus dorsolateralis anterior; *n.dors.med.ant.*, nucleus dorsomedialis anterior; *n.lat.hyp.*, nucleus lateralis hypothalami; *n.med.ant.thal.*, nucleus medialis anterior thalami; *n.microcell.*, nucleus microcellularis; *n. perivent.hyp.*, nucleus periventricularis hypothalami; *n.reuns.pars cent.*, nucleus reuniens pars centralis; *n.reuns.pars dif.*, nucleus reuniens pars diffusa; *n.rot.*, nucleus rotundus; *n.tr.tect.thal.cruc.*, nucleus tractus tecto-thalami cruciati; *olf.proj.tr.+inters.n.*, olfactory projection tract and interstitial nucleus; *st.med.*, stria medullaris; *tr.op.*, tractus opticus; *tr.thal.str.interm.*, tractus thalamo-striatalis intermedius; *V.III*, ventriculus tertius.

994

lateral forebrain bundle.   However, the differentiation of these nuclear groups varies in distinctness with the reptile under consideration.   This is evident in a study of various reptilian thalami in process of preparation but not ready as yet for publication.   There may be tectal connections through the periventricular system but these are not definitely demonstrable.   According to *Cairney*, this nucleus is interconnected with the habenula and to this region, at least, *de Lange* carried a mammillo-thalamic tract.   (For homologies, see page 1060.)

The nucleus dorsolateralis anterior, earlier regarded as forming, with the nucleus dorsomedialis anterior, a discrete nuclear mass, in Alligator (*Huber* and *Crosby*, '26), Sphenodon (*Cairney*, '26; *Durward*, '30), and other reptiles is distinguishable from this latter nucleus, for it consists of distinctly larger, somewhat pyramidal shaped cells, resembling far more clearly those of the nucleus rotundus than those of the nucleus dorsomedialis anterior (see figs. 483 and 484). The nucleus dorsolateralis anterior has its beginning near the anterior end of the diencephalon.   At first it is situated between the nucleus ovalis and the nucleus dorsomedialis anterior but soon lies between this latter nucleus and the nucleus geniculatus lateralis.   At first the nucleus in question is confined to more lateral parts of the diencephalon but gradually increases in size until its ventromedial angle reaches almost to the midline while its dorsolateral portion approaches the marginal optic tract.   This latter portion is somewhat differentiable from the remainder of the nucleus, although clearly of similar cell character, and appears to receive collaterals and possibly terminal fibers of the optic tract.   Gradually the cells of the ventromedial portion thin out, their place being taken by the lateral forebrain bundle which passes to the nucleus rotundus.   At a level about through the middle of the latter nucleus, the nucleus dorsolateralis anterior disappears.   Its connections (figs. 386, 486) are distinctive; it is in relation with lateral forebrain fibers by way of the anterior thalamo-striatal path and is connected with the tectum through the tractus tecto-thalamicus lateralis.   Short internuclear fibers bring this nucleus into intimate relation with the nucleus dorsomedialis anterior and the nucleus rotundus.   The reception of optic impulses by the differentiated dorsolateral portion of the nucleus has been mentioned previously.   (For homologies, see page 1060.)

The nucleus ovalis of the alligator consists of relatively small or medium sized, but deeply staining and distinctly grouped cells, oval in outline and situated near the anterior end of the diencephalon between the tractus cortico-habenularis lateralis posterior and the stria terminalis.   Dorsal to the nucleus, and in part through it, pass fibers of the medial olfacto-habenular tract on their way to join the stria medullaris.   Actual proof of the synapse of this tract around cells of the nucleus is lacking but the alligator material certainly suggests such a connection.   Collaterals of the tractus cortico-habenularis lateralis posterior turn in toward the cells of the oval nucleus.   This nucleus occurs in Sphenodon (*Cairney*, '26; *Durward*, '30).

The main mass of the nucleus geniculatus lateralis (termed the nucleus geniculatus lateralis pars ventralis, *Cairney*) is a prominent nuclear mass in most reptiles, extending from near the frontal end of the diencephalon until well toward its posterior pole.   This is indicated in figures 483 and 485.   In the alligator it appears immediately behind the nucleus ovalis, being situated lateral and ventrolateral to the nucleus dorsolateralis anterior and medial to the marginal optic tract.   It is characterized in Varanus (*Beccari*, '23), in the alligator (*Huber* and *Crosby*, '26), and, to a slight extent apparently, in Sphenodon (*Cairney*, '26), by the appearance of a perpendicular row of cells which the silver prepara-

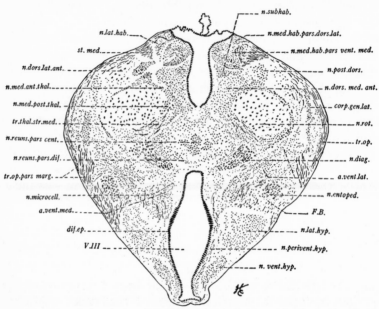

FIG. 484.   Section through the middle of the nucleus rotundus showing the majority of the larger nuclei of the dorsal thalamus and giving their relative positions with regard to one another.   Alligator mississippiensis.   Toluidin-blue preparation. *Huber* and *Crosby*.

a.vent.lat., area ventrolateralis; *a.vent.med.*, area ventromedialis; *corp.gen.lat.*, corpus geniculatum laterale; *dif.ep.*, differentiated ependyma; *F.B.*, forebrain bundle; *n.diag.*, nucleus diagonalis; *n.dors.lat.ant.*, nucleus dorsolateralis anterior; *n.dors.med.ant.*, nucleus dorsomedialis anterior; *n.entoped.*, nucleus entopeduncularis; *n.lat.hab.*, nucleus lateralis habenulae; *n.lat.hyp.*, nucleus lateralis hypothalami; *n.med.ant.thal.*, nucleus medialis anterior thalami; *n.med.hab.pars dors.lat.*, nucleus medialis habenulae pars dorsolateralis; *n.med.post.thal.*, nucleus medialis posterior thalami; *n.microcell.*, nucleus microcellularis; *n.perivent.hyp.*, nucleus periventricularis hypothalami; *n.post.dors.*, nucleus posterodorsalis; *n.reun.pars cent.*, nucleus reuniens pars centralis; *n.reun.pars dif.*, nucleus reuniens pars diffusa; *n.rot.*, nucleus rotundus; *n.subhab.*, nucleus subhabenularis; *n.vent.hyp.*, nucleus ventralis hypothalami; *st.med.*, stria medullaris; *tr.op.*, tractus opticus; *tr.op.pars marg.*, tractus opticus pars marginalis; *tr.thal.str.med.*, tractus thalamostriatalis medialis; *V.III*, ventriculus tertius.

tions indicate send dendrites out in either direction.   Among these branches are more scattered neurons forming a marginal layer on either side of the perpendicular row of cells.   This part of the lateral geniculate nucleus has been recognized by various students of the reptilian diencephalon, among whom may be mentioned *Bellonci* ('88), *Ramón* ('96), *C. L. Herrick* ('93), *Edinger* ('99 and '08), *de Lange* ('13), *Ariëns Kappers* ('21), *Beccari* ('23), *Huber* and *Crosby* ('26), *Cairney* ('26), *Durward* ('30), *Shanklin* ('30), and *Frederikse* ('31).   *Cairney* ('26) termed it the nucleus geniculatus lateralis pars ventralis; a second more dorsal group, which also receives optic fibers, he termed the pars dorsalis. *Abbie* ('33), studying the blood supply, misquoted *Cairney* and termed the main nuclear mass, the pars dorsalis. This pars dorsalis of *Cairney* is present in Anolis and other lizards (*Huber* and *Crosby*, '33), and possibly in all reptiles (see fig. 485), but not equally well differentiated. *Shanklin* ('30), following *Ramón*, described a pars inferior, a pars intermedia, and a pars superior for the lateral geniculate nucleus. His pars intermedia is comparable to the pars ventralis, his pars superior (as in figure 5, p. 431) to *Cairney's* pars dorsalis, and his pars inferior is probably the nucleus tractus tecto-thalamici cruciati referred to in the following paragraph.

Optic tract fibers from the marginal and the axillary optic tracts reach the ventral part of the lateral geniculate nucleus, which is connected with the tectum by the ventrolateral tecto-thalamic tract and with lower centers by the tractus geniculatus descendens (see figs. 482 and 485). This latter tract, described first by *Beccari* ('23) and later by *Huber* and *Crosby* ('26) and by *Cairney* ('26), arises in the nucleus and runs caudalward, but its final termination is not known. A connection from the ventral part of the lateral geniculate nucleus with the hypothalamus has been described under the name of tractus geniculo-hypo-thalamicus. Internuclear fibers connect the lateral geniculate nucleus with a cell group found at its ventral border and probably part of the complex. This nucleus tractus tecto-thalamici cruciati (figs. 482 and 483) consists of scattered cells showing none of the linear arrangement character'stic of the lateral genicu-late. It receives not only the crossed tecto-thalamic tract but also appears to be in relation with the tractus tecto-thalamicus ventrolateralis. A further cell group intervening between the lateral geniculate nucleus and the area ventralis anterior (fig. 484) has been termed the area triangularis in the alligator. Possibly it falls within the zona incerta of mammals (p. 1060).

The nucleus rotundus (figs. 482 to 485, 487, 488), has long been known to students of the reptilian brain. Thus *Stieda* ('75) described in Varanus "einen kugelrunden Komplex" and appears to have recognized its fiber relations with the forebrain. *C. L. Herrick* ('91) and *Humphrey* ('94) also identified the cell group, although they described it under other names. It has been seen and described by practically all the later workers (*Edinger*, '08; *de Lange*, '13; *Ariëns Kappers*, '21; *Huber* and *Crosby*, '26; *Cairney*, '26; *Durward*, '30; *Shanklin*, '30; *Frederikse*, '31). In all reptiles it is characterized in sections by the outline which gives it its name. In general it is somewhat irregularly spherical in form and consists of large multipolar cells, comparable in Alligator and Sphenodon to those constituting the nucleus dorsomedialis anterior, from which it is not sharply separable anteriorly. It is so generally known and so easily recognized that further account of it appears unnecessary. It receives a distinct component of the lateral forebrain bundle (figs. 386, 485, 488) and is related with the tectum and the pretectal areas by a tractus tecto-thalamicus dorsomedialis anterior (*Huber* and *Crosby*, '26; fig. 482), which probably carries impulses in both directions. Internuclear fibers relate it to surrounding areas and, according to *Cairney*, it receives fibers of the habenulo-thalamic tract. It has been suggested that this nucleus may receive ascending lemnisci fibers, particularly trigeminal fibers from the chief sensory trigeminal nucleus, but such a connection has not been demonstrated as yet.   This nucleus is regarded by certain observers as homologous with a part of the nucleus medialis of mammals (*Ariëns Kappers*, '21 ; *Frederikse*, '31), but there is also much to be said in favor of its possible homology with the ventral nucleus of these latter forms, as *Ingvar* ('23), *Hines* ('23, but not '29), *Huber* and *Crosby* ('26), and others have suggested. *Rioch* ('31) suggested that it is homologous with the noyau centré median de Luys of mammals.

In reptiles, ventral and ventrolateral to the nucleus rotundus and medial to the lateral geniculate nucleus, is an area ventrolateralis (fig. 484) occupied to a very considerable extent by fibers of passage with some intercalated neurons.   For the most part the region shows no distinct nuclear grouping, but in the more ventral part of the area there is a suggestion of such an arrangement, the neurons being in linear arrangement with intercalated fiber bundles.   Dorsal to the nucleus rotundus in the alligator is the nucleus posterodorsalis, which has been described earlier (p. 990).

Surrounding the nucleus rotundus on all sides is a capsule of fibers and interstitial cells.   Such cells are not clearly separable, dorsally and medially, from the medial nuclear group.   To this medial group may be assigned in Alligator an anterior division of medium-sized cells, the nucleus medialis anterior, and a posterior division of larger cells, the nucleus medialis posterior.

The nucleus medialis anterior (fig. 484), in the material available, is not clearly definable from the nucleus dorsomedialis anterior.   It extends between the ventricular wall and the nucleus rotundus and over the dorsal border of that nucleus, continuous with its capsule.   It consists of medium-sized cells.   The tractus thalamo-striatalis intermedius relates this nucleus to the striatum. Possibly it also receives fibers from the tractus thalamo-striatalis medialis.

The nucleus medialis posterior (fig. 484) begins on the medial side of the nucleus rotundus as a group of larger cells.   As the caudal end of the nucleus rotundus is reached, the nucleus medialis posterior swings caudal to the nuclear mass and forms a rather conspicuous, relatively large-celled group in the caudal part of the thalamus.   The tractus thalamo-striatalis, the tractus tecto-thalamicus medialis, and internuclear fibers to surrounding nuclear masses provide the main connections of this cell group.

Ventral to the nucleus medialis posterior of the alligator, and in close relationship with it, although distinguishable by a slight difference in cell character and cell staining, is the nucleus posterocentralis.   This nucleus swings dorsalward and occupies the central part of the dorsal field behind the nucleus medialis posterior.   The homology of this nucleus with cell masses in this general region in other reptiles is unknown at present.   *Shanklin* ('30) has figured a nucleus posterocentralis in the chameleon which he regards as comparable to the nucleus of that name in the alligator.   The caudal end of the alligator diencephalon resembles the homologous region in birds.   A nucleus lentiformis (diencephali) has been described in various other reptiles as a clear cut nuclear mass caudal to the nucleus rotundus by *Ariëns Kappers* ('21), *Beccari* ('23), *Durward* ('30), *Frederikse* ('31), and others.

The midline group of nuclei are represented in many reptiles, including snakes, crocodiles, and alligators, by the so-called nucleus reuniens (figs. 482 to 484, 487), which was described first for the snake by *Rabl Rückhard* ('94). It consists of a central more dense portion in Alligator, comparable with the nucleus reuniens of *Edinger* ('99), and a frame of scattered cells, the pars diffusa, comparable to a part of the nucleus diffusus of *Edinger* ('99). The central part makes its appearance in front of·the level of the habenular commissure as a rounded midline group of cells joining the two dorsal thalami. In front the pars diffusa and the tractus thalamo-striatalis medialis separate the pars centralis from the medial nuclei, to which it is slightly ventromedial. Farther caudally the pars diffusa separates it from the nucleus medialis posterior and an underlying nucleus diagonalis. The round outline gradually changes to an oblong shape, thus increasing in size. Then the nucleus begins to lose its characteristic form and, beginning on the ventral side, the mass gradually breaks up and becomes continuous with the pars diffusa. The pars diffusa consists of scattered cells separating the pars centralis from surrounding nuclear masses. Specific connections to the pars diffusa have not been established. Probably it receives collaterals or even stem fibers from the tracts associated with the pars centralis, which are a thalamo-striate component of the lateral forebrain bundle and the tractus tecto-reuniens (fig. 482). *Papez* (to be published) has suggested the probable homology of the caudal end of the nucleus reuniens with the mammalian nucleus geniculatus medialis pars dorsalis, basing his interpretation on its relations to the tractus tecto-reuniens.

Ventrolateral to the cephalic portion of the nucleus reuniens a small group of deeply staining cells appears, the nucleus diagonalis (fig. 484). This group increases in size caudally and takes on comma shape, the thicker portion occupying the original position of the nucleus and the thinner part intermingling with fibers extending dorsolaterally. Gradually this lateral part becomes somewhat larger and more nearly round and is ultimately cut off from the medial portion by the tractus tecto-reuniens. The nucleus is related to the tractus tecto-reuniens and appears also to send fibers dorsolaterally to the pretectal or tectal areas.

The majority although not all of the nuclei thus far considered appear to belong to the dorsal thalamus. The ventral thalamus is not nearly so highly differentiated as is the dorsal thalamus, yet it also contains representative nuclear areas. Most oral of these is the area ventralis anterior, a region extending from the hippocampal commissure frontally and the preoptic area ventrally and ventrolaterally to the area triangularis, from which it is indistinctly separated caudally. It lies ventral to the nucleus dorsomedialis anterior, below the sulcus medius. Ventrolateral to it is the olfactory projection tract with its interstitial nucleus. The bed nucleus of the hippocampal commissure, continued back through the area as a bed nucleus for the medial cortico-habenular tract, is differentiable through its smaller type of cells. This area ventralis anterior is partly an interstitial area for fibers of passage such as the stria terminalis, with which it is in part in synaptic relation.

The nucleus decussationis supraopticae dorsalis (fig. 483) is that portion of the entopeduncular group which is not only in synaptic relation with collaterals and perhaps even stem fibers of the lateral forebrain bundle but also with dorsal supraoptic fibers. It appears to contribute fibers to pretectal and dorsal thalamic regions. The nucleus consists of relatively large cells situated in the anterior diencephalic region at the place where the anterior thalamo-striatal component of the lateral forebrain bundle swings downward from the nucleus dorsolateralis anterior to join the other components of the lateral forebrain bundle.

The nucleus entopeduncularis proper (fig. 484) has been described by *Edinger* ('99) for Varanus griseus, by *de Lange* ('13) for Varanus salvator and Draco volans, and by *Huber* and *Crosby* ('26) for Alligator mississippiensis. It lies among the fibers of the ventral peduncle of the lateral forebrain bundle, with which it is in synaptic relation. A special differentiation of this entopeduncular group is the midbrain entopeduncular group, regarded as the forerunner of the substantia nigra (see page 986).

The area ventromedialis (fig. 484) consists of somewhat scattered gray, appearing at about the level of the anterior end of the nucleus reuniens and extending to a plane through about the middle of the commissura posterior. At first it is round in outline. Where best developed it consists of a mass of medium-sized cells intermingled and bordered medially by some very tiny cells (the nucleus microcellularis). The nucleus microcellularis (fig. 484) increases in size and ultimately unites the nucleus ventromedialis proper with the nucleus periventricularis hypothalami. This area appears to include in part at least the interstitial nucleus of the fasciculus geniculatus descendens of *Beccari* ('23).

THE NUCLEAR MASSES OF THE HYPOTHALAMUS WITH FIBER CONNECTIONS

The hypothalamic area is continuous forward without sharp break into the preoptic region. It consists of several nuclear masses: the nucleus periventricularis hypothalami, the nucleus hypothalamicus anterior, the nucleus hypothalamicus lateralis, and the nucleus hypothalamicus ventralis.

The first mentioned nucleus, nucleus periventricularis hypothalami (figs. 483 484, 488), was described by *de Lange* ('13) for Draco and by *Huber* and *Crosby* ('26) for Alligator mississippiensis. It appears at the anterior end of the hypothalamus as rows of deeply stained neurons fused with interstitial cells of the olfactory projection tract. At first round in outline, it soon becomes triangular with the apex pointed dorsalward and then this portion fuses with a mass of cells along the ventricle, forming the typical nucleus periventricularis described for the forms studied by *de Lange*. The nucleus periventricularis hypothalami can be traced throughout practically the whole extent of the hypothalamus.

Somewhat in front of the habenular commissure, ventral to the forebrain bundles and lateral to the periventricular hypothalamic nucleus, is the nucleus lateralis hypothalami (*de Lange*, '13, Draco; *Huber* and *Crosby*, '26, Alligator), which is indicated in figures 483, 484, 488. It extends caudalward to a plane slightly behind the habenular commissure. Cytologically it consists of medium-sized cells.   A nucleus of similar character and having relatively similar relations farther cephalad has been termed the nucleus hypothalamicus anterior.   The two nuclei are not sharply separated from each other.   Both receive forebrain fibers.

A ventral hypothalamic nucleus (fig. 484) was described by *de Lange* ('13). A similar nucleus is present in the alligator and in other reptiles, although smaller and particularly characterized by its relation with the ventral hypothalamic commissural system.

The posterior end of the hypothalamus is occupied chiefly by a deeply staining, fairly compact nucleus which *de Lange* ('13) termed the corpus mamillare, since he succeeded in carrying the fornix bundle to it and found it giving rise to a connection with the anterior thalamic nucleus, which he regarded as the tractus mamillo-thalamicus or Vicq d'Azyr fasciculus (fig. 488).   To the similarly situated nucleus in Alligator it has not been possible to demonstrate such a connection, probably through faulty impregnation of the tract.

The major connections of the hypothalamic regions may be summarized briefly, although there are considerable gaps as yet regarding the details of origin and specific distribution of the various tracts.   A fornix system from the projection cells of the hippocampal region to the hypothalamic areas has been described by numerous observers, among whom are *Edinger* ('88 and '96), *C. L. Herrick* ('90), *Adolf Meyer* ('92), *C. J. Herrick* ('10, for Alligator), *de Lange* ('11), *Crosby* ('17), *Ariëns Kappers* ('21), *Hines* ('23), and others.   The basal olfactory centers on the medial wall of the hemisphere are interconnected with the hypothalamic centers by way of the hypothalamic component of the medial forebrain bundle.   The amygdaloid complex, the nucleus of the lateral olfactory tract, and the piriform lobe complex are interrelated with preoptic, hypothalamic, and perhaps midbrain areas by way of the stria terminalis and olfactory projection paths (which include the various amygdalo-hypothalamic paths of *Cairney*, '26).   The detailed accounts of these paths are given under the description of the telencephalon (p. 1351).   Lateral forebrain fibers, through the strio-hypothalamic component, distribute to the hypothalamus, particularly to the lateral and anterior hypothalamic nuclei.   The hypothalamic areas are probably connected with the tectum by way of the periventricular systems, but it is difficult here to trace individual bundles for any great distance.   Undoubtedly there are ascending fibers to the region from lower centers but these have not been clearly established for reptiles.   In reading the above account of the hypothalamic connections reference should be made to figures 386, 482, 485, 486, and 487.

RÉSUMÉ OF CERTAIN MAJOR FIBER PATHS RELATING TO BOTH
MESENCEPHALIC AND DIENCEPHALIC CENTERS

a. Optic Tract.   The optic nerves in reptiles are completely crossed in the chiasma region, where they interlace in the characteristic manner described for the alligator by *Gross* ('03).   The bundles are medullated.   The main or marginal bundle of fibers (figs. 485 to 488) runs caudalward and dorsalward to the optic tectum, which it enters, forming the stratum opticum.   The optic tract fibers

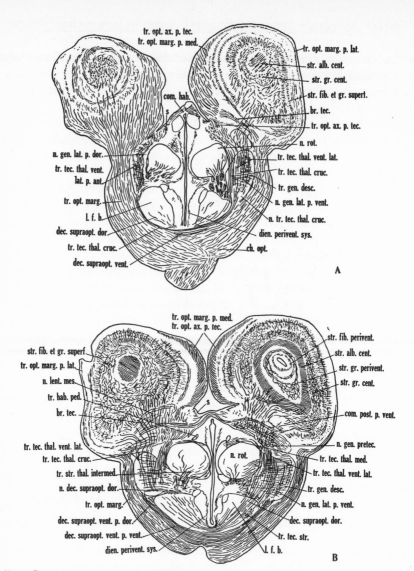

FIG. 485. Cross sections of pyridin silver preparations; *A* and *B*, Anolis carolinensis. *Huber* and *Crosby.*

br.tec., brachium tecti; *ch.opt.*, chiasma opticum; *com.hab.*, commissura habenularum; *com.post.p.vent.*, commissura posterior pars ventralis; *dec.supraopt.dor.*, decussatio supraoptica dorsalis; *dec.supraopt. vent.p.dor.*, decussatio supraoptica ventralis pars dorsalis; *dec.supraopt.vent.p.vent.*, decussatio supraoptica ventralis pars ventralis; *dien.perivent.sys.*, diencephalic periventricular system; *l.f.b.*, lateral forebrain bundle; *n.dec.supraopt.dor.*, nucleus decussationis supraopticae dorsalis; *n.gen.lat.p.dor.*, nucleus geniculatus lateralis pars dorsolateralis; *n.gen.lat.p.vent.*, nucleus geniculatus lateralis pars ventralis; *n.gen. pretec.*, nucleus geniculatus pretectalis; *n.lent.mes.*, nucleus lentiformis mesencephali; *n.rot.*, nucleus rotundus; *str.alb.cent.*, stratum album centrale; *str.fib.et gr.superf.*, stratum fibrosum et griseum superficiale; *str.fib.perivent.*, stratum fibrosum periventriculare; *str.gr.cent.*, stratum griseum centrale; *str.gr. perivent.*, stratum griseum periventriculare; *tr.gen.desc.*, tractus geniculatus descendens; *tr.hab.ped.*, tractus habenulo-peduncularis; *tr.opt.ax.p.tec.*, tractus opticus axillaris pars tectalis; *tr.opt.marg.*, tractus opticus marginalis; *tr.opt.marg.p.lat.*, tractus opticus marginalis pars lateralis; *tr.opt.marg.p.med.*, tractus opticus marginalis pars medialis; *tr.str.thal.intermed.*, tractus strio-thalamicus intermedius; *tr.tec.str.*, tractus tecto-striatalis et strio-tectalis; *tr.tec.thal.cruc.*, tractus tecto-thalamicus (et thalamo-tectalis) cruciatus; *tr.tec.thal.med.*, tractus tecto-thalamicus medialis; *tr.tec.thal.vent.*, tractus tecto-thalamicus et thalamo-tectalis ventromedialis; *tr.tec.thal.vent.lat.p.ant.*, tractus tecto-thalamicus et thalamo-tectalis ventrolateralis pars anterior.

enter the tectum along its outer border (fig. 485), sometimes close to the surface, occasionally slightly deeper, in part leaving a potential molecular layer.   Their termination is within the underlying stratum fibrosum et griseum superficiale. As they reach the tectum the marginal optic tract in most reptiles splits into two parts, a medial and a lateral, the latter added to through much of its extent from the main bundle.   These fibers distribute to the dorsal part of the optic tectum and, followed back, contribute bundles which swing dorsalward and forward over the tectum to constitute the pars caudalis.   The medial division of the marginal optic tract encapsulates the ventral, medial, and dorsomedial portions of the tectum, the dorsal portion swinging caudalward and approaching the caudal part of the lateral tract as it swings over the dorsal part of the tectum. In some reptiles it does not reach quite all of the dorsal part of the tectum. In its course toward the tectum, collaterals, and stem fibers as well, are given off to the lateral geniculate nucleus.   In the chiasma region in Alligator, certain of the more dorsal fascicles swing away from the marginal bundle, cut across the extreme lateral edge of the lateral forebrain bundle, and then rejoin the main tract ; this they accompany to the nucleus geniculatus lateralis to which they distribute (see fig. 486).   A few of these fascicles accompany the marginal optic tract to the tectum.   This inner bundle has been termed the tractus opticus pars axillaris.   *Bellonci* ('88), working on optic connections in various verte- brates, included a study of the relations of this system in the turtle and the lizard.   In addition to the superficial optic tract he described two deeper bundles. Of these latter the more lateral is undoubtedly the axillary bundle of the alligator and of various lizards.   The more medial has not as yet been demonstrated in this latter reptile unless it is represented in that portion of the supraoptic system termed the tractus tecto-thalamicus cruciatus (*Huber* and *Crosby*, '26).   *Ramón* ('96) regarded a similar bundle (fasciculo optico-commissural) in reptiles as composed in part of optic and in part of supraoptic fibers, although uncertain of the relationships and components.   The axillary optic tract is formed of fibers crossing in the deeper part of the chiasmal ridge and entering, to a considerable extent, into the medial and ventral parts of the pars ventralis of the lateral geniculate nucleus.   Many of these fibers reach the optic tectum.

A basal optic bundle (figs. 482, 486, 488), similar to that described in amphib- ians (*Wlassak*, '93 ; *Herrick*, '17, '25) and in mammals (*Marburg*, '03 ; *Bochenek*, '08 ; *Tsai*, '25, and others), has been demonstrated in reptiles.   *De Lange* ('13) gave the designation "basalis opticus Wurzel" to an apparently similar tract in a figure of Draco but did not describe it.   *Beccari* ('23) for Varanus, *Huber* and *Crosby* ('26) for the alligator and ('33) for other reptiles, *Shanklin* ('30, '34) for Chameleon and other reptiles, *Frederikse* ('31) for Varanus, and various other observers have recognized this root and traced it to its nucleus.   Recently *Shanklin* ('33) described it under the name used by *Bochenek* and *Tsai* — that of tractus opticus accessorius posterior.

b. *Uncrossed Tecto-thalamic and Thalamo-tectal Systems.*   The dorsal thalamus in reptiles develops hand in hand with, and largely under the influence of, the tectal areas.   The greater number of the ascending sensory systems terminate primarily in the tectum and the impulses are then relayed by means of tecto-thalamic paths to dorsal thalamic centers. Moreover, the tectum is probably a region of synapse for descending impulses from thalamic to lower centers. It is to be expected that tecto-thalamic and thalamo-tectal paths will be well developed in these forms, and such is indeed the case. Such paths, for convenience of description, may be subdivided into two groups, uncrossed and crossed tecto-thalamic paths (*Huber* and *Crosby*, '26). To the uncrossed group belong various fiber bundles, the most prominent of which are described briefly in the following paragraphs. The reader interested in further details concerning these connections should consult the original papers cited.

The tractus tecto-thalamicus et thalamo-tectalis ventrolateralis (*Huber* and *Crosby*, '26, '33; figs. 482, 485, 486) has connections with both the medial and lateral sides of the tectum, with the pretectal nucleus, and with the nucleus lentiformis mesencephali by either collaterals or by stem fibers or by both. It contains both afferent and efferent fibers with respect to the tectum. It is included within the tractus tecto-thalamicus ventrolateralis of *Cairney* ('26), along with certain other tecto-thalamic systems from the nucleus rotundus and the nucleus dorsolateralis anterior, and carries fibers from both dorsal and ventral parts of the lateral geniculate nucleus. In many reptiles it has fibers from the nucleus tractus tecto-thalamici cruciati (nucleus geniculatus lateralis inferior of *Shanklin*, '30), which run to the tectum where they enter the stratum fibrosum et griseum superficiale, and consequently are largely thalamo-tectal in their direction of conduction. They probably constitute the tractus geniculo-tectalis anterior of *Shanklin* ('30), although in the majority of reptiles they are part of a continuous system. The main part of the tractus tecto-thalamicus et thalamo-tectalis ventrolateralis (probably the tractus geniculo-tectalis intermedius of *Shanklin*) is largely a tecto-geniculate system. Whether this part of the tract includes the tractus geniculo-tectalis posterior of *Shanklin* or whether this latter fiber bundle is represented by fine black fibers (chrome-silver preparations) which constitute the most caudal bundle of the tractus tecto-thalamicus et thalamo-tectalis ventrolateralis is at present uncertain.

The tractus tecto-thalamicus (et thalamo-tectalis) dorsomedialis anterior of *Huber* and *Crosby* ('26 and '33; fig. 482) includes the tractus tecto-thalamicus ventralis of *Cairney* ('26). It is homologous, to some extent at least, with the bundle described by *Edinger* ('99) and *de Lange* ('13, p. 102) as the tractus tecto-thalamicus, and presumably is the homologue of the similarly named tract of *Beccari* ('23). The tractus rotundo-tectalis, with the associated tractus rotundo-mesencephalicus profundus and tractus rotundo-geniculo-pretectalis, represents the homologous bundle in *Shanklin's* terminology. A cephalic part of the tract (a tecto-rotundus system) was recognized by this latter observer. Figures C and D, plate 11, of *Huber* and *Crosby* ('33) are from sections cut in favorable planes with reference to this system. Traced from the nucleus rotundus and the nucleus medialis posterior, the tractus tecto-thalamicus dorsomedialis anterior proceeds almost directly caudolaterally until it reaches the dorsal division of the ventral supraoptic decussation with which it continues tectalward.

While a few of its fibers may enter the more superficial receptive layer, the majority of them are continuous with the stratum album centrale (and the efferent bundles within the stratum griseum centrale in the turtle), so that this caudal part of the system is regarded chiefly as a tecto-thalamic path.   Coursing with this caudal portion of the tractus tecto-thalamicus (et thalamo-tectalis) dorsomedialis anterior are found fascicles to the nucleus geniculatus pretectalis and to the tegmental region, and particularly to the nucleus lateralis profundus mesencephali.   A cephalic part of the tract under discussion swings forward and dorsalward, paralleling the tractus tecto-thalamicus ventrolateralis, and enters the efferent tectal layer, thus, functionally considered, constituting mainly a tecto-thalamic system.

The regions immediately ventral to the posterior commissure and to the periventricular gray are reached by fascicles of efferent tectal fibers, at least in certain reptiles.   These fibers are few in number and difficult to demonstrate by reason of the relatively large number of fibers of passage through the area. They constitute a so-called tractus tecto-thalamicus dorsomedialis posterior. It is not certain that they are present in all reptiles.

To the nucleus medialis anterior and the nucleus medialis posterior come fibers from the stratum album centrale constituting a tecto-thalamic system. In certain reptiles these fibers form a distinct path, the tractus tecto-thalamicus medialis (as in the alligator; fig. 482); in other forms they constitute a component of the tract passing from the tectum to the nucleus rotundus.

The establishment of a direct connection between the tectum and the nucleus reuniens presents difficulties.   In the alligator, fibers (fig. 482, tr. tec. reun.) can be followed almost directly lateralward from the nucleus reuniens to a position on the inner border of the pars ventralis of the ventral supraoptic decussation, where it lies in relation with cells of a nuclear mass.   To this cell mass various designations have been given : geniculatum internum of *Bellonci* ('88), nucleo *S* of *Beccari* ('23), nucleus *Z* of *Huber* and *Crosby* ('26), and nucleus commissurae transversae of *Frey* ('33).   (For its homology see page 1007).   To what extent the fiber bundle traced lateralward from the nucleus reuniens proceeds beyond the nucleus *Z* (etc.) is uncertain, but it is believed that in the alligator, at least, some bundles proceed to the tectum.   The direction of conduction is probably from the tectum to the nucleus reuniens.   In reptiles where the nucleus reuniens is smaller or where it has no midline representative, although it may be represented by some gray at either side, the bundle may be smaller and more difficult to follow.

The pretectal and subtectal nuclear groups, such as the nucleus geniculatus pretectalis, the nucleus lentiformis mesencephali, and the pretectal nucleus, have interconnections with the tectum.   It is probable that, in most cases, fiber groups provide for the conveyance of impulses in both directions.   The nucleus lateralis profundus mesencephali receives fibers from the tectum.

c. Supraoptic or Postoptic Decussations.   The crossed tecto-thalamic and thalamo-tectal systems are composed of the postoptic or supraoptic commissures which are well developed in reptiles.   In the description of this system the terms, decussatio supraoptica ventralis and decussatio supraoptica dorsalis,

used by *Ariëns Kappers* ('21) are retained here.   The following account is based
chiefly on the descriptions given for various reptiles by *Huber* and *Crosby* ('26
and '33).

The ventral supraoptic decussation (figs. 481, 482, 485 to 487) is divisible in
Alligator into a pars ventralis and a pars dorsalis.   The pars dorsalis constitutes
the most rostral part of the optic complex at its decussation.   The fibers appear

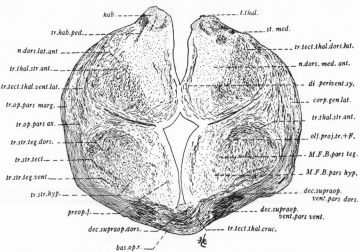

Fig. 486.   Cross section showing the dorsal supraoptic decussation; tractus
tecto-thalamicus cruciatus is also indicated as it crosses the midline.   Alligator
mississippiensis.   Pyridin-silver preparation.   *Huber* and *Crosby.*
bas.op.r., basal optic root; *corp.gen.lat.*, corpus geniculatum laterale; *dec.*
supraop.dors., decussatio supraoptica dorsalis; *dec.supraop.vent.pars dors.*, decussatio supraoptica ventralis pars dorsalis; *dec.supraop.vent.pars vent.*, decussatio supraoptica ventralis pars ventralis; *di.perivent.sy.*, diencephalic
periventricular system; *hab.*, habenula; *M.F.B.pars hyp.*, medial forebrain
bundle hypothalamic part; *M.F.B.pars teg.*, medial forebrain bundle tegmental
part; *n.dors.lat.ant.*, nucleus dorsolateralis anterior; *n.dors.med.ant.*, nucleus
dorsomedialis anterior; *olf.proj.tr. + F.*, olfactory projection tract and fornix;
preop.f., preoptic fibers; *st.med.*, stria medullaris; *t.thal.*, taenia thalami; *tr.*
hab.ped., tractus habenulo-peduncularis; *tr.op.pars ax.*, tractus opticus pars
axillaris; *tr.op.pars marg.*, tractus opticus pars marginalis; *tr.str.hyp.*, tractus
strio-hypothalamicus; *tr.str.tect.*, tractus strio-tectalis; *tr.str.teg.dors.*, tractus
strio-tegmentalis dorsalis; *tr.str.teg.vent.*, tractus strio-tegmentalis ventralis;
tr.tect.thal.cruc., tractus tecto-thalamicus cruciatus; *tr.tect.thal.dors.lat.*, tractus
tecto-thalamicus dorsolateralis; *tr.tect.thal.vent.lat.*, tractus tecto-thalamicus
ventrolateralis; *tr.thal.str.ant.*, tractus thalamo-striatalis anterior.

as a compact bundle immediately caudal to the optic tract decussation.   They
turn caudalward and lateralward, for the first part of their course surrounded by
optic tract fibers.   Then as this latter tract swings dorsalward, the decussatio
supraoptica ventralis pars dorsalis swings to a position internal to the optic fibers
and, in this position, joined by fibers of the anterior part of the dorsomedial
tecto-thalamic tract, passes to the tectum.   In the caudal part of their course
these fibers are in close association with the posterior part of the dorsomedial
tecto-thalamic system.   The tract in question distributes largely to the optic
tectum, affording thus a commissural connection between the tecta of the two
sides.   A small slip of the tract can be followed to the nucleus isthmi.

The pars ventralis of the ventral supraoptic decussation (figs. 482, 485, 486) crosses slightly posterior and ventral to the decussation of the pars dorsalis. However, its fascicles lie among fibers of the optic tract, differentiable from this latter by differences in the character of their staining in chrome-silver preparations.   The ventral division joins the dorsal division, the two forming more or less distinctly a single band until separated by tecto-reuniens fibers, which swing between them.   The ventral division distributes to the optic tectum, in part to the stratum fibrosum et griseum superficiale and the adjacent stratum griseum centrale, and in part to the stratum album centrale, and apparently sends some bundles with the tractus tecto-reuniens to the torus semicircularis. Some of the fibers, before reaching the optic tectum, come into synaptic relation with a nucleus Z, which was recognized by *Huber* and *Crosby* ('26, fig. 25) and discussed but unnamed by *Cairney* ('26) in relation with this fiber system. *Frey* ('33a) has discussed the ventral supraoptic system in reptiles and regarded this nucleus as does *Papez* ('35, to be published) as representative of the mammalian medial geniculate nucleus (p. 1170).   The connections of this system suggest that it carries both afferent and efferent fibers.

The tractus tecto-thalamicus (et thalamo-tectalis) cruciatus (figs. 482, 485, 486), a part of the supraoptic system of reptiles, is the apparent homologue of the tractus opticus commissuralis noted in Chameleon by *Ramón* ('96).   There was some question in the mind of this observer and in that of *Edinger* as to whether or not this tract should be regarded as optic or supraoptic in character. It is our present opinion that the latter is the case but the matter requires experimental proof for its final elucidation.   Its nucleus constitutes the corpus geniculatum laterale of *Shanklin* ('30, figs. 5 and 6).   This tractus tecto-thalamicus (et thalamo-tectalis) of *Huber* and *Crosby* ('26 and '33) is included in the dorsal part of the ventral supraoptic decussation of *Cairney* ('26).   Its relations in the caudal part of its course, together with its general connections, suggest a more intimate relation with the dorsal supraoptic system; in fact it has the appearance of forming the ventrolateral part of a great portion of the decussating fibers, of which the major portion consists of fascicles of the dorsal supraoptic system proper.   In the alligator material the tract (fig. 486) appears as a band of fine, unmedullated fibers crossing the chiasmal ridge and then swinging internal to the optic tract from which, in chrome-silver preparations, the different staining reaction of its fibers distinguishes it.   Joined by fibers from adjacent preoptic and hypothalamic areas (?), it swings dorsalward, between the lateral forebrain bundle and the ventral supraoptic decussation, to its nucleus, the nucleus tractus tecto-thalamici, where part of its fibers terminate while the others swing dorsalward with the ventrolateral tecto-thalamic tract.   Certain of the more posterior fibers run to the pretectal and tectal areas as a relatively distinct tract, keeping in their course to the medial side of the ventral supraoptic decussation and its associated tracts.   The system is both afferent and efferent with respect to the tectum.

The dorsal supraoptic decussation (figs. 482, 485, and 486) has been figured under various names by students of reptilian brains, among whom may be mentioned *Edinger* ('99), *de Lange* ('13), *Ariëns Kappers* ('21), and *Huber* and *Crosby* ('26 and '33).   The fibers in the alligator cross in close association with a portion of the tractus tecto-thalamicus cruciatus.   After decussating they swing dorsalward and lateralward, in part mingling with and in part lying medial to, the lateral forebrain bundle.   Some of the more anterior and medial fibers appear to come into direct relation with the dorsal thalamus.   A considerable portion of these are in synaptic relation with the nucleus decussationis supra-

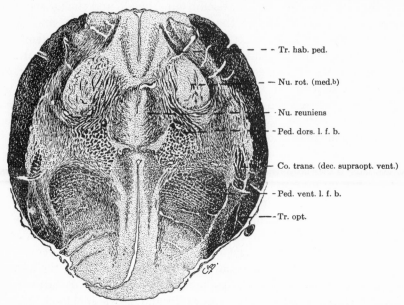

FIG. 487.   Cross section through the diencephalon of Crocodilus porosus.   *Ariëns Kappers.*

Co.trans.(dec.supraopt.vent.), commissura transversa (decussatio supraoptica ventralis); *Nu.reuniens*, nucleus reuniens; *Nu.rot.(med.b)*, nucleus rotundus (nucleus medialis b of Ariëns Kappers); *Ped.dors.l.f.b.*, dorsal peduncle of lateral forebrain bundle; *Ped.vent.l.f.b.*, ventral peduncle of lateral forebrain bundle; *Tr.hab.ped.*, tractus habenulo-peduncularis; *Tr.opt.*, tractus opticus.

opticae dorsalis, situated among the fascicles of the lateral forebrain bundle.   It was not possible to demonstrate the presence of a striatal connection of this system in the alligator, but in view of the findings in birds, in all probability such a connection does exist.   The more caudal portions of the dorsal supraoptic system reach the tectal region (and possibly the tegmental regions), accompanied by secondary fibers from the nucleus.   They pass to the tectum, entering in part the receptive layers on both the medial and lateral sides of the tectum, in part receiving fibers from the efferent stratum album centrale.   The dorsal supraoptic system also sends some few fascicles to the periventricular layer of fibers.   With these tectal connections of the system course bundles which pass to the nucleus lentiformis mesencephali as well as shorter internuclear fibers for tegmental and diencephalic areas.

In chrome-silver preparations, darkly staining fibers cross in the chiasmal ridge behind the decussation of the dorsal supraoptic system.   These are the fibrae ansulatae which have been described by *Bellonci* ('88) and *Beccari* ('23). The latter observer carried them in Varanus into relation with the interstitial nucleus of the medial longitudinal fasciculus.   This relation and the fact that fibers entered the fasciculus were substantiated for Alligator by *Huber* and *Crosby* ('26).   It has been suggested (*Ariëns Kappers*) that these may represent the ascending bulbar system described by *Wallenberg* ('04) as crossing in this commissure in birds.

d. Lateral Forebrain Bundle.   The lateral forebrain bundle (figs. 386, 482, 485 ; see also pp. 1353 to 1356) will be discussed in detail in the account of the reptilian telencephalon and the cognate literature will be given consideration. It is the purpose here merely to give a brief résumé of the various components as they separate from each other to distribute to appropriate thalamic and mesencephalic centers.

At the point where it enters the diencephalon, the lateral forebrain bundle is a more or less compact mass of fibers, but almost immediately the anterior thalamo-striatal tract becomes separated — the nucleus of the dorsal supraoptic decussation lying in the angle between it and the main fiber bundle — runs dorsalward and slightly caudalward, and then bends forward again into the nucleus dorsolateralis anterior (see figs. 386 and 486).

A second portion is given off caudal and medial to the last mentioned nuclear group.   This runs caudalward, terminating in the nucleus rotundus and the nucleus medialis anterior.   This tract, tractus thalamo-striatalis intermedius (fig. 386), forms a capsule of fibers around the nucleus rotundus.   The nucleus medialis posterior, and possibly the nucleus medialis anterior, is in relation with fibers from the tractus thalamo-striatalis medialis, which runs dorsomedialward around the medial side of the nucleus rotundus.   A tractus thalamo-striatalis internus (fig. 386) runs downward and medialward to the nucleus reuniens and to a part of the nucleus diagonalis.   For convenience these tracts have been described as passing toward the thalamic nuclei.   The anterior, intermediate, and internal tracts carry thalamo-striatal impulses in Alligator, although they may also carry impulses in the other direction, for which, however, the evidence is not conclusive.   In Chameleon, *Ramón y Cajal* showed neuraxes of neurons of the nucleus rotundus entering the thalamo-striatal tract, as did *Frederikse* ('31) in the lizard.   The tracts, as given by *Edinger* for reptiles, with their homologues in Alligator, may be listed as follows (from the contribution by *Huber* and *Crosby*, '26, p. 156) : "In the following brief statement of *Edinger's* findings the homologous tracts according to our terminology are given in parentheses.   That observer described a tractus anterior to nucleus anterior (pars anterior to nucleus dorsolateralis anterior), tractus medius to nucleus rotundus (probably the exact homologue of our pars intermedius to that nucleus), tractus internus to nucleus diffusus (apparently our pars medialis to nucleus medialis posterior, certainly not the tract to nucleus reuniens), and a tractus lateralis to the lateral geniculate body (this tract we have not been able to identify)."

The ventral peduncle of the lateral forebrain bundle for convenience has been split into a tractus strio-hypothalamicus, a tractus strio-tegmentalis dorsalis, a tractus strio-tegmentalis ventralis, and a tractus strio-tectalis (see fig. 486; also fig. 481). The first mentioned tract constitutes the most ventromedial and ventral portion of the forebrain bundle. After reaching

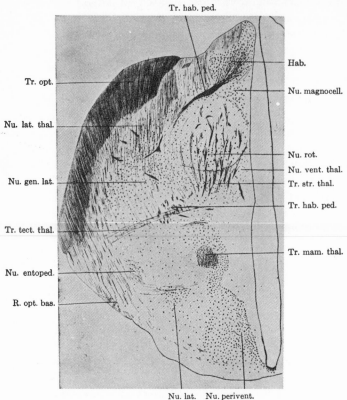

FIG. 488. Cross section through the diencephalon of Draco volans. The figure taken from the 1913 paper of *de Lange* is labeled according to his interpretation. The accompanying labels, given below in parentheses, represent *Ariëns Kappers'* interpretation of this same figure as presented in the earlier edition of the present text.

Hab., habenula; *Nu.entoped.*, nucleus entopeduncularis; *Nu.gen.lat.*, nucleus geniculatus lateralis (nucleus lateralis thalami); *Nu.lat.thal.*, nucleus lateralis thalami (nucleus geniculatus lateralis); *Nu.lat.hypothal.*, nucleus lateralis hypothalami; *Nu.magnocell.*, nucleus magnocellularis (regio subhabenularis, nucleus anterior?); *Nu.perivent.*, nucleus periventricularis; *Nu.rot.*, nucleus rotundus (nucleus medialis); *Nu.vent.thal.*, nucleus ventralis thalami; *R.opt.bas.*, basal optic root; *Tr.hab.ped.*, tractus habenulo-peduncularis; *Tr.hab.ped.*, tractus habenulo-peduncularis (tractus tecto-thalamicus); *Tr.mam.thal.*, tractus mamillo-thalamicus (tractus bulbo-thalamicus et hypothalamicus); *Tr.opt.*, tractus opticus; *Tr.str.thal.*, tractus strio-thalamicus (tractus thalamo-striatalis); *Tr.tect.thal.*, tractus tecto-thalamicus.

diencephalic centers it swings ventralward to terminate in the lateral and anterior hypothalamic nuclei. This is the component emphasized by *de Lange* in his term of tractus strio-hypothalamicus for the ventral part of the lateral forebrain bundle.

The dorsal strio-tegmental tract runs through the diencephalon to the level of the entopeduncular nucleus, where, either with or without a synapse, and accompanied by fibers of this nucleus, it swings into the tegmental region. Its final termination is in tegmental regions, particularly the substantia nigra of the present terminology (*Huber* and *Crosby*, '33). Its fibers are somewhat intermingled with those of the posterior part of the dorsal supraoptic decussation.

The ventral strio-tegmental tract lies ventral to the dorsal tract just described and does not contribute, apparently, to the entopeduncular nucleus. Its fibers distribute to tegmental areas of the mesencephalon. There is some slight suggestion that certain bundles may extend even farther caudalward.

The most lateral part of the ventral portion of the lateral forebrain bundle is occupied by the strio-tectal tract, which swings dorsalward behind the plane of the posterior commissure to the tectum and probably the more dorsal part of the tegmentum. Short connections between the hypothalamic areas and the tegmentum accompany the more ventral of the forebrain fibers, constituting a hypothalamo-tegmental tract.

De Lange ('13) described a thalamo-bulbar tract in Varanus. Fibers similarly situated can be identified in other reptiles, but for these at present neither the nuclei of origin or termination appear to have been recognized.

RÉSUMÉ (See also résumé, page 1057.)

The foregoing consideration of the reptilian mesencephalic and diencephalic centers permits of certain generalizations which may give some bases for a further comprehension of the functional significance of these important centers. Within the tectum a fundamental pattern has been demonstrated, and the *raison d'être* of this fundamental pattern (as well as its variations) has been related to its dual activity, since on the one hand it serves as a sensory correlation center and on the other hand as a discharge center for efferent impulses. Stratification, simple or complex, is a morphologic expression of the subdivisions into afferent and efferent centers. The main efferent centers and fiber tracts occupy the more central portion and thus separate a superficial receptive correlation layer from a deep or periventricular layer, primarily receptive and correlative, but also efferent in function. The trend of development, as one passes from amphibians to reptiles and birds, is toward an increase in the richness and complexity of the afferent sensory impulses — optic, tactile, pain, and temperature impulses from the body and the head and correlated somatic impulses from the dorsal thalamus of the same and opposite sides, together with rich intertectal connections — so that the tectum with the intimately related dorsal thalamic centers becomes the main sensory correlation center of the brain, overshadowing in richness of correlation and degree of morphologic differentiation the developing forebrain in these forms. The alternating layers of gray and white within the receptive area undoubtedly permit a localization of impulses within this area.

The ventrodorsal correlation systems and the acoustico-optic fibers, carrying in auditory impulses from the inferior colliculus, have been described as coming into relation with the neurons of the periventricular gray. These neurons, through the spread of their dendrites into the stratum fibrosum et griseum super-ficiale, serve to correlate within themselves optic, tactile, pain, and temperature impulses, with auditory impulses and with impulses brought in through the periventricular system, which, in part at least, are olfacto-visceral in character. Since the periventricular layer and fiber paths which influence it are large in the reptilian tectum, they must be regarded as of distinct significance in any con-sideration of it as a sensory correlation center. The high development and differentiation of both of these receptive layers in reptiles and in birds is morpho-logic evidence that in these forms the tectum has reached the peak of its develop-ment as a sensory correlation center. The efferent paths in the reptilian (and avian) tectum are also well developed, discharge being made to diencephalic, tegmental, cerebellar, and bulbar centers, with few if any tecto-spinal paths. Of particular interest are the tecto-thalamic connections, for the dorsal thalamus receives at best few lemnisci fibers and is dependent for its development upon the various sensory impulses which reach it by way of the bulbo-tectal and tecto-thalamic paths, the development of the dorsal thalamus going hand in hand with the development of the tectum in these forms.

In former paragraphs the close interrelation of the dorsal thalamus and the tectum has been discussed. It needs to be emphasized that the growth of the nonolfactory telencephalon is structurally and functionally dependent upon the relative development of the dorsal thalamus. Even a cursory examination indicates a marked increase in the size and differentiation of nuclear patterns and fiber connections of the dorsal thalamus of reptiles as compared with lower vertebrates, and with this increase a corresponding growth in size and differentia-tion of the neopallial, primordial pallial, and certain striatal areas of the hemi-spheres. Not only the dorsal thalamus, but the ventral thalamus (subthalamus) as well, shows an appreciable advance in nuclear differentiation as compared with that demonstrated in vertebrates below the phylogenetic level of reptiles.

Huber and *Crosby* regard the development of the ventral thalamus as based on two criteria: the first depends on ansa lenticularis relations to phylogeneti-cally developing, interrupted nuclear columns related to the ventral peduncle of the forebrain bundle, out of which differentiate nuclear groups; the sec-ond depends on the extent of differentiation of said nuclear groups, which is cor-related with the specificity of their connections, secondarily acquired, with the spinal cord, medulla oblongata, tegmentum or tectum. Thus far it has been possible to identify in reptiles all of the generally accepted ventral thalamic nuclei with the exception of the nucleus subthalamicus and this latter nucleus is present in anlage. This differentiation of the ventral thalamus can be correlated both structurally and functionally with the higher degree of differentiation of the striatum and particularly its lenticular portion. The degree of development of the hypothalamic centers and the numerous connections from the telenceph-alon to both epithalamus and hypothalamus, and from the hypothalamus to the telencephalon, and particularly to the olfactory cortex, indicate a marked interrelation between such olfactory telencephalic centers and the hypothalamic and epithalamic areas.

THE AVIAN MESENCEPHALIC AND DIENCEPHALIC CENTERS

GENERAL RELATIONS.   INTERNALLY SECRETING PORTIONS

The avian brain exhibits marked morphologic differences from that of reptiles. Associated with these gross changes there are changes in the internal arrangement of the nuclei and fiber tracts, which are very confusing to the student of the avian brain, and make it particularly difficult to establish homologies.   Such gross changes are due probably to many factors, among which may be mentioned the

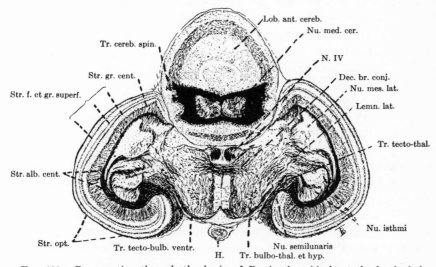

FIG. 489.   Cross section through the brain of Pratincola rubicola at the level of the nucleus isthmi.   *Ariëns Kappers.*

Dec.br.conj., decussation of brachium conjunctivum; *H.*, hypophysis; *Lemn.lat.*, lemniscus lateralis; *Lob.ant.cereb.*, lobus anterior cerebelli; *N.IV*, nervus trochlearis; *Nu.med.cer.*, nucleus medialis cerebelli; *Nu.mes.lat.*, nucleus mesencephalicus lateralis; *Nu.isthmi*, nucleus isthmi; *Nu.semilunaris*, nucleus semilunaris; *Str.alb.cent.*, stratum album centrale; *Str.f.et gr.superf.*, stratum fibrosum et griseum superficiale; *Str.gr.cent.*, stratum griseum centrale; *Str.opt.*, stratum opticum; *Tr.bulbo-thal.et hyp.*, tractus bulbo-thalamicus et hypothalamicus; *Tr.cereb.spin.*, tractus cerebello-spinalis; *Tr.tecto-bulb.ventr.*, tractus tecto-bulbaris ventralis; *Tr.tecto-thal.*, tractus tecto-thalamicus.

compression of the brain by the skull, the space within having been narrowed relatively by reason of the conspicuous development of the telencephalon in avian forms.   The pressure exercised by the increased brain mass upon the segments lying behind and beneath the hemispheres is particularly manifested in the lateral shifting of the two halves of the optic tectum, which in many birds are connected here only by a thin lamella and the ventricle of which is reduced to a narrow furrow (fig. 489).   Thus the optic tectum in the majority of birds consists of two very conspicuous lateral eminences proportionally larger than in other forms, as is to be expected with the relatively great development of the eyes and with their importance in reflex activities in these animals.   The migration ventralward may also be aided by the neurobiotactic influence of the optic tract fibers in these animals (*Ingvar*, '23).

Unlike the condition in lizards, the homologue of the torus semicircularis, which in birds is termed the ganglion laterale (*Wallenberg*, '98) or nucleus mesencephalicus lateralis, pars dorsalis (*Ariëns Kappers*, '21), in most birds is entirely embedded in the gray of the midbrain wall, and the nucleus isthmi is deep and not perceptible from the surface.   The effect of the pressure of the enlarged forebrain hemispheres appears in the position of the epiphysis in birds, which has shifted considerably backward in these forms and adheres closely to the cerebellum. In bird embryos a pineal and a parapineal anlage are present (*Cameron*, '03–'04; *Livini*, '06).   A parietal eye, however, does not develop and the epiphysis in birds is generally smaller than in lizards and often scarcely shows a glandular structure.   In cocks, where it is rather large, its amputation, according to *Foà* ('12), effects an hypertrophy of the testicles and the crest, indicating that the gland is concerned with the primary and secondary sex characteristics.   This statement has been contradicted by *Badetscher* (*Ariëns Kappers*, '21).

The ventricles of the diencephalon are narrowed also in consequence of the intracranial pressure.   Their walls are usually flattened against each other and do not show very distinct fissures.   The sulcus subhabenularis and sometimes a trace of the sulcus medius may be seen, although the latter is not very distinct in adults.

Just as in reptiles, in the upper infundibular region in birds there is an area characterized by the increased development and peculiar vascularization of its ependyma (modified ependyma occurs also in the subcommissural organ in the region of the commissura posterior).   As the position which this secretory ependyma occupies (compare figures 453, 459, and 473A and B) is exactly the same as that in other animals, it may be concluded that it is a rather constant feature of this region.

There is scarcely any lumen in the lower part of the infundibulum.   The recessus postopticus and the recessus preopticus are not clearly defined and the hypophysis in birds, compared with that in mammals, is small (fig. 489).   The hypothalamus in these animals is relatively small (although it has considerable nuclear differentiation), an accompaniment of the microsmatic character of these animals.

A cursory examination of the avian thalamus suggests that it is very different from that of reptiles, but a closer study — and particularly an understanding of the fiber pattern — indicates that while the form relations are very different in the two types, they both have a common pattern which is merely modified in the bird. Naturally the conditions in the bird are most readily compared with those in lizards, crocodiles, and alligators.   In most birds there is a relative reduction of the olfactory centers, although the degree of this reduction varies between considerable limits.

THE NUCLEAR STRUCTURE AND FIBER CONNECTIONS OF THE OPTIC TECTUM

A consideration of the microscopic structure of the avian mesencephalic and diencephalic regions may begin with a review of the optic tectum (figs. 489 to 495, 496), which is developed even more elaborately in avian than in reptilian forms.

There is a difference of opinion among various observers as to the number of layers into which it should be divided. Thus *Bellonci* ('88) recognized seven layers, *Ramón y Cajal* ('91, '11) and *Ramón* ('98) fifteen layers, *van Gehuchten* ('92) three layers, *von Kölliker* ('96), working with Weigert material, and *Ris* ('99), using Golgi material, nine layers. Almost any one of these several subdivisions may be verified, the differences listed depending on the kind of material used, the method of preparation followed, and upon the personal predilection of the individual observer. Until accurate proof of the functional significance of the layering in terms of the details of the relations of incoming and outgoing paths shall be forthcoming, it is perhaps futile to discuss which one of the several systems of layering is to be recommended as the one deserving special consideration. In favorably sectioned preparations through the tectum the fifteen layers of *Ramón* and *Ramón y Cajal* ('11) can be quite readily identified. It may be noted here that the relations in birds are directly comparable to those in reptiles (see p. 976); that in birds as in reptiles the external layer constitutes the stratum opticum; that internal to this layer, comprising layer 14 of *Ramón* and *Ramón y Cajal*, is found a field of alternate gray and white (fiber bundles and regions of synapse) which constitutes a major receptive field and is comparable to the reptilian stratum fibrosum et griseum superficiale of the terminology of *Huber* and *Crosby* ('33a, '34) and that internal to this layer is found a gray layer giving rise to efferent paths (zone 13 of *Ramón* and *Ramón y Cajal*), a stratum griseum centrale, bordered internally by the efferent tectal layer, the stratum album centrale. On the ventricular side of this last stratum are the layers of the stratum griseum periventriculare (including the cells of the mesencephalic nucleus of the trigeminal), with the stratum fibrosum periventriculare intervening between this gray layer and the ependymal lining of the ventricle. The periventricular layers are relatively greatly reduced in birds, more of the gray having migrated peripherally.

The fiber connections of the optic tectum are numerous and the present knowledge of them has been an outgrowth of the work of many observers. Many of these connections cannot be understood satisfactorily without reference to the diencephalic and pretectal centers. Consequently a list of the major tectal connections is given here, which is followed by a brief account of the tecto-bulbar tracts, while reference is made in the list to descriptions of other tracts to be found in the present chapter. Certain major connections of the avian optic tectum are: tractus opticus marginalis (p. 1044); tractus thalamo-frontalis intermedialis (p. 1052); tractus strio-tegmentalis et strio-cerebellaris (the tectal division) (p. 1053); tractus septo-mesencephalicus pars dorsalis (p. 1056); tractus tecto-thalamicus ventrolateralis (p. 1049); tractus tecto-thalamicus cruciatus (p. 1046); decussatio supraoptica dorsalis pars lateralis (p. 1046); decussatio supraoptica ventralis, pars dorsalis and pars ventralis (p. 1047); tractus tecto-spiriformis lateralis (p. 1024); tractus tecto-spiriformis medialis (p. 1024); internuclear connections with the nucleus ectomamillaris, the nucleus externus, the nucleus pretectalis, the nucleus subpretectalis, the nucleus superficialis magnocellularis, the nucleus principalis precommissuralis, and other diencephalic nuclei; tractus tecto-thalamicus dorsalis (p. 1049); tractus tecto-thalamicus et thalamo-tectalis nuclei rotundi (p. 1049); commissura posterior pars dorsalis et pars ventralis (p. 1024); tractus tecto-bulbaris dorsalis (see below); tractus tecto-bulbaris ventralis (see below); connections with the nucleus of the oculomotor and internuclear connections with the nucleus isthmo-opticus and the nucleus isthmi pars principalis.

The tecto-bulbar systems in birds are directly comparable to certain of these systems in reptiles. They have been described by many workers in this field, a very adequate description having been given relatively early by *Edinger* and *Wallenberg* ('99). The dorsal tecto-bulbar system (figs. 491, 498), after leaving the tectum through the stratum album centrale, passes medialward, accompanied by tecto-oculomotor fibers which terminate in the oculomotor nuclei, while the main path, decussating in part in the dorsal tegmental decussation, turns caudalward in intimate relation with the medial longitudinal fasciculus. The ventral tecto-bulbar system (figs. 489, 491, 498) is large and its fibers form conspicuous components of the tegmental region through which it passes and to which it undoubtedly contributes. After undergoing a partial decussation near the base of the midbrain, it forms a descending system of fibers in the ventrolateral part of the brain stem. It loses fibers in its course caudalward, but has been followed well toward the lower end of the medulla oblongata, and may extend even farther caudalward.

NUCLEUS MESENCEPHALICUS LATERALIS PARS DORSALIS AND ITS FIBER CONNECTIONS

At about the level of the posterior commissure, in such forms as the dove, a cellular mass, the nucleus mesencephalicus lateralis pars dorsalis (figs. 491 and 492), makes its appearance along the inner side of the ventricle. Its cells are similar in type to those forming the periventricular cell layer of the optic tectum and continuous with this layer. Gradually the cell mass, which consists of medium-sized cells, thickens and is continuous behind the ventral part of the posterior commissure with the periventricular gray which runs toward the midline. At about the middle of the optic ventricle an ovoid mass of larger neurons makes its appearance among these more scattered cells and represents the cell mass of the nucleus proper, the scattered cells forming a capsule about it. This nucleus mesencephalicus lateralis pars dorsalis (*Ariëns Kappers*, '21) is presumably the homologue of the torus semicircularis of reptiles and the inferior colliculus of mammals. Gradually the larger-celled central part of the nucleus decreases in size, becoming first crescent shaped and then represented merely by a small patch of cells which soon disappears. Behind this central part the scattered, medium-sized cells form a capsule. The above account is based on the dove, but the relations are essentially similar in many other birds, with due allowance for slight differences in form relations. The main connections of this nuclear mass are the decussatio supraoptica ventralis, pars ventralis (p. 1047), the lemniscus lateralis (p. 484), the tractus isthmo-mesencephalicus, and internuclear connections with the tectum. This nucleus has been recognized by various observers.

The term nucleus isthmi does not appear to have been used with consistency throughout vertebrates.   Much of the controversy as to its fiber relations and its homologies are probably due to these differences in usage.   A nucleus situated in the dorsal part of the mesencephalon, medial to the tectum, and about the level of the oculomotor nucleus, has been recognized by a number of observers.

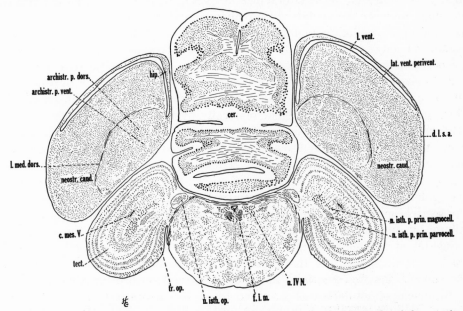

FIG. 490.   Cross section through the brain of the sparrow at the level of the nucleus isthmo-opticus and the nucleus of the fourth nerve.   Toluidin-blue preparation.   *Huber* and *Crosby*.
  archistr.p.dors., archistriatum pars dorsalis;   *archistr.p.vent.*, archistriatum pars ventralis; *c.mes.V*, cells of the mesencephalic root of the trigeminal nerve;   *cer.*, cerebellum;   *d.l.s.a.*, dorsolateral surface area (corticoid); *f.l.m.*, fasciculus longitudinalis medialis; *hip.*, hippocampus; *l.med.dors.*, lamina medullaris dorsalis; *l.vent.*, lateral ventricle; *lat.vent.perivent.*, lateroventral periventricular gray; *n.isth.op.*, nucleus isthmo-opticus; *n.isth.p.prin.magnocell.*, nucleus isthmi pars principalis magnocellularis; *n.IV N.*, nucleus of the fourth nerve; *neostr.caud.*, neostriatum caudale; *tect.*, tectum; *tr.opt.*, tractus opticus.

Bellonci ('88), and *Jelgersma* ('96) termed it the ganglion opticum dorsale; *Perlia* ('89) called it the medial optic nucleus; *Edinger* and *Wallenberg* ('99) named it the ganglion isthmi.   *Craigie* ('28), in his study of the humming bird, gave to this cell mass the name of the nucleus tractus isthmo-optici.   This nucleus consists in the sparrow (*Huber* and *Crosby*, '29; fig. 490, nucleus isthmo-opticus) of a round or oval nuclear mass with an outer layer of compact cells and an inner layer of more scattered neurons.   In the dove the nucleus is greatly folded and the inner core is reduced.   In stained material the nucleus can be identified macroscopically.   Its connections are the isthmo-optic component of the optic tract (figs. 493 and 495), and internuclear connections with the tectum and with the nuclei of the oculomotor and trochlear nerves.

Ariëns Kappers, following the work of *Pedro Ramón* and *S. Ramón y Cajal*, described another, more ventrally situated nucleus in birds, to which the name of nucleus isthmi is also applied.   For this portion *Craigie* ('28) suggested the term nucleus isthmi pars parvocellularis or pars principalis.   The latter term is here used (figs. 490 and 492).   The two portions of this nucleus are designated the pars principalis parvocellularis and the pars principalis magnocellularis.   The former makes its appearance in the sparrow in a plane passing through the middle of the habenular region dorsally and the hypophysis ventrally ; it is ventral and slightly ventromedial to the lateral mesencephalic nucleus.   Its slightly irregular, oval shape soon breaks secondarily into an inner and an outer curved band, the pars principalis parvocellularis making its appearance within the latter.   The magno-cellular portion remains about the same size for a considerable distance but the parvocellular part increases very considerably.   This latter portion consists of medium-sized cells, arranged in dorsoventrally radiating rows, with a hilus apparent on the dorsal side.   Gradually the pars parvocellularis elongates and forms a long column of cells capped ventrolaterally by the nucleus principalis magno-cellularis.   As the smaller-celled part decreases in size, the magnocellular portion about it assumes somewhat the shape of a flattened crescent, with its outer and inner bands of cells still discernible.   Then the whole nuclear mass decreases rapidly and first the small-celled and then the large-celled portion disappears. The nucleus isthmi pars principalis receives fibers or collaterals of the decussatio supraoptica ventralis and of the lateral lemniscus, is connected with the cere-bellum by an isthmo-cerebellar path, is interconnected with the tectum by isthmo-tectal and tecto-isthmal paths, and has an isthmo-mesencephalic bundle, which runs dorsalward to the nucleus mesencephalicus lateralis pars dorsalis. The connections are essentially the same as those described for Alligator.

A nucleus semilunaris was described by *Ariëns Kappers* ('21 ; also fig. 489). *Mesdag* ('09) divided it into lateral and medial portions.   Presumably the former is the pars magnocellularis ventralis of *Craigie*, although in many birds it is not large-celled as compared with the remainder of the nucleus isthmi.   For this portion the name of nucleus semilunaris has been retained to avoid a multi-plication of synonyms.   This nucleus extends medialward to the small-celled part of the nucleus isthmi.   Its cells resemble those of adjacent portions of this latter nucleus and in places the two nuclei appear continuous.   Caudally the nucleus increases in size, becomes more or less semilunar in outline, and occupies a position dorsomedial to the lateral part of the nucleus semilunaris (nucleus lemnisci lateralis).   The more lateroventral part of the nucleus extends ventral-ward in the tegmentum along the course of the lateral lemniscus fibers.   Both parts of the nuclear mass here described receive collaterals of the lateral lemniscus and the medial portion, or the nucleus semilunaris proper, is interconnected with the nucleus isthmi pars principalis.   A figure (fig. 29) illustrating this nucleus may be found in the 1929 paper of *Huber* and *Crosby*.

The connections of the lateral lemniscus with the nuclei last described — that is, the nucleus mesencephalicus lateralis, pars dorsalis, the nucleus isthmi pars principalis, the nucleus semilunaris and the associated nucleus of the lateral lemniscus — have been mentioned on preceding pages.   It is necessary only to emphasize the fact that this tract represents a connection, crossed and uncrossed, between the cochlear centers of the medulla and the above-mentioned centers, which then become the midbrain representatives of the auditory areas in the bird. Beyond this midbrain center auditory paths have not been traced in birds.

TEGMENTAL AREAS OF THE MESENCEPHALON

The tegmental centers have been described in part before.   Prominent among such are the nuclei of the oculomotor and trochlear nerves and the reticular

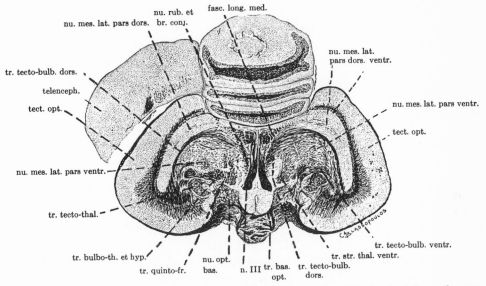

FIG. 491.   A cross section through the brain of Pratincola rubicola at the level of the oculomotor nucleus.   (Drawn from material at the Amsterdam Institute; *Ariëns Kappers*.)

fasc. long. med., fasciculus longitudinalis medialis; *n. III*, nucleus oculomotorius; *nu.mes.lat.pars dors.*, nucleus mesencephalicus lateralis pars dorsalis; *nu.mes.lat.pars ventr.*, nucleus mesencephalicus lateralis pars ventralis; *nu.opt.bas.*, nucleus opticus basalis; *nu.rub.et br.conj.*, nucleus ruber et brachium conjunctivum; *tect.opt.*, tectum opticum; *telenceph.*, telencephalon; *tr.bulbo-th.et hyp.*, tractus bulbo-thalamicus et hypothalamicus; *tr.opt.bas.*, tractus opticus basalis; *tr.quinto-fr.*, tractus quinto-frontalis; *tr.str.thal.ventr.*, tractus strio-thalamicus ventralis; *tr.tecto-bulb.dors.*, tractus tecto-bulbaris dorsalis; *tr.tecto-bulb.ventr.*, tractus tecto-bulbaris ventralis; *tr.tecto-thal.*, tractus tecto-thalamicus; *ventr.*, ventricle.

centers, particularly the intercalated cells of *Cajal* (the superior mesencephalic reticular nucleus) and the red nucleus (figs. 327 and 491).   This latter consists of conspicuously large cells situated near the midline at the level of emergence of the oculomotor roots and resembling in important respects the homologous nucleus in the alligator.   It is the nucleus of termination of a very considerable portion of the superior cerebellar peduncle, which swings ventralward and medialward from that center, crosses the midline, and terminates around the large cells of the red nucleus.   Into this nucleus also, with tectal connections to the oculomotor nuclear group, come fibers from tectal areas (partly crossed and partly uncrossed).   The neuraxes of the large cells cross the midline and descend but it has not been possible to trace them to their final termination.   They undoubtedly represent a rubro-bulbar path, or possibly a rubro-spinal path.

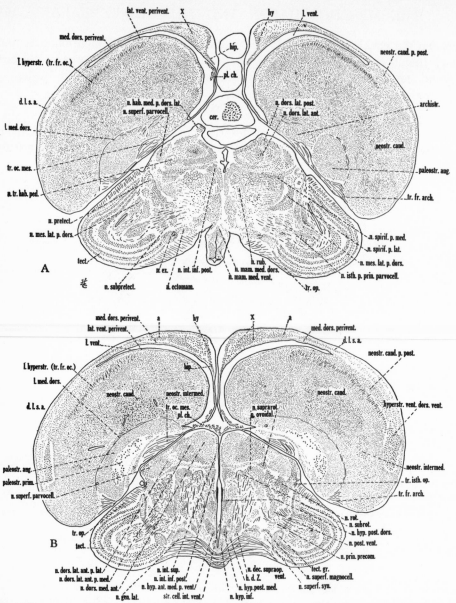

Fig. 492. *A*, cross section through the brain of a sparrow, in the posterior diencephalic and pretectal areas. Toluidin-blue preparation. *B*, cross section through the brain of a sparrow at the level of the hyperstriatum ventrale pars dorsoventrale, showing more particularly the positions and relations of nuclear masses in the more dorsal portion of the thalamus. Toluidin-blue preparation. *Huber* and *Crosby*.

a, differentiated portion of hyperstriatum accessorium; *archistr.*, archistriatum; *cer.*, cerebellum; *d.l.s.a.*, dorsolateral surface area (corticoid); *h.d.Z.*, h.d.Z. of *Rendahl*; *hip.*, hippocampus; *hy* probably comparable to hippocampus pars dorsalis of the alligator, the area entorhinalis of *Rose* for birds, mammalian homologies uncertain; *l.hyperstr.(tr.fr.oc.)* lamina hyperstriatica (tractus fronto-occipitalis); *l.med.dors.*, lamina medullaris dorsalis; *l.vent.*, lateral ventricle; *lat.vent.perivent.*, lateroventral periventricular gray; *med.dors.perivent.*, mediodorsal periventricular gray; *n.dec.supraop.vent.*, nucleus decussationis supraopticae ventralis; *n.dors.lat.ant.*, nucleus dorsolateralis anterior; *n.dors.lat.ant.p.lat.*, nucleus dorsolateralis anterior pars lateralis; *n.dors.lat.ant.p.med.*, nucleus dorsolateralis anterior pars medialis; *n.dors.lat.post.*, nucleus dorsolateralis posterior; *n.ectomam.*, nucleus ectomamillaris; *n.ent. sup.*, nucleus entopeduncularis superior; *n.ex.*, nucleus externus; *n.gen.lat.*, nucleus geniculatus lateralis;

1020

An interpeduncular nucleus is present in birds.   Its best known connection is the well-developed habenulo-peduncular tract (fig. 494).

The two nuclei characteristic of the reptilian fasciculus longitudinalis medialis, as described by *Beccari* ('23, see bibliography for reptiles), have been recognized by *Rendahl* ('24) in the chicken.   These extend from the level of the anterior part of the oculomotor nuclei forward and downward toward the diencephalon, being situated near the midline, and occurring in many, and possibly in all, birds (*Huber* and *Crosby*, '29; *Craigie*, '31).

The nucleus ectomamillaris (*Edinger* and *Wallenberg*, '99; *Kosaka* and *Hiraiwa*, '15; *Groebbels*, '24, and others; fig. 492), comparable to the nucleus of the basal optic root of reptiles and the nucleus opticus tegmenti of mammals, receives basal optic root fibers, is interconnected with the tectum, and has fiber connections with the interstitial nucleus of Cajal and the oculomotor nucleus.   The nucleus externus (*Rendahl*, '24) is related to the optic tract and the tectum (figs. 492 and 493, in latter see tr. tect. thal. n. ex.).

PRETECTAL AND SUBPRETECTAL AREAS AND THEIR FIBER CONNECTIONS

On the line between the mesencephalon and the diencephalon are nuclei to which the general term of the pretectal group may be applied since they appear to be concerned, to a very considerable extent, in the interrelation of tectal with diencephalic and other centers.   To this group four major nuclei have been assigned; whether the nucleus superficialis parvocellularis and the nucleus magnocellularis superficialis might not equally well be so assigned is as yet an open question.   For the present the latter are included in the diencephalon.   The four members of the pretectal group thus referred to are the nucleus pretectalis, the nucleus principalis precommissuralis, the nucleus spiriformis pars lateralis and pars medialis, and the nucleus subpretectalis.   With these belong the lenticular mass of gray continuous with the gray of the tectum which has been designated the lateral optic nucleus by *Craigie* ('28), the nucleus of the optic tract (pretectal) by *Papez* ('29), and merely tectal gray by *Huber* and *Crosby* ('29).

---

n.hab.med.p.dors.lat., nucleus habenularis medialis pars dorsolateralis; *n.hyp.ant.med.p.vent.*, nucleus hypothalamicus anterior medialis pars ventralis; *n.hyp.post.dors.*, nucleus hypothalamicus posterior dorsalis; *n.hyp.post.med.*, nucleus hypothalamicus posterior medialis; *n.hyp.post.med.*, nucleus hypothalamicus posterior medialis; *n.hyp.inf.*, nucleus hypothalamicus inferior; *n.int.inf.post.*, nucleus internus inferior posterior; *n.int.sup.*, nucleus internus superior; *n.isth.p.prin.parvocell.*, nucleus isthmi pars principalis parvocellularis; *n.mam.med.dors.*, nucleus mamillaris medialis pars dorsalis; *n. mam.med.vent.*, nucleus mamillaris medialis pars ventralis; *n.mes.lat.p.dors.*, nucleus mesencephalicus lateralis pars dorsalis; *n.ovoidal.*, nucleus ovoidalis; *n.post.vent.*, nucleus posteroventralis; *n. pretect.*, nucleus pretectalis; *n.prin.precom.*, nucleus principalis precommissuralis; *n.rot.*, nucleus rotundus; *n.rub.*, nucleus ruber; *n.spirif.p.lat.*, nucleus spiriformis pars lateralis; *n.spirif.p.med.*, nucleus spiriformis pars medialis; *n.subpretect.*, nucleus subpretectalis; *n.subrot.*, nucleus subrotundus; *n.superf.magnocell.*, nucleus superficialis magnocellularis; *n.superf.parvocell.*, nucleus superficialis parvocellularis; *n.superf.syn.*, nucleus superficialis synencephali of *Rendahl*; *n.suprarot.*, nucleus suprarotundus; *n.tr.hab.ped.*, nucleus tractus habenulo-peduncularis; *neostr.caud.*, neostriatum caudale; *neostr.caud.p.post.*, neostriatum caudale pars posterior; *neostr.intermed.*, neostriatum intermediale; *paleostr.aug.*, paleostriatum augmentatum; *paleostr.prim.*, paleostriatum primitivum; *pl.ch.*, plexus choroideus; *str.cell.int.vent.*, stratum cellulare internum ventrale; *tect.*, tectum; *tect.gr.*, tectal gray; *tr.fr.arch.*, tractus fronto-archistriaticus et neostriaticus; *tr.isth.op.*, tractus isthmo-opticus; *tr.oc.mes.*, tractus occipito-mesencephalicus et bulbaris; *tr.op.*, tractus opticus; *X*, area *X*.

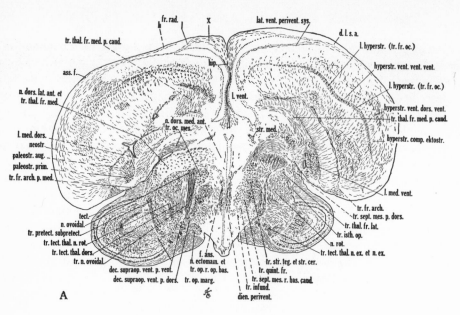

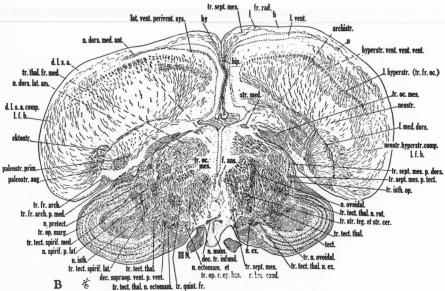

Fig. 493. *A*, cross section of the brain of a sparrow through the midthalamus region; *B*, cross section of the brain of a sparrow through the level of the pretectal nuclei and the decussation of the tractus infundibuli. Pyridine-silver preparation. *Huber* and *Crosby*.

archistr., archistriatum; *ass.f.*, association fibers; *d.l.s.a.*, dorsolateral surface area (corticoid); *d.l.s.a. comp.l.f.b.*, dorsolateral surface area component to lateral forebrain bundle; *dec.supraop.vent.p.dors.*, decussatio supraoptica ventralis pars dorsalis; *dec.supraop.vent.p.vent.*, decussatio supraoptica ventralis pars ventralis; *dec.tr.infund.*, decussatio tractus infundibuli; *dien.perivent.*, diencephalic periventricular fiber system; *ektostr.*, ektostriatum; *f.ans.*, fibrae ansulatae; *fr.rad.h.*, frontal radiations of dorsolateral surface area; *fr.rad.l.*, frontal radiations of lamina frontalis suprema; *hip.*, hippocampus; *hy*, hippocampus pars dorsalis probably of alligator, area entorhinalis of *Rose*, mammalian homologies uncertain; *hyperstr.comp.ektostr.*, hyperstriatal component of ektostriatum; *hyperstr.vent.dors.vent.*, hyperstriatum ventrale dorsoventrale; *hyperstr.vent.vent.vent.*, hyperstriatum ventrale ventroventrale; *l.hyperstr.(tr.fr. oc.)* lamina hyperstriatica (tractus fronto-occipitalis); *l.med.dors.*, lamina medullaris dorsalis; *l.med. vent.*, lamina medullaris ventralis; *l.vent.*, lateral ventricle; *lat.vent.perivent.sys.*, latero-ventral periventricular fiber system; *n*, region of fusion of laminae frontalis superior et suprema; *n.dors.lat.ant.et tr.*

The nucleus pretectalis (figs. 492, 493) has been described by workers on avian brains since the early accounts of *Edinger* ('96, '08). Even before that time *Turner* ('91) had made mention of the mass, terming it the nucleus posterior. In section it consists of a deeply staining cell mass situated dorsal to the nucleus spiriformis, medial to the tectal area, and not far ventral to the medial optic tract. It is interconnected with a larger mass of more scattered cells lying ventral to the more ventral part of the tectum, the nucleus subpretectalis of *Rendahl* ('24). This latter is probably the homologue of the nucleus pretectalis of reptiles, which has shifted ventralward with the ventral shifting of the tectum with which it is connected by internuclear fibers. Like most other members of the pretectal group, the nucleus pretectalis receives fibers from the posterior commissure. Its connection with the nucleus subpretectalis by means of a fiber bundle (tractus pretectalis-subpretectalis; fig. 493), which runs lateral to the nucleus spiriformis pars lateralis, has already been mentioned. Internuclear fibers connect it with the surrounding regions — with the tectum, the two portions of the spiriform nuclei and the nucleus superficialis parvocellularis. It receives also a small slip of the tractus septo-mesencephalicus pars dorsalis (fig. 495).

Medial and lateral portions of the nucleus spiriformis were described by *Edinger* and *Wallenberg* ('99). In most birds the lateral portion (figs. 492 and 493) consists of large, deeply staining, multipolar cells ventral to the nucleus pretectalis, dorsal to the nucleus subpretectalis and medial to the tectal centers, but separated from them by the pretectal-subpretectal fiber bundles. The medial portion of the nucleus (fig. 492), termed by *Rendahl* ('24) the nucleus dorso-caudalis, is pyramidal shaped with the apex of the pyramid toward the midline. Its cells are more densely arranged than those of the lateral portion and, at the region of the posterior commissure, it extends well toward the midline. The medial and lateral portions of the nucleus were recognized by *Huber* and *Crosby* ('29). *Craigie* recognized what appear to be homologous portions which he termed ventral and dorsal spiriform nuclei in the humming bird, although

---

thal.fr.med., nucleus dorsolateralis anterior et tractus thalamo-frontalis medialis; *n.dors.med.ant.*, nucleus dorsomedialis anterior; *n.ectomam.et tr.op.r.op.bas.*, nucleus ectomamillaris et tractus radix opticum basale; *n.ex.*, nucleus externus; *n.isth.*, nucleus isthmi; *n.mam.*, nucleus mamillaris; *n.pretect.*, nucleus pretectalis; *n.ovoidal.*, nucleus ovoidalis; *n.rot.*, nucleus rotundus; *n.spirif.p.lat.*, nucleus spiriformis pars lateralis; *neostr.*, neostriatum; *neostr.hypostr.comp.l.f.b.*, neostriatal-hypostriatal component to the lateral forebrain bundle; *paleostr.aug.*, paleostriatum augmentum; *paleostr.prim.*, paleostriatum primitivum; *str.med.*, stria medullaris; *tect.*, tectum; *tr.fr.arch.*, tractus fronto-archistriaticus; *tr.infund.*, tractus infundibuli; *tr.isth.op.*, tractus isthmo-opticus; *tr.n.ovoidal.*, tractus nuclei ovoidalis; *tr.oc.mes.*, tractus occipito-mesencephalicus et bulbaris; *tr.op.marg.*, tractus opticus marginalis; *tr. pretect.subpretect.*, tractus pretectalis-subpretectalis; *tr.quint.fr.*, tractus quinto-frontalis; *tr.sept.mes.*, tractus septo-mesencephalicus; *tr.sept.mes.p.dors.*, tractus septo-mesencephalicus pars dorsalis; *tr.sept. mes.p.tect.*, tractus septo-mesencephalicus pars tectalis; *tr.sept.mes.r.bas.caud.*, tractus septo-mesencephalicus, ramus basalis caudalis; *tr.str.teg.et str.cer.*, tractus strio-tegmentalis et strio-cerebellaris; *tr. tect.spirif.lat.*, tractus tecto-spiriformis lateralis; *tr.tect.spirif.med.*, tractus tecto-spiriformis medialis; *tr.tec.thal.*, tractus tecto-thalamicus et thalamo-tectalis; *tr.tec.thal.dors.*, tractus tecto-thalamicus et thalamo-tectalis dorsalis; *tr.tect.thal.n.ectomam.*, tractus tecto-thalamicus et thalamo-tectalis nuclei ectomamillaris; *tr.tect.thal.n.ex.*, tractus tecto-thalamicus et thalamo-tectalis nuclei externus; *tr.tect. thal.n.rot.*, tractus tecto-thalamicus et thalamo-tectalis nuclei rotundi; *tr.tect.thal.n.ex.et n.ex.*, tractus tecto-thalamicus et thalamo-tectalis nuclei externi et nucleus externus; *tr.thal.fr.lat.*, tractus thalamo-frontalis lateralis; *tr.thal.fr.med.p.caud.*, tractus thalamo-frontalis medialis pars caudalis; *III N.*, third nerve.

earlier ('30) he spoke of the nucleus as consisting typically of medial and lateral or ventromedial and ventrolateral portions.   He found it inconspicuous in Apteryx. It does not seem probable that his nucleus subpretectalis represents the ventral part of the nucleus spiriformis.   The nucleus spiriformis pars medialis is intimately associated with the ventral part of the posterior commissure and, according to *Wallenberg* ('04), receives fibers of the medial longitudinal fasciculus.   In addition to its connections with this system it is related to the pars lateralis of the spiriform nucleus by short internuclear fibers, with the hemisphere by an occipito-mesencephalic path (p. 1015), and with the tectum by the tractus tecto-spiri-formis medialis (fig. 493).   This latter tract runs lateralward from its nucleus to the more dorsal part of the tectal area.   A similar tract connects the nucleus spiriformis pars lateralis with the tectum (fig. 493).   This lateral portion is interconnected with surrounding nuclei — that is, the nucleus pretectalis and the nucleus spiriformis pars medialis.   It also receives fibers from the pars ventralis of the posterior commissure and probably from the medial longitudinal fasciculus.

The nucleus principalis precommissuralis (*Rendahl*, '24 ; *Huber* and *Crosby*, '29 ; *Craigie*, '30 and '31) is a nuclear mass lateral to the nucleus rotundus, between that latter nucleus and the tectal gray (fig. 492).   It extends caudalward until replaced by the lateral portion of the nucleus subpretectalis and the nucleus spiriformis.   In addition to internuclear connections with the tectum and the posterior commissure (ventral portion) this nucleus receives fibers of the pars ventralis of the ventral supraoptic decussation.

THE POSTERIOR COMMISSURE IN RELATION TO THE PRETECTAL, TECTAL, AND
SUBPRETECTAL AREAS

The posterior commissure (figs. 494 and 497) is so intimately related with the tectal and pretectal areas that a summary of its components can best be considered at this time.   There are numerous references to the various components of this fiber system in birds (*Ariëns Kappers*, '21 ; *Craigie*, '28, and others). The following account, which is based on the sparrow material (*Huber* and *Crosby*, '29), illustrates reasonably well the conditions found in most birds.   The relations are very comparable to those described previously for the alligator.   The system is divisible into a dorsal and a ventral portion.   The dorsal portion is essentially an interconnection of the two halves of the optic tectum.   The fibers cross the midline and for the most part turn just dorsal to the optic ventricle.   The ventral division is concerned chiefly with the interconnection of areas below the optic ventricle including the nucleus mesencephalicus dorsalis pars lateralis and the pretectal areas, with the exception of the nucleus subpretectalis.   This ventral division of the posterior commissure forms an almost continuous sheet of fibers, among which are situated, and partly encapsulated, the nucleus pretectalis and the two subdivisions of the nucleus spiriformis.   A slip runs medialward and caudalward from the nucleus principalis precommissuralis to the commissure.   The most medial portion of the posterior commissure fibers swings down around the periventricular gray to come into relation with the medial longitudinal fasciculus and to end in the associated interstitial nuclei of this fasciculus, particularly the dorsal nucleus.   For further details of this last relationship, reference should be made to the work of *Wallenberg* ('04) and *Beccari* ('23, for reptiles).

THE MEDIAL LONGITUDINAL FASCICULUS AND ITS RELATION TO PRETECTAL AREAS

Another important coördination bundle must receive consideration at this time.   In preceding chapters, and particularly in Chapter IV, emphasis was laid on certain component fiber tracts of the medial longitudinal fasciculus.   At the pretectal levels certain important constituents are added to this bundle, which has its origin near the boundary between the mesencephalon and the diencephalon and extends caudalward, occupying a position near the ventricular floor and close to the somatic efferent nuclear groups until the caudal end of the medulla oblongata is reached, where it continues into the ventral white funiculus of the spinal cord. Here only a brief summary of the various components will be attempted, based on the accounts of *Edinger* ('08), *Ramón y Cajal* ('11), *Muskens* ('14), *Groebbels* ('24), and others.   This bundle (figs. 276, 278, 325, 490, and 491) is said to contain :

1. Uncrossed secondary vestibular fibers from the ventrolateral (or *Deiters'*) vestibular nucleus.   The homolateral fibers (*Wallenberg*, '05) ascend for the most part in the middle third of the medial longitudinal fasciculus, with scattered fibers medial and lateral to it, and distribute to the different nuclei of the bulbar reticular gray, to the trochlear and oculomotor nuclei, and to the nucleus spiriformis pars dorsomedialis.   Certain fascicles are believed to decussate in the supraoptic or postoptic decussation in order to reach the tuber cinereum of the opposite side. The homolateral descending bundle, according to *Wallenberg* ('05), occupies a position adjacent to the medial tecto-spinal tract (or fasciculus predorsalis) and terminates in a part of the hypoglossal nucleus and the ventral horn nuclei of the cervical cord.

2. Crossed secondary vestibular fibers from the Deiters' nucleus (ventrolateral vestibular nucleus).   The ascending contralateral fibers (*Wallenberg*, '05) terminate in the reticular formation, the nuclei of the medial longitudinal fasciculus, the oculomotor nuclei (the dorsolateral, not supplied by the homolateral fibers) and the tuber cinereum after crossing above the optic chiasma.   The dorsomedial nuclear group of the hypoglossal nerve, together with the cells of the ventral horn of the spinal cord, receive contralateral descending fibers of the bundle.

3. Components from the nuclei of the medial longitudinal fasciculus and the gray associated with the posterior commissure.   Certain of the bundles cross immediately in the commissure to reach the fasciculus of the other side.   The longest fibers of the fasciculus arise in this region and extend into the spinal cord. The descending paths have been emphasized particularly by *Muskens* ('14), who termed them the tractus interstitio-spinalis and tractus commissuro-medullaris.

THE NUCLEAR PATTERN AND FIBER CONNECTIONS OF THE EPITHALAMUS AND PARTICULARLY THE STRIA MEDULLARIS

Turning now to a consideration of the diencephalon, the usual divisions into epithalamus, thalamus, and hypothalamus are observed.   The epithalamus will receive consideration first.

Coincident with the reduction of the olfactory system in most birds, the epithalamic olfacto-somatic correlations are correspondingly reduced, but just as there are all gradations from forms in which the olfactory components bear a close resemblance to those of reptiles to those which show but slight development of these fibers, so there are all degrees of development of the habenula and its associated fiber tracts. The following account is based primarily on the dove, which may be regarded as typical of those avian forms in which the olfactory system, while reduced, still has representatives centrally of the major tracts and centers.

Most workers on the avian brain have recognized medial and lateral habenular nuclei (*Edinger* and *Wallenberg*, '99; *Rendahl*, '24; *Groebbels*, '24; figs. 492, 494, and 496). *Münzer* and *Wiener* ('98) termed them respectively the "zentrale Zellpartie" and the "habenular ganglion." Only one nuclear mass was identified by *Mesdag* ('09), who worked, as did *Rendahl* ('24, see above), on chick embryos. Although smaller, the two nuclei are so similar to those described for Alligator as to make further description unnecessary. A superficially placed, small-celled nucleus just ventrolateral to the habenula was recognized and described by *Rendahl* ('24) as the nucleus superficialis epithalamicus (fig. 496). It appears to be intercalated in the course of stria medullaris fibers.

The major incoming path to the habenula is the stria medullaris (fig. 493). To this belong several components, of which the first to be described are the tractus cortico-habenularis medialis and the tractus septo-habenularis or tractus parolfacto-habenularis. The portion contributed by the dorsomedial hemisphere wall is small in the dove; it increases in lower birds where the olfactory regions are better developed and decreases in such avian forms as the parrakeet. The greater part of the fibers arise from the lateral septal area and from the bed nuclei of the anterior and pallial commissures, constituting a septo-habenular tract. Accompanying the fibers for a considerable distance from the region of the bed nucleus are scattered cells which constitute a sort of bed nucleus for the tract. The components of this tract are shown best in figure 609.

The tractus taenio-habenularis (*Huber* and *Crosby*, '29) is the homologue in part of the reptilian tractus cortico-habenularis lateralis anterior and in part of the tractus olfacto-habenularis posterior. In reptiles there are two components of the tract from the nucleus ventromedialis (or nucleus taenia of birds) to the stria which, during the latter part of their course, fuse into a common tract. In birds the taenio-habenular tract represents the component from this nucleus to the stria as represented in both tracts. The bundle might equally well be termed the tractus olfacto-habenularis posterior as *Craigie* ('30) has done, but the avian tract is more inclusive than the reptilian tract of that name. The ventromedial nucleus of the alligator, in the same sense as the nucleus taenia of birds, is a part of the archistriatal complex. This tract is illustrated in figure 609.

The tractus archistriato-habenularis et precommissuralis is an amygdalo-habenular system comparable in part with the tractus cortico-habenularis posterior of Alligator. In this reptile the posterior part of the so-called nucleus olfactorius lateralis (included within the avian and reptilian archistriatum), the overlying piriform lobe cortex, and the lower part of the dorsolateral area contribute to this tract, but in the dove and sparrow (*Huber* and *Crosby*, '29) thus far it has been traced only from the archistriatal region. *Craigie* ('30) described a tract from the cortex overlying the archistriatum, which passed through the archistriatum without apparent synapse, but otherwise had the course to be described for the tractus archistriato-habenularis. One component of the reptilian system appears to have been identified in the dove and the other in the kiwi. The avian tractus archistriato-habenularis et precommissuralis swings directly medialward from its origin in the archistriatum and passes dorsal to the stria terminalis fibers. It soon forms a relatively compact bundle easily distinguishable in the chrome-silver material studied, because of its orange color, which is in contrast with the grayish black color of the stria terminalis fibers. A few of the fibers can be traced into the stria medullaris (the archistriato-habenular component); the majority of them synapse in the region of the bed nuclei of the commissures and the septal areas, constituting an archistriato-precommissural component — the homologue of the tractus epistriato-precommissuralis of *Schroeder* ('11). Reference is made here to figure 609.

Small bundles join the stria medullaris on its medial side as this bundle courses dorsalward toward the habenula. They come from the preoptic and anterior hypothalamic regions and are comparable with the reptilian tractus olfacto-habenularis of *Ariëns Kappers* or the tractus olfacto-habenularis medialis of *Herrick* ('10), *Crosby* ('17), and *Huber* and *Crosby* ('26) for reptiles and *Huber* and *Crosby* ('29) for birds (fig. 609).

The various components collectively form the stria medullaris, which swings along the dorsal diencephalic surface to the habenula. Part of these bundles run ahead of the main group and distribute to the medial habenular nucleus. Certain of the more medial fibers appear to terminate on the same side; the lateral fibers cross in part to the opposite side. A small component from the septo-mesencephalic tract joins the tractus taenio-habenularis on its medial side. This is accompanied by fibers from the nucleus lateralis and the nucleus superficialis parvocellularis.

The chief path from the habenula is the habenulo-peduncular system. Primarily it consists of two main bundles, a medial, associated with the medial habenular nucleus, and a lateral, associated with the lateral habenular nucleus. These two divisions will now be described. They are illustrated in figure 494.

The fibers from the lateral division swing ventrolateralward from the lateral habenular nucleus to a position just dorsal to the nucleus rotundus. In that position a small bundle is given off from the tract which runs ventrolateralward along the outer part of the capsule of the nucleus rotundus toward the tectum. Neither the final termination of the bundle nor the direction of the impulses passing over it is known at present. Probably it interconnects the tectum and the habenula. Internal to this component fibers swing into and through the nucleus rotundus and, to some extent, appear to be in synaptic relation with this nuclear mass. The main fiber mass of the lateral division of the habenulo-peduncular tract lies medial to this small component to the nucleus rotundus; it runs downward and medialward, consisting of a portion which passes through the edge of the nucleus rotundus and a part which swings ventromedialward

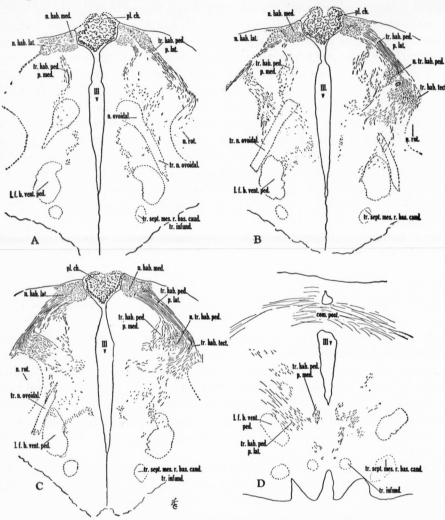

FIG. 494. A series of outline drawings (*A, B, C,* and *D*) showing, with relations, the several components of the habenulo-peduncular system. From cross sections of the brain of the dove. Pyridine-silver preparations. *Huber* and *Crosby.*

com.post., commissura posterior; *l.f.b.vent.ped.*, lateral forebrain bundle ventral peduncle; *n.hab. lat.*, nucleus habenularis lateralis; *n.hab.med.*, nucleus habenularis medialis; *n.ovoidal.*, nucleus ovoidalis; *n.rot.* nucleus rotundus; *n.tr.hab.ped.*, nucleus tractus habenulo-peduncularis; *pl.ch.*, plexus choroideus; *tr.hab. ped.p.lat.*, tractus habenulo-peduncularis pars lateralis; *tr.hab.ped.p.med.*, tractus habenulo-peduncularis pars medialis; *tr.hab.tect.*, tractus habenulo-tectalis; *tr.infund.*, tractus infundibuli; *tr.sept.mes.r.bas.caud.*, tractus septo-mesencephalicus, ramus basalis caudalis; *tr.n.ovoidalis*, tractus nuclei ovoidalis; *III V.*, third ventricle.

between this nucleus and the nucleus tractus habenulo-peduncularis and is, to a considerable extent, in synaptic relation with this last mentioned nucleus. This latter constitutes an habenulo-diencephalic and perhaps also a diencephalohabenular tract.   From the nucleus of the tractus habenulo-peduncularis fibers join the tract and proceed ventromedialward and caudalward with it to the nucleus interpeduncularis.   A few of these fibers appear to cross before entrance to their terminal nucleus.

The medial division of the habenulo-peduncular tract has its origin from the medial habenular nucleus and a considerable portion of its fibers parallel the course of the lateral division of the habenulo-peduncular tract.   Its outermost fibers are likewise in synaptic relation with the nucleus of the habenulo-peduncular tract, but its inner fibers pass medial to this cell group.   The most medial fascicles of the medial division do not accompany the remainder of the bundle lateralward but cut straight through the dorsal thalamus.   Their course is that of a slight double curve, the convexities of which are first medialward and then lateralward.   Ventralward they cut through the occipito-mesencephalic tract. Gradually the various parts of the system converge and pass to the interpeduncular nucleus.

THE AVIAN THALAMUS AND ITS FIBER CONNECTIONS

The thalamus proper is very well differentiated in birds.   In many ways its nuclear pattern represents an elaboration of that found in reptiles and particularly in lizards, crocodiles, and alligators, although there is a marked difference in form relations.

The work of *Edinger* and *Wallenberg* ('99) constitutes a point of departure for all later studies of the diencephalon.   It must be supplemented by the studies of *Bellonci* ('88), *Perlia* ('89), *Singer* and *Münzer* ('90), and others on the optic thalamus to which reference will be made later.   *Edinger's* text ('08) and the German edition of the *Ariëns Kappers* book ('21) contain reviews of this earlier work. The account of the development of the nuclear centers of the brain of the chick given by *Mesdag* ('09) contains a brief description of certain thalamic centers. *Ingvar's* ('23) paper on the evolution of the thalamus will be considered later. The thalamic and midbrain centers and certain of their fiber connections in the dove and chicken were described by *Groebbels* ('24).   In the same year *Rendahl* published an account of the thalamic nuclei in the chicken.   He concerned himself with the question of segmentation within the diencephalon (dividing the areas into a parencephalon anterius, a parencephalon posterius, and a synencephalon) and with the progressive development of the nuclei of the diencephalon, which are considered through various embryonic and young stages of chick brain to adult conditions.   Several accounts which include descriptions of the avian diencephalon have been published in relatively recent years, and among these mention is made of a contribution dealing with the brain of the humming bird by *Craigie* ('28), a paper dealing with the diencephalic centers of the sparrow, the dove, the duck, the chicken, and the parrakeet by *Huber* and *Crosby* ('29), which contribution was followed by an account of the diencephalic centers of the humming bird by *Craigie* ('31).   While the following account of the avian diencephalon is based primarily on the forms studied by *Huber* and *Crosby* ('29) and on other avian material available at the Laboratory of Comparative Neurology,

University of Michigan, due regard has been given to the pertinent literature. For convenience the nuclear masses are described from in front caudalward.

a. Area Ventralis Anterior. The bed nuclei of the anterior and pallial commissures become continuous with a mass of scattered cells which occupies the more frontal part of the diencephalon, medial and ventromedial to the occipito-mesencephalic tract. It is the homologue of the similarly named area in Alligator, the area ventralis anterior (fig. 496).

b. Nuclei of the Upper Portion of the Thalamic Wall with Fiber Connections. The dorsomedial part of the anterior thalamic wall is soon occupied by a mass of medium-sized cells, usually deeply staining in cytologic material. This is the area dorsalis of *Rendahl* ('24) or the nucleus dorsomedialis anterior of *Huber* and *Crosby* ('29) and of *Craigie* ('30). It is probably the homologue of the reptilian nucleus dorsomedialis anterior described in Alligator (*Huber* and *Crosby*, '26) and in Sphenodon (*Cairney*, '26). Minor differences in its relations are to be found in various birds, for which the literature should be consulted. In the sparrow (figs. 493 and 496) it appears slightly in front of the level of the interventricular foramen and disappears at a plane about through the middle of the habenular nuclei. It varies somewhat in shape, being a slightly curved mass at its anterior extremity, with the nucleus dorsolateralis anterior in the hollow of the curve. Farther caudalward it becomes triangular in outline and then gradually disappears. In addition to fibers to the diencephalic periventricular system, this nucleus is related by short internuclear fibers with the nucleus dorsolateralis anterior pars medialis.

The lateral half of the dorsal diencephalic wall is occupied to a considerable extent by the nucleus dorsolateralis anterior (figs. 492 to 493, 495), divided, in certain avian forms (sparrow), into a pars lateralis and a pars medialis. In the sparrow the pars medialis makes its appearance near the level of the interventricular foramen. In this position it consists of a somewhat triangular-shaped mass of deeply stained cells lying immediately lateral to the nucleus dorsomedialis anterior. It soon becomes oval in outline and then irregularly rectangular, reaching its greatest size at a plane through the beginning of the habenular nuclei. Beyond this level it gradually decreases in size, reassumes an oval shape in sections, and disappears at about the middle of the habenular gray, being replaced by the nucleus dorsalis posterior. Around the main nuclear mass, particularly evident on its lateral side, are larger, more scattered cells (intercalated in the course of fiber bundles), which become continuous laterally with a more compact but similarly stained nuclear mass, which has been termed the pars lateralis. This latter nucleus, although relatively distinct in the sparrow, is much less clear in certain other avian forms, the area occupied by the pars medialis and the pars lateralis in the sparrow appearing to contain a single nuclear mass (*Huber* and *Crosby*, '29) in some birds, or in certain birds showing other groupings (*Craigie*, '31). In the sparrow the pars lateralis appears near the anterior end of the diencephalon, cephalad to the frontal limits of the nucleus dorsomedialis anterior and the nucleus dorsolateralis anterior. Its medial boundary is formed by fascicles of the lateral forebrain bundle, its lateral boundary by the nucleus superficialis parvocellularis or nucleus tractus septo-mesencephalici. Its posterior boundary is not clearly delimited for it passes over without sharp demarcation into the intercalated cells associated with the forebrain bundle and into the nucleus dorsolateralis posterior (fig. 492). The nucleus dorsolateralis posterior, at the level of the habenula, gradually encroaches upon the area formerly occupied by the pars medialis of the nucleus dorsolateralis anterior.

To recapitulate, the variations in the region are many but the differences are rather those of degree of development than of fundamental pattern. Roughly speaking, the area between the nucleus superficialis parvocellularis (nucleus tractus septo-mesencephalici) and the ventricular wall has been termed, by several observers, the nucleus dorsalis. In the bird brains available and in *Rendahl's* material, this nuclear area can be divided into medial and lateral portions. Of these the medial falls within the medial parts of the nuclei dorsalis anterior and posterior as these were described by *Edinger* and *Wallenberg* ('99). Anteriorly this medial part includes the area dorsalis of *Rendahl* and the nucleus dorsomedialis anterior of *Huber* and *Crosby* ('29) and that of *Craigie* ('30 and '31). The lateral parts of the nucleus dorsalis anterior and posterior, as described by *Edinger* and *Wallenberg* ('99), are relatively clear in the dove, the form on which they worked, and are readily distinguishable in the duck, the chicken, and the sparrow. In the sparrow the nucleus dorsolateralis is further divided into medial and lateral parts. The distinctness with which this nuclear group may be subdivided into two parts is dependent to a considerable extent on the form studied. This point was emphasized in the *Huber* and *Crosby* account, for in the chicken ('29, on page 74) they found no separation into lateral and medial parts and so indistinct a separation into a nucleus dorsolateralis anterior and a nucleus dorsolateralis posterior as to justify *Rendahl's* account of this area as composed of a single nucleus (A_2). *Craigie* found also no division into medial and lateral parts in Apteryx. In the humming bird (in his 1930 paper) he found a somewhat different grouping of small and large cells within the nucleus dorsolateralis anterior and a small-celled nuclear group caudal to the larger main mass of the nucleus dorsolateralis anterior, which small-celled group apparently is the homologue of the nucleus dorsolateralis posterior, though it is not definitely separated from the nucleus dorsolateralis anterior and is included in this latter nuclear group by *Craigie* ('31). In the parrakeet the nucleus consists of closely arranged, deeply staining neurons, with a pars lateralis which is difficult to distinguish. As was stated previously, the variations appear to be modifications of a pattern fundamental to all forms studied, so that not the amount of variation but the extent of agreement among the different birds is significant. To the whole area *Edinger* ('08), *Ariëns Kappers* ('21), and *Groebbels* ('24) applied the term of the nucleus dorsalis.

The connections of the nucleus dorsolateralis anterior pars medialis are by way of the tractus thalamo-frontalis medialis (figs. 602 and 603), the tractus tecto-thalamicus dorsalis (figs. 493 and 495), and internuclear connections with the pars lateralis, with the nucleus dorsomedialis anterior, and with the nucleus dorsolateralis posterior. The pars lateralis is in relation with the tractus thalamo-frontalis lateralis (fig. 602, or externus, figs. 604 to 608) and the tractus thalamo-frontalis medialis, and has internuclear connections with the pars medialis and the nucleus superficialis parvocellularis, while the nucleus dorsolateralis posterior, in addition to the internuclear connection to which reference is made above, gives rise to the tractus thalamo-frontalis medialis.

"Nucleus superficialis parvocellularis" is the name given by *Rendahl* ('24) to the gray band which occupies the most lateral part of the dorsal diencephalon throughout the greater part of the extent of this latter region. This is the nucleus superficialis parvocellularis of *Huber* and *Crosby* ('29) and *Craigie* ('30), except that this nucleus, as described by *Rendahl*, is regarded by *Huber* and *Crosby* as including both the nucleus lateralis of earlier workers and the "Kern des Scheidewandbündel" of *Edinger* and *Wallenberg* ('99, fig. 5), which nucleus then is the place of synapse of the tract associated with its neurons, that is represents the nucleus of the septo-mesencephalic tract of these authors. The name of nucleus lateralis was retained by *Huber* and *Crosby* for the portion so designated earlier. There is some question as to the suitability of the name "nucleus superficialis parvocellularis" for the remainder of this cell mass. This name has been retained for the present because to *Rendahl* belongs the credit of recognizing the extent of this nuclear mass and because his account is most readily homologized with the material available. This nucleus is in synaptic relation with the tractus septo-mesencephalicus but also with other fiber systems. *Craigie* ('30), in his paper on the kiwi, suggested the retention of the name of the nucleus tractus septo-mesencephalici for a part of this nucleus superficialis parvocellularis (apparently the more ventral and cephalic portion). He stated: "As the nucleus of the septo-mesencephalic tract is, however, at least in many adult birds, a very definitely circumscribed body, even though derived from this layer, it seems desirable to retain its specific designation, and confine the term nucleus superficialis parvocellularis to the remainder of the area." Such a terminology could be applied to the forms studied by *Huber* and *Crosby*. It is difficult to reconcile the above statements with those in *Craigie's* later paper on the humming bird, where he stated that the above mentioned nucleus tractus septo-mesencephalici of the kiwi is not differentiable as a distinct nucleus and that the nucleus lateralis anterior (recognizable as a distinct nucleus in the kiwi) is the nucleus tractus septo-mesencephalici of the humming bird.

The nucleus superficialis parvocellularis (figs. 492 and 495), irrespective of the name employed, appears in the sparrow at the anterior end of the diencephalon as a round or oval cell mass continuous at its upper end with a band of cells, which forms the nucleus lateralis. Gradually the oval outline changes to a triangular and then a band-like form, and the whole cell mass swings somewhat dorsalward. It can be followed to about the level of the posterior commissure. In other birds it has essentially similar relations, although it varies somewhat in shape. It may be very much intermingled with the ventrally running "tail" of cells from the nucleus lateralis. Associated with this nucleus in all the avian forms available for study are the bundles of the tractus septo-mesencephalicus pars dorsalis and the ventral, cephalic part of the nucleus is especially connected with this system (figs. 493, 495, and 602).

The nucleus lateralis, so termed first by *Edinger* and *Wallenberg* ('99), was homologized by these workers with the "Kern der Decussatio inferior" of *Münzer* and *Wiener* ('98). Its homologies with other previously described centers is less clear. The homology made by *Groebbels* ('24) with his nucleus geniculatus lateralis externus appears to be open to question. The so-called nucleus lateralis anterior of certain observers may possibly be homologous. The nucleus lateralis of the present description is that of *Huber* and *Crosby* ('29, in fig. 16). In the sparrow it is represented by a band of cells, conspicuous for their deeply stained character, which lies along the dorsolateral margin of the diencephalon. Its cells define it clearly from the nucleus superficialis parvocellularis throughout its more cephalic extent but farther caudally its cells become more or less intermingled with those of the other nucleus so that it becomes impossible to draw any boundary line between the two cell groups. In one- and eight-day-old doves, the nucleus lateralis is not distinguishable from the nucleus superficialis parvocellularis but is present at the ten-day stage although not so large as in the adult. In adult birds it consists of a mass of cells distinguishable along the dorsal surface of the dien-cephalon through about the extent of the anterior half of the habenula. Cephali-cally it is comet shaped, the "tail" extending into the nucleus superficialis parvocellularis. Farther caudally the lower part disappears, leaving an oval mass of cells which decreases gradually. The nucleus lateralis occurs in the duck, the parrakeet, and the chicken, although in each the form relations are slightly differ-ent. It is present also in the kiwi and the humming bird (*Craigie*, '30 and '31). It receives impulses, largely through collaterals, from the tractus isthmo-opticus, and is related by short, internuclear connections with the nucleus superficialis parvocellularis and the lateral habenular nucleus.

In doves, sparrows, ducks, and chickens (*Huber* and *Crosby*, '29) and in the humming bird (*Craigie*, '31), a nucleus associated with the habenulo-peduncular tract has been seen. In the dove and the sparrow, where the relations are essentially similar, the main mass of the nucleus lies directly dorsal to the nucleus rotundus and at some levels apparently continuous with it. It has been desig-nated by *Rendahl* ('24) in the chicken as nucleus A_3. As yet it has not been possible to recognize it in the parrakeet although there is every reason to believe that it is present. Cells of this nucleus in the dove and the sparrow are large, multipolar neurons; similar scattered cells can be followed along the course of the tract as it passes medialward and ventromedialward. The nucleus is in synaptic relation with the tract, the name of which it bears (fig. 494).

c. *The Nucleus Rotundus.* Of all the nuclear groups of the avian diencepha-lon, the nucleus rotundus has probably been the most generally recognized. The cell mass was termed "zentraler Kern" by *Bellonci* ('83) and the corpus geniculatum externum by *Turner* ('91). Most observers (*Stieda*, '69; *Edinger* and *Wallenberg*, '99; *Edinger*, '08; *Ariëns Kappers*, '21; *Groebbels*, '24; *Craigie*, '28, '30, and '31; *Papez*, '29; *Huber* and *Crosby*, '29, and others) called it the nucleus rotundus. *Rendahl* ('24) designated it A_1 in the chicken. In spite of its name, in many birds at least, the nucleus is round only in certain planes; in other planes it varies in outline, sometimes having a straight inner and a convex

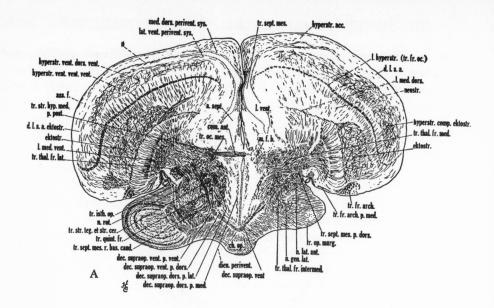

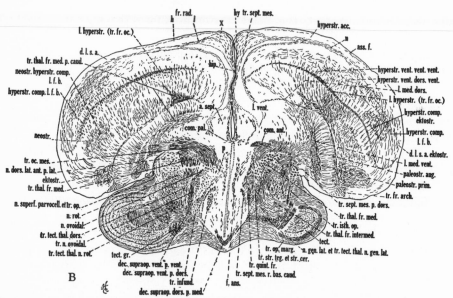

Fig. 495. *A*, cross section through brain of a sparrow, passing through the anterior commissure and the tectum; *B*, cross section of the brain of a sparrow, passing slightly caudal to the level of the anterior commissure and showing numerous diencephalic fiber connections. Pyridine-silver preparations. *Huber and Crosby.*

a.sept., area septalis; *ass.f.*, association fibers; *ch.op.*, chiasma opticum; *com.ant.*, commissura anterior; *com.pal.*, commissura pallii; *d.l.s.a.*, dorsolateral surface area (corticoid); *d.l.s.a.ektostr.*, dorsolateral surface area component to ektostriatum; *dec.supraop.dors.p.lat.*, decussatio supraoptica dorsalis pars lateralis; *dec.supraop.dors.p.med.*, decussatio supraoptica dorsalis pars medialis; *dec.supraop.vent.*, decussatio supraoptica ventralis; *dec.supraop.vent.p.vent.*, decussatio supraoptica ventralis pars ventralis; *dien.perivent.*, diencephalic periventricular fiber system; *ektostr.*, ektostriatum; *f.ans.*, fibrae ansulatae; *fr.rad.h.*, frontal radiations from dorsolateral surface area; *fr.rad.l.*, frontal radiations from lamina frontalis suprema; *hip.*, hippocampus; *hy*, hippocampus pars dorsalis of alligator, area entorhinalis *Rose*, mammalian homologies uncertain; *hyperstr.acc.*, hyperstriatum accessorium; *hyperstr.comp. ektostr.*, hyperstriatal component to ektostriatum; *hyperstr.comp.l.f.b.*, hyperstriatal component to lateral forebrain bundle; *hyperstr.vent.dors.vent.*, hyperstriatum ventrale dorsoventrale; *hyperstr.vent.vent.vent.*,

1034

outer border, sometimes being somewhat irregular in outline.   Its large cells are multipolar, and the nucleus is so evident in all sections where it occurs and so generally recognized that it does not require further description (figs. 492 to 498). It is associated with the following fiber bundles: tractus thalamo-frontalis lateralis (p. 1052), tractus tecto-thalamicus et thalamo-tectalis nuclei rotundi (p. 1049), tractus tecto-thalamicus dorsalis (p. 1049), and the tractus bulbo-thalamicus (*Wallenberg*, '00; p. 1049).   Internuclear fibers interconnect this nucleus with the nucleus ovoidalis, the nucleus subrotundus, and the nucleus postrotundus.

A band of dark staining cells, multipolar in type, extends diagonally downward from the region medial to the nucleus ovoidalis, along the medial surface of the nucleus rotundus, constituting the nucleus subrotundus.   Its relations are essentially the same in all the avian material available for study.   The nucleus was first described and named by *Rendahl* ('24) in the chicken and later by *Huber* and *Crosby* ('29) in the dove, the parrakeet, the chicken, the duck, and the sparrow.   A cell mass dorsal to the nucleus rotundus is the nucleus suprarotundus of *Huber* and *Crosby* ('29; fig. 492).   It receives impulses by way of the tractus thalamo-frontalis lateralis (p. 1052).

Medial to the nucleus rotundus is a bundle of fibers recognized by earlier workers (*Edinger* and *Wallenberg*, '99) under the name of the stilus corporis geniculati.   Among the fibers are certain scattered nerve cells as well as neuroglia cells.   Near the base of this region is situated the nucleus intercalatus of *Edinger* and *Wallenberg* ('99), *Ariëns Kappers* ('21), *Craigie* ('28), and *Huber* and *Crosby* ('29) — a cell mass previously identified by *Münzer* and *Wiener* ('98) as the nucleus interstriaticus.   *Edinger* ('08) called it the nucleus ventralis, while *r* was used by *Rendahl* ('24) to designate the cell group.   Apparently it is rather generally present throughout the avian series.   It is illustrated in figure 496.

The nucleus anterior ventralis of *Edinger* and *Wallenberg* ('99) is the nucleus *B* of *Rendahl*.   For this nuclear mass the name of nucleus ovoidalis was proposed

hyperstriatum ventrale ventroventrale; *l.hyperstr.*(*tr.fr.oc.*), lamina hyperstriatica (tractus fronto-occipitalis); *l.med.dors.*, lamina medullaris dorsalis; *l.med.vent.*, lamina medullaris ventralis; *l.vent.*, lateral ventricle; *l.vent.perivent.sys.*, latero-ventral periventricular fiber system; *m.f.b.*, medial forebrain bundle; *med.dors.perivent.sys.*, mediodorsal periventricular fiber system; *n*, region of fusion of laminae frontalis superior et suprema; *n.dors.lat.ant.p.lat.*, nucleus dorsolateralis anterior pars lateralis; *n.gen.lat.*, nucleus geniculatus lateralis; *n.gen lat.et tr.tect.thal.n.gen.lat.*, nucleus geniculatus lateralis et tractus tecto-thalamicus nuclei geniculati lateralis; *n.lat.ant.*, nucleus lateralis anterior; *n.ovoidal.*, nucleus ovoidalis; *n.rot.*, nucleus rotundus; *n.superf.parvocell.et tr.op.*, nucleus superficialis parvocellularis et tractus opticus; *neostr.*, neostriatum; *neostr.hyperstr.comp.l.f.b.*, neostriatal-hyperstriatal component to lateral forebrain bundle; *p.*, fibers from *tr.oc.mes.* to *n.inf.post.*; *paleostr.*, paleostriatum augmentatum; *paleostr.prim.*, paleostriatum primitivum; *tect.*, tectum; *tect.gr.*, tectal gray; *tr.fr.arch.*, tractus fronto-archistriaticus et neostriaticus; *tr.fr.arch.p.med.*, tractus archistriaticus et neostriaticus pars medialis; *tr. infund.*, tractus infundibuli; *tr.isth.op.*, tractus isthmo-opticus; *tr.n.ovoidal.*, tractus nuclei ovoidalis; *tr.oc.mes.*, tractus occipito-mesencephalicus et bulbaris; *tr.op.marg.*, tractus opticus marginalis; *tr.quint.fr.*, tractus quinto-frontalis; *tr.sept.mes.*, tractus septo-mesencephalicus; *tr.sept.mes.p.dors.*, tractus septo-mesencephalicus pars dorsalis; *tr.sept.mes.r.bas.caud.*, tractus septo-mesencephalicus, ramus basalis caudalis; *tr.str.teg.et str.cer.*, tractus strio-tegmentalis et strio-cerebellaris; *tr.str.hyp.med.p.post.*, tractus strio-hypothalamicus medialis pars posterior; *tr.tect.thal.dors.*, tractus tecto-thalamicus et thalamo-tectalis dorsalis; *tr.thal.fr.intermed.*, tractus thalamo-frontalis intermedialis; *tr.tect.thal.n.rot.*, tractus tecto-thalamicus et thalamo-tectalis nuclei rotundi; *tr.thal.fr.lat.*, tractus thalamo-frontalis lateralis; *tr.thal.fr. med.*, tractus thalamo-frontalis medialis; *tr.thal.fr.med.p.caud.*, tractus thalamo-frontalis medialis pars caudalis.

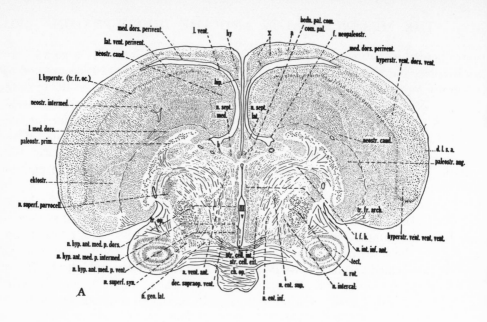

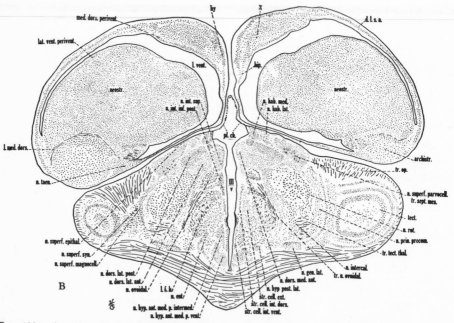

FIG. 496. *A*, cross section of the brain of a sparrow slightly caudal to the anterior commissure, giving the nuclear pattern in the more anterior portion of the diencephalon; *B*, cross section through the brain of a dove, showing positions and relations of many of the more important diencephalic nuclei. Toluidin-blue preparations. *Huber* and *Crosby.*

a, differentiated portion of hyperstriatum accessorium; *archistr.*, archistriatum; *a.vent.ant.*, area ventralis anterior; *b*, lateral continuation of the bed nucleus of the pallial commissure; *bedn.pal.com.*, bed nucleus of the pallial commissure; *ch.op.*, chiasma opticum; *com.pal.*, commissura pallii; *d.l.s.a.*, dorsolateral surface area (corticoid); *dec.supraop.vent.*, decussatio supraoptica ventralis; *ektostr.*, ektostriatum; *f.neopaleostr.*, fissura neopaleostriata; *hip.*, hippocampus; *hy*, probably comparable to hippocampus pars dorsalis of the alligator, the area entorhinalis of *Rose* for birds, mammalian homologies uncertain; *hyperstr.vent.dors.vent.*, hyperstriatum ventrale pars dorsoventrale; *hyperstr.vent.vent.vent.*, hyperstriatum ventrale pars ventroventrale; *l.f.b.*, lateral forebrain bundle; *l.hyperstr.(tr.fr.oc.)*, by *Craigie* ('28) for the humming bird and adopted by *Huber* and *Crosby* ('29). This nucleus (figs. 492 to 496) appears as a sharply delimited nuclear mass, oval in outline, and consisting of medium-sized to large multipolar cells, rather closely packed together.   Secondary cell groupings are relatively evident within the nuclear mass.   The 1931 paper of *Craigie* should be consulted for the correct position of this nucleus in the humming bird.   In the sparrow and the parrakeet the nucleus is relatively far lateralward, being situated dorsolateral to the forebrain bundles.   In the dove and the chicken it is near the midline, medial to the nucleus rotundus, dorsal to the forebrain bundle, and immediately lateral to the nucleus internus.   The position of the nucleus in the duck is more nearly comparable to that in the sparrow than to that in the dove, although it is intermediate in position between the two.   In each form the position of the nucleus is constant with reference to that of the nucleus rotundus.   It gives rise to fibers of the tractus nuclei ovoidalis (figs. 493 to 496), is in relation with the tractus thalamo-frontalis medialis (p. 1054), the tractus thalamo-frontalis intermedialis (p. 1052), and the tractus tecto-thalamicus dorsalis (p. 1049), and has internuclear connections with the nucleus rotundus and the nucleus subrotundus.   *Papez* (to be published) has regarded it as homologous to the dorsal part of the mammalian medial geniculate.

d. Nucleus Tractus Tecto-thalamici Cruciati, Nucleus Lateralis Anterior and the Geniculate Complex, with Connections.   A small nucleus situated at the place where the diencephalon becomes continuous with the preoptic area has been termed, from its associated fiber bundle (fig. 602), the nucleus tractus tecto-thalamici cruciati (*Huber* and *Crosby*, '29; *Craigie*, '31).   Caudally, in the sparrow, this mass is not sharply differentiated from the nucleus intercalatus.   The round or oval cell mass lateral and then slightly dorsolateral to it is the nucleus lateralis anterior (fig. 602) of *Edinger* and *Wallenberg* ('99), *Huber* and *Crosby* ('29), and *Craigie* ('30), but *Craigie* ('31) has labeled the same area, the nucleus tractus septi.

The nucleus geniculatus lateralis of avian forms in general is band-like in outline, consisting of a layer of larger, more deeply staining cells bounded on

---

lamina hyperstriatica (tractus fronto-occipitalis); *l.med.dors.*, lamina medullaris dorsalis; *l.vent.*, lateral ventricle; *lat.vent.perivent.*, lateroventral periventricular gray; *med.dors.perivent.*, mediodorsal periventricular gray; *n.dors.lat.ant.*, nucleus dorsolateralis anterior; *n.dors.lat.post.*, nucleus dorsolateralis posterior; *n.dors.med.ant.*, nucleus dorsomedialis anterior; *n.ent.*, nucleus entopeduncularis; *n.ent.inf.*, nucleus entopeduncularis inferior; *n.ent.sup.*, nucleus entopeduncularis superior; *n.gen.lat.*, nucleus geniculatus lateralis; *n.hab.lat.*, nucleus habenularis lateralis; *n.hab.med.*, nucleus habenularis medialis; *n.hyp. ant.med.p.dors.*, nucleus hypothalamicus anterior medialis pars dorsalis; *n.hyp.ant.med.p.intermed.*, nucleus hypothalamicus anterior medialis pars intermedialis; *n.hyp.ant. med.p.vent.*, nucleus hypothalamicus anterior medialis pars ventralis; *n.hyp.post.lat.*, nucleus hypothalamicus posterior lateralis; *n.int.inf.ant.*, nucleus internus inferior anterior; *n.int.inf.post.*, nucleus internus inferior posterior; *n.int. sup.*, nucleus internus superior; *n.intercal.*, nucleus intercalatus; *n.ovoidal.*, nucleus ovoidalis; *n.rot.*, nucleus rotundus; *n.sept.lat.*, nucleus septalis lateralis; *n.sept.med.*, nucleus septalis medialis; *n.superf. epithal.*, nucleus superficialis epithalamicus; *n.superf.magnocell.*, nucleus superficialis magnocellularis; *n.superf.parvocell.*, nucleus superficialis parvocellularis; *n.superf.syn.*, nucleus superficialis synencephali; *n.taen.*, nucleus taenia; *neostr.*, neostriatum; *neostr.caud.*, neostriatum caudale; *neostr.intermed.*, neostriatum intermediale; *paleostr.aug.*, paleostriatum augmentatum; *paleostr.prim.*, paleostriatum primitivum; *pl.ch.*, plexus choroideus; *str.cell.ext.*, stratum cellulare externum; *str.cell.int.*, stratum cellulare internum; *str.cell.int.dors.*, stratum cellulare internum dorsale; *str.cell.int.vent.*, stratum cellulare internum ventrale; *tect.*, tectum; *tr.fr.arch.*, tractus fronto-archistriaticus et neostriaticus; *tr.n.ovoidal.*, tractus nuclei ovoidalis; *tr.op.*, tractus opticus; *tr.sept.mes.*, tractus septo-mesencephalicus; *tr.tect. thal.*, tractus tecto-thalamicus et thalamo-tectalis; *III V.*, third ventricle.

either side, but particularly ventrolaterally, by more scattered, smaller cells. This cell group has been described under various names in the literature. By *Bellonci* ('88), *Münzer* and *Wiener* ('98), and *Edinger* and *Wallenberg* ('99) it was named corpus geniculatum. *Edinger* ('96 and '08) and *Ariëns Kappers* ('21) designated it as the corpus geniculatum laterale; *Rendahl* ('24), while terming it a medial superficial layer, favored the name of corpus geniculatum thalamicum, since he considered it only in part the homologue of the lateral geniculate nucleus of mammals. This nucleus may be seen in figures 492, 496, and 602.

Lateral to the main mass of the lateral geniculate nucleus is a small group of large cells to which optic fibers distribute. This belongs to the geniculate complex of *Craigie* and *Brickner* ('27) and *Craigie* ('28) and is the nucleus superficialis synencephali of *Rendahl* ('24), *Huber* and *Crosby* ('29), and *Craigie* ('30 and '31). In it are included the nucleus geniculatus lateralis externus and nucleus geniculatus tertius anterius of *Groebbels* and undoubtedly it is associated with the main lateral geniculate gray. An extension of tectal gray lies just lateral to the lower part of the nucleus superficialis synencephali (fig. 492).

Frey ('33a) has described a medial geniculate nucleus in birds as located near the lateral geniculate nucleus (it is not a part of it in the *Huber* and *Crosby* figure of sparrow as he stated). His supposition is interesting and possibly correct but needs verification in cell and other fiber material.

e. Nucleus Postrotundus, Nucleus Posterointermedialis and Nucleus Postero-ventralis with Fiber Connections. *Ariëns Kappers* ('21) first applied the name of nucleus postrotundus to a group lying behind the nucleus rotundus, but did not delimit it definitely from other nuclear masses to be found there. *Craigie* ('28) described a nucleus postrotundus in the humming bird, applying the name to an area behind the nucleus rotundus but not definitely delimited. In an attempt to follow the *Craigie* terminology, the region labeled by him was termed by *Huber* and *Crosby* ('29) the nucleus postrotundus and the group medial to the nucleus postrotundus, the nucleus posterointermedialis. As the name was used by these observers, the nucleus postrotundus consists of a mass of medium-sized cells applied to the posterior and posteromedial surfaces of the nucleus rotundus. First it is triangular in outline, but gradually decreases in size and disappears in a plane passing through the cephalic end of the oculomotor nucleus. A column or cell mass, termed the nucleus posterointermedialis, lies dorsomedial to the nucleus rotundus and postrotundus and consists of relatively large neurons. It can be followed caudalward to planes through the caudal end of the habenular nucleus in the sparrow. *Craigie* ('31) stated that he included in his nucleus postrotundus of the 1928 paper both the nucleus postrotundus and the nucleus posterointermedialis of the account of *Huber* and *Crosby* ('29). In his 1931 contribution, *Craigie* termed the former nuclear group the nucleus postrotundus of *Huber* and *Crosby*. However, he stated that the nucleus postrotundus (either as earlier identified by himself or as described by *Huber* and *Crosby*) is not the nucleus so termed by *Ariëns Kappers* (personal communication) but the nucleus principalis precommissuralis enjoys that distinction. In such a case it would appear better to discard the name nucleus postrotundus since its application to two distinct nuclear masses is confusing, and further, a large and conspicuous portion of the nucleus principalis precommissuralis is lateral to the nucleus rotundus.   In fact, in the sparrow the nucleus principalis precommissuralis does not extend so far medialward in its more caudal part as it does in the humming bird (*Craigie*), the nucleus posteroventralis lying more directly behind the main mass of the nucleus rotundus in the sparrow than is the case in the latter bird. Such variations are to be expected, otherwise all birds would be either sparrows or humming birds.   For the positions of the nuclei mentioned in the foregoing paragraph the papers referred to should be consulted.

The tractus thalamo-frontalis lateralis and the tractus tecto-thalamicus et thalamo-tectalis nuclei rotundi are in relation with the nucleus postrotundus.   The tractus bulbo-thalamicus of *Wallenberg* ('04) probably also distributes to this area and its cells are in connection with the nucleus rotundus.   The nucleus is present in other avian forms although it varies somewhat in size.   It is demonstrable in the chicken but is of small size.   In these forms the connections of this nucleus are not known ;   neither are the connections of the nucleus posterointermedialis.

The nucleus posteroventralis (*Huber* and *Crosby*, '29) replaces the nucleus rotundus as the series are followed caudalward.   It begins as a group of small cells which fits into a notch on the side of the nucleus rotundus and then swings dorsalward behind this latter nucleus.   This nucleus, while present, is less developed in the chicken, so that it was included by *Rendahl* ('24) in his nucleus *A*, homologous to nucleus rotundus.   It is present in the parrakeet and *Craigie* ('31) found it in the humming bird.   Its specific connections are not known.

f. The Entopeduncular Nuclear Group and Its Connections.   Scattered along the course of the lateral forebrain bundle are a series of cell masses which may be grouped as entopeduncular nuclei (figs. 492 and 496).   These are in synaptic relation with stem fibers or collaterals of the forebrain tract and are differentiable in general through their large, multipolar cells, which resemble those of the paleostriatum primitivum.   The groups vary somewhat in different birds.   In the avian forms available for study there are demonstrable, in addition to more scattered groups, dorsal and ventral entopeduncular groups, associated with the ventral peduncle, which occasionally can be further subdivided.   A nucleus decussationis supraopticae dorsalis (fig. 602), a part of the entopeduncular group, is present among the fibers of the dorsal peduncular portion and in association with that as well as with the fibers of the dorsal supraoptic decussation.   A bed nucleus for the tractus thalamo-frontalis internus may also be seen.   A nucleus praestriaticus was described by *Rendahl* ('24) for the chicken.   This can be identified in other birds and frequently appears to be a part of the entopeduncular group.   However, *Rendahl's* studies indicate that it has a different origin embryologically.   The main entopeduncular groups, essentially as described above, were recognized by *Craigie* ('30 and '31) in the kiwi and the humming bird.

g. Periventricular and Hypothalamic Gray with Fiber Connections.   The diencephalic periventricular gray and the hypothalamic areas grade over into each other in so many regions that they can be considered best together.   The periventricular gray has been described more or less completely for birds by a number of writers, among whom may be mentioned *Edinger* and *Wallenberg* ('99), *Edinger* ('08), *Groebbels* ('24), *Rendahl* ('24), *Huber* and *Crosby* ('29), *Craigie* ('30 and '31), and others.   German writers in general speak of a "zentrales Höhlengrau."   This has two portions, a medial nucleus magnocellularis strati grisei and a lateral (and more caudal) nucleus parvocellularis strati grisei.   *Rendahl* ('24) and *Huber* and *Crosby* ('29) have given more detailed accounts of the region which agree very satisfactorily with each other in spite of differences in nomenclature.   It has not been possible to homologize very closely the earlier accounts with these later descriptions.   The terminology here employed is that of the paper of *Huber* and *Crosby* ('29), with due reference to *Rendahl's* nomenclature in particular and to other workers where it has been possible to draw homologies.

Cephalically the diencephalic periventricular gray is not sharply delimitable from the periventricular preoptic areas and any line drawn between the two regions in the following account is necessarily arbitrary.   The narrow cellular band, the stratum cellulare internum of the preoptic area, becomes continuous with a similarly named band in the diencephalic region (fig. 496).   Directly continuous with this stratum in the sparrow, in the posterior part of the preoptic region (below the anterior commissure), is a somewhat indistinct nuclear mass, which in passing caudally gradually becomes more definitely delimited.   It is the nucleus internus inferior anterior (*Huber* and *Crosby*, '29).   Caudally it is continuous with the nucleus internus inferior of *Rendahl* ('24), which is termed the nucleus internus inferior posterior (fig. 492) in the *Huber* and *Crosby* terminology.   This latter nucleus (which *Craigie*, '31, also found in the humming bird) is present in all avian forms available for study.   It lies just ventral to the nucleus internus superior and in many cases medial to the nucleus ovoidalis.   The nucleus varies in outline in different forms, apparently being relatively larger in such birds as the sparrow where the nucleus ovoidalis is situated farther lateralward.   A nucleus internus inferior anterior is present in other birds, as the dove and parrakeet, and *Craigie* ('31) found it in the humming bird.   The nucleus varies in shape in the different forms, although occupying homologous positions. It is relatively better developed, more clearly defined, and more deeply stained in the dove than in the sparrow ; and consists in the parrakeet of a small band of deeply stained, large cells, capped by spindle-shaped cells.   Apparently it is very well developed and distinct in the humming bird.   Between the nucleus dorsomedialis anterior and the ventricle in the dove, the parrakeet, and the duck, and also in the humming bird (*Craigie*, '31) is a band of cells to which the name of nucleus internus superior anterior is applied.   This is represented merely by a few scattered cells in the sparrow and does not appear to be present in the chicken. Farther caudally a well-defined nucleus is present in the sparrow and chicken as well as certain other avian forms, which *Rendahl* ('24), *Huber* and *Crosby* ('29), and *Craigie* ('31) called the nucleus internus superior (fig. 492).

Reference to the avian telencephalon (p. 1381 ; also fig. 594) will show that in the preoptic area in the chicken a conspicuous group of large cells can be demonstrated to which the name of nucleus magnocellularis interstitialis has been applied.   This nucleus may be divided further into lateral, dorsal, and medial portions, and the medial portion subdivided into various parts. *Huber* and *Crosby* ('29) were unable to find the nucleus in this differentiated form in the other birds studied, although there are indications of its presence in a less highly developed form. *Craigie* ('31) also found a comparable nucleus in the humming bird, but showing only a dorsal prolongation of cells. The apparent absence of a nucleus internus inferior anterior and a nucleus internus superior anterior in the chicken suggests that portions of the nucleus magnocellularis interstitialis may substitute in the chicken for these centers in other birds, for while it is not possible to homologize definitely portions of the general nuclear mass of the nucleus magnocellularis interstitialis, nevertheless one of the subdivisions of the medial group suggests the nucleus internus inferior anterior of the parrakeet, the dove, and certain other avian forms and another subdivision, the nucleus internus superior anterior of the dove.

The ventral part of the periventricular diencephalic region may be subdivided into various areas, some of which are rather sharply definable, while others merge into one another without establishing definite boundaries. In general, this ventral area just lateral to the stratum cellulare internum may be divided into lateral and medial parts, which are respectively the nucleus hypothalamicus anterior lateralis and the nucleus hypothalamicus anterior medialis (part of K_1 of *Rendahl*, '24, also part of the nucleus periventricularis hypothalami of reptiles as described by *de Lange*, '13, for Draco, and *Huber* and *Crosby* for Alligator, '26). Nucleus supraopticus (Kl_1 of *Rendahl*) lies just above the supraoptic decussation. Nucleus hypothalamicus anterior medialis becomes divided further caudally into a pars dorsalis (Kc of *Rendahl*), a pars intermedialis (Ka of *Rendahl*), and a pars ventralis (K_2 of *Rendahl*). Nucleus hypothalamicus inferior (m of *Rendahl*) consists cephalically of somewhat scattered cells and caudally of an admixture of small and medium-sized cells which surround the ventral side of the ventricle and bulge out on either side. It replaces the nucleus supraopticus and lies, throughout much of its extent, ventral to the pars ventralis of the nucleus hypothalamicus anterior medialis. Farther caudally it is not sharply definable from the nucleus hypothalamicus posterior medialis, while lateral to it is the nucleus hypothalamicus lateralis, and lateral and ventral a small, scattered cell mass, the *H.d.z.* of *Rendahl*. Between this last-mentioned group and the supraoptic system is a small-celled mass designated as the nucleus decussationis supraopticae ventralis. Figures 492 and 496 should be consulted to determine the position of the above-mentioned nuclei and those in the following paragraph.

In following a series from the more frontal regions caudalward, the three portions of the nucleus hypothalamicus anterior medialis gradually disappear, beginning with the more dorsal and then with the intermediate part. The place of this nucleus is taken by the nucleus hypothalamicus posterior medialis, which soon becomes a discrete nuclear mass. A nucleus hypothalamicus posterior lateralis replaces the anterior lateral hypothalamic group, and a small nuclear group, the nucleus hypothalamicus posterior dorsalis, is to be found in the upper portion of the field. The nucleus hypothalamicus inferior (m of *Rendahl*) is replaced by a somewhat dense cell mass which is secondarily divisible into dorsal and ventral portions which *Rendahl* ('24) and *Huber* and *Crosby* ('29) termed the nuclei mamillaris medialis dorsalis and ventralis. Of these the dorsal group forms an unpaired median nucleus. Scattered cells along the outer border of the dorsal nuclear group represent the nucleus mamillaris lateralis. The various mammillary nuclei described above were identified by *Craigie* ('31) in the humming bird. Apparently the subdivision between the dorsal and the ventral parts is more evident cephalically in the humming bird, since the observer was unable to trace the nucleus mamillaris medialis into relation with the nucleus hypothalamicus inferior. It must be emphasized that the homologies of the mammillary nuclei with the corresponding nuclei of mammals can be only suggested at present. Further work on fiber relations and fiber connections in the region is necessary before such homologies can be definitely established. Reference is made again to figures 492 and 496.

With regard to the fiber connections for the periventricular and hypothalamic gray, much needs to be done. It is possible that the variations in the nuclear pattern and the relative distinctness of this pattern are due to slight differences in the size and the course of the related fiber bundles. The following summary of the connections of this area, regarded as not quite complete, is based on observations by *Huber* and *Crosby* ('29). For the position of these tracts the figures in this section and those on the avian forebrain should be consulted. In order to conserve space and avoid repetition the evidence at hand is here presented in a condensed form in a table:

NUCLEAR MASSES	FIBER CONNECTIONS
	c. HYPOTHALAMUS
h. d. Z	Decussatio supraoptica ventralis
Nucleus decussationis supraopticae ventralis	Collaterals of the decussation
Nucleus hypothalamicus anterior lateralis	Tractus occipito-mesencephalicus Medial forebrain bundle
Nucleus hypothalamicus anterior medialis pars dorsalis	Tractus occipito-mesencephalicus Decussatio supraoptica dorsalis pars medialis Other portions of the diencephalic periventricular system Internuclear connections with nucleus hypothalamicus posterior dorsalis, nucleus internus inferior posterior, nucleus hypothalamicus anterior lateralis, pars intermedialis of nucleus hypothalamicus anterior medialis, and probably with other hypothalamic centers
Nucleus hypothalamicus anterior medialis pars intermedialis	Tractus occipito-mesencephalicus Tractus strio-tegmentalis et strio-cerebellaris Decussatio supraoptica dorsalis pars medialis and other fibers of the diencephalic periventricular system

	Internuclear connections with pars dorsalis and pars ventralis of the nucleus and with nucleus hypothalamicus anterior lateralis and other hypothalamic centers
Nucleus hypothalamicus anterior medialis pars ventralis	Decussatio supraoptica ventralis
	Diencephalic periventricular system
	Internuclear connections with pars intermedialis and adjacent areas
Nucleus hypothalamicus posterior dorsalis	Tractus occipito-mesencephalicus
	Internuclear connections with nucleus internus inferior posterior, nucleus hypothalamicus anterior medialis pars dorsalis, and other hypothalamic areas
	Diencephalic periventricular system
Nucleus hypothalamicus posterior lateralis	Tractus strio-tegmentalis et strio-cerebellaris
	Tractus septo-mesencephalicus, ramus basalis caudalis
	Internuclear connections with adjacent areas
Nucleus hypothalamicus inferior	Probably, diencephalic periventricular fibers and internuclear connections with surrounding areas
Nucleus internus inferior anterior	Tractus occipito-mesencephalicus
	Tractus olfacto-habenularis medialis
	Diencephalic periventricular system
	Internuclear connections with adjacent areas
Nucleus internus inferior posterior	Tractus occipito-mesencephalicus
	Decussatio supraoptica dorsalis pars medialis and other fibers of the diencephalic periventricular system
	Tractus nuclei ovoidalis
	Internuclear connections with nucleus ovoidalis and subrotundus and with adjacent hypothalamic regions
Nuclei mamillares	Tractus septo-mesencephalicus, ramus basalis caudalis?
Stratum cellulare externum	Tractus strio-tegmentalis et strio-cerebellaris
	Tractus olfacto-habenularis medialis
	Medial forebrain bundle
	Tractus occipito-mesencephalicus
	Decussatio supraoptica dorsalis pars medialis
	Internuclear connections with adjacent areas
Stratum cellulare internum dorsale	Diencephalic periventricular system
Stratum cellulare internum ventrale	Tractus occipito-mesencephalicus
	Diencephalic periventricular system
	Internuclear connections with adjacent areas

RÉSUMÉ OF CERTAIN AVIAN MESENCEPHALIC AND DIENCEPHALIC FIBER SYSTEMS

Throughout the preceding account reference has been made to fiber connections of the various nuclei. Numbers of such connections have been discussed but the accounts of other tracts with relations either with many centers or with widely separated centers have been postponed until the various centers had been described and located.

This is deemed the appropriate place to give further and more specific attention to the optic and supraoptic systems, the tecto-thalamic systems, the bulbo-thalamic and hypothalamic tracts, the forebrain bundles, the occipito-mesencephalic tract, the septo-mesencephalic tract, and the tractus infundibularis. For details concerning these connections the original articles to which reference is made should be consulted.

a. *Optic Tract*. The recognition of the optic tract in birds dates back to the work of the earlier observers, and the tract has been the subject of repeated observations. Among the earlier workers should be mentioned *Bellonci* ('88), *Perlia* ('89), *Wallenberg* ('98a), *Edinger, Wallenberg*, and *Holmes* ('03), and *Kosaka* and *Hiraiwa* ('15). An excellent account of the optic tract in various vertebrates, including birds, is to be found in the paper of *Bellonci*. *Perlia*, by use of experimental methods, studied this system in cuckoos, chickens, and sparrows. He was able to demonstrate that the avian optic nerves undergo a complete decussation and to make clear the presence of medial and lateral optic tracts. The lateral optic tract he carried to the tectum. This constitutes the marginal optic tract of later descriptions and carries impulses to the lateral geniculate nucleus, the nucleus externus, and the nucleus superficialis synencephali, as well as to the tectum (*Huber* and *Crosby*, '29). It runs along the periphery in its caudal course (figs. 495, 497, 602, and 603).

The medial optic tract or tractus isthmo-opticus (sometimes termed the axillary optic tract) *Perlia* ('89) related to a nuclear mass which he termed the nucleus opticus medialis but which has been known by various other names, such as the ganglion opticum basale (*Jelgersma*, '96) and the nucleus isthmi (*Wallenberg*, '98a). Unfortunately an entirely different group has been termed the nucleus isthmi in various vertebrate brains. *Craigie* ('28) proposed the name of nucleus isthmo-opticus for the nucleus opticus medialis of *Perlia*, thus relating it to the nucleus isthmi, and this name was adopted by *Huber* and *Crosby*. There has been question as to the direction of conduction of the optic fibers related to the nucleus isthmo-opticus. *Perlia* believed these fibers were concerned with the pupillary reactions and had a centrifugal course, and *Jelgersma* ('96) and *Wallenberg* ('98a) gave further experimental evidence for such a direction of conduction, by showing that direct injury of the nucleus produced degeneration in the optic tract. Sections of the brain of a dove, blind in one eye, showed a degeneration of the optic tract fibers and the outer layer of the optic tectum (stratum opticum), and a failure of the nucleus isthmo-opticus to develop. In certain birds, at least, a part of the axillary or isthmo-optic tract runs through the lateral geniculate nucleus in its course to the nucleus isthmo-opticus, but it is uncertain to what extent (if

any) it is related with the geniculate gray.   As it courses along the nucleus superficialis parvocellularis, small fascicles, joined by similar fine bundles from the
marginal optic tract, turn in toward the nucleus superficialis parvocellularis and
certain ones appear to reach the nucleus lateralis.   The tractus isthmo-opticus is
accompanied by fibers which either join it from the tectum or leave it to enter
the tectum.   It is to be emphasized that the main relations of the isthmo-optic

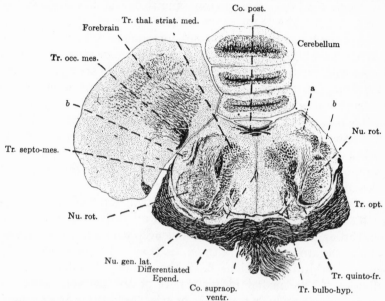

Fig. 497. A cross section through the diencephalon of Pratincola rubicola,
passing dorsally through the posterior commissure and ventrally through the optic
chiasma. Modified slightly as to labels from the original figure in the German text.
  a, nucleus anterior thalami of Ariëns Kappers, a part of the dorsolateral nuclear
complex of Huber and Crosby and of Craigie; b, nucleus lateralis anterior of Ariëns
Kappers, modified portion of the nucleus superficialis parvocellularis of Rendahl
and of Huber and Crosby, which is particularly in relation to the tractus septo-
mesencephalicus — might be termed nucleus tractus septo-mesencephalici; Co.
post., commissura posterior; Co.supraop.ventr., commissura supraoptica ventralis;
Nu.gen.lat., nucleus geniculatus lateralis; Nu.rot., nucleus rotundus; Tr.bulbo-hyp.,
tractus bulbo-hypothalamicus; Tr.occ.mes., tractus occipito-mesencephalicus; Tr.
opt., tractus opticus; Tr.quinto-fr., tractus quinto-frontalis; Tr.septo-mes., tractus
septo-mesencephalicus; Tr.thal.striat.med., tractus thalamo-striatalis medialis.

tract are with the nucleus isthmo-opticus and that all other connections are distinctly secondary and should be regarded merely as accompanying fibers.   Relatively recent accounts of the isthmo-optic tract are to be found in the papers of
Craigie and *Brickner* ('27), *Craigie* ('28), and *Huber* and *Crosby* ('29) and its
position is shown in figures 493, 495, and 602.
    The basal optic root has been described along with other optic tract fibers by
Kosaka and *Hiraiwa* ('15) and by other observers.   This root (tr. op. r. op. bas.,
fig. 493), which is larger and consequently more easily followed in birds than in
reptiles, can be traced through the decussating fibers of the optic chiasma and
almost directly caudalward to the nucleus ectomamillaris (or nucleus of the
basal optic root), at the level of the emerging fibers of the oculomotor nerve

and just lateral to them. The nucleus ectomamillaris has connections with the oculomotor nucleus, with the interstitial nucleus of *Cajal* (*Huber* and *Crosby*, '29), and probably with the tectum. These are similar to the connections described for reptiles by *Beccari* ('23), *Huber* and *Crosby* ('26), and *Shanklin* ('30, '33; see bibliography for reptiles). The nucleus ectomamillaris is said to have connections also with the spiriform nucleus (*Ariëns Kappers*, '21).

b. *Supraoptic Systems.* The present knowledge of the supraoptic systems, which is far from complete, is the result of a slow accumulation of evidence regarding the courses and relations of the various components. Particularly to be mentioned in this connection are the descriptions of the connections of the dorsal part of the system with the telencephalon, given in the 1903 paper of *Edinger, Wallenberg,* and *Holmes,* and the account and figures of certain medullated components of this system as described and figured by *Ariëns Kappers* ('21) in the earlier edition of this text. The following account is based particularly on the relations as seen in the sparrow and dove, because of a greater familiarity with these forms on the part of *Huber* and *Crosby.*

The supraoptic system, and particularly its dorsal portion, is relatively very well developed in birds. The dorsal supraoptic decussation (figs. 495, 498, and 602) forms a relatively wide band of compactly arranged fibers in the region of the chiasma which, shortly after crossing, breaks up into smaller bundles. These radiate out through nearly all parts of the diencephalic wall from the periventricular regions to the areas just above the optic tract. For purposes of description three relatively arbitrary divisions have been made, a medial, a lateral, and a ventral division. The medial forms a part of the periventricular system of fibers, carrying bundles which terminate or arise (or both) in the nucleus internus inferior anterior or among the cells of the stratum cellulare internum, and those of the stratum cellulare externum. A few fibers run farther caudalward, possibly to come into relation with the nuclei of the medial longitudinal fasciculus. Certain fascicles run dorsalward and caudalward between the ventricular wall and the forebrain bundles, and, distributing in part to the areas through which they pass, continue caudalward to reach the more lateral portions of the medial area of the diencephalon. In this more medial portion is included the homologue of Ganser's commissure, as found in mammals.

The main mass of fibers of the dorsal supraoptic decussation — the lateral division — is, in particular, the homologue of the dorsal supraoptic decussation of reptiles. Such fibers, after decussating in the chiasmal ridge, swing dorsolateralward, running in part medial to the forebrain bundle and in part intermingled with it, particularly with the more anterior fascicles which accompany the forebrain bundle to the basal lateral hemisphere wall. Some fibers of this portion of the lateral division are in synaptic relation with a nucleus decussationis supraopticae dorsalis, which lies in the angle between the main mass of the forebrain bundle and the thalamo-striatal tracts given off at the level (fig. 602).

The ventral division of the dorsal supraoptic decussation is the homologue of the tractus tecto-thalamicus cruciatus of Alligator (*Huber* and *Crosby*, '26; see also '29). In the sparrow its fibers run directly lateralward, synapsing in part in the nucleus of the tract and sending collaterals to the lateral geniculate nucleus. Strengthened by fibers from these nuclear masses, the bundle passes to the tectum. Whether or not it is accompanied by optic fibers has not been definitely determined. It is the opinion of *Huber* and *Crosby* that it is probably supraoptic in character rather than optic. Certain of the above described relations are illustrated in figure 602.

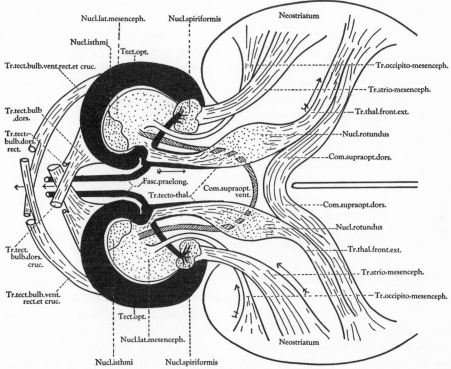

Fig. 498. A schematic representation of the course of the supraoptic commissures and certain connections of the mesencephalon and diencephalon in Pratincola rubicola. (See also figure 549.) *Ariëns Kappers.*

Com.supraopt.dors., commissura supraoptica dorsalis; *Com.supraopt.vent.*, commissura supraoptica ventralis; *Fasc.praelong.*, fasciculus prelongitudinalis; *Nucl.isthmi*, nucleus isthmi; *Nucl. lat.mesenceph.*, nucleus mesencephalicus lateralis; *Nucl.rot.*, nucleus rotundus; *Nucl.spiriformis*, nucleus spiriformis; *Tect.opt.*, tectum opticum; *Tr.occipito-mesenceph.*, tractus occipito-mesencephalicus; *Tr.strio-mesenceph.*, tractus strio-mesencephalicus; *Tr.tect.bulb.dors.*, tractus tecto-bulbaris dorsalis; *Tr.tect.bulb.dors.cruc.*, tractus tecto-bulbaris dorsalis cruciatus; *Tr.tect.bulb.dors. rect.*, tractus tecto-bulbaris dorsalis rectus; *Tr.tect.bulb.vent.rect.et cruc.*, tractus tecto-bulbaris ventralis rectus et cruciatus; *Tr.tect.thal.*, tractus tecto-thalamicus; *Tr.thal.front.ext.*, tractus thalamo-frontalis externus.

The ventral supraoptic decussation is divisible into dorsal and ventral portions, the former being represented in part in the commissura transversa of *Craigie* and *Brickner's* account ('27). Both parts decussate in the chiasmal ridge between the dorsal supraoptic system dorsally and the optic tract ventrally, and swing lateralward together to a position just dorsal to the lateral geniculate nucleus. Here they become distinct from each other, the ventral fibers lying lateral and ventrolateral to the pars dorsalis. The dorsal part distributes to the optic tectum and sends a few bundles to pars principalis of the nucleus isthmi; the ventral part likewise reaches the tectum. For the details of their relatively complex course, the *Huber* and *Crosby* ('29) paper and figures 493, 495, 498, 602, and 603 should be consulted. In its course toward the tectum, the ventral supraoptic decussation gives off fibers. Such fascicles of this system, in their course lateralward, are believed by *Frey* ('33a) to reach the nucleus geniculatus medialis identified by him.

c. *Tecto-thalamic and Thalamo-tectal Paths.* As is to be expected in forms in which the optic tectum is so highly differentiated and the diencephalic centers so well developed, the connections between these brain areas are numerous and varied. A part of such connections find representation in certain components of the supraoptic system, as is evident from the above account. A large number of such connections fall within the scope of what may be termed tecto-thalamic and thalamo-tectal paths. Among these latter pathways there have been described for birds the following: tractus nuclei ovoidalis, tractus tecto-thalamicus et thalamo-tectalis nuclei rotundi, tractus tecto-thalamicus ventrolateralis, tractus tecto-thalamicus et thalamo-tectalis ectomamillaris, and tractus tecto-thalamicus et thalamo-tectalis nuclei externi. These interconnections of the thalamus and tectum are supplemented by connections between pretectal and subpretectal nuclei and the tectum.

The tract from the nucleus ovoidalis was identified by *Edinger, Wallenberg*, and *Holmes* ('03), and earlier by *Münzer* and *Wiener* ('98), as a mammillo-thalamic tract, the nucleus ovoidalis being termed by them the nucleus anterior ventralis. Later *Edinger* ('08) applied the name nucleus anterior to the area dorsalis of *Rendahl* ('24). *Ariëns Kappers* ('21) called into question the homology of the tract with the Vicq d'Azyr tract of mammals, pointing out that *Edinger, Wallenberg*, and *Holmes* ('03) had indicated that the direction of conduction was efferent with reference to their nucleus anterior ventralis (or nucleus ovoidalis). The termination of the tract is still in question, its distribution being a matter for experimental verification. An attempt was made to analyze it in chrome-silver preparations of the sparrow brain, and the following account is given (figs. 493, 495, and 603) with due appreciation of the fact that the statements made here are subject to revision in the light of subsequent experimental evidence. Arising from the nucleus ovoidalis (*Edinger, Wallenberg*, and *Holmes*, '03) and joined by fibers from the nucleus subrotundus and probably from the nucleus internus inferior posterior, the fibers run almost directly ventralward just internal to the nucleus rotundus, between that nucleus and the ventral peduncle of the lateral forebrain bundle. Along their course is the nucleus intercalatus with which they probably have synaptic relations and which probably both receives from and contributes fibers to the tract. The fibers gradually acquire a somewhat more caudal position, particularly during the more ventral part of their course, and here the bundle lies in close relation to the supraoptic system. From this region some of the fibers appear to swing lateralward to join the tecto-thalamic and thalamo-tectal tract; other fascicles join the dorsal supraoptic decussation, in part to decussate and in part to distribute to the tectum of the same side.   *Papez* (to be published) has considered it comparable to the reptilian tractus tecto-reuniens, and the nucleus ovoidalis as a primitive medial geniculate nucleus (p. 1037).   Other bundles of the tract could not be traced.

The connection of the nucleus rotundus with the tectum has been recognized for many years, usually under the name of the tecto-thalamic tract.   This tract has been described by *Edinger* and *Wallenberg* ('99), by *Ariëns Kappers* ('21), whose collection of material of Cacatua, of Paleornis, and of Gallus domesticus, stained by the Weigert method, shows this system very well, further by *Craigie* ('28), and by *Huber* and *Crosby* ('29).   The fibers of this system accumulate in the ventral part of the nucleus rotundus and, caudal to that nuclear mass, become intermingled with the fibers of the nucleus posteroventralis, with which gray, in all probability, they have some synaptic relations.   In this region they are joined by other fiber systems related to the tectum, and thereafter cannot be distinctly separated from them but can be traced lateralward in company with such systems to the tectum.   The tract in question is joined by fibers to the tectum from the nucleus principalis precommissuralis, and it gives fibers to and receives fibers from the nucleus subpretectalis.   As the tectal regions are reached, the main bundle becomes continuous with the stratum album centrale (or deep medullary layer), suggesting that the direct conduction is tecto-thalamic, but it is probable that there is some distribution to the more peripheral tectal layers of certain thalamo-tectal fibers.   The tractus tecto-thalamicus to the nucleus rotundus is illustrated in figures 493 and 495.

A bundle of fine fibers gradually accumulates on the medial side of the tractus tecto-thalamicus to the nucleus rotundus.   This bundle interconnects the nucleus dorsolateralis anterior, the nucleus tractus habenulo-peduncularis, the capsule on the ventral side of the nucleus rotundus (and possibly that nucleus), with the tectum.   The tract has been termed the tractus tecto-thalamicus (et thalamo-tectalis) dorsalis, but the direction of conduction is uncertain (*Huber* and *Crosby*, '29; also figs. 493 and 495).

The optic tectum is connected with the lateral geniculate nucleus by means of small fascicles which run medialward from the tectal region, passing in part through and in part ventral to the nucleus superficialis synencephali of *Rendahl* ('24).   This tract is the tractus tecto-thalamicus ventrolateralis of *Huber* and *Crosby*.   The nucleus externus also is connected with the tectum (fig. 493), and tectal connections with an unknown direction of conduction relate the nucleus ectomamillaris with the tectum.

d. Bulbo-thalamic and Hypothalamic Systems.   Tractus Cerebello-diencephalicus. The most complete account of ascending paths from bulbar centers to diencephalic areas is to be found in the work of *Wallenberg* ('04), who traced, by means of degeneration methods, fibers from the bulbar centers to the diencephalon. This bulbo-thalamic tract, which he homologized with the mammalian medial lemniscus, he carried forward to the nucleus rotundus, the nucleus intercalatus, the red nucleus, and the nucleus of the strio-mesencephalic tract (a part of the nucleus superficialis parvocellularis).   This tract he believed to be accompanied by bulbo-hypothalamic fibers to the infundibular region, the tuber cinereum, and the commissura transversa, which bulbo-hypothalamic component he homologized with the mammalian mammillary peduncle.

Muskens ('14, also '29, '30, and '30a; see also page 1025), in his work on forced movements and postures in birds, repeated *Wallenberg's* experiments on these bulbo-thalamic and hypothalamic paths. He made more localized lesions and his results, in so far as carried out, support the suggestion of *Wallenberg* ('04) that the cuneate nucleus is the source of the bulbo-mesencephalic (or bulbo-thalamic) tract, but the matter is not regarded as definitely determined by the work of either of these observers. The bulbo-mesencephalic tract appears to have a more ventral origin than does the bulbo-hypothalamic tract. After its origin the former tract was traced forward by *Muskens* along the inner border of the lateral lemniscus until it reached a position close to the interpeduncular nucleus, when it passed to the level of the nucleus ectomamillaris (nucleus nervi optici basalis), to which it contributed. Other fibers terminated in the basal region of the mesencephalon, including large cells ventrolateral to the red nucleus. In another case *Muskens* traced fibers through the supraoptic decussation to corresponding areas on the other side. *Muskens* traced the tractus bulbo-hypothalamicus farther forward to the nucleus intercalatus, the capsule of the nucleus rotundus, and the commissura transversa, but with such particular emphasis on the connections with the nucleus intercalatus that he suggested the name of tractus bulbo-intercalatus instead of tractus bulbo-hypothalamicus. The distribution of the tracts, as given by *Wallenberg* and *Muskens* respectively, is such that much of the system, as described by the latter, falls within the bulbo-thalamic tract of the former, while with his more limited lesions, *Muskens* did not degenerate that portion of the bulbo-hypothalamic tract of *Wallenberg* which passes to the infundibular and hypothalamic gray, although he may have included the fibers through the supraoptic system.

In checking his results physiologically in a typical case following a small lesion of the bulbo-mesencephalic and hypothalamic system in the medulla oblongata of the pigeon, *Muskens* found that a bird thus experimented upon maintained a crouched position with a tilting forward and downward. By a comparison with results in other experiments, *Muskens* believed he was able to show that the results obtained were not due to impulses passing over other major systems injured by the lesion. His results suggest that "the forced movements forward and downward have their anatomic basis in the bulbo-intercalatus system of fibers," which he compared to the mammillary peduncle of mammals. Not satisfied that his results permitted a final decision in the matter, *Muskens* tried a series of experiments in which lesions were made in the nucleus intercalatus, and found in nearly all cases a tendency toward a downward movement and a degeneration of descending paths — the homolateral, and to some extent the contralateral tractus intercalato-trapezius. The lesion also evidenced a degenerated path from the nucleus intercalatus forward to the paleostriatal region (nucleus basalis of the older account). The results attained thus far appear confirmatory of an important involvement of the nucleus intercalatus in forced movements and postures of birds.

In connection with these ascending tracts to the diencephalon, note should be taken of the tractus cerebello-diencephalicus. A considerable amount of experimental work on pigeons indicated that certain lesions in or near the cerebellum (*Weir Mitchell*, '61; *Ten Cate*, '26; *Bremer* and *Leys*, '27; *Muskens*, '30a, and others) produce a rearing backward (backward cullubation, *Muskens*) of the animals. The lesions which led to such behavior involved the deeper part of the cerebellum or the cerebellar peduncle, and *Muskens* believed them to be due to injury of the medial cerebellar nucleus or of the tract emanating from it to pass either to mesencephalic or to diencephalic centers. *Muskens* found that severance of the commissure connecting the two medial cerebellar nuclei (which he homologizes with the mammalian nuclei tecti) or destruction of both nuclei produces marked backward cullubation. He believed that this tract, which he termed the tractus cerebello-diencephalicus, crosses immediately in the commissure and then swings forward to the diencephalon to terminate in a nuclear mass which he called the nucleus anterior ventralis and which appears to be the nucleus anterior ventralis of *Edinger, Wallenberg,* and *Holmes* ('03) and the nucleus ovoidalis of certain later observers. Further confirmation would be desirable.

e. *Occipito-mesencephalic Tract.* Certain tracts connect telencephalic and thalamic centers, and for the greater part these are considered more satisfactorily after the former centers have been discussed. In this connection, brief reference is made to such tracts, while the detailed accounts, together with a discussion of the literature concerned, are to be found in Chapter IX. Reference is made here to the occipito-mesencephalic tract, the septo-mesencephalic tract, the tractus infundibuli, the medial forebrain bundle, and the lateral forebrain bundle.

The occipito-mesencephalic and bulbar tract arises from the archistriatum (*Huber* and *Crosby*, '29; *Craigie*, '30) and the neostriatum caudale (*Huber* and *Crosby*), swings medialward, accompanied by true commissural fibers, passes dorsal to the forebrain bundle, and takes up a position along the dorsomedial angle of that bundle, proceeding caudalward in that position. In the diencephalic region the position of the tract varies with reference to the nucleus ovoidalis, being medial to this nucleus in the sparrow and ventromedial to it in the dove. The tract gives off fibers (or at least collaterals) in its course to the nucleus preopticus lateralis, to the bed nucleus of the anterior commissure, to the area anterior ventralis, to the nucleus internus inferior anterior, and to the stratum cellulare externum. Part of the bundle distributes to the pars medialis of the spiriform nucleus; other fascicles extend farther caudalward. For the relations of this tract, figures 493, 495, 497, 498, 603, 606, 607, and 608 should be consulted.

Craigie ('28) described a strio-bulbar tract in the humming bird, which forms the portion of the occipito-mesencephalic tract of the above account arising from the neostriatum, and possibly constitutes the more caudally coursing fibers of the occipito-mesencephalic system described above. The remainder of the system *Hermann* ('25) and *Craigie* have termed the archistriato-mesencephalic system. *Craigie's* strio-bulbar tract does not appear to *Huber* and *Crosby* to be homologous to the tract described by *Wallenberg* ('02) as fronto-bulbar, mentioned by *Groebbels* ('24) and again referred to by *Muskens* ('29) as the tractus strio-mesencephalicus et reticularis.   Although *Wallenberg* ('28) appears to have favored such an homology, *Craigie* ('30) expressed some doubt about it but stated that he termed his tract the fronto-bulbar tract in conformity with the usage of *Wallenberg*.   It appears probable that the tract so labeled in Apteryx may be the *Wallenberg* tract (of this there is some uncertainty), but if so, it is not the homologue of *Craigie's* earlier described strio-bulbar bundle.   The strio-bulbar system of the earlier account accompanies or is a part of the occipito-mesencephalic et bulbar system, which appears to *Huber* and *Crosby* to be analogous to the noncommissural part of the reptilian stria terminalis.   The tract described by *Wallenberg* ('02) as fronto-bulbar and by *Muskens* ('30; see also '29) as tractus strio-mesencephalicus et reticularis is ventral to the occipito-mesencephalic system in the more ventral part of the lateral forebrain bundle.   A tract recently described by *Wallenberg* ('33) as fronto-bulbar, however, does appear to be homologous with the tract designated fronto-bulbar by *Craigie*.   This tract *Wallenberg* has carried back to the vestibular and trigeminal centers.

f. Lateral Forebrain Bundle.   The lateral forebrain bundle in birds is very well developed and it has been described as a whole or in part by numerous students of avian forms, among whom may be mentioned *Bumm* ('83), *Edinger* and *Wallenberg* ('99), *Wallenberg* ('02), *Edinger, Wallenberg,* and *Holmes* ('03), *Schroeder* ('11), *Ariëns Kappers* ('21), *Hunter* ('23), *Groebbels* ('24), *Craigie* and *Brickner* ('27), *Craigie* ('28 and '30), *Huber* and *Crosby* ('29), and others.   This literature is briefly reviewed in the account of the avian telencephalon, where details of the connections are given, and the interested reader is referred to pages 1388 to 1394.   The following paragraphs contain merely a brief résumé of the relations of the lateral forebrain bundle to the diencephalic and mesencephalic centers and are based primarily on the sparrow, with which *Huber* and *Crosby* are more particularly familiar, but the relations, in the main essentials, are the same for other birds.

At the point where the lateral forebrain bundle enters the diencephalon its components, beginning at the outer side (fig. 602), are as follows : the tractus thalamo-frontalis lateralis, the tractus thalamo-frontalis intermedialis, the tractus strio-tegmentalis (with which are found the striatal fibers of the dorsal supraoptic decussation and the quinto-frontal tract), the tractus thalamo-frontalis medialis, and the tractus strio-hypothalamicus medialis.

The tractus thalamo-frontalis lateralis or externus (figs. 493, 495, 498, 602, 604, 605, 607, and 608) connects the nucleus rotundus, the lateral part of the nucleus dorsolateralis anterior, and the nucleus postrotundus with the hyperstriatal region of the hemisphere, passing in course through the ectostriatal regions where it may form connections with other forebrain systems (see p. 1391). The direction of conduction is efferent with respect to the diencephalic nuclei, although the work of *Edinger, Wallenberg,* and *Holmes* ('03) indicated that certain afferent fibers to the nucleus rotundus are present.

The direction of conduction of the tractus thalamo-frontalis intermedialis is unknown at present, although it appears probable that in large part it is afferent to the forebrain.   In this group are to be found fibers associated with the tectum, with the lateral geniculate nucleus, with the nucleus intercalatus, with the nucleus lateralis anterior, and with the nucleus tractus tecto-thalamici cruciati.   From tectal areas, the tectal components swing medialward above the lateral geniculate nucleus, are joined by fibers to or from that nucleus and the nucleus tecto-thalamicus cruciatus, and come ultimately into relation with the nucleus intercalatus, where they increase in size, after which they swing into a position internal to the lateral thalamo-frontal path, which they accompany to the hemispheres. This tract is illustrated in figures 495, 602, and 603.

The strio-cerebellar tract has been described for birds by various observers, including *Schroeder* ('11), *Craigie* ('28 and '30), *Huber* and *Crosby* ('29), and *Sanders* ('29).   In the sparrow, through the more cephalic part of its course, the tract lies in relatively close relation to the strio-tegmental system, but becomes separated in the midbrain in order to swing dorsocaudalward to the cerebellum (figs. 493 and 495).   The strio-cerebellar path described by *Muskens* ('29 and '30) appears to have the same relations through mesencephalic and diencephalic areas, but this observer is not ready to affirm its exact homology with the strio-cerebellar tract of *Schroeder* and others.

The strio-tegmental tract arises in the sparrow from frontal, middle, and caudal regions of the paleostriatum (and from the dorsal medullary lamina and the ectostriatum also).   In chrome-silver preparations, which show the fascicles to be numerous, these various components appear to constitute a continuous system of fibers, which runs caudalward from its origin through the more ventral part of the diencephalon to the midbrain (figs. 493 and 495).   It distributes to entopeduncular nuclear groups along its course and to a special nuclear group in the kiwi, and probably in other birds, to which nuclear group the name of nucleus tractus strio-tegmentalis (*Craigie*, '30) has been given.   It seems probable that this nucleus may correspond to the nuclear group described in reptiles as substantia nigra (?) by *Beccari* ('23), as entopeduncular nucleus by *Shanklin* ('30), and as substantia nigra by *Huber* and *Crosby* ('33), to which reference has been made on page 986.   With this strio-tegmental tract run fibers constituting a connection with the tectum, the direction of conduction of which is unknown.

In approximately the region occupied by the strio-tegmental tract of the sparrow, *Edinger* and *Wallenberg* ('99) described two tracts, a tractus strio-thalamicus ventralis medius, from the frontal striatal region through the ventral peduncle to the caudal end of the thalamus, and a tractus strio-mesencephalicus (*Münzer* and *Wiener*, '98; *Boyce* and *Warrington*, '99), from the lateral and caudal end of the hemisphere to the lateral part of the spiriform nucleus, to the tectum, and to the deep centers of the tegmentum.   The strio-mesencephalic tract of *Craigie* ('28 and '30) corresponds to that part of the last mentioned bundle which enters the lateral part of the spiriform nucleus.   The strio-tegmental tract of *Huber* and *Crosby* ('29) includes the strio-mesencephalic tract of *Edinger* and *Wallenberg* ('99) and the greater part at least of the tractus strio-thalamicus ventralis medius of these observers.   *Muskens* ('29 and '30; see also '27) described a tractus strio-mesencephalicus and reticularis which obviously falls within the strio-tegmental tract just described (the term tegmentum implying that it is related to basal and not tectal regions of the midbrain).   With *Groebbels* ('24) and others, *Muskens* thought that the strio-mesencephalic tract of his terminology carries both ascending and descending fibers, that of these fibers the centripetal are the finer and that they arise from the frontal region of the spiriform nucleus "which is concerned with the circus movements, form the mediolateral part of the peduncle, and end in the lateral part of the nucleus striatus (*Münzer* and *Wiener*) or neostriatum."   The descending components *Muskens* carried in two bundles to the spiriform nucleus, one reaching the anterior and the other the posterior part of that nuclear complex.

The fronto-bulbar tract of *Wallenberg* ('02) appears to belong among the bundles of the components of the strio-tegmental system.   In position it does not appear to be associated with the occipito-mesencephalic tract but rather with the quinto-frontal tract (p. 1055).   The fronto-bulbar tract described by *Wallenberg* in 1933 is part of the occipito-mesencephalic system.

The tractus thalamo-frontalis medialis (tractus thalamo-frontalis medius of *Edinger, Wallenberg*, and *Holmes*, '03; *Ariëns Kappers*, '21; *Huber* and *Crosby*, '29; *Craigie*, '30, and others) in the sparrow constitutes a connection between the nucleus dorsolateralis anterior, the nucleus dorsolateralis posterior, and the nucleus ovoidalis, and the hemisphere wall.   After entering the hemisphere, part of the fibers run dorsomedialward and in part forward, constituting the pars frontalis of the tract.   These pass to the medial side of the frontal and intermediate portions of the neostriatum and are related to the periventricular gray, with a possible connection with the medial portion of the hyperstriatum ventrale.   The pars caudalis distributes to the medial part of the caudal hemisphere wall, particularly to the neostriatum caudale and periventricular gray of the region.   It is to be noted that, while the frontal and caudal parts of the system are relatively discrete bundles in Weigert preparations, in chrome-silver preparations they constitute merely the more dense fascicles of a continuous fan of fibers.   The tractus thalamo-frontalis medialis is illustrated in figures 493, 495, 602, and 603.

Certain fibers from the paleostriatal region run with fibers of the tractus thalamo-striatalis medialis and on the medial side of the bundle such fascicles, largely nonmedullated and so probably not recognizable in Weigert preparations, are joined by fibers from the medial part of the dorsal medullary lamina and the periventricular gray.   Such bundles have been grouped under the name of the tractus strio-hypothalamicus medialis (*Huber* and *Crosby*, '29; figs. 495 and 602).

The crossed and uncrossed tractus strio-thalamicus internus of *Hunter* ('23), *Ariëns Kappers* ('21 and '24), *Huber* and *Crosby* ('29), and *Craigie* ('30) represents another efferent system from striatal regions to lower centers.   The uncrossed path terminates in part in hypothalamic centers (constituting a medial strio-hypothalamic system) but it may also reach subthalamic regions of the diencephalon and possibly other centers as well.

In conclusion, it may be stated that in any comparison of the components of the lateral forebrain bundle of different birds, due account should be taken of the methods employed in preparing the material.   In Weigert material, in which only the well-medullated fiber tracts are stained, certain of the fiber bundles stand out clearly as relatively well-marked and fairly discrete bundles, while, when chrome-silver preparations are used, such bundles are seen to be only portions of an enormous fan of fibers.

g. *Quinto-frontal Tract.* There are two other systems which in reality are not a portion of the lateral forebrain bundle, although at times they have been recognized as a part of it, but are associated with it through a part of its course and are largely fibers of passage for mesencephalic and diencephalic regions. They are here described as the striatal component of the dorsal supra-optic decussation, discussed on page 1046, and the quinto-frontal tract of *Wallenberg* ('98b, '03). The credit for the discovery of this latter tract belongs to *Wallenberg*, who first traced it forward from the isthmus region as an isthmo-striatal system and later showed that it had specific origin in the chief sensory nucleus of the trigeminal and renamed it the quinto-frontal tract. Extending forward from this nucleus of the trigeminal nerve, the bundle undergoes a partial decussation at the transverse level of the trochlear nucleus and courses through the upper end of the mesencephalon and through the diencephalon in intimate relation with the strio-tegmental tract. The bundles enter the forebrain, distributing to the striatum. *Schroeder* ('11) reaffirmed *Wallenberg's* account, and divided the striatal portion into two components. Such components are present in the sparrow, distributing partly to accessory hyperstriatal and hyperstriatal areas (dorsal component) and partly to the neostriatal basal nucleus and ectostriatal areas (basal component). The tract has been identified in many birds (*Ariëns Kappers*, '21) and probably is present in all avian forms. It brings forward tactile impulses entering over the trigeminal nerve to the neostriatal and hyperstriatal regions of the hemispheres and the nucleus basalis, in which latter region they probably come into interrelation with such olfactory impulses as may be present. The quinto-frontal tract is illustrated in figures 493, 495, 497, and 602.

h. *Medial Forebrain Bundle. Septo-mesencephalic Tract.* Delicate fibers from the septal (or parolfactory) region of the hemisphere swing into relation with the medial strio-hypothalamic component of the forebrain bundle, which they accompany to the hypothalamic regions. This group of fibers is probably the avian representation of the reptilian medial forebrain bundle and can be seen in figures 495 and 602.

The septo-mesencephalic tract (Scheidewandbündel), one of the earliest recognized in the avian brain, has been described by *Boyce* and *Warrington* ('98), *Edinger*, *Wallenberg*, and *Holmes* ('03), *Kalischer* ('05), *Wallenberg* ('06), *Ariëns Kappers* ('21), and several later observers. To *Wallenberg* ('06) is due particular credit for the analysis of this bundle. The name, septo-mesen-cephalic tract, is not very satisfactory, as the degeneration experiments of both *Kalischer* ('05) and *Wallenberg* ('06) indicated, since in large part the bundles accumulate from the dorsal and dorsomedial portions of the hemisphere, more specifically stated for the sparrow, from the accessory hyperstriatal and corticoid areas, as far lateralward as the line of fusion of the hyperstriatal area with the

superficial corticoid areas, and from the various centers of the dorsal and dorsomedial hemisphere walls, including hippocampal areas.   All these bundles form
a relatively compact fiber system (figs. 493, 495, and 602 to 608), which courses
ventralward through the septal areas, where collaterals or stem fibers are given off
to septal areas and fascicles from the septal areas join the tract.   After the septo-
mesencephalic tract has reached a position medial to the forebrain bundle, it
turns sharply and proceeds lateralward, ventral to the forebrain bundle, inclos-
ing this bundle in the angle formed by its fibers.   This shows very clearly in
preparations of the brain material of Cacatua, Paleornis (*Ariëns Kappers*), and
Gallus domesticus (*Huber* and *Crosby*) stained after the Weigert method.   After
this turn the major part of the bundle extends lateralward and the ramus basalis
frontalis of *Wallenberg* is given off to the frontal hemisphere region (fig. 602).   This
connection is discussed further in the chapter on the telencephalon (page 1397).

Other fibers of this septo-mesencephalic tract, after coursing somewhat
farther caudalward, gradually shift dorsalward to a position dorsal to the optic
tract and lateral to the lateral forebrain bundle, and form the dorsal part of
the septo-mesencephalic tract (figs. 493, 495, 602, and 603), which comes into relation with the nucleus superficialis parvocellularis, a ventral portion of which
might well be termed the nucleus of the septo-mesencephalic tract.   In the sparrow (*Huber* and *Crosby*, '29), small fascicles of this dorsal part lie in relation
with the nucleus lateralis and pass through the pretectal nucleus on their way to
the tectum (fig. 493).   The degree to which synapse occurs in the nucleus lateralis and nucleus pretectalis is uncertain.   The connection with the tectum was
described by *Craigie* ('28) in the humming bird, although differences in the position of the tectum affect the direction of the course of the tectal component.

The ramus basalis caudalis of the septo-mesencephalic tract, described by
Wallenberg ('06) in degeneration preparations of the various bird brains, was
homologized by him with the tractus cortico-septo-spinalis of *Kalischer* ('05).
It had been described by *Boyce* and *Warrington* ('98) as "chiasma fibers of the
tractus septo-mesencephalicus" and given the provisional name of tractus
septo-mesencephalicus by *Edinger*, *Wallenberg*, and *Holmes* ('03).   This tract
is the caudal continuation of the septo-mesencephalic tract, which instead of
coursing lateralward, ventral to the forebrain bundle, swings caudalward with
that bundle into the diencephalic region.   In *Wallenberg's* preparations it could
be seen to extend to the caudal end of the thalamus in the dove, into the
midbrain in the goose, and into the bulb in the duck.   The ramus basalis
caudalis is seen in figures 493, 495, and 602.

i. Tractus Infundibuli.   The tractus infundibuli is a bundle delimited by
Jelgersma ('96) in extirpation experiments.   He believed that this tract had
origin from basal telencephalic regions and accompanied the ventral peduncle
of the forebrain bundle caudalward into diencephalic regions, where the
bundle decussated and passed to the oculomotor nuclear centers.   *Schroeder*
('11), in reaffirming *Jelgersma's* description, termed the bundle the septo-
oculomotor tract and homologized it with the ramus basalis of *Wallenberg*.
Schroeder regarded the tract as homologous, in a physiologic sense, with the

mammalian pyramidal tract, but such an homology does not appear probable. Moreover, the tractus infundibuli of *Jelgersma* and the ramus basalis caudalis are separate systems, as *Wallenberg* has pointed out. The tractus infundibuli apparently is partially homologous with the tractus olfactorius basalis of *Ariëns Kappers* ('21; see also *Craigie*, '30), who regarded it as arising from paleo-striatal and septal areas and ending in the oculomotor nuclei, the nucleus peduncularis, and the tegmentum of the midbrain.

In normal preparations of the sparrow brain, *Huber* and *Crosby* ('29) were able to trace fibers of the tractus infundibuli from the region of the bed nuclei of the commissures and adjoining areas (including the septum) into a bundle which coursed caudalward in very close relation to the ramus caudalis and the medial forebrain bundle, but gradually shifted medialward and caudalward as a distinct fiber mass, decussated in the postinfundibular commissure, and passed to the region of the oculomotor centers (fig. 493).

CERTAIN RESULTS DERIVED FROM EXPERIMENTAL STUDIES OF THE AVIAN DIENCEPHALON

There is need of much further study, including anatomical and experimental observations, before a relatively complete account of the functions of the avian diencephalon can be given. Destruction of diencephalic areas produces more profound changes than removal of the cerebral hemispheres alone, and the bird usually does not live for any great length of time after appreciable destruction of the diencephalon. After such operations the bird is not aroused through starving and loses weight very rapidly. Complete destruction of the region (*Rogers*, '24 and '24a) results in great loss of body water, diuresis, and a fall of arterial pressure greater than that following the destruction of the hemispheres. The destruction of the hypothalamus in particular (*Rogers*, '21b and '23) results in an inability to maintain the normal body temperature, but maintenance of such temperature by artificial means results in spontaneous movements on the part of the bird and a behavior in many ways resembling that of a decerebrated bird. The flattened feathers seen in the bird with hypothalamic injury and a temperature below normal are seen in the decerebrated bird when a pilocarpine injection reduces the temperature. As long as midbrain centers are intact, disturbances of muscular activity, rigidity, or muscular incoördination were not found by *Rogers*. All of the above statements indicate that in the diencephalon in birds, as probably in mammals, there are centers which exert a directive influence of a certain type over various lower centers formed by preganglionic neurons of the autonomic nervous system (or sympathetic nervous system in the broader use of this term). The experiments of *Muskens* related to the diencephalon have been referred to earlier (see p. 1050).

RÉSUMÉ OF GRAY MASSES AND FIBER CONNECTIONS OF THE AVIAN DIENCEPHALON CONSIDERED IN THEIR PHYLOGENETIC RELATIONS

On the preceding pages is presented an account of the main nuclear masses and fiber connections of the avian mesencephalon and diencephalon, with due consideration of the pertinent literature. In the literature are found many incidental comparisons of the bird diencephalon with that of other vertebrate forms; in addition there are contributions dealing chiefly with such comparisons and homologies and these deserve further consideration. Deserving especial notice, more particularly by reason of the stimulating suggestions contained, is the 1923 paper of *Ingvar*, "On Thalamic Evolution." *Ingvar* undertook to homologize in detail avian and mammalian thalamic centers, regarding the avian nucleus rotundus as homologous with the nucleus ventralis of mammals and, with this as a basis, established homologies between the several avian and mammalian centers, and believed that he could identify in birds the chief mammalian thalamic nuclei with the exception of the nucleus anterior and the nucleus lateralis. For details of such homologies the original paper should be consulted. Among his general conclusions is to be emphasized his statement that the avian thalamus differs from the mammalian thalamus through the higher development of the mammalian nucleus lateralis and that the factors which produced the differences in form relations are directly coördinated with the differences in the relative position of the respective tecta. *Rendahl* ('24), after presenting the embryology and the adult cellular structure of the thalamus of the chicken and considering briefly the development and adult nuclear structure of the reptilian thalamus, presented homologies of certain reptilian and avian diencephalic centers which are further homologized with certain mammalian diencephalic centers. *Craigie* and *Brickner* ('27) discussed homologies between teleostean and avian diencephalic centers; certain of their homologies appear to have been substantiated by later investigations — others require reconsideration by reason of the increase in knowledge relative to the avian diencephalon since their paper was published. *Huber* and *Crosby* ('26 and '29), in their consideration of the reptilian and avian diencephalic centers, have incidentally discussed certain homologies which in a general way influence the following discussion.

It is obvious that the avian mesencephalon and diencephalon are very highly developed and this development affects more particularly the tectal region and the dorsal thalamus. In previous pages attention has been called to the fact that the high degree of differentiation of the tectum is related to its importance as a correlation center and as a way station for impulses to the dorsal thalamus.

The nucleus mesencephalicus lateralis pars dorsalis of birds is regarded by many observers as the homologue of the torus semicircularis of reptiles and the corpus posterius of lower forms, but there is still difference of opinion as to whether these structures are the homologue of the mammalian inferior colliculus (see *Palmgren*, '21). The avian nucleus isthmi, as this name was used in the previous discussion, includes more than its reptilian homologue, which constitutes the pars principalis of the avian nucleus and which presents distinctly less differentiation. The nucleus isthmo-opticus of the avian isthmal nuclear complex, as such, has not been recognized in reptiles, although evidence is at hand that it has a representation. Further study is required before it can be definitely stated that the tegmentum of the avian mesencephalon has acquired an approximately equivalent degree of differentiation.   It is obvious that the avian red nucleus is the homologue of that of reptiles and is comparable in a general way with the magnocellular portion of the mammalian red nucleus.

The nucleus ectomamillaris, with its associated optic root, is better developed in birds than its reptilian representative, the nucleus of the basal optic root, or its mammalian equivalent, the nucleus tractus peduncularis transversi (*Marburg*, '03 and '03a; posterior accessory optic tract of *Bochenek*, '08; see mammalian bibliography).   The nuclear masses associated with the medial longitudinal fasciculus, as described for both reptiles and birds, and the ventrally situated gray of the medial longitudinal fasciculus of carnivores (*Rioch*, '29a) are regarded here as homologous nuclear masses.

In birds the pretectal and subpretectal regions are highly developed, and present relatively clear nuclear differentiation, perhaps more so than in other vertebrate forms.   Nuclear groups associated with the avian posterior commissure phylogenetically repeat the reptilian nuclear pattern as presented for Varanus by *Beccari* ('23) and as substantiated in other reptilian forms.   To this posterior commissure nuclear group, *Huber* and *Crosby* would allocate the medial portion of the nucleus spiriformis, although recently *Craigie* ('31) has described a dorsal nucleus of the posterior commissure.   The subpretectal nucleus of birds is the homologue of the pretectal nucleus of reptiles, while the avian pretectal nucleus is homologous to a small cell group of reptiles designated by the letter *m* in figure 482.   The pretectal and subpretectal nuclei of birds are interconnected by fiber bundles associated with scattered cells so that in a sense they may be considered parts of the same nuclear complex, as may their reptilian homologues.   Probably the reptilian pretectal nucleus and the nucleus lentiformis mesencephali are represented in the mammalian pretectal nucleus and the large-celled nucleus of the optic tract respectively, and the lateral and medial parts of the avian nucleus spiriformis in the rodent posterior nucleus and dorsal nucleus of the posterior commissure.

Avian and mammalian epithalamic centers repeat in essential the reptilian pattern, with the reservation that the size and degree of differentiation are correlated with the development of the olfactory system in the particular bird or mammal under consideration.   The homologies of the relatively conspicuous avian nucleus rotundus with the reptilian nucleus of the same name have been questioned by certain observers.   However, in the light of available evidence, *Huber* and *Crosby* feel that such homology is warranted, and they would also homologize the reptilian and the avian nucleus rotundus with some portion of the mammalian nucleus ventralis, as *Ingvar* ('23), *Le Gros Clark* ('29, '32, see bibliography for mammals, as nucleus ventralis medialis or submedius), and others have done.   Certain other workers (as *Ariëns Kappers*, '21) have homologized the reptilian nucleus rotundus with the medial nucleus of mammals.

The avian nucleus dorsolateralis anterior and nucleus dorsomedialis anterior have their homologues in the reptilian nuclei of the same name.   The latter nucleus is represented in the mammalian anterior (probably antero-medial) nuclear group. The former may represent in part, portions of the mammalian ventral nucleus (*Le Gros Clark*, '32; *Abbie*, '34, see p. 1059), in part the nucleus antero-ventralis and the pars dorsalis of the lateral geniculate (see also *Abbie*).

The midline gray of certain reptiles is comparable in a general way to certain of the mammalian midline thalamic nuclei. The avian nucleus of the habenulo-peduncular tract probably may be homologized with the mammalian nucleus of that tract. There is some justification for homologizing the avian nucleus superficialis parvocellularis and the reptilian nucleus ovalis.

The so-called lateral geniculate nucleus of birds is homologous to the ventral part of the mammalian and the main part of the reptilian lateral geniculate (see p. 995). The dorsal part of the lateral geniculate has representation in reptiles (possibly in birds) and reaches the peak of its differentiation in mammals (see pp. 1154 to 1159; *Cairney*, '26, and *Huber* and *Crosby*, '33, bibliography for reptiles; *Huber* and *Crosby*, '29, and *Le Gros Clark*, '32, bibliography for mammals; *Herrick*, '33, bibliography for amphibians).

The phylogeny of the mammalian medial geniculate nucleus (see p. 1170) has aroused much interest. Probably it has no representation in the reptilian nucleus isthmi (see, however, *Ariëns Kappers*, '29). Possibly the homologue of its ventral part is the nucleus of the transverse decussation of *Frey* ('33, for birds and reptiles) and, of its dorsal part, the avian nucleus ovoidalis, as *Papez* (to be published) has suggested, but these homologies need further confirmation.

Turning now to a consideration of the ventral thalamus it becomes evident that the reptilian area ventralis anterior has representation in the similarly designated avian area. Entopeduncular nuclear groups are present along the course of the lateral forebrain bundles of both reptiles and birds, and along the ansa lenticularis of mammals, where in part they are designated by special names. The nucleus decussationis supraopticae dorsalis constitutes a special differentiation of this cell group in all three groups. *Ingvar* ('23) homologized the avian nucleus intercalatus with the mammalian zona incerta. It appears probable that the avian nucleus intercalatus, possibly, together with the nucleus subrotundus, falls within the area ventrolateralis of the alligator (*Huber* and *Crosby*, '26). This area, together with the area triangularis, has certain relations to other thalamic areas (see figs. 483 and 484) and to the fasciculus geniculatus descendens and fascicles of the ventral peduncle of the lateral forebrain bundle that suggest its homology with the mammalian zona incerta, but again much in the way of further direct evidence would be desirable. For somewhat similar interpretations the papers of *de Lange* ('11, bibliography for reptiles) and *Le Gros Clark* ('32, bibliography for mammals) should be consulted. A reptilian forerunner of the substantia nigra of mammals has been suggested by *Beccari* ('23) and *Huber* and *Crosby* ('33).

The avian and reptilian hypothalamic areas are comparable in general, although the establishment of detailed homologies is not possible in all cases. The most complete comparison of these regions in the two forms has been made by *Rendahl* ('24), to whom reference is made here. Undoubtedly the mammalian pattern is foreshadowed in reptiles, but attempts at detailed homologies are reserved for a later account.

A further phase of the studies on the avian diencephalon deserves emphasis, that concerned with the embryologic development of the nuclear pattern, since this portrays in ontogeny the phylogenetic development of the diencephalic nuclear pattern. For the details of such nuclear development the reader is referred to the accounts of *Mesdag* ('09) and *Rendahl* ('24) and their contained bibliographies.

The Mammalian Mesencephalon and Diencephalon

GROSS RELATIONS

The mesencephalon and diencephalon of mammals vary greatly from the corresponding regions in birds. One of the most marked differences to be noted in gross preparations is the presence of two eminences, the inferior colliculi (or posterior quadrigeminal bodies), in the region caudal to the superior colliculi (or anterior quadrigeminal bodies). Usually the inferior colliculi are separated from the superior colliculi by a sulcus, the sulcus transversus laminae quadrigeminae (fig. 501). Near their caudal ends the inferior colliculi often do not touch each other but are united by a thin lamella which fuses with the anterior medullary velum. In most mammals the inferior eminences are smaller than are the superior (figs. 501 and 522) but in several mammals they are of about equal size, while in others — such as certain carnivores and more particularly cetaceans (fig. 499), certain chiropteres (such as the bat, fig. 499), and insectivores (such as the mole) — they are larger. This relative increase in the size of the inferior colliculi may be due to an actual increase in these centers, associated with a very great development of the lateral lemniscus system as in carnivores, cetaceans, and chiropteres (fig. 499), or to a decrease in the superior colliculi associated with an atrophy of the optic system as in chiropteres and insectivores. In comparison with the remainder of the brain stem, the superior colliculi are relatively smaller in mammals than in lower vertebrates and probably this decrease is associated with the very great development of the thalamic optic centers. Occasionally in mammals (including man) the superior colliculi of the two sides are separated, as in frogs and crocodiles, by a pars impar mesencephali which lies immediately behind the root of the epiphyseal stalk. A subcommissural organ and Reissner's fiber occur in the human fetus and infant (*Keene* and *Hewer*, '35, J. Anat., vol. 69, p. 501).

The superior and inferior colliculi constitute the tectal portion of the midbrain. The remainder of the region is divided into an upper portion, the pars tegmentalis, and a lower portion, the pars peduncularis. The latter includes the cerebral peduncle and its associated gray, the substantia nigra. Usually its upper border is indicated on the lateral surface of the brain by a deep sulcus, the sulcus lateralis mesencephali, clearly visible although unlabeled in figure 500. The pars tegmentalis is the region between the tectal and peduncular parts.

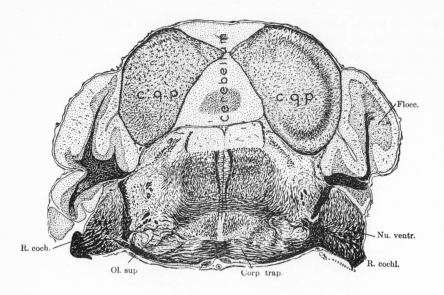

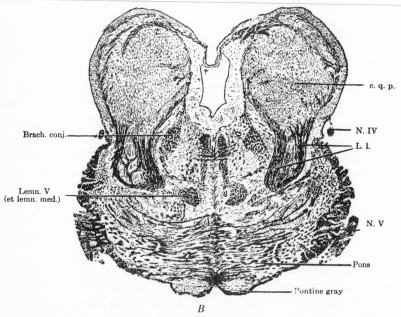

B

Fig. 499. *A*. Section through the inferior colliculi or corpora quadrigemina posteriora and the cochlear nuclei of Vesperugo noctua. *c.q.p.*, corpus quadrigeminum posterius; *Corp.trap.*, corpus trapezoideum; *Flocc.*, flocculus; *Nu.ventr.*, nucleus ventralis; *Ol.sup.*, superior olive; *Pyr.*, pyramid; *R.cochl.*, ramus cochlearis.

B. Section through the corpora quadrigemina posteriora (inferior colliculi) and the lateral lemnisci in Phocaena communis (drawn from a preparation by *Jelgersma*). *Brach.conj.*, brachium conjunctivum; *c.q.p.*, corpus quadrigeminum posterius; *L.l.*, lemniscus lateralis; *Lemn.V* (et lemn. med.), lemniscus trigeminalis (and lemniscus medialis); *N.IV*, nucleus trochlearis.

The tegmental portion has increased in size in mammals. This increase is due not so much to the greater size of its nuclear masses as to the increase in its fibers of passage.

The most conspicuous change in the midbrain is found in the peduncular portion. The cerebral peduncles occupy an increasingly large portion of the ventral field in passing from lower to higher mammals (compare figs. 522 and 500, and figs. 505 and 503). These peduncles carry the great fiber pathways between the motor centers of the cortex and those of the brain stem and spinal cord, and the fiber systems discharging from the association areas of the cortex to the

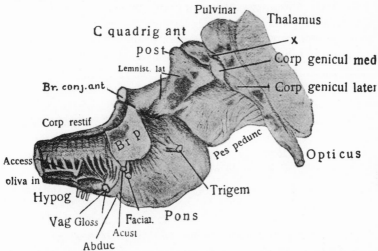

FIG. 500. Lateral view of the brain stem of man. *X* indicates the portion of the optic tract passing to the superior colliculus or corpus quadrigeminum anterius. The greater part of the optic nerve ends in the lateral geniculate nucleus. The remaining labels are so obvious that it does not appear necessary to list them.

pontine gray. Consequently their size varies in the different species in proportion to the development of the neopallial cortical areas from which the systems originate and is greatest in man. In consequence of their bilateral origin in the cortex, the cerebral peduncles converge caudalward (fig. 500), forming thus a triangle at the base of the midbrain, the trigonum interpedunculare or interpeduncular fossa, at the base of which the nucleus interpeduncularis and the roots of the oculomotor nerves are found (fig. 503). The region immediately in front of the roots of the oculomotor is penetrated by a great number of smaller vessels and in consequence is called the substantia perforata posterior. In front of this latter region are the mammillary bodies, the caudal ends of which mark the line between the mesencephalon and the diencephalon.

The ventricular pattern is relatively simple in the mesencephalon and the diencephalon. The fourth ventricle narrows down toward the upper part of the pons region where it continues into the aqueduct (aqueduct of Sylvius) which extends forward through the mesencephalon and opens into the third ventricle at the caudal end of the diencephalon. The third ventricle is narrow, particularly in the dorsal part of the thalamus above the sulcus medius. In about

30 per cent of human thalami the ventricle is obliterated in part in this region by a fusion of the dorsal thalami of the two sides, forming the commissura media or commissura mollis.   In many mammals the nuclei of the midline are very highly developed and their fusion occurs throughout a large part of the dorsal thalami.   The third ventricle extends directly forward into the telencephalon medium and here the border between the diencephalon and telencephalon in adult material is a line drawn from the floor of the interventricular foramen to near the caudal end of the preoptic recess.   In certain mammals, as for instance in the dog, in the region of the ventral thalamus, traces of an hypertrophied, highly vascularized, and apparently secretory ependyma is to be seen, although not so typically as in teleosts (fig. 453), reptiles (fig. 473), and birds (fig. 497).

The diencephalon shows a relatively greater increase in size in mammals than does the mesencephalon and its form and internal structural relations show more marked variations.   In adult mammals the sulci along the walls of the third ventricle are almost entirely obliterated, or at best indistinct.   However, in certain mammalian embryos the frontal continuation of the sulcus limitans is still discernible in the diencephalon.   In the rabbit it ends in the recessus preopticus (*Droogleever Fortuyn*, '12) after having sent out a branch, the sulcus medius (fig. 423, from *Herrick*), which forms the boundary between the dorsal and ventral segments of the thalamus.

Dorsally a small posterior commissure marks the line between the diencephalon and the mesencephalon and directly in front of this is the epiphysis, a glandular structure present in most mammals but absent in Dasypus (*Creutzfeldt*, '12), in Myrmecophaga and other edentates (*Krabbe*), and in Manatus and Halicore (*Murie*, '85).[5]   It is relatively small in the elephant and microscopically small in Phocaena.   The epiphysis is large in Echidna (*Krabbe*), in marsupials (see fig. 503), in rodents, and in ungulates (*Cutore*, '10, and *Biondi*, '16).   It varies considerably in form.   Thus it is small and elongated in the guinea pig, club shaped in rabbits, round in goats, and bean shaped in man.[6]   A brief review of its microscopic structure may be found under the discussion of the epithalamus, page 1101.   In front of the anterior stalk of the epiphysis, on either side of the midline, lie the habenular nuclei, connected by an habenular commissure and receiving the stria medullaris.   These structures, together with a part of the posterior commissure and the choroid plexus of the third ventricle, constitute the epithalamic region of the diencephalon.

The most obvious increase in size within the diencephalon has occurred in the dorsal thalamus and takes place in several directions.   The increase in size in the frontal direction results in the bulging out of the lateral wall of the region lying between the habenular nuclei, the interventricular foramen becomes large, and over it the stria medullaris travels for a considerable distance in order to reach the habenular nuclei.   From this region of the habenulae forward to the

[5] *Marburg* ('20), however, was able to trace remnants of it in Halicore.

[6] A trace of a parietal organ was described in man by *Marburg*, but if present occasionally, it is certainly very inconstant.   It is possible that a prepineal structure, which was found by *Krabbe* in the Talpa embryo, is the homologue of a parietal organ.

foramen, a thin roof is stretched between the two striae medullares, forming the choroid plexus of the third ventricle. The so-called line of attachment of this roof is the taenia thalami, which merely marks the place where the thickened wall of the brain passes over into the thin choroid plexus. A velum transversum, comparable to that in lower forms, is present in the embryo (*Bailey*, '16) but disappears later, and the choroid plexus of the third ventricle becomes continuous with the choroid plexus of the lateral ventricle in the region of the foramen.

The maximum lateral extension of the diencephalon, and particularly of its dorsal portion, occurs immediately in front of the midbrain. In man it bulges caudalward in this region, lateral to the collicular regions of the midbrain, forming the pulvinar. As a consequence of this lateral and frontal development, the diencephalon, as seen from above, has the shape of an isosceles triangle, the apex of which (the tuberculum anterius) forms the caudal wall of the interventricular foramen, while the base of the triangle lies against the midbrain. On each side, the caudolateral portion of this triangle has been designated the pulvinar or cushion of the thalamus because the hemisphere rests against it. The pulvinar increases in size from lower to higher mammals. The caudal end of the diencephalon in the kangaroo extends only to the middle of the superior collicular region. In man its caudal limit corresponds almost to that of the inferior colliculus (fig. 501).

The enormous development of the dorsal thalamus, and particularly of its neothalamic portions, brings the lateral wall of the diencephalon into relation with the caudomedial wall of the telencephalon. The region where the medioventral telencephalic wall approaches the thalamus is called the lamina affixa telencephali. As a result of the expansion of the neostriatum and the neothalamus in mammals and the increase in the tracts interconnecting these areas, the connection between the two regions is very much broader than in lower forms and the thalamus is bounded laterally by the internal capsule and the striatum. Dorsal to this thickening, and marking the line between the lateral thalamus and the striatum, is a groove (fig. 501) in which lies the stria terminalis or stria semicircularis. This tract can be followed from the level of the anterior commissure along the medial border of the caudate nucleus; since it marks the line between the thalamus and the striatum it has been called the stria terminalis. It is accompanied by a blood vessel, the vena terminalis. The blood in this vessel aids in the recognition of the structure, frequently giving the line a dark color, and this color has led to its designation occasionally as the stria cornea.

Since the dorsal thalamus is larger than the ventral, the lateral walls of the diencephalon converge ventralward. Along the lateral wall passes the optic tract. The posterior end of this tract is the superior colliculus and along its course and receiving a very large part of its fibers is the lateral geniculate nucleus, an eminence visible on the superficial surface close to the pulvinar (fig. 500). Between the lateral geniculate and the superior colliculus lies the medial geniculate nucleus (fig. 500). The medial and lateral geniculate nuclei

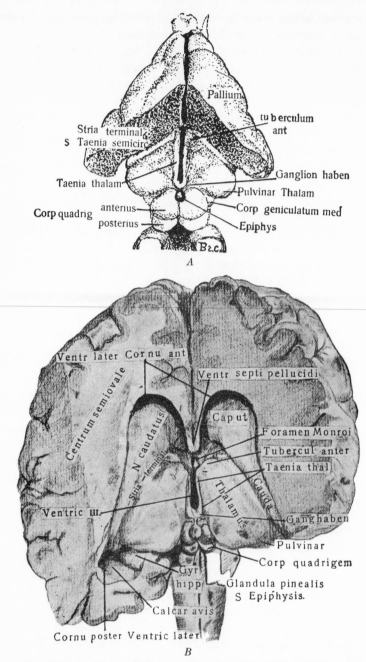

FIG. 501. *A.* The midbrain and thalamus of a kangaroo (Macropus robustus).
B. The midbrain, thalamus, and striatum of a man, as seen from above.

form the metathalamus of human anatomy.   They mark the transition in topographical and, in a certain sense, in functional respects between the midbrain and the diencephalon.

The ventral thalamus lies below the sulcus medius and above and, for the most part, lateral to the hypothalamus. All of its major subdivisions are demonstrable in gross preparations of the human brain, with the exception of the nucleus entopeduncularis, but they are better understood if the knowledge gained from gross preparations is supplemented by an account of their microscopic structure and fiber connections.

The base of the diencephalon, the hypothalamic portion, shows greater surface differentiation in mammals than in birds and reptiles. Behind the chiasm the mammalian tuber cinereum has attained greater prominence. The hypophysis with its infundibulum varies considerably in size in different mammals. Behind the hypophyseal stalk lie the mammillary bodies, sometimes called the corpora candescantia because of their white color. In many animals they are unpaired externally, although they are divided generally into paired nuclei internally. They are particularly well developed in macrosmatic animals but are also well developed in man.

In the following account the nuclear pattern of the mesencephalon and the diencephalon will be considered. With each group the major fiber connections, as far as they are known, will be listed. The account of the nuclear configuration and general fiber relations of each group will be followed by a description of certain of the more prominent fiber systems.

THE MESENCEPHALIC NUCLEI AND THEIR CONNECTIONS IN MAMMALS

The nuclei and fiber connections of the mammalian midbrain vary in certain important details from those described for reptiles and birds. These variations are due to the particularly strong development of certain mesencephalic regions and are usually superimposed upon a structural pattern which shows the primary relations of the region. As was stated earlier, the mesencephalon may be divided into a tectal portion, a tegmental portion, and a peduncular portion. The tectal regions will be considered first.

The Inferior Colliculi, Their Fiber Connections and Their Functions

The tectal regions in mammals consist primarily of the inferior and superior collicular centers. The inferior colliculi are regarded by many observers as the homologues of the tori semicirculares of reptiles, which may bulge out into the ventricle, as in Alligator, or may form eminences on the surface, as in lizards and snakes, similar to those formed by the inferior collicular eminences of mammals. *Palmgren* ('21) believed that the corpus posterius of amphibians is not homologous (as evidenced by its embryologic development) with the mammalian inferior colliculus. *Herrick* ('25; see bibliography for amphibians) stated that the corpus posterius has the general relations and functions of an inferior colliculus, even if not in all respects homologous embryologically. Evidences of its phylogenetic relation to the reptilian torus semicircularis are seen in the massiveness of the structure of the inferior colliculus and in the fact that its central nucleus is a caudal extension and expansion of the stratum griseum periventriculare, while the capsular portion represents a similar extension but a reduction of the layers peripheral to this gray stratum (*Huber* and *Crosby*). These suggest the relations of the torus semicircularis to the reptilian superior colliculus. This extension is evident in paramedian but not in midsagittal sections of the brains of many mammals.

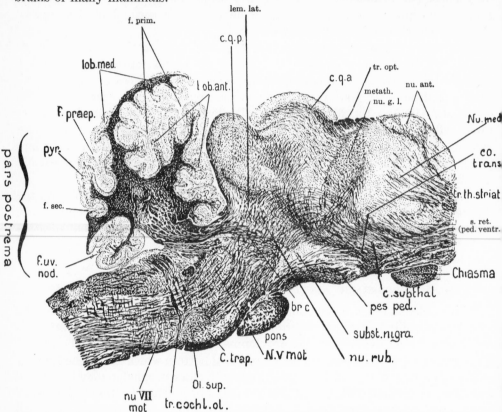

Fig. 502.   A sagittal section through the brain of a marsupial, Onychogale frenata.
br.c., brachium conjunctivum; *c.q.a.*, corpus quadrigeminum anterius (superior colliculus); *c.q.p.*, corpus quadrigeminum posterius (inferior colliculus); *c.subthal.*, corpus subthalamicus; *c.trap.*, corpus trapezoideum; *co.trans.*, commissura transversa; *f.praep.*, fissura praepyramidalis (in *Ingvar's* usage); *f.prim.*, fissura prima; *f.sec.*, fissura secunda; *f.uv.nod.*, fissura uvulo-nodularis; *lem.lat.*, lemniscus lateralis; *lob.ant.*, anterior lobe of cerebellum; *lob.med.*, median lobe of cerebellum; *metath.*, metathalamus; *nu.ant.*, nucleus anterior thalami; *nu.med.*, nucleus medialis; *nu.g.l.*, nucleus geniculatus lateralis; *nu.rub.*, nucleus ruber; *N.V mot.*, motor nucleus of the trigeminal nerve; *nu.VII mot.*, motor nucleus of the facial nerve; *ol.sup.*, superior olivary nucleus; *ped.ventr.*, ventral peduncle; *pes ped.*, pes pedunculi; *s.ret. (ped.ventr.)*, substantia reticularis (pedunculus ventralis); *subst. nigra*, substantia nigra; *tr.cochl.ol.*, tractus cochleo-olivaris; *tr.opt.*, tractus opticus; *tr.th.striat.*, tractus thalamo-striatalis.

Each inferior colliculus (fig. 499) shows a differentiation into (1) an inner segment or central nucleus (comparable in general to the main mass of the nucleus mesencephalicus lateralis pars dorsalis in avian forms, probably to the nucleus lateralis mesencephali of teleosts and to the nucleus medialis tegmenti of plagiostomes), and (2) a capsular portion which contains more fibers than the central part and gives a white appearance to the surface.   According to *Held* ('93), *von Kölliker* ('96), and *Ramón y Cajal* ('11), the neurons forming the central nucleus are large and multipolar, with dendrites passing out in all directions from the cell bodies but not beyond the circumference of the nucleus. For the most part the neuraxes of these cells pass through the capsular portion in order to enter the peduncle of the inferior colliculus (the brachium of the medial geniculate nucleus). A smaller number of these neuraxes are believed to descend to lower centers. At the periphery of the inferior colliculus there are smaller neurons which, according to *Ramón y Cajal* ('11), send their processes either into the medial geniculate nucleus or into the inferior intercollicular commissure. Neuraxes of certain of these cells pass to the deeper part of the superior colliculus.

In mammals the primary function of each inferior colliculus is that of a reflex auditory center, as is evidenced by its fiber connections. Entering it are fibers of the lateral lemniscus (see also page 496), bringing auditory impulses from contralateral and homolateral cochlear centers (*Kreidl*, '14) and thus providing a path for the projection of the impulses from each ear on to both sides of the brain (*Mott*, '07). A discharge path from the inferior colliculus (by way of the tangential fibers of *Ramón y Cajal*, '11) to the medial geniculate nucleus of the metathalamus is provided through the brachium of the inferior colliculus, and acoustico-optic fibers transmit impulses from the inferior to the superior colliculus. The paths from this midbrain auditory region to lower centers are not equally well developed in all mammals. Most observers grant that the tecto-spinal tracts in the majority of mammals arise to a variable extent from the inferior as well as from the superior colliculus. In the opossum *Tsai* ('25a) described a tecto-pontine tract arising from the whole length of the tectum, but particularly from the inferior colliculus. This system lies just internal to the superficially placed brachium of the inferior colliculus until the caudal end of this latter fiber bundle is reached and then occupies the brain surface until it shifts medially in order to reach the lateral nucleus of the pons. Earlier *Pavlow* ('00e) had described a tecto-pontine bundle. This tract has been questioned by various observers and it is not clear as yet exactly what the significance of the relation with the pontine gray may be. *Tsai* ('25a) traced a medial tecto-bulbar system arising largely from the inferior colliculus, and a lateral tecto-bulbar system from both the inferior and superior colliculi to the substantia nigra (tractus tecto-nigralis), to the pontine gray, and to the tegmental region of the midbrain. *Rioch* ('29a) described medial and lateral tecto-nigral and nigro-tectal tracts in carnivores, all of which are associated particularly with the inferior collicular portion of the midbrain roof.

The Superior Colliculi, Their Fiber Connections and Functions

The superior colliculus differs in certain particulars from the optic tectal region described for lower forms such as reptiles and birds. The most marked of these differences is the presence of a less evident lamination in this region in mammals and a relatively smaller size. The reduction of the superior colliculus phylogenetically is to a considerable extent in inverse proportion to the development of the dorsal part of the lateral geniculate nucleus, since this latter center assumes some of the functions formerly carried out by the superior colliculus.

The following strata may be recognized :

1. A stratum zonale, comparable to the fibrille periferiche of *Tartuferi* ('85), the äussere weisse Lage or stratum zonale of *von Kölliker* ('96), W_1 of *Frankl-Hochwart* ('02), the stratum zonale of *Ramón y Cajal* ('11), *Winkler* and *Potter* ('14), and *Tsai* ('25), and the strato marginale of *Castaldi* ('23).

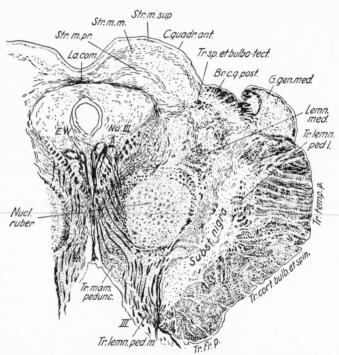

Fig. 503.   A section through the right half of the midbrain in man, showing particularly the red nucleus, the substantia nigra and the basis pedunculi.

Br.c.q.post., brachium of the corpus quadrigeminum posterius; *C.quadr. ant.*, corpus quadrigeminum anterius; *E.W.*, Edinger-Westphal nucleus; *La.com.*, lamina commissuralis; *Lemn.med.*, lemniscus medialis; *G. gen. med.*, nucleus geniculatus medialis; *Nucl.ruber*, nucleus ruber; *Nu.III*, nucleus of the oculomotor nerve; *Str.z.*, stratum zonale; *Str.op.*, stratum opticum; *Str.a.m.*, stratum album medius; *Subst.nigra*, substantia nigra; *Tr.cort.bulb.et spin.*, tractus cortico-bulbaris et spinalis; *Tr.fr.p.*, tractus fronto-pontinus; *Tr.lemn.ped.l.*, tractus lemniscalis pedunculi lateralis; *Tr.temp.pont.*, tractus temporo-pontinus.

2. A peripheral gray layer, the stratum griseum superficiale, which forms the oberflächliches Grau of *Ganser* ('82), the cappa cinerea of *Tartuferi* ('85) and *Castaldi* ('23), the äussere graue Zone of *von Kölliker* ('96), *gl* of *Frankl-Hochwart* ('02), the zone centré of *Ramón y Cajal* ('11), and the stratum griseum superficiale of *Winkler* and *Potter* ('14) and of *Tsai* ('25).

3. A stratum opticum, which is the oberflächliches Mark of *Ganser* ('82). This (with the next two layers) constitutes the strato bianco cinereo superficiale of *Tartuferi* ('85), and is the mittlere weisse Lage of *von Kölliker* ('96), the zone des fibres optique of *Ramón y Cajal* ('11), the stratum medullare superficiale of

Winkler and *Potter* ('14), the strato ottico of *Castaldi* ('23), and the stratum opticum of *Tsai* ('25).   (See here fig. 503, str. m. sup.)

4. A middle gray layer (sometimes grouped with the two succeeding layers) which is the stratum griseum mediale; it constitutes the mittlere graue Schicht of *Obersteiner* ('01), or the mittlere graue Zone of *von Kölliker* ('96), the mittleres Grau of *Ganser* ('82), is included in strato bianco cinereo superficiale of *Tartuferi* ('85), and, with the next layer, in the zone ganglionnaire on des fibres horizontales of *Ramón y Cajal* ('11), and is the stratum griseum intermedium of *Winkler* and *Potter* ('14), the strato bianco cinereo superficiale of *Castaldi* ('23), and the stratum griseum medius of *Tsai* ('25).

5. A middle white layer, the stratum album mediale, comparable to the mittleres Mark of *Ganser* ('82) and the innere weisse Lage of *von Kölliker* ('96), included in the strato bianco cinereo superficiale of *Tartuferi* ('85) and in the zone ganglionnaire on des fibres horizontales of *Ramón y Cajal* ('11), the W_3 of *Frankl-Hochwart* ('02), the stratum medullare intermedium of *Winkler* and *Potter* ('14), the strato sensitivo ascendente of *Castaldi* ('23), and the stratum album medius of *Tsai* ('25).

6. A deep gray layer, the stratum griseum profundum, which is the tiefe graue Schicht of *Obersteiner* ('01), homologous with the tiefes Grau of *Ganser* ('82) and the innere graue Zone of *von Kölliker* ('96).   The strato bianco cinereo profundo, grigio centrale o del acquediotto del Silvio of *Tartuferi* ('85) includes this layer and the next also, as does *Ramón y Cajal's* ('11) zone de la substance grise centrale.   It is W_4 of *Frankl-Hochwart* ('02), and it appears to be the strato bianco cinereo profondo of *Castaldi* ('23) and the stratum griseum profundum of *Winkler* and *Potter* ('14) and of *Tsai* ('25).

7. A deep white or medullary layer, the stratum album profundum, is the tiefe alba Schicht (*Obersteiner*, '01), and is represented, in addition to the citations made in the preceding paragraph, by W_4 of *Frankl-Hochwart* ('02), midollo profondo of *Castaldi* ('23), stratum medullare profundum of *Winkler* and *Potter* ('14), and the stratum album profundum of *Tsai* ('25).

8 and 9. A stratum griseum periventriculare and a stratum fibrosum periventriculare (somewhat intermingled) lie near the ventricle.   In the gray, *Castaldi* ('23) described a grigio centrale and a strato germinativo.

The cell types found in the different layers are illustrated in figure 504 (taken from the text of *Ramón y Cajal*, '11), which shows the more superficial part of the optic tectum of an eight-day rabbit brain, prepared according to the Golgi method.   The cell types and the general arrangement are sufficiently clear in the figure to require no further explanation.   The deeper position of the optic fibers in the tectum of mammals than in that of lower vertebrates is worthy of note.   In part this may be associated with the decrease in the thalamo-tectal systems, other than those from the lateral geniculate nucleus, and with the decreased importance of the lemnisci connections to the tectum, which no longer affords for them a major way station to the dorsal thalamus.   Thus the relative size of the underlying layer in the region is somewhat decreased.   This may be furthered slightly by migration peripheralward (external to the optic tract) of certain cells of the receptive gray toward the fine fibers in the stratum zonale, which are partly intrinsic (and correlative) fibers and partly neuraxes of cortico-collicular fibers (*Bailey, Strong,* and *Elwyn's* Histology, '25). It has been suggested that these differences may be associated with certain functional relations peculiar to mammals, since certain optic reflexes are more highly developed in mammals than in lower vertebrates. However, the deeper position of the optic fibers in mammals does not decrease the number of synapses necessary for the passage of the impulses through the tectum, since the optic fibers in reptiles and birds

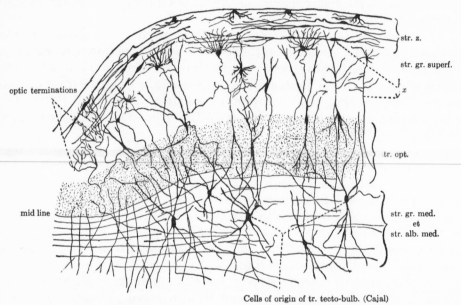

Cells of origin of tr. tecto-bulb. (Cajal)

Fig. 504. The finer structure of the upper two thirds of the optic tectum of a mammal. *Ramón y Cajal.* Terminology is modified.

str.z., stratum zonale; *str.gr.superf.*, stratum griseum superficiale; *str.opt.*, stratum opticum; *str.gr.med.et str.alb.med.*, stratum griseum mediale and stratum album mediale. The terminations of the optic tract are indicated in part on the left-hand side of the figure. At *x* attention is called to the horizontal or vertical course of the processes indicated.

synapse not only with intermediate correlative cells but directly with neurons, the neuraxes of which constitute the major efferent systems. That other forms show indications of this migration inward is evidenced by the presence of a stratum zonale in various lower forms, such as fishes, frogs, and turtles. The gray external to the optic tract, the stratum griseum superficiale, belongs in its development to the stratum fibrosum et griseum of submammals. The remainder of this submammalian stratum is represented in mammals by the stratum griseum mediale and the stratum album mediale (the stratum lemnisci with its gray and white layers, in part). The stratum griseum centrale and the stratum album centrale of submammals find expression in the stratum griseum profundum and the stratum album profundum of mammals. The mammalian stratum griseum periventriculare has neurons of the mesencephalic root of the trigeminal nerve (fig. 179) scattered along its outer border. Otherwise its cells have no highly characteristic appearance or arrangement in toluidin blue stained material.   In part intermingled with this last mentioned stratum, in part internal to it, are fascicles derived from periventricularly coursing bundles of the acoustico-optic system, the dorsal longitudinal fasciculus and other systems, which are representative of a stratum fibrosum periventriculare.   It is obvious then that the stratification pattern in mammals is directly related to that of lower forms.

The pretectal nucleus (*Tsai*, '25 ; *Rioch*, '31 ; *Ingram*, *Hannett*, and *Ranson*, '32, and others ; not that of *Le Gros Clark*, '32, '32a) is essentially mesencephalic in many mammals.   In marsupials and rodents, at levels where well developed, it lies between the posterior nucleus (of *Gurdjian*, '27) and the stratum griseum mediale of the tectum, ultimately extending into the tectum to become continuous with this stratum.   In carnivores the anterior part has a pretectal position, but the gray extends back into the collicular eminence.   In man (*Huber* and *Crosby*, to be published) the nucleus, although distinguishable from the optic tectum, being cephalo-ventral to it in general, is essentially part of the superior collicular eminence as recognized in human anatomy.   It is convenient to deal with this nucleus in connection with the lateral nuclear group of the dorsal thalamus (pp. 1133, 1141, and 1153), and there the pertinent literature and homologies are discussed.

Major afferent connections of the superior colliculus are the optic tract, the peduncle of the superior colliculus (in certain mammals), the cortico-tectal tracts, fibers from lemnisci systems, acoustico-optic and other periventricular systems, and from superior collicular and posterior commissures.   Major efferent connections are the peduncle of the superior colliculus (particularly in lower mammals), tecto-oculomotor, tecto-rubral, tecto-tegmental, tecto-nigral, and tecto-spinal tracts and superior collicular and posterior commissure fibers, supplemented, in certain forms, by tecto-hypothalamic (*Hines*, '29, Ornithorhynchus) and tecto-isthmal (*Ariëns Kappers*, '21, Tamandua) tracts.

In forms in which complete decussation of the optic tract occurs within the chiasma, obviously all optic fibers to the tectum are crossed.   It is sometimes stated that in mammals in general (*Brouwer*, '27) this center receives only crossed fibers, but *Minkowski* ('20) found a small percentage of uncrossed fibers reaching this region in man.   Optic fibers carry both light and visual impulses.   Those carrying light impulses are said to terminate in the pretectal nucleus (according to workers in Ranson's laboratory (*Ranson* and *Magoun*, '33) ; see also *Barris*, and *Ingram*, '34, small drawing, fig. 526) in carnivores.   Presumably similar relations hold for most other mammals, but since the pretectal nucleus is within the superior colliculus in man (*Huber* and *Crosby*, to be published), a differentiated part of this latter region becomes the human light reflex center (fig. 526), and from this portion (and probably from the pretectal nucleus of lower mammals) light impulses are discharged to the Edinger-Westphal nucleus, partly after decussation in the posterior commissure, and from that nucleus pass as preganglionic fibers of the oculomotor nerve to the ciliary ganglion, and, after synapse, to the sphincter of the pupil and the ciliary muscle.   Dilation of the pupil is elicited by stimulation of various regions of the nervous system, including tegmental areas (*Ingram*, *Hannett*, and *Ranson*, '32), the hypothalamus (*Ranson* and *Magoun*, '33a), the subthalamic nucleus (*Karplus* and *Kreidl*, '13; see also p. 1136), and probably deep portions of the tectum.   Pain and possibly other impulses, reaching the optic tectum by secondary ascending paths, may serve as stimuli to produce such dilation when discharged from that as from other centers.   Light impulses entering the optic tectum over the optic nerve do not produce dilation.   On the contrary, when discharged to the tegmental centers by tecto-tegmental paths, or to the intermediolateral column via medial tecto-spinal paths, presumably they exert a regulatory or inhibitory effect over such centers.   The medial tecto-spinal tract, to which reference was made above, carries both visual and regulatory impulses.   Often it is said to be both a crossed and an uncrossed path.   In the cat (*Rasmussen*, '35, Anat. Rec., vol. 61, p. 41) it decussates, the crossing occurring in the dorsal tegmental decussation.   The fibers, together with uncrossed fascicles, course caudalward in company with the medial longitudinal fasciculus.   According to *Rasmussen* ('32, '32a) the medial tecto-spinal tract in the cat extends only to the end of the cervical cord.   In view of the rather greater extent of the tracts of the cord in man as compared with carnivores, it seems reasonable to suppose that the medial tecto-spinal tract may end directly on the intermediolateral column (1 to 4 Th.) in the human cord, where are situated the preganglionic neurons, the fibers of which pass, by way of a synapse in the superior cervical sympathetic ganglion, to the dilator apparatus of the eye.   If the medial tecto-spinal tract does not have sufficient caudal extent in man (and this requires further proof) it may be supplemented by a short intercalary neuron.   Another possible discharge path from the tectum would be by tecto-tegmental paths to the tegmental gray and then caudalward by reticulo-spinal paths.   These paths are diagramed by various observers (for example, *Huber* and *Crosby*, '29; *Rasmussen*, '32a) and are illustrated in figure 526.

Between the lateral geniculate nucleus and the superior colliculus there is a band of fibers long known as the peduncle of the superior colliculus.   This peduncle carries chiefly tecto-geniculate fibers in lower mammals (as in reptiles, *Huber* and *Crosby*, '29, '33; see p. 1004), forming an important efferent path to the ventral nucleus of the lateral geniculate, from which area, after synapse, connections are made with efferent centers such as the zona incerta.   Whether this peduncle carries a few afferent fibers from the dorsal nucleus of the lateral geniculate in lower mammals is uncertain, although there is some evidence (according to Ranson's laboratory) to the contrary.   In man, where only a small percentage of the uncrossed optic fibers reach the tectum directly, presumably they must be supplemented by geniculo-tectal fibers, visual impulses traveling over such uncrossed paths, synapsing for the most part in the dorsal nucleus of the lateral geniculate, and then passing by geniculo-tectal paths to the optic tectum for visual reflexes.   These differences are emphasized in the large and small diagrams in figure 526.   They find substantiation in the results of experimental and clinical work.   Thus clinical evidence indicates (*Tilney* and *Riley*, '21) that destruction of the human thalamic optic center leads to the abolishment of many visual reflexes as well as to a loss of visual consciousness. This indicates that the superior colliculus is unable to mediate many visual reflexes in man. However, in many mammals this center serves visual as well as light reflexes. For the rabbit *Brouwer* ('27, p. 10) stated : "This ganglion is in rabbits of much higher significance for sight than in higher mammals and does not merely serve for lower reflex movements." In rabbits, but somewhat less definitely in monkeys, *Brouwer* and his co-workers found a localization of optic fibers within the tectum of such type that the upper quadrants of the retina find representation in the caudal and lateral portions of the superior colliculus and the lower quadrants in the more oral and medial parts of the area. From the tectum, discharge to motor centers of the brain stem and cord is effected over tecto-tegmental (*Winkler* and *Potter*, '11 ; *Tsai*, '25a, and others), crossed and uncrossed tecto-oculomotor, and crossed and uncrossed lateral and medial tecto-bulbar and tecto-spinal paths (*Edinger*, '08 ; *Ramón y Cajal*, '11 ; *Winkler* and *Potter*, '11 and '14 ; *Rasmussen*, '31, '32 ; *Tsai*, '25, *Rioch*, '29 ; figs. 526, 528 ; for tecto-spinals, Chap. II ; also figs. 526 and 528). Crossed and uncrossed tecto-rubral tracts occur (*Rioch*, '29 ; fig. 510). To pontine gray passes the tecto-pontine path as described by *Pavlow* ('00e), *Tsai* ('25), and *Rasmussen* ('31). Tecto-nigral and nigro-tectal paths have been described by *Tsai* ('25), *Kodama* ('29), and *Rioch* ('29). These are discussed further on page 1094 and shown in figure 510.

Collaterals from various ascending systems bringing in sensory impulses from body and face, auditory impulses from the inferior colliculus by way of the periventricularly running acoustico-optic tract, and impulses from the thalamus by tecto-thalamic fibers (*Gurdjian*, '27, and others) and from the hypothalamus by the dorsal longitudinal fasciculus may modify visual impulses reaching the tectum, or, in the absence of such impulses, may themselves give rise to discharges over efferent paths.

Means of cortically conditioning the tectal reflexes are provided by cortico-tectal fascicles which swing down from the occipital regions of the cortex, pass through the dorsal thalamus, where they may receive some additions from the pulvinar (opinions differ with regard to this), and enter the tectum through the stratum album mediale and adjoining gray (figs. 515 and 526). Another small cortical path, probably not from the occipital cortex, has been described to the stratum zonale (*Bailey*, *Strong*, and *Elwyn*, '25, and others). This has been followed in a number of mammals by *Huber* and *Crosby* (to be published).

The superior collicular commissure interconnects the tectal areas of the two sides and carries a variable number of crossed fascicles of efferent tracts, such as the tecto-spinals. The posterior commissure, in so far as it is concerned with the tectum, probably serves for interconnecting fibers between subtectal and contralateral tectal areas and carries discharge paths for the pretectal nucleus.

The mammalian superior colliculus, then, is an important way station in the visual reflex path, is a center through which cortical conditioning of such reflexes may occur, is a region where they may be modified on the reflex plane by other afferent impulses, and serves as an efferent center for other types of reflexes, also. Moreover it serves as a light reflex center in man although it may be relieved of this function in other mammals by pretectal areas. Slight cortical conditioning of the light reflex is said to occur in man; if so this must be through the superior colliculus, possibly through the position corresponding to the pretectal nucleus.

The Tegmental Nuclei of the Mesencephalon with Fiber Connections

The most complete analysis of the tegmental region in mammals is to be found in the series of papers by *Castaldi* ('23, '24, and '26) on the guinea pig, to which series those interested in the detailed structure of this region are referred. It is impossible within the limits of the present chapter to present the detailed

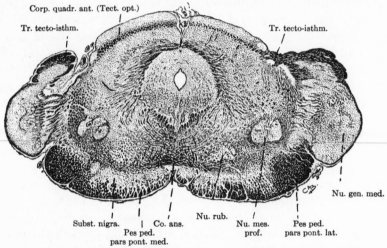

FIG 505. A cross section through the midbrain of an anteater (Tamandua tetradactyla).

Co.ans., commissura ansulata; *Corp.quadr.ant.(Tect.opt.)*, corpus quadrigeminum anterius (tectum opticum); *Nu.gen.med.*, nucleus geniculatus medialis; *Nu.mes.prof.*, nucleus mesencephalicus profundus; *Nu.rub.*, nucleus ruber; *Pes ped.pars pont.med.*, tractus cortico-pontinus medialis (fronto-pontine); *Pes ped.pars pont.lat.*, tractus cortico-pontinus lateralis; *Subst.nigra*, substantia nigra; *Tr.tecto-isthm.*, tractus tecto-isthmalis of Ariens Kappers.

relations described in these most thorough and most instructive accounts. Only certain of the better recognized nuclear masses will be described here.

Several of the nuclear masses of the midbrain have been considered in other sections of this text, in which consideration has been given to special nuclear groups. Thus the nuclei of the oculomotor and of the trochlear nerves have been described with the other motor nuclei of the brain stem (Chapter V, pp. 612 to 618). The reticular groups of the midbrain, including the tegmental nuclei, have been described in Chapter VI. Certain nuclear groups deserving of further or special discussion are considered here; these are the nucleus interstitialis of *Ramón y Cajal*, the ventral interstitial nucleus of the medial longitudinal fasciculus, the nucleus of Darkschewitsch, the red nucleus, and the nucleus interpeduncularis.

a. Nuclei Associated with the Medial Longitudinal Fasciculus. Relations and Functions of the Fasciculus. In mammals, near the frontal end of the nucleus ruber are scattered cells, which forward and dorsalward are continuous with similar cells lying among the bundles of the medial longitudinal fasciculus. Taken together these cells constitute the interstitial nucleus of *Ramón y Cajal* ('11). As figured by that observer, the cells are relatively large and multipolar and their neuraxes enter the medial longitudinal fasciculus. A more ventral interstitial nucleus of the fasciculus longitudinalis medialis is present in many mammals, lying at the caudal end of the diencephalon near the midline and in front of the oculomotor nuclei. It, too, contributes fibers to the medial longitudinal fasciculus.

Dorsal to the interstitial nucleus of *Ramón y Cajal* ('11) is the nucleus of Darkschewitsch, sometimes termed the nucleus of the medial longitudinal fasciculus or the nucleus of the commissura posterior. These latter names illustrate the two types of connections for which this nucleus is believed to be responsible. Its cells resemble in general character those of the nucleus interstitialis just described. Its dendrites extend out between the fascicles of the posterior commissure and certain of its neuraxes may be traced from the cell bodies into the bundles of the medial longitudinal fasciculus (*Ramón y Cajal*, '11). By various observers it has been stated that a certain per cent of its neuraxes enter the posterior commissure, decussate there, and pass to the medial longitudinal fasciculus of the other side. The nucleus of Darkschewitsch is shown in figures 507 and 527 (following the interpretation of *Ramón y Cajal*, '11).

In Delphinus delphis *Hatschek* and *Schleisinger* ('02) described, as corpus ellipticum, a differentiated part of the central gray dorsal to the oculomotor nucleus and considered it characteristic of the brain of water animals. *Riese* ('24a) agreed with these observers. A comparable nuclear mass has been described by *Hines* ('29) in Ornithorhynchus. She found the nucleus composed of large, polymorphic cells and traced fibers from it to the pretectal and interstitial nuclei and "a few of which may mingle with the striatal and longitudinal fasciculus group."

In connection with these nuclei it appears desirable to review the relations and connections of the medial longitudinal fasciculus. This path (fig. 506) begins cephalically as small fascicles emanating from its ventral interstitial nuclei (in the region of the subthalamic caudal boundary) and extends dorsalward to the region of its main interstitial nucleus (mentioned in the preceding paragraphs), from which region it is easily recognizable. It extends caudalward, occupying a position near the midline, not far from the floor of the ventricle and in very evident relation to the nuclei of the somatic motor column at the respective levels. As the lower end of the medulla oblongata is reached, behind the level of the sensory decussation, the medial longitudinal fasciculi, with the associated medial tecto-spinal and probably the ventral spino-thalamic bundles, overlie the pyramids. As fascicles of the pyramids cross in the motor decussation to form the lateral cortico-spinal tracts, they pass between the above mentioned bundles, and these (the medial longitudinal fasciculi and their associated tracts) swing lateralward and ventralward to become continuous with the ventral ground bundle of the spinal cord.

The medial longitudinal fasciculus or, as it is termed frequently, the posterior longitudinal fasciculus, serves many functions.   In part it is made up of short fibers interconnecting brain stem nuclei, and particularly the motor nuclei of various levels.   In part it interrelates eye muscle nuclei with contralateral and probably with homolateral vestibular nuclei.   Recent work, and particularly that of *Muskens* ('30), indicates that the bundle carries very important connections between vestibular centers and the contralateral and homolateral nuclei commissurales posteriores and the nucleus interstitialis.   The list of more important connections of the fasciculus follows, many of which will not be rediscussed since they have received consideration in Chapter IV.   However, a brief account of the significance of the connections with the nuclei of the medial longitudinal fasciculus will be presented.   According to *Muskens* ('14), the arrangement of the bundles within the medial longitudinal fasciculus of the cat is such that the homolateral fibers occupy a lateral position; internal to them are found the bundles arising from the opposite side of the brain stem, and still more medial the centrifugal components of the bundle.   A comparison of the components considered below with those described for birds by *Wallenberg* (see p. 1025) and others shows many resemblances between avian and mammalian forms.

Thus, among other fiber bundle components, the medial longitudinal fasciculus contains (see fig. 506) :

1.   Fibers from the contralateral and, according to *Ramón y Cajal* ('11), homolateral nuclei of the posterior commissure.   Those from the homolateral nucleus constitute the fasciculus commissuro-medullaris of *Muskens* ('14).   Fibers from the homolateral interstitial nucleus of the medial longitudinal fasciculus constitute the fasciculus interstitio-spinalis of *Muskens* ('14).   These bundles have been seen in the medial longitudinal fasciculus in normal preparations or after lesions in the region of the posterior commissure by *Held* ('93), *Boyce* ('94), *Redlich*, ('99), *van Gehuchten* ('04), *Probst* ('00a), *Karplus* and *Economo* ('09), *Economo* ('11), *Ramón y Cajal* ('11), *Muskens* ('14, '22, and '30), and others.

2.   Bundles which interconnect the eye muscle nuclei and which associate them with the accessory nucleus and motor nuclei of the cervical spinal cord.

3.   Reticulo-spinal fibers which descend from the reticular or tegmental gray to the cord according to *von Monakow* ('95), *Kohnstamm* and *Quensel* ('08), *Probst* ('02a), *van Gehuchten* ('04), *Papez* ('26), and others.   These are discussed on pages 269, 270, and 290, and 659 to 662 and diagramed in figure 506.

4.   Fibers connecting the oculomotor nuclei with the nucleus of the facial nerve, coming there into relation with those neurons which supply the corrugator supercilii and the orbicularis oculi, providing thus for the correlation of the movements of these muscles with those of the levator superioris — also fibers connecting the hypoglossal and the contralateral facial nucleus.   Both of these connections may be regarded as typical of various similar connections through the medial longitudinal fasciculus.

5.   Fibers from the superior vestibular nucleus to the homolateral oculomotor, trochlear, and abducens nuclei, fibers from the inferior vestibular nuclei to the

contralateral motor centers of the upper cord, and fibers from the medial vestibular nuclei, which, after crossing the midline, bifurcate and supply both the eye muscle nuclei and centers of the upper part of the spinal cord. The above

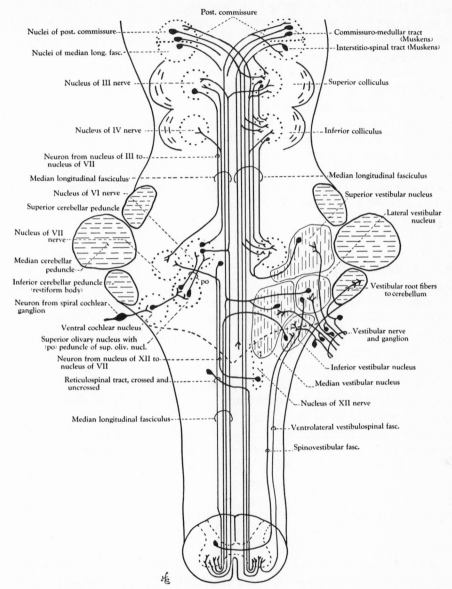

Post. commissure

Nuclei of post. commissure

Nuclei of median long. fasc.

Nucleus of III nerve

Nucleus of IV nerve

Neuron from nucleus of III to nucleus of VII

Median longitudinal fasciculus

Nucleus of VI nerve

Superior cerebellar peduncle

Nucleus of VII nerve

Median cerebellar peduncle

Inferior cerebellar peduncle (restiform body)

Neuron from spiral cochlear ganglion

Ventral cochlear nucleus

Superior olivary nucleus with (po) peduncle of sup. oliv. nucl.

Neuron from nucleus of XII to nucleus of VII

Reticulospinal tract, crossed and uncrossed

Median longitudinal fasciculus

Commissuro-medullar tract (Muskens)

Interstitio-spinal tract (Muskens)

Superior colliculus

Inferior colliculus

Median longitudinal fasciculus

Superior vestibular nucleus

Lateral vestibular nucleus

Vestibular root fibers to cerebellum

po

Vestibular nerve and ganglion

Inferior vestibular nucleus

Median vestibular nucleus

Nucleus of XII nerve

Ventrolateral vestibulospinal fasc.

Spinovestibular fasc.

FIG. 506. A diagram presenting the chief components of the medial longitudinal fasciculus. *Huber* and *Crosby*.

connections of the vestibular centers with the medial longitudinal fasciculus follow the account of *Gray* ('26) for the cat. Certain observers regarded the crossed bifurcated fibers as arising from the lateral vestibular nucleus instead of the medial vestibular nucleus, and other observers (*Rasmussen*, '32) carried fiber bundles into the contralateral medial longitudinal fasciculus from the medial and homolateral descending from the lateral vestibular nuclei. Other observers (*Winkler*, '07), working on the rabbit, regarded certain fibers as arising in the Deiters' nucleus and as ascending, at first slightly lateral to, and then as a part of, the homolateral medial longitudinal fasciculus, after the level of the trochlear nucleus is reached. According to *Winkler*, this homolateral fasciculus has rich connections with the eye muscle nuclei; however, he also recognized contralateral ascending and descending fibers from the nucleus of Deiters. *Probst* ('02), *Frazer* ('02), *van Gehuchten* ('04), *Winkler* ('07), *Muskens* ('14), *Gray* ('26), *Rasmussen* ('32), and others have demonstrated descending fibers from the vestibular nuclei to regions of the spinal cord through the medial longitudinal fasciculus, but opinions differ with regard to the origin of this fasciculus from the respective vestibular nuclei, certain of the observers regarding it as arising from the medial or triangular nucleus, other observers regarding it as arising from the lateral vestibular nucleus. A homolateral descending tract has been described as arising from the medial or triangular nucleus (see *Muskens*, '14, p. 54).

6. Fibers from the lateral and medial (or triangular) vestibular nuclei to the contralateral medial longitudinal fasciculus which ascend in the fasciculus and cross (*Muskens*, '22, p. 477) through the posterior commissure to the nucleus commissuralis posterior and the nucleus interstitialis of the medial longitudinal fasciculus; also fibers from the superior vestibular nucleus by way of the homolateral medial longitudinal fasciculus, apparently to decussate in the posterior commissure (*Muskens*, '22, p. 477) in order to reach the nucleus commissuralis posterior.

The connections discussed under number 6 deserve further consideration. *Muskens* ('14) executed a series of physiological experiments on the cat with a view to establishing certain connections, and particularly of determining the vestibular components of the medial (or posterior) longitudinal fasciculus and their relations, and hence the relations of the fasciculus to forced movements. He found that the degeneration of the crossed vestibulo-mescencephalic tract, which he diagrammed as passing cephalad in the medial part of the medial longitudinal fasciculus to the nucleus commissuralis posterior, or at least to the region of this nucleus, was associated with the appearance of circus movements on the side opposite to that in which the partially degenerated medial longitudinal fasciculus was found, just so long as other portions of the vestibular system remained uninjured. *Muskens* obtained these results whether he destroyed the vestibular nuclei (including the triangular or medial and the remainder or lateral nucleus of Deiters) or placed a lesion directly within the medial longitudinal fasciculus. Conjugate deviation was obtained by the degeneration of the uncrossed ascending tract from the superior vestibular nucleus, which he carried to the nucleus commissuralis posterior. He interconnected the nuclei of the posterior commissure through fibers of the commissure. Later studies led him to the conclusion that the "secondary vestibular tract which ascends in the posterior longitudinal bundles crosses the midline by way of the posterior commissure before entering the nucleus commissurae posterioris and nucleus interstitialis." The crossing of the middle and lateral parts of the medial longitudinal fasciculus which are to supply the commissural nuclear groups of the posterior commissure has been seen by *C.* and *O. Vogt* ('19), *Riese* ('24b), and *Groebbels* ('27, for birds).

In an experimental lesion of the posterior commissure of the cat, *Muskens* ('22) found that, on the side of the lesion, degeneration occurred in both the commissuro-medullaris and the interstitio-spinalis tracts, that is, in the tracts from the nucleus commissurae posterioris to the medulla oblongata regions and from the nucleus interstitialis to the spinal cord regions, indicating the direction of conduction of these paths. A degeneration of the contralateral interstitio-spinal tract may have been due to an injury of the medial longitudinal fasciculus of the other side. A similar but more limited lesion was made in a rabbit brain.

The preceding account indicates clearly that the medial longitudinal fasciculus is a very important coördinating system of the brain stem; (1) that it interrelates motor nuclei, serving to coördinate their discharge; (2) that it serves as a discharge path from the reticular gray to the efferent centers of the spinal cord; (3) that it connects vestibular nuclei with the eye muscle centers and the upper regions of the spinal cord; (4) that through its bundles, which integrate the vestibular with the contralateral commissural nuclei and the descending pathways through the fasciculus, it forms an important part of the pathway concerned with forced movements.

Since the connections of the commissural nuclei with the higher centers apparently have a close functional relation to the connections of these centers with the medial longitudinal fasciculus, such secondary connections can be discussed best at this time, although they belong in part with the ansa lenticularis, to be considered later.

The experimental lesions of the posterior commissure of the rabbit and the cat, to which reference has been made above, permitted not only an analysis of the descending paths but also allowed *Muskens* ('22) to postulate the presence of ascending fibers from the commissural nuclei to the striatal region. In the cat material, which was prepared by the Marchi method, he found evidence of degenerating fibers which "disappear in the direction of the globus pallidus." *Muskens* believed also that the globus pallidus sends efferent fibers to the com-missural nuclei. He ('22, p. 468) stated: "I therefore conclude from this evidence that the commissural nuclei are in neuronal continuity with the globus pallidus of the same side. This connection consists of at least two neurons between the globus pallidus and the commissural nuclei, whereas in the reverse direction but one neuron exists." *Muskens* ('22) found that injuries to the connections of the globus pallidus with the commissural nuclei or to the oral end of the globus pallidus itself are associated with a lateral conjugate deviation of the head and the eyes to the injured side, with circus movements which persist, and with a tendency on the part of the animal to fall toward the injured side. With these results of *Muskens* ('14 and '22) certain anatomical observations and certain experimental and clinical work appear to be in agreement, although much further confirmation and explanation of the details, particularly of the details of the ascending path, would be desirable. *C.* and *O. Vogt* ('19) and *Riese* ('24a), in a study of normal material, reached the conclusion that there exist interconnections between the commissural nuclei and the globus pallidus. The results of the experimental work of *Feliciangeli* ('10) on the dog and *Rogers* ('24) on the opossum are in agreement in general with the results obtained by *Muskens*, who in turn considered his work as in accord with that of *Probst* ('00a) and with that of *Gerstmann* ('16) and probably with that of *Polimanti* ('06), although in the absence of a microscopic check of the material, the work of the last mentioned observer is more difficult to correlate. *Morgan* ('27) described in the cat a bundle of fibers from the globus pallidus which coursed partly through the nucleus subthalamicus and partly around its caudal pole in order to reach the caudal portion of the field (H$_2$) of Forel, the nuclei of the oculomotor nerve, including the Edinger-Westphal nucleus, the nucleus commissurae posterioris (or nucleus of Darkschewitsch), and the interstitial nucleus of the medial longitudinal fasciculus. This bundle appears to correspond with the connection advocated by *Muskens* ('14, '22, '30, etc.) between the globus pallidus and the commissural nuclei of the posterior commissure.

Muskens ('30) presented a study of certain experimental material, prepared for other purposes by various observers, and reached the conclusion that the destruction of the globus pallidus was accompanied by evidences of atrophy in the nucleus commissurae posterioris, while the medial longitudinal fasciculus on the side of the lesion was smaller. *Hinsey, Ranson,* and *McNattin* ('30) have shown that progressive locomotion is impossible where the level of transection of the brain stem in a cat is caudal to a plane which passes through the cephalic pole of the tectum dorsally and the cephalic end of the mammillary body ventrally. *Muskens* ('30) called attention to the fact that such lesions left intact the commissura posterior, the associated nuclei, and the medial longitudinal fasciculus, and, having emphasized again the significance of the tractus commissuro-medullaris in conjugate deviation of the head and eyes and of the tractus interstitio-spinalis for rolling or circus movements, concluded that "Die Symptome nach Verletzung des Globus pallidus sind vollkommen in Uberein-stimmung mit dieser Korrelation. Diese posturalen locomotorischen Funktionen sind absonderlich im Globus pallidus lokalisiert."

However, not all observers have agreed that the paths passing to the commissural nuclei and the nuclei of the oculomotor nerves are striatal in origin. For example *Kodama* ('29) discusses the possibility that such connections are cortical, and cortical paths to the commissural nuclei have been described by various observers (as for example *Villiger*, '25) and rather generally there have been recognized cortico-oculomotor fibers (as for example *Bechterew*, '94). That both cortical and striatal fibers may be present, although not necessarily in the same tracts, seems probable, at least with regards to the oculomotor centers.

It seems fair to conclude that there is evidence suggesting striatal connections from the globus pallidus to the commissural nuclei (nucleus commissuralis posterior and nucleus interstitialis) by way of fascicles which, in the broader meaning of the term, are called the ansa lenticularis.   The evidence for an ascending path is less clear, at least much is to be desired in the way of a demonstration of its course.   Those particularly interested in the details of this important work on the relations of the medial longitudinal fasciculus to forced movements are referred to the articles quoted above and to those listed in the bibliography.

b. *Nucleus Interpeduncularis.*   Nucleus interpeduncularis has been studied by numerous observers.   Among the earlier workers may be mentioned *Forel* ('72), *Ganser* ('82), *Ramón y Cajal* ('11), and others.   It has been recognized by practically all of the later students of this region of the mammalian mesencephalon. Phylogenetically it is old, having been identified in fishes, amphibians, reptiles, and birds.   It is particularly well developed in macrosmatic mammals, since one of its primary functions is to serve as an end station for the habenulo-peduncular tract.   *Ramón y Cajal* ('11) recognized in this nucleus an unpaired mass of gray consisting of two layers of cells: (1) a superficial zone, and (2) a deep zone.   The superficial zone contains ovoid, fusiform, or triangular, multi-polar neurons.   Many of these neurons have dendrites which extend more or less parallel to the surface of the brain and which show marked varicosities and many fine branches.   Neuraxes of these neurons often follow a very sinuous course among the processes of the deeper cells of the area, and ultimately pass over into the overlying tegmental gray.   The deep zone has smaller, star-shaped cells with greatly branched processes radiating out in all directions from the cell body, and a larger type of cell similar to those found in the superficial zone.   The neuraxes of the larger cells of the deep zone likewise enter the teg-mental region.   Probably both they and the cells of the superficial zone contribute to the formation of the pedunculo-tegmental tract.   The neuraxes of the smaller cells of the deep zone, according to *Ramón y Cajal*, break up into numerous arborizations in regions near the cell body.   This nucleus is illustrated in figures 507, 509, and 510.

The main incoming connection to the nucleus is the habenulo-peduncular tract, figures 507, 512, 527, which arises from the habenular nuclei.   On entrance to the interpeduncular nucleus the fibers of this tract follow a most peculiar course, for they swing across the nucleus to the opposite side of the brain, then curve back again to break up ultimately in terminal arborizations on the side on which they enter.   Collaterals are given off from this main fiber tract, particularly during the latter part of its course through the nucleus, and such collaterals arise at right angles.   Certain of the fibers of the tract, on entrance to the nucleus, bifurcate, and the branches follow the course just described for single fibers but distribute in different planes.   This curious course of the terminal bundles of the habenulo-peduncular tract has been most excellently illustrated by *Ramón y Cajal* ('11) and has been verified by other observers.   Into the interpeduncular nucleus come fibers from the mammillary bodies, consti-tuting a mammillo-peduncular tract.   Arising from the cells of the inter-peduncular nucleus is the tractus pedunculo-tegmentalis described first by

Ganser ('82), who called it "faisceau de la calotte du ganglion inter-pedunculaire." This tract terminates in the dorsal tegmental nucleus. The interpeduncular nucleus is a way station in the discharge of impulses from the hypothalamic

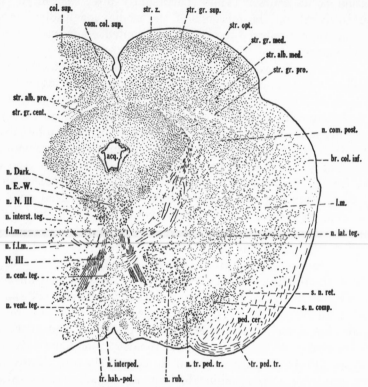

Fig. 507. Transverse section through the level of the root of the oculo-motor nerve. Adult cat. Toluidin-blue preparation. *Rioch.*

acq., acqueductus; *br.col.inf.*, brachium colliculi inferioris; *col.sup.*, colliculus superior; *com.col.sup.*, commissura colliculi superioris; *f.l.m.*, fasciculus longitudinalis medialis; *l.m.*, lemniscus medialis; *n.cent.teg.*, nucleus centralis tegmenti; *n.com.post.*, nucleus commissurae posterioris; *n.Dark.*, nucleus of Darkschewitsch; *n.E.-W.*, nucleus of Edinger-Westphal; *n.f.l.m.*, nucleus fasciculi longitudinalis medialis; *n.interped.*, nucleus interpeduncularis; *n.in-terst.teg.*, nucleus interstitialis tegmenti; *n.lat.teg.*, nucleus lateralis tegmenti; *n.N.III*, nucleus nervi oculomotorii; *n.rub.*, nucleus ruber; *n.tr.ped.tr.*, nucleus tractus peduncularis transversi; *n.vent.teg.*, nucleus ventralis tegmenti; *N.III*, nervus oculomotorius; *ped.cer.*, pedunculus cerebri; *s.n.comp.*, substantia nigra compacta; *s.n.ret.*, substantia nigra reticularis; *str.alb.med.*, stratum album mediale; *str.alb.pro.*, stratum album profundum; *str.gr.cent.*, stratum griseum centrale; *str.gr.med.*, stratum griseum mediale; *str.gr.pro.*, stratum griseum profundum; *str.gr.sup.*, stratum griseum superiore; *str.opt.*, stratum opticum; *str.z.*, stratum zonale; *tr.hab.-ped.*, tractus habenulo-peduncularis; *tr.ped.tr.*, tractus peduncularis transversus.

olfacto-visceral and epithalamic olfacto-somatic correlation centers to the teg-mental regions of the midbrain. From the dorsal tegmental nucleus these impulses distribute by the dorsal longitudinal fasciculus to the efferent centers of the brain stem, perhaps including the preganglionic centers such as the dorsal efferent nucleus of the vagus (*Huber* and *Crosby*, '29; *Piersol's* Anatomy,

'30), thus constituting a way in which impulses from these regions may affect the sympathetic nervous system.

c. *Nucleus Ruber.* The nucleus ruber is a conspicuous element of the tegmental region of the midbrain and easily recognizable in all mammalian forms. It is situated at superior collicular levels, occupying a position ventral to the oculomotor nuclei and ventrolateral to the dorsal tegmental decussation. In certain higher mammals, such as man, the nucleus extends forward into the subthalamic region. It has been subdivided in several ways and it is uncertain to what extent the subdivisions are directly comparable in the different mammals (see *Foix* and *Nicolesco*, '25). Nucleus ruber has been described and figured so frequently that it is felt unjustifiable to quote any large proportion of the pertinent literature. An attempt is here made to present briefly certain representative contributions and it is suggested that the reader particularly interested in the relations of this nucleus in respective animal forms or in particular fiber connections or functional activities of this center, consult the contributions quoted for more extended bibliographic references. This nucleus is illustrated in figures 503, 505, 507 to 510, 521, and elsewhere in the text.

Fundamental studies of the red nucleus, which have greatly influenced all later work, were carried on by *von Monakow* ('95), who recognized in the cephalic third of the red nucleus of the rabbit a large-celled ventral portion, a dorsal reticular nucleus, and a nucleus gelatinosus (which was also reticular but was placed dorsolaterally). In addition to the above mentioned divisions, the middle third presented a nucleus minimus and a lateral horn. *Von Monakow* regarded the lateral horn as fused with the nucleus gelatinosus in the cephalic third of the nucleus. *Hatschek* ('07) recognized magnocellular and parvocellular portions within the red nucleus and, in tracing the phylogenetic development of this center, showed that the magnocellular part predominates in lower mammals and the parvocellular becomes more conspicuous in higher forms. *Ariëns Kappers* ('21) confirmed the conclusions of *Hatschek*. *Winkler* and *Potter* ('11) described a magnocellular portion and dorsolateral and ventrolateral small cell divisions, which divisions correspond very well with the portions recognized by *Tsai* ('25) in the opossum, for which form this observer noted a nucleus ruber medialis (receiving the lenticular fasciculus of Forel and giving origin to the rubro-spinal tract), which may be compared with the magnocellular portion of the rabbit, and a nucleus ruber lateralis, the connections of which were not given but which in position suggest the remaining portions of the red nucleus. The red nucleus of carnivores has been described by several observers, among whom may be mentioned *Winkler* and *Potter* ('14), *Rademaker* ('26), *Rioch* ('29a), and *Davenport* and *Ranson* ('30). The nucleus appears to extend farther forward in the cat than in the rabbit (*Winkler* and *Potter; Magnus*, '24; *Davenport* and *Ranson*). In the dog *Rioch* described a more compact caudal portion having very large cells and a more loosely arranged oral portion with intermingled large and small cells. In both the rabbit and the cat, *Davenport* and *Ranson* found large cells closely packed within the caudal pole of the nucleus and a more diffuse rostral portion which has large cells and scattered small cells. They suggested that a division into compact and diffuse portions best characterizes the nucleus. The nucleus minimus of *von Monakow* was identified in the cat and they called attention to a small group of cells in a lateral position to the cephalic part of the nucleus within the reticular gray of the region which they stated "might conceivably be regarded as a small-celled component of the red nucleus in the cat and rabbit."

Magnocellular and parvocellular divisions were found by *Friedemann* ('12) in Cercopithecus and by *Mingazzini* ('28) and others in man, the large-celled portion constituting the caudal portion of the nuclear complex and the small-celled portion its oral part. In man the large cells are multipolar with dendrites extending in all directions but terminating in end brushes largely within the nucleus; the cells have a cytoplasm within which are granules. The cells are rich in chromatin and the neurofibrils form a network close to the nucleus (*Mingazzini*). The neuraxis may arise either directly from the cell body or it may arise from a main dendrite. Frequently it gives off two collaterals (*Ramón y Cajal*, '11), which divide and redivide among the cells of the nucleus. The main neuraxes enter the rubro-spinal tract (*Mingazzini* and others). According to *Mingazzini* ('28), very large cells containing yellow pigment are found in the more ventral and medial regions of the human red nucleus. Triangular and spindle-shaped cells with rich granulations characterize the parvocellular portion of the red nucleus of man. Such cells have dendrites similar to those of the large cells and fine neuraxes which, after their origin, may give rise to collaterals and then pass into efferent paths, supposedly into the rubro-thalamic and possibly into the rubro-spinal and the rubro-reticular tracts.

The major connections of the red nucleus are: the dento-rubral and rubro-thalamic tracts, the rubro-reticular, rubro-bulbar, rubro-spinal, tecto-rubral, strio-rubral, incerto-rubral, subthalamo-rubral, and cortico-rubral tracts or paths, and shorter internuclear fibers.

The dento-rubral tract or path (a part of the dento-rubro-thalamic system) constitutes the main mass of the superior cerebellar peduncle. It arises in the dentate nucleus and swings downward and forward to decussate in the tegmental region of the midbrain, then turns forward into the red nucleus where it terminates. It is accompanied by dento-thalamic fibers, which are joined at the level of the red nucleus by a rubro-thalamic component. The dento-rubro-thalamic tract, in front of the red nucleus, joins the trigeminal lemniscus, which it accompanies to the anterior part of the ventral nucleus of the thalamus (prelemniscal fascicles of *Vogt*, '09). Thus the red nucleus serves as an important way station for proprioceptive and vestibular impulses on their way to higher centers. The discharge from the red nucleus occurs over the rubro-bulbar and rubro-spinal paths. These tracts arise from the red nucleus, decussate immediately in the ventral tegmental decussation, swing lateralward under the lemnisci systems, occupy a position dorsal to and in close relation with the lateral tecto-spinal tract, and so proceed caudalward, distributing to efferent centers of the bulb and cord. That impulses passing through the red nucleus may be conditioned by cortical centers appears probable since a number of observers have described cortico-rubral paths (*von Monakow*, '95 and '05; *Ramón y Cajal*, '11; *Foix* and *Nicolesco*, '25, and others).   In addition to these important relations, some workers regard the red nucleus as an important relay center between the lenticular nucleus and the motor centers of the brain stem and cord, the impulses reaching the red nucleus by way of the ansa lenticularis (*von Monakow*, '95 and '05; *Déjérine*, '01; *Ramón y Cajal*, '11; *Foix* and *Nicolesco*, '25, and others).   A further discussion of the relations of the red nucleus to the ansa lenticularis may be found on pages 1449 and 1450.   The red nucleus is connected also with the tectum by way of crossed and uncrossed tecto-rubral fibers, with the zona incerta by an incerto-rubral tract, with the nucleus subthalamicus by a subthalamo-rubral path, and with the substantia nigra by short internuclear fibers (*Foix* and *Nicolesco*, '25). According to *Rioch* ('29a) the connections between the tectal regions and the red nucleus run in three bundles: a most medial one intimately associated with the tecto-oculomotor system and crossed in the dorsal tegmental decussation, an intermediate group, crossed and uncrossed from the whole tectal area, and a lateral system connecting the red nucleus and tegmentum with the superior colliculus.   These are illustrated in figure 510.   Through the commissure of Forel the red nucleus is put into relation with the hypothalamus of the other side (*Foix* and *Nicolesco*, '25) and with the contralateral nucleus subthalamicus (*Déjérine*, '01).   The red nucleus is connected with its homologue on the other side of the brain and with the contralateral tegmental region of the midbrain through fibers of the posterior commissure (*Foix* and *Nicolesco*, '25).

   d. Results of Experimental Observations on the Red Nucleus.   No discussion of the red nucleus could claim to present a fair picture of the present knowledge of this important center without some reference to the great store of experimental observations concerned with it, but in summarizing experimental observations involving the red nucleus it must be acknowledged that at the present time there is still want of unanimity of view as to the functions of this nucleus.   The literature here especially discussed was chosen with the aim of presenting distinctive views of the functional relations of the red nucleus, and for the evidence supporting said views the original papers must be consulted and the extensive bibliographies, there presented, must be reviewed.   The following review opens with a consideration of the work of *Weed*.

   The red nucleus was regarded by *Weed* ('14) as the center concerned in postural reactions.   In 1917, working with young decerebrated kittens, this observer reached the conclusion that animals under 10 days of age showed prolonged progressive movements but only rarely decerebrate rigidity, while older decerebrate animals showed much less evidence of progressive movements but extensor rigidity.   These observations of *Weed* received confirmation in a series of studies by *Langworthy* ('24, '28, and '29), who used not only kittens but also puppies, young rabbits, and young guinea pigs.   According to this latter observer the time of possible appearance of decerebrate rigidity is dependent on the relative maturity of the animal.   Thus decerebration following birth produces decerebrate rigidity in guinea pigs which are relatively mature but only progressive movements in kittens and rabbits which are relatively immature. As an exception to this, *Langworthy* ('29) cited a case of a newborn kitten in which the nervous system appeared somewhat unusually advanced in its development, and in which he was able to see an onset of rigidity in the neck muscles.   Langworthy found that in rabbits quite a lapse of time must occur before decerebration is followed by decerebrate rigidity.   *Weed* and *Langworthy* ('25) failed to obtain extensor rigidity in pouch-young opossums until they had reached 82 days of age.   *Langworthy* ('24 and '29) believed that the time of development of decerebrate rigidity about coincides with that of the animal's ability to stand and is associated with the myelinization of the rubro-spinal tract.   *Langworthy* ('33) found the beginning of myelinization in the red nucleus in his late fetal stage.

Somewhat different results were obtained by *Laughton* ('24, '26), who studied decerebrate rigidity in kittens from 4 hours to 7 weeks of age, rabbits from 24 hours to 2 weeks of age, and puppies from 6 hours to 6 weeks of age.   In kittens, regardless of age, decerebration was followed by extensor rigidity in the forelegs but in no case by such rigidity in the hindlegs.   Rigidity in both forelegs and hindlegs and in tail and neck muscles appeared when decerebration was carried out on animals of 5 weeks or more of age.   The position of the head in space, as was shown by *Magnus* and *de Kleijn* ('12), affected the rigidity in these kittens.   *Laughton* found that extensor rigidity appeared in the forelimbs of the youngest rabbits studied by him, that it increased gradually as older rabbits were studied, and that it was very marked in rabbits 10 days of age. In all rabbits from 10 days of age on (and in the adult rabbits also) the rigidity, while present in both limbs, was more marked in the forelimb than in the hindlimb.   Again the position of the head of the decerebrate animal influenced the rigidity, as *Magnus* ('25) had shown.   *Laughton's* results on puppies were in essential agreement with those obtained by him on kittens.   *Laughton* concluded from his experiments that extensor rigidity appears in the forelimbs of rabbits, kittens, and puppies only a few hours old as the result of decerebration and that it increases progressively as the animals grow older ; that extensor rigidity of the hindlimb does not appear, in any of the three types studied, as a result of decerebration of the very young animals, but appears later in their ontogenetic development.

Windle ('29), in a series of experiments carried out on dogs (2 to 4 days old) and kittens (from late fetal life to 26 days of age), arrived at the conclusion that it was the level of transection and not the age of the animal which determined whether decerebration was followed by progressive movements or rigidity. Transections removing all or nearly all of the red nucleus were followed by hypertonicity in the extensor muscles, particularly of the foreleg.   *Windle* regarded this as indicating that decerebrate rigidity is not dependent for its development upon the red nucleus. He stated: "It is evident that the postural reaction is independent of the red nucleus and that it develops before the rubro-spinal tract is myelinated."   *Griffin* and *Windle* ('31), in a further study of newborn and young rabbits, reached the conclusion, in agreement with *Windle's* earlier work, that the level of the transection is more important than the age of the animal in predicting the occurrence of decerebrate rigidity.

Various other observers have believed that decerebrate rigidity may develop after destruction of the red nucleus or after lesions caudal to it, which cut off the rubro-spinal tract, such results indicating that this nucleus is not a necessary center for the production of rigidity. Thus *Thiele* ('05) obtained increasing rigidity in cats and monkeys by various coronal transections of the brain beginning from a plane through the caudal end of the thalamus to a plane involving the trapezoid nucleus, with the rigidity disappearing at the latter level. *Sherrington* ('06) found that various transections of the midbrain produced rigidity. This observer, who ('96) gave the name decerebrate rigidity to the prolonged contraction seen in destruction of the hemispheres and basal nuclei of the cerebrum, showed ('06) that animals with the cerebellum removed still showed such rigidity. *Bazzett* and *Penfield* ('22) obtained decerebrate rigidity in animals in which the red nucleus was almost completely lacking and in others in which a median section of the mesencephalon destroyed the rubro-spinal tracts at their decussation. *Ranson* and *Hinsey* ('29) found that the red nucleus could be removed completely in cats and still have the appearance in the animal of the highest type of decerebrate rigidity.

The work of *Rademaker* ('26) and *Magnus* ('25) indicated that decerebrate rigidity develops quite independently of the red nucleus. However, they considered that rigidity is not produced necessarily by transection above the midbrain level, since they regarded the centers necessary for maintaining normal muscle tonus situated within that segment. *Mella* ('23) and *Laughton* ('26) believed that, due to modification through other reactions, decerebrate rigidity might not appear from section of the caudal part of the thalamus. That decerebrate rigidity occurs as a result of section of the hypothalamus or the upper mesencephalic regions is substantiated in the work of various observers, including *Thiele* ('05), *Sherrington* ('06), *Weed* ('14), *Cobb, Bailey*, and *Holtz* ('17), and *Ranson* and *Hinsey* ('29).

Rademaker ('26) regarded the red nucleus as a chief center concerned in the regulation of normal muscle tone and in labyrinth and body righting reflexes. Those body righting reflexes acting on the head of the animal, together with the neck righting reflexes, are said to be present after removal of the cerebellum. The center for body righting impulses is said to be also in the red nucleus, but such impulses are lacking after removal of the cerebellum (*Rademaker*), although, according to *Magnus* ('25), there is no positive evidence for the influence of the cerebellum on postural activity. Removal of the cerebellum and transection behind the inferior colliculus showed well marked decerebrate rigidity according to *Beritoff* and *Magnus* ('14). The work of *Gray* ('26) on the vestibular mechanism in cats appears to indicate that the rubro-spinal tract is not concerned in tonic and rolling movements, since these movements do not appear unless the direct vestibulo-spinal tract is severed. *Muskens* ('14, '23, '30, etc.), whose work has been quite fully quoted on pages 1080 to 1082, believed it is the commissural nuclei associated with the posterior commissure, with their connections from the vestibular centers through the medial longitudinal fasciculus, which are concerned in forced movements. *Muskens* is of the opinion that the striatal connections usually ascribed to the red nucleus really pass through its capsule to the commissural nuclei.

Mussen ('27), after destruction of the caudal end of the red nucleus and its associated rubro-spinal tract, found that loss of righting reflexes or of rigidity did not follow. Destruction of the parvocellular portion led to a diminution of muscle tone and tendon reflexes, with a complete loss of righting reflexes; however, this loss was not permanent, a gradual improvement occurring in the days immediately following the operation, so that in a few weeks only a slight unsteadiness in balancing remained, together with a slight turning of the head to the right. According to *Mussen*, the destruction of the parvocellular portion of the red nucleus is associated with the degeneration of a crossed rubro-cervical tract which lies in close relation with the main rubro-spinal tract throughout its course.

Graham Brown ('15) found that kittens presented rhythmically progressive movements following removal of the cerebral cortex and the basal ganglia. *Laughton* ('24) found that the caudal two-thirds of the thalamus must remain uninjured in order that coördinated progressive movements might be present in the dog and the cat, while the cephalic two-thirds of the pontine region must remain uninjured for normal progressive movements in the rabbit. *Laughton* ('28) arrived at similar conclusions in his study of very young animals. In this connection, the emphasis which *Ranson* and *Hinsey* ('29) laid on the difference in the cephalic extent of the red nucleus in different animals should be borne in mind. Even a casual examination of normal preparations corroborates fully their statement, based particularly on behavior reactions, "that a mesencephalic rabbit is a very different preparation from a mescencephalic cat." *Hinsey* and *Ranson* ('28) found that an intact red nucleus and hypothalamus were associated with normal righting movements and walking. These observers in a later communication (*Ranson* and *Hinsey*, '29) stated that either the red nucleus or the tegmental region immediately adjacent to it plays a part in the inhibiting of the crossed extensor after-discharge in the de-afferented muscle. The work of *Hinsey, Ranson,* and *Dixon* ('30) indicated that the tegmental region of the midbrain, perhaps the red nucleus itself or the surrounding reticular formation, has motor functions. The responses which they obtained following stimulation of the tegmental region in the cat were extension of the forelimbs on the opposite side of the body and flexion on the same side. The response obtained from the hindlimbs was not always the same. They eliminated other possible sources for initiating this response such as the basis pedunculi, the tectum, and the medial longitudinal fasciculus. Section of the ventral tegmental decussation showed that the nervous impulse which produced this response did not travel by the rubro-spinal path and they suggest a rubro-reticular and a reticulo-spinal pathway.

Windle ('29) showed that in cats, when the level of the transection did not involve the red nucleus but extended forward to the optic chiasma from the rostral border of the superior colliculus, the righting reflexes and normal progression remained intact, but that if the region close to the cephalic end of this nucleus or its rostral tip were injured, then interference with the righting reflexes and with normal progression appeared. *Windle* was of the opinion that an uninjured red nucleus and possibly other structures in the hypothalamus were necessary for locomotion of a normal type in the animals studied.

An attempt to reach definite conclusions with regard to the functions of the red nucleus either in experimental animals or man is not an easy task. Obviously it is a way station for proprioceptive impulses from the cerebellum to the cortex by way of a synapse in the dorsal thalamus, and it represents one of the main discharge centers of the cerebellum. In spite of a lack of agreement on the matter, it seems probable that it is one of the series of discharge centers for the striatum (which is concerned with the coördination of associative movements) through the ansa lenticularis. There is at present no unanimity of opinion as to its relation to tonic and righting movements. The balance of evidence at present seems against its being the center concerned with the production of decerebrate rigidity, although it may exert, under given conditions, an inhibitory effect over such rigidity. Either the nucleus itself or the gray in its vicinity (such as diencephalic gray) appears to be necessary for normal walking in the experimental animals studied. A man with the nervous system severed in the caudal end of the diencephalon would not show such reflex walking. The danger of carrying over unmodified the results of experimental procedure on lower mammals as interpretations of the normal behavior of man has been emphasized by *Spatz* ('27), who pointed out that cerebral cortex dominance of necessity modifies the rôle played by the red nucleus in man as compared with its rôle in lower mammals.

Basis Pedunculi

The pars peduncularis of the mesencephalon shows greater changes than do other portions of the midbrain segment, and there is considerable difference in its development in passing from lower to higher mammals. It contains, as has been stated previously, the substantia nigra and the paths connecting the cortex with the pontine gray and with the motor centers of the brain stem and the spinal cord. On the border between the peduncular and tegmental portions of the midbrain, is found the nucleus tractus peduncularis transversi (figs. 507 to 509).

a. *Nucleus Tractus Peduncularis Transversi*. The nucleus tractus peduncularis transversi (nucleus opticus tegmenti, *Tsai*, '25a) lies along the inner border of the substantia nigra, between that nucleus and the mammillary body in the rat (*Kosaka* and *Hiraiwa*, '15; also fig. 508); it has been identified in other rodents, such as the guinea pig (*Castaldi*, '23), and in some but not all other mammals. This nucleus lies at the border between the peduncular and tegmental regions of the midbrain, and is sometimes allocated to one region and sometimes to the other. Although the fiber bundles may have thin medullary sheaths and so be hard to see in Marchi preparations (*Kosaka* and *Hiraiwa*, '15), experimental evidence indicates that this nucleus receives bundles which enter with the optic nerve (*Münzer* and *Wiener*, '02; *Wallenberg*, '04; *Loepp*, '12; *Kosaka* and *Hiraiwa*, '15; *Brouwer*, '23, and *Castaldi*, '23). Behind the chiasma these fibers swing caudalward over the cerebral peduncle and then turn dorsalward to reach the nucleus. They probably constitute the tractus peduncularis transversus of *Marburg* ('03) and are comparable, that observer indicated, with the basal optic root of birds and reptiles, while their nucleus is homologous to the avian nucleus ectomamillaris. They have been described by *Bochenek* ('08) and *Tsai* ('25a) under the name of the posterior accessory optic fasciculus. Connections of the nucleus tractus peduncularis transversi with the substantia nigra have been described by *Castaldi* ('23). *Sterzi* ('14–'15) traced fibers of the tractus peduncularis transversus (or posterior accessory optic tract) directly to substantia nigra. In reptiles and birds a connection with the oculomotor nucleus has been established for the gray homologous to the mammalian nucleus tractus peduncularis transversi. A similar connection was described by

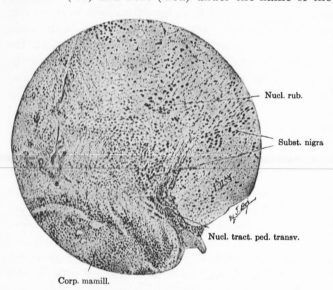

Nucl. rub.

Subst. nigra

Nucl. tract. ped. transv.

Corp. mamill.

FIG. 508. The nucleus tractus peduncularis transversi (*Nucl. tract.ped.transv.*) and the nucleus ruber (*Nucl.rub.*) in the rat. *Subst.nigra*, substantia nigra. *Kosaka* and *Hiraiwa*.

Edinger ('08) for mammals, but his results could not be substantiated in the material *Tsai* had available for study. The probable connection between these optic centers led to *Edinger's* suggestion that efferent fibers for the ciliary muscle and iris (as well as incoming fibers from the retina) were supplied from the nucleus peduncularis transversus.

b. The Substantia Nigra and Its Connections. The substantia nigra is a cell mass overriding the cerebral peduncle throughout the greater part of its extent in the mesencephalon and, in higher mammals, projecting forward into the ventral part of the diencephalon, and, in certain animals (as the cat, *Winkler* and *Potter*, '14, and the elephant, *Přecechtěl*, '25), caudalward into continuity with the gray matter of the pons. The cells of the region vary in size from small or medium sized elements to certain relatively large neurons with deeply staining granulations. *Morgan* ('27) believed that he could recognize within it motor and sensory regions on the basis of the cell types of the area. He described a medial group which he considered motor, a central group having sensory cells of the type so recognized by *Malone* ('10), and a lateral group comparable to the interpeduncular nucleus of *Jacobson* ('09). There appears to be more justification, at least in higher mammals, for the subdivision suggested by *Friedemann* ('12) in primates. This observer recognized a zona compacta and a zona reticulata. Similar subdivisions were found in carnivores by *Rioch* ('29a) and in man by *Foix* and *Nicolesco* ('25). In the cat, as indicated in *Rioch's* paper and in the material at present available for study, the zona compacta extends from

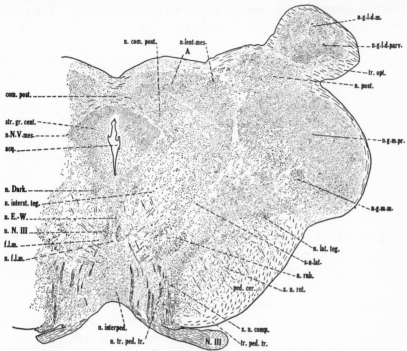

FIG. 509. Transverse section through the root of the oculomotor nerve. Adult dog. Toluidin-blue preparation. *Rioch.*

A, presumably area pretectalis (1931); *acq.*, aqueduct; *com.post.*, commissura posterior; *f.l.m.*, fasciculus longitudinalis medialis; *n.com.post.*, nuclei commissurae posterioris; *n.Dark.*, nucleus of Darkschewitsch; *n.E-W.*, nucleus of Edinger-Westphal; *n.f.l.m.*, nucleus fasciculi longitudinalis medialis; *n.g.l.d.m.*, nucleus geniculatus lateralis dorsalis, lamina magnocellularis; *n.g.l.d.parv.*, nucleus geniculatus lateralis dorsalis, lamina parvocellularis; *n.g.m.m.*, nucleus geniculatus medialis, pars magnocellularis; *n.g.m.pr.*, nucleus geniculatus medialis, pars principalis; *n.interped.*, nucleus interpeduncularis; *n.interst.teg.*, nucleus interstitialis tegmenti; *n.lat.teg.*, nucleus lateralis tegmenti; *n.lent.mes.*, nucleus lenticularis mesencephali; *n.N.III*, nucleus nervi oculomotorii; *n.N.V.mes.*, nucleus nervi trigemini mesencephalici; *n.post.*, nucleus posterior; *n.rub.*, nucleus ruber; *n.tr.ped.tr.*, nucleus tractus peduncularis transversi; *N.III*, nervus oculomotorius; *ped.cer.*, pedunculus cerebri; *s.n.comp.*, substantia nigra compacta; *s.n.lat.*, substantia nigra, pars lateralis, *s.n.ret.*, substantia nigra reticularis; *str.gr.cent.*, stratum griseum centrale; *tr.opt.*, tractus opticus; *tr.ped.tr.*, tractus peduncularis transversus.

a plane caudal to the mammillary body to the beginning of the pons, lying along the internal surface of the cerebral peduncle. There its caudal, scattered cells form a nucleus continuing dorsolaterally along the beginning of the tectal bundles. The zona compacta is a comma shaped structure rostrally (*Rioch*, '29a) and a band shaped mass caudally. Separated from the zona compacta by a fiber band, the stratum intermediale, is the zona reticulata, which makes its appearance as scattered cells intercalated among the fibers of the cerebral peduncle. In carnivores this zone reaches its greatest extent in planes through the oculomotor nuclei. In addition to the zona compacta and the zona reticulata, *Rioch* described a pars lateralis lying dorsolateral to the other portions of this substantia nigra. Its position is indicated in figure 509 and the various subdivisions seen in carnivores are illustrated in figures 507 and 509 to 511. The cells of this region are somewhat larger than those of the zona reticulata but in other ways resemble them closely.

The substantia nigra, like other subthalamic nuclei, receives bundles of the ansa lenticularis, including fibers from the field H_2 of *Forel* (*von Monakow*, '95, '05; *Tsai*, '25a; *Foix* and *Nicolesco*, '25; *Morgan*, '27; *Rioch*, '29a, and others). It is connected by fibers with the nucleus subthalamicus (*Mirto*, '96a; *Bauer*, '09; *Sano*, '10; *Kodama*, '29, and *Rioch*, '29a; see also fig. 511), which may be termed the tractus subthalamo-nigralis. *Tsai* ('25a) found that it received fibers of the pretectal, tectal, and tegmental systems and also fascicles from the cerebello-tegmental bundles, and *Rioch* ('29a; *Spitzer* and *Karplus*, '07) described a series of tectal connections which are well marked in the cat and presumably of considerable functional importance (see also fig. 510). Thus he found superficial nigro-tectal tracts (tractus nigro-tectalis lateralis and tractus nigro-tectalis medialis) entering the tectum along its lateral surface and a deeply situated tecto-nigral system (tractus tecto-nigralis). Connecting the substantia nigra with the overlying tegmentum is the latter observer's (*Rioch's*) tractus nigro-tegmentalis (fig. 510). He was able also to establish short internuclear connections with the surrounding regions, including the nucleus tractus peduncularis transversi, the nucleus interpeduncularis, and the ventral nucleus of the lateral lemniscus. Considerable difference of opinion exists as to two other connections which have been described for the substantia nigra. One of these is a possible cortico-nigral connection either as a separate tract or as collaterals of cortico-bulbar or cortico-spinal fibers. *Von Monakow* ('05) believed that the frontal pole of the hemisphere, the anterior island region, and the anterior part of the operculum are related to the substantia nigra. *Mingazinni* ('89), *von Kölliker* ('96), *Anton* and *Zingerle* ('02), *Bauer* ('09), and *Foix* and *Nicolesco* ('25) described fibers to this nucleus from the cerebral peduncle, and *Ramón y Cajal* ('11) thought that collaterals of the motor tracts within the peduncle reach the cells of the substantia nigra. *Münzer* and *Wiener* ('02) denied the presence of cortico-nigral fibers and many other observers have been unable to establish them to their own satisfaction. *Jurmann* (see *Kodama* '29) believed that fibers from the medial lemniscus enter the substantia nigra although *Probst* ('00) could not obtain such connections and *Kodama* ('29) questioned their origin and termination. *Papez* ('29) described such connections for mammals and *Rioch* ('29a) found a similar connection in the dog at the caudal end of the substantia nigra.

There appears to be much more provision for bringing impulses to the substantia nigra than for discharging them therefrom, and various suggestions have been made as to what constitutes the most important efferent path of this system. Aside from the connection with the tectum, which may be considered as established, the most probable discharge path is to the tegmentum of the midbrain and then caudalward through one of the various tegmento-bulbar or reticulo-bulbar systems. Such a discharge path has been hypothecated (*Foix* and *Nicolesco*, '25). Various other connections might be mentioned, the significance of which are as yet not clear. Among such may be the relation of the mammillary peduncle to this nucleus as described by *Papez* ('29).

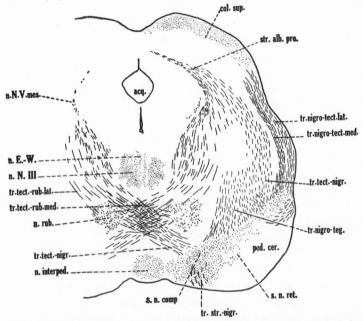

Fig. 510.   Transverse section passing through the red nucleus behind the level of emergence of the oculomotor nerve.   Three-day-old puppy.   Pyridine-silver preparation.   *Rioch.*

acq., acqueductus; *col.sup.*, colliculus superior; *n.E.-W.*, nucleus of Edinger-Westphal; *n.interped.*, nucleus interpeduncularis; *n.N.III*, nucleus nervi oculomotorii; *n.N.V.mes.*, nucleus nervi trigemini mesencephalici; *n.rub.*, nucleus ruber; *ped.cer.*, pedunculus cerebri; *s.n.comp.*, substantia nigra compacta; *s.n.ret.*, substantia nigra reticularis; *str.alb.pro.*, stratum album profundum; *tr.nigro-tect.lat.*, tractus nigro-tectalis lateralis; *tr.nigro-tect.med.*, tractus nigro-tectalis medialis; *tr.nigro-teg.*, tractus nigro-tegmentalis; *tr.str.nigr.*, tractus strio-nigralis; *tr.tect.-nigr.*, tractus tecto-nigralis; *tr.tect.-rub.lat.*, tractus tecto-rubralis lateralis; *tr.tect.-rub.med.*, tractus tecto-rubralis medialis.

It must be admitted that the functions of the substantia nigra, in spite of the very considerable amount of work that has been done upon this center, are very poorly understood. That it constitutes a center in an extrapyramidal path is relatively obvious, but the exact way in which its functions differ from those of certain other tegmental centers is problematical. It has been shown to exhibit structural changes in patients with the Parkinsonian syndrome (see *Foix* and *Nicolesco*, '25), one marked structural change being the disintegration of the pigment within the cells and its collection in clumps between the cells. In the discussion of the experimental work on the red nucleus, it was pointed out that various observers regard an intact red nucleus and possibly intact closely associated gray and hypothalamic gray as necessary for normal walking in such mammals as the cat and the dog. *Környey* ('27), working on the cat, reached the conclusion that the substantia nigra rather than the red nucleus was the midbrain center, the integrity of which was necessary for properly coördinating movements for reflex walking. The lesion made by him was large, including considerable portions of the tegmentum and the red nucleus of one side. *Hinsey, Ranson,* and *Dixon* ('30), in their study of the reflex functions of the mesencephalic tegmentum, reached the conclusion that the substantia nigra was unnecessary for bringing about the typical tegmental response, since this response could be elicited when the substantia nigra had been removed almost completely. Until further and more generally confirmatory observations are at hand, the conclusion would appear warranted that the major mesencephalic centers may complement one another and perhaps with different stress in different mammalian forms.

c. *Fiber Tracts of the Basis Pedunculi.* Fiber paths which form the most superficial portion of the pars peduncularis vary in size in the different mammals. Thus *Gierlich* ('16) found that in insectivores this basal portion constitutes 2 per cent of the whole peduncle, in marsupials 2.7 per cent, in ungulates and chiropteres 4.5 per cent, and in carnivores 5.4 per cent. It reaches its greatest percentage on the one hand in water animals, forming there around 10 per cent of the whole peduncular region, and on the other hand in apes, where it constitutes 11 per cent and in man approximately 20 per cent. The peduncle carries frontal cortico-pontine, temporal and occipital cortico-pontine, cortico-bulbar, and cortico-spinal fibers. The cortico-spinal fibers constitute in man about the middle three-fifths of the cerebral peduncle, being bounded medially by the frontal cortico-pontine system and laterally by the occipital and temporal cortico-pontine fibers. The medial and lateral cortico-bulbar systems are situated somewhat less superficially than the tracts just mentioned. The medial tract lies in close relation with the frontal cortico-pontine and the lateral near to the cortico-spinal system (figs. 503, 505, and 634). The frontal cortico-pontine fibers have their origin in the frontal regions of the cortex and pass through the anterior limb of the internal capsule to terminate in the pontine gray. The occipital and temporal cortico-pontine fibers arise from temporal and probably occipital association areas (pp. 1463 and 1464), pass through the internal capsule between the auditory and optic radiations, occupy the lateral one-fifth of the cerebral peduncle, and terminate in homolateral pontine gray. The cortico-spinal and cortico-bulbar paths have their origin in the precentral and adjacent paracentral gyri, those from the cortico-bulbar arising nearer the great horizontal fissure than those from the cortico-spinal. Some of the fibers converge and pass through the genu and posterior limb of the internal capsule (see fig. 634) and then enter the middle three-fifths of the cerebral peduncle.

Associated for a part of their course with these main fiber bundles of the cerebral peduncle are some other smaller tracts which have aroused more than passing interest among workers. Among these are fibers (fig. 503) of the fasciculi laterales pontis of *Marburg* ('10) or laterale pontine Bündel, *Poppi* ('27). This bundle has received a variety of names, such as Fuszschleife of *Flechsig* ('76), pes lemniscus profond of *Déjérine* ('95–'01, and '14), and laterale Haubenfuszschleife of *von Monakow* ('05). *Déjérine* followed this bundle from a position in relation to the outer two-fifths of the pes pedunculi, dorsalward and caudalward through the substantia nigra to join the medial lemniscus, which it accompanied caudalward into the medulla oblongata. This bundle takes no part in the sensory decussation, but, according to *Déjérine*, is a descending path which he considered an aberrant portion of the peduncular paths. *Marburg* ('10) considered this bundle as an aberrant pyramidal system. Those observers who regard the tract, in part at least, as an extrapyramidal system, believe its course to be of significance in explaining certain clinical syndromes, since the bundles provide cortico-bulbar fibers to various efferent nuclei of the cranial nerves, certain of which nuclei receive impulses over more than a single efferent path. *Déjérine* ('14) gave an instructive figure in which the aberrant pyramidal paths are clearly delineated. *Wallenberg* ('22), *Jakob* ('23), and *Riese* ('24) regarded the fasciculus lateralis pontis as composed neither of ascending lemnisci fibers nor of descending pyramidal tract fibers, but as a bundle of fibers found in company with other components of the ansa lenticularis, which arises from the globus pallidus, separates from other bundles of the ansa to enter the capsule of the nucleus subthalamicus, and extends caudalward into the substantia nigra, through which it runs for a very considerable distance, separating from this gray after contributing collaterals to it (*Jakob*), in order to enter the tegmental region of the pons, where it distributes to the lateral tegmental region. These constitute the pallido-nigral and pallido-tegmental tracts of *Jakob*. *Poppi* ('27), who made a study of this system, was able to trace it, with the aid of a hand lens, from the border of the pons forward to the capsule of the nucleus subthalamicus, an indication of the relative conspicuousness of the fascicles. He believed that the lateral pontine bundle or tractus fronto-pontinus tegmenti, as he preferred to call it, is frequently confused with other bundles. He found that the lateral pontine bundle does not degenerate in complete atrophy of the medial lemniscus system, and that it does not degenerate, except for occasional associated pyramidal fibers, with complete degeneration of the pyramidal tract, so that it seems not to constitute a pyramidal system. He appears to have regarded it as arising from the frontal lobe of the hemisphere but as occupying a lateral position in the rostral portion of the pons, gradually shifting medialward, and, in the region of the substantia nigra, entering the fronto-pontine system, hence the name of tractus fronto-pontinus tegmenti. Confused with this tract (*Poppi*) are fibers from the globus pallidus which pass to the substantia nigra, constituting a fasciculus pedunculo-mesencephalicus which is present when the cortical paths have atrophied. Certain fibers of this system pass through as a fasciculus mesencephalicus to the tegmentum of the midbrain, coursing through the lemnisci fibers in their course. *Ronge* ('29) recognized the pallido-tegmental system described by *Poppi*.

Another bundle which is present in certain individuals and is associated with the peduncle is the so-called faisceau en écharpe of *Féré* (see *Testut*, '11), to which *Elliot Smith* ('07) gave the name of the fasciculus obliquus crucis cerebri. This bundle, according to *Elliot Smith*, passes from the most lateral part of the crus, obliquely backward and medialward to enter the brain in the region of the interpeduncular fossa, and so to reach the pontine gray. *Poppi* ('27) thought it might pass also to the nucleus reticularis tegmenti pontis. *Elliot Smith* and others have found that, with very few exceptions, it is better developed on the left than on the right side, and it may be present on the left side only, though in three out of one hundred cases of this anomaly, *Elliot Smith* found the tract only on the right side. *Poppi*, who confirmed the observations of *Elliot Smith* with regard to the relations of this bundle in the midbrain and pons regions, believed that it arises from the temporal region of the telencephalon and termed it the fasciculus temporo-pontinus tegmenti. *Ronge* ('29), while confirming in many respects the work of *Poppi*, presented a somewhat different interpretation of the system just discussed. He believed that at the proximal end of the midbrain intermediate portions of the peduncle send fibers dorsalward. Such fibers unite with fascicles from the globus pallidus (forming in this way the pallido-tegmental tract of *Poppi*) which pass through the substantia nigra in order to unite with the medial lemniscus. From the lateral and medial parts of the peduncle, fascicles with somewhat similar courses pass to the lemniscus, the medial fibers occupying a separate field. In their course the medial fibers (pes médian, *Ronge*) meet the fibers of the faisceau en écharpe or fasciculus obliquus cruris cerebri. With the pedunculo-tegmental fibers formed by these various aberrant fibers are pedunculo-nigral fascicles, and, at least with the intermediate bundle (pes profond, *Ronge*), pallido-tegmental fascicles. *Ronge* found numerous variations, but believed that the system represented an intermingling of phylogenetically younger and older systems.

In general (*Déjérine*, '14, *Ranson*, '32), the aberrant paths may be subdivided into (*a*) those directly from the peduncle (medial and lateral cortico-bulbar) which join the medial lemniscus and terminate in motor nuclei of the oculomotor, abducens and accessory nerves, (*b*) pontine bundles joining those in (*a*) and passing to the motor trigeminal nucleus and the hypoglossal nucleus, and (*c*) bulbo-pontine fascicles to the motor facial nucleus and to the nucleus ambiguus and the nucleus hypoglossi.

Certain Mesencephalic Commissural Systems

a. Superior Cerebellar Decussation. Before concluding this brief review of the mammalian midbrain, attention must be directed to certain commissural systems which are related with various mesencephalic centers. The first of these is the decussation of the superior cerebellar peduncle. This decussation occupies the central portion of the field at transverse levels through the inferior colliculus and the nucleus of the fourth nerve. It lies immediately caudal to the red nucleus. Its cells of origin are situated in the dentate nucleus and the nucleus fastigii of the cerebellum. The neuraxes of these neurons accumulate, forming a large fiber mass which constitutes the major portion of the superior cerebellar peduncle (figs. 522 and 511).   This peduncle turns ventralward and forward toward the midline, decussating in the region indicated, and then swings forward to the red nucleus for which it forms a part of the capsule.   The superior cerebellar decussation contains dento-rubral and dento-thalamic fibers.   In addition to these components there are crossed and uncrossed fibers to the tegmental regions of the midbrain and pons (cerebello-tegmental or dento-tegmental fibers) and crossed fibers to the motor nuclei of the cranial nerves (fastigio-bulbar components).   These have been discussed in Chapter VII (pp. 808 and 816) and shown in figure 422.

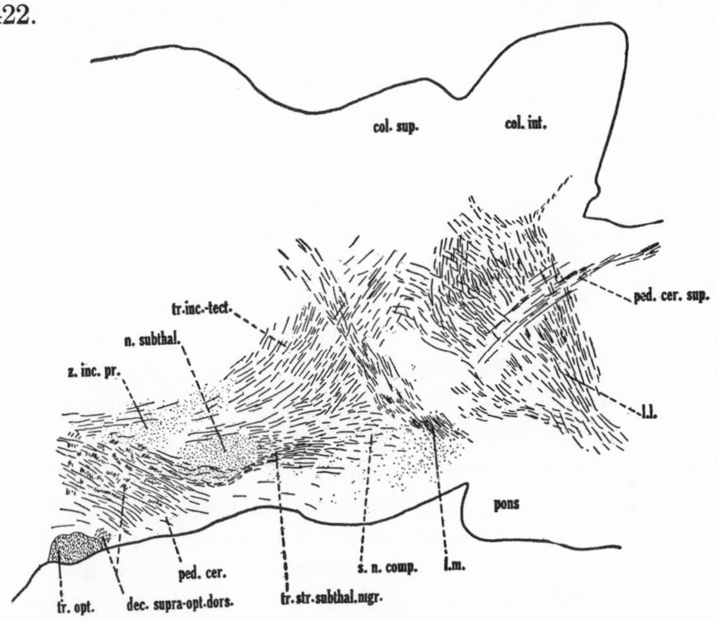

FIG. 511.   Sagittal section in a plane through the lateral margin of the superior cerebellar peduncle.   Three-day-old puppy.   Pyridine-silver preparation.   *Rioch.*
   col.inf., colliculus inferior; *col.sup.*, colliculus superior; *dec.supra-opt.dors.*, decussatio supraoptica dorsalis; *l.l.*, lemniscus lateralis; *l.m.*, lemniscus medialis; *n.subthal.*, nucleus subthalamicus; *ped.cer.*, pedunculus cerebri; *ped.cer.sup.*, pedunculus cerebelli superior; *pons*, pons; *s.n.comp.*, substantia nigra compacta; *tr.inc.-tect.*, tractus incerto-tectalis; *tr.opt.*, tractus opticus; *tr.str.subthal.nigr.*, tractus strio-subthalamico-nigralis; *z.inc.pr.*, zona incerta proper.

b. Dorsal and Ventral Tegmental Decussations.   At the level of the superior colliculus and near the caudal end of the red nucleus appears the ventral tegmental decussation or decussation of Forel.   This consists of fibers with cells of origin in the red nucleus and with neuraxes which cross in the ventral tegmental decussation and then turn backward as the rubro-bulbar and rubro-spinal tract (fig. 422) or tract of von Monakow.   The dorsal tegmental decussation appears also at the level of the superior colliculus and the red nucleus, however, in most mammals in planes slightly cephalic to that of the ventral tegmental crossing.   This dorsal tegmental decussation or decussation of Meynert consists of fibers the cells of origin of which are situated in the tectum, largely in the superior colliculus.   The neuraxes of such cells swing along the central gray forming the so-called radiations of Meynert (fig. 526) and cross at the level of the oculomotor nuclei as the dorsal tegmental decussation. From this point on most of the fibers proceed caudalward ventral to the medial longitudinal fasciculus as the medial tecto-spinal tract. A part of the crossed fibers end in the oculomotor nuclei.

c. *Supramammillary Commissure.* The commissure of Forel is situated near the line between the diencephalon and the mesencephalon, usually dorsal and sometimes slightly caudal to the mammillary bodies. As a consequence it is sometimes called the supramammillary and sometimes the retroinfundibular commissure. It carries several systems of fibers: (1) crossed fibers of the fornix system which separate from the main fornix bundle and decussate in the commissure to reach the midbrain region of the other side, termination unknown (according to *Foix* and *Nicolesco* in the mammillary body, '25, p. 491, fig. 333); (2) fibers interconnecting the subthalamic nuclei; and (3) crossed fibers of the ansa lenticularis. The components just mentioned have received relatively general recognition and are given in most of the larger texts on neurology (*Foix* and *Nicolesco*, '25). In addition to these, various minor connections have been described, such as crossed connections between the substantia nigra and the nucleus subthalamicus. It is shown in figure 505 under the name of the ansulate commissure, which title it also bears.

d. *Posterior Commissure.* At the line between the mesencephalon and diencephalon, sometimes considered with one division and sometimes with the other, is situated the posterior commissure, which in higher mammals and man is to be regarded as a relatively reduced fiber system. It is known to contain several types of fibers: (1) commissural fibers between the superior colliculi; (2) decussating and commissural fibers between the pretectal region of one side and the superior colliculus and pretectal areas of the other, and some from the pretectal nucleus at least passing to the contralateral Edinger-Westphal nucleus; (3) fibers arising from the nucleus of the posterior commissure, decussating in the commissure and entering the medial longitudinal fasciculus of the other side, forming the tractus commissuro-medullaris and tractus interstitio-spinalis (*Muskens*, '14, '22); and (4) probably ascending secondary vestibular fibers as described on pages 1078 to 1082. The commissure is shown in figures 506 and 509.

THE DIENCEPHALIC NUCLEI AND THEIR CONNECTIONS IN MAMMALS

The diencephalon of mammals has the usual divisions into epithalamus, dorsal thalamus, ventral thalamus or subthalamus, and hypothalamus. The several divisions will receive consideration in the order named. In this consideration of the diencephalic centers these are described beginning with the rostral and extending to the caudal end of the area, since this procedure makes comparisons with the literature somewhat easier.

The Epithalamus, Particularly Its Nuclei and Connections

The epithalamic region of the diencephalon contains endocrine components, the epiphysis and the choroid plexus of the third ventricle, a non-olfactory portion, comprising a part of the posterior commissure, which has just received consideration, and an olfactory correlation center, the habenula, with its habenular commissure and its associated fiber bundles, including the stria medullaris.

The choroid plexus has been considered in Chapter I.   The epiphysis (figs. 501A and B) is an outgrowth of the dorsal wall of the diencephalon in the region immediately in front of the posterior commissure.   Various theories regarding its function in mammals have been advocated.   Certain observers have considered it as a vestigial structure, a remnant of the parietal eye of lower forms.   By many observers it is described as a bloodvascular gland (*Cutore*, '12; *Krabbe*, '11 and '15, and many others).   *Jordan* ('11 and '12) regarded it as essentially neural in structure.   By still other investigators it has been considered as formed entirely of neuroglia tissue in mammals (*Weigert*, '95; *Edinger*, '08), while *Mihalkovicz* ('74) regarded it as exclusively ependymal.   Certain other observers have regarded it as showing resemblance to a lymph gland.   However, the more modern workers believe that they have established the glandular character of the epiphysis or pineal gland.   Usually three types of cells are recognized : neuroglia cells, parenchyma cells, and certain scattered cells regarded as non-functional ganglion cells.   The parenchymal cells are either large cells having a granular cytoplasm and deeply staining, relatively large nuclei, or smaller cells with basophilic or eosinophilic granules and vesicular nuclei.   The supporting tissue is neuroglial in character except where prolongations of connective tissue of the capsule extend down into the gland tissue.   *Tilney* and *Warren* ('19) have studied with great care the pineal gland in various vertebrates and have discussed the various theories regarding it.   They reached the conclusion that this gland does not represent any type of vestige of the parietal eye and *Herring* ('27) arrived at a similar conclusion.   Those interested in the development of this gland are referred to the papers quoted above.   It appears that in higher mammals hyposecretion of the gland produces early sexual development and hypersecretion is in some way associated with fat storage within the body (*Marburg*, '09).   A history of the development of the pineal gland is to be found in the work of *Krabbe* ('11, '15).

Each habenula (figs. 512, 513, 515, 516, 518, 523, 527) consists of two nuclei, a lateral habenular nucleus and a medial habenular nucleus.   Frequently the medial habenular nucleus can be divided, in its more anterior part, into a pars dorsomedialis and a pars ventromedialis (*Gurdjian*, '25, and *Tsai*, '25).   The cells of the lateral habenular nucleus are smaller and somewhat more scattered than those of the medial habenular nucleus.

The habenula receives its impulses through the stria medullaris which carries : (1) fibers from the hippocampal region of the cortex, the tractus cortico-habenularis medialis (*Ganser*, '82; *Honegger*, '90; *Lotheissen*, '94; *Déjérine*, '01; *Edinger*, '11, and many others; *Ramón y Cajal*, '11, denied its existence); (2) septo-habenular fibers from the lateral septal nucleus to the habenula (*Déjérine*, '01; *Gurdjian*, '25); (3) amygdalo-habenular fibers through connections with the stria terminalis (*Honegger*, '90; *Lotheissen*,' 94; *von Kölliker*, '96; *Johnston*, '23;

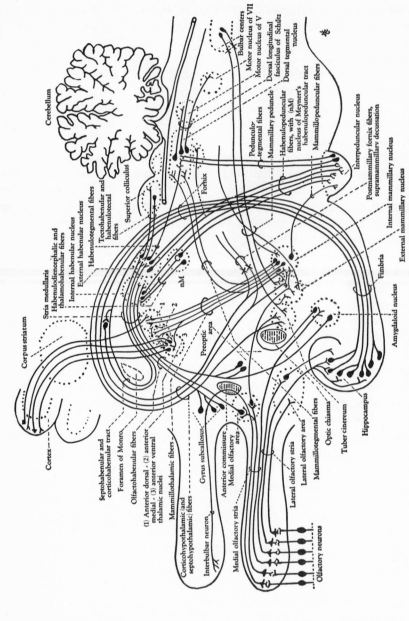

FIG. 512. A diagram of the olfactory connections of the diencephalon. *Huber and Crosby.*

Gurdjian, '25) ; (4) fibers from the bed nucleus of the stria terminalis and the anterior commissure similar to those in lower forms (*Crosby*, '17, for reptiles ; *Gurdjian*, '25) ; (5) lateral and medial olfacto-habenular tracts (*Gurdjian*, '25) comparable to those in reptiles (*Herrick*, '10 ; *Crosby*, '17, and *Hines*, '23 ; see bibliography for reptiles) ; and (6) lateral cortico-habenular fibers (sometimes termed the lateral olfacto-habenular tract) from the piriform lobe and the nucleus of the lateral olfactory tract.   (7) Another important connection of the habenula is with the optic tectum (tecto-habenular and habenulo-tectal tracts). By means of this connection impulses of a somatic character are brought to the habenula so that it becomes an olfacto-somatic correlation center.

The main outgoing path from the habenula is the tractus habenulo-peduncularis.   This arises from the lateral and medial habenular nuclei and follows a somewhat curved course, proceeding ventralward and caudalward to the interpeduncular nucleus where its fibers cross and then curve back again to terminate in the homolateral portion of the nucleus, having given off, however, during their course, collateral fibers to all of the nuclear gray.   This tract, which frequently is designated the fasciculus retroflexus of Meynert, has been recognized and described by many observers (*Edinger*, '08 ; *Ramón y Cajal*, '11, and many others).   Accompanying the tract are habenulo-diencephalic fibers which terminate in relation to the nucleus of the habenulo-peduncular tract and possibly other portions of the medial division of the dorsal thalamus.   With them may be thalamo-habenular fibers.   The habenulo-diencephalic tract was described by *Edinger* ('08) and has been recognized since by several observers, and more recently by *Hines* ('29).   These connections of the habenula are illustrated in figure 512.

The General Relations of the Mammalian Dorsal Thalamus

The dorsal thalamus is bounded medially by the third ventricle, its dorsal limit being indicated on the ventricular wall by the sulcus epithalamicus dorsalis, its ventral limit by the sulcus medius.   Laterally it is bounded by the caudate nucleus and the posterior limb of the internal capsule, dorsally in man (fig. 501) it forms in part the free surface of the brain and in part lies within the lateral ventricle.   Ventrally it is bounded by the zona incerta and certain hypothalamic regions.   In most mammals the lateral and medial geniculate nuclei are demonstrable in gross material, lying at the posterior end of the diencephalon and along the lateral surface of the midbrain at the level of the superior colliculus.   Gross inspection of appropriate cross sections of many mammalian brains indicates that the dorsal thalamus is divisible into an outer and an inner part separated by a band of medullated fibers — the lamina medullaris interna — which bifurcates dorsally to include within its branches a gray mass which is known usually as the nucleus anterior.   In this way the anterior, internal (or medial), and external (or lateral) nuclei have been delimited by many workers (for example, *Foix* and *Nicolesco*, '25).   Microscopic study indicates that these nuclear groups may be subdivided further into discrete nuclei, distinguishable on a basis of nuclear pattern and frequently of fiber connections.

In the following account of the nuclear groups in mammals, no plan of phylogenetic development is implied by the order in which the various forms are discussed, although in general the nuclear groups are considered from their simpler to their complex developments. The arrangement is a matter of convenience, since the various nuclear patterns are considered in the order which makes easiest a recognition of their homologies and interrelation, in the light of the present understanding of these groups.

Study of the literature and of sections indicates that the dorsal thalamus may be subdivided into an internal or medial portion and an external or lateral part. To the medial subdivision may be relegated three major nuclear groups — (a) an anterior group, (b) a medial group, and (c) a midline group.

The Nuclear Pattern of the Anterior Nuclear Group of the Mammalian Dorsal Thalamus

The anterior nuclear group of mammals has been described frequently as a single nuclear mass (*Déjérine*, '01; *Foix* and *Nicolesco*, '25, and others). However, the majority of observers who have had available material suitable for study of the nuclear pattern have been able to subdivide the anterior nucleus into two or three secondary divisions or nuclei. Such secondary divisions have been recognized in mammals from marsupials through primates, although they have received various designations and show differences in the degree of their development in the various forms.

a. Monotremes and Marsupials. The nucleus anterior of Ornithorhynchus was described by *Hines* ('29) as crescent-shaped and as situated immediately beneath the stria medullaris. The nucleus lies in front of the nucleus medialis and medial to it, and is differentiable from this latter (*Hines*) through the small size and more compact arrangement of its constituent neurons.

In the opossum, *Tsai* ('25) labeled two anterior nuclei, a more dorsal nucleus anterior *a* and a more ventrolateral nucleus anterior *b*. However, his contribution does not contain a description of these nuclear masses. Recently *Chu* ('32) described in the opossum a nucleus anterodorsalis, a nucleus anteroventralis, and a nucleus anteromedialis, which correspond to the similarly named centers in higher mammals (see the succeeding paragraphs). *Chu* found that the nucleus anterodorsalis, which lies in the rostral part of the diencephalon, just lateral to the stria medullaris, is composed of large, closely packed cells of multangular form which show a marked affinity for basic stains, while the nucleus anteroventralis of the opossum, situated ventrolateral to the nucleus anterodorsalis, has smaller and less closely arranged cells of relatively uniform size showing less deep staining in basic stains than do the cells of the nucleus anterodorsalis. The nucleus anteroventralis is the largest of the three anterior nuclei in the opossum. It may receive fascicles from the superior thalamic radiations which pass through it. The nucleus anteromedialis of the opossum (*Chu*, '32) constitutes a cell group of intermingled small and rather large multipolar nerve cells which lies caudoventral to the nucleus anterodorsalis and ventral and medial to the nucleus anteroventralis. The position of the anterior nuclear group in Ony-chogale is indicated in figures 502 and 522.

b. *Edentates and Rodents.* Papez ('32) divided the anterior nuclear group in an edentate, the armadillo, into nucleus anterior and nucleus anterodorsalis. The nucleus anterior, although representing the anteroventral and anteromedial nuclei of forms such as rodents, is a single nuclear mass of a typical cytologic char-acter with no separation into two distinct portions in the armadillo. The nucleus anterodorsalis is a group of deeply staining cells found in the cephalic end of the thalamus in the "angle formed by the medial dorsal, the anterior, and the lateral anterior nuclei" (Papez, '32, p. 79; see also figure 523 of present text).

Several very excellent accounts of the subdivisions of the anterior nuclear group among rodents are contained in the literature. *Münzer* and *Wiener* ('02), for the rabbit, and *Gurdjian* ('27), for the rat, described a nucleus anterior dor-salis, a nucleus anterior ventralis, and a nucleus anterior medialis; the first two are homologous with the anterior nuclei *b* and *a*, respectively, of *Winkler* and *Potter* ('11). A noyau antero-dorsal, a noyau antero-ventral, and a noyau antero-medial were recognized in the rabbit by *d'Hollander* ('13) and similar nuclei were described in the mouse under other names by *Ramón y Cajal* ('11). In the rat *Gurdjian* found that the nucleus anterior dorsalis, the most dorsal of the three (see fig. 513), extends forward to a plane passing through the posterior end of the anterior commissure, that it reaches its greatest size near the anterior end of the habenula, and then rather quickly disappears. Throughout most of its extent it is medial to the nucleus lateralis and dorsomedial to the nucleus anterior ventralis. It is connected with its fellow of the opposite side by a com-missural nucleus, nucleus commissuralis interanterodorsalis, and associated fibers. In the rabbit *d'Hollander* ('13) described the noyau antero-dorsal as cap shaped and as consisting of cells closely packed and of medium size, while *Winkler* and *Potter* ('11) found large cells in the corresponding nucleus in this rodent. The nucleus anterior dorsalis of the rat is the homologue of the noyau angulaire described by *Ramón y Cajal* ('11) for the mouse.

The nucleus anterior ventralis of the rat (*Gurdjian*, '27; see also fig. 513) is distinguishable from the nucleus just described through the smaller size of its cells and their fainter staining in toluidin blue preparations. It appears at about the same cephalic level as does the nucleus anterior dorsalis, occupying a position dorsolateral to the ventricle. Gradually it increases in size and extends ventromedialward, lying between the nucleus anterior dorsalis and the nucleus reticularis, while the nucleus anterior medialis appears to ·be more or less con-tinuous with it medially in many planes. It is very small by the time the caudal end of the nucleus anterior dorsalis is reached and soon thereafter disappears. The nucleus anterior ventralis here described is comparable with the noyau dorsal supérieure of *Ramón y Cajal* ('11) for the mouse, and the nucleus anterior ventralis of *Münzer* and *Wiener* ('02), the nucleus anterior *a* of *Winkler* and *Potter* ('11), and the noyau antero-ventral of *d'Hollander* ('13) for the rabbit.

Nucleus anterior medialis of *Münzer* and *Wiener* ('02) and of *Gurdjian* ('27) is the noyau dorsal inférieure of *Ramón y Cajal* ('11) for the mouse, and the nucleus antero-medial of *d'Hollander* ('13) for the rabbit. This nucleus (fig. 513), which is not always distinguishable in its cephalic part from the nucleus anterior ventralis, frequently becomes more sharply defined farther caudalward. In the mouse and the rat, the nuclei of the two sides approach each other and are interconnected by a noyau interdorsal (*Ramón y Cajal*, '11) or nucleus com-

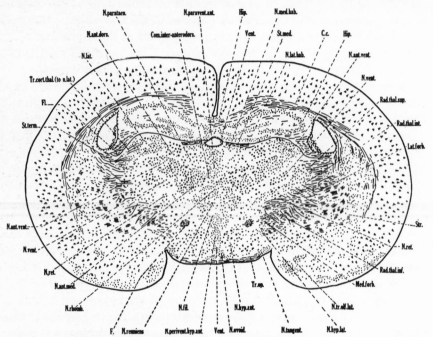

FIG. 513. Cross section of the brain of the albino rat passing through the rostral extreme of the ventral thalamic nucleus. Note in particular the thalamic nuclei of the midline. Toluidin-blue preparation. *Gurdjian.* (Redrawn.)

C.c., corpus callosum; *F.*, fornix; *Fl.*, fimbria fornicis; *Hip.*, hippocampus; *Lat.forb.*, lateral forebrain bundle (capsula interna); *Med.forb.*, medial forebrain bundle; *N.ant.-dors.*, nucleus antero-dorsalis; *N.ant.-med.*, nucleus antero-medialis; *N.ant.-vent.*, nucleus antero-ventralis; *N.fil.*, nucleus filiformis; *N.hyp.ant.*, nucleus hypothalamicus anterior; *N.hyp.lat.*, nucleus hypothalamicus lateralis; *N.lat.*, nucleus lateralis thalami; *N.lat.hab.*, nucleus lateralis habenulae; *N.med.hab.*, nucleus medialis habenulae; *N.ovoid.*, nucleus ovoidus; *N.parataen.*, nucleus parataenialis; *N.paravent.ant.*, nucleus paraventricularis anterior; *N.perivent.hyp.ant.*, nucleus periventricularis hypothalamicus anterior; *N.ret.*, nucleus reticularis thalami; *N.reuniens*, nucleus reuniens; *N.rhomb.*, nucleus rhomboidalis; *N.tangent.*, nucleus tangentialis; *N.tr.olf.lat.*, nucleus tractus olfactorii lateralis; *N.vent.*, nucleus ventralis thalami; *Rad.thal.inf.*, radiatio thalamica inferior; *Rad.thal.int.*, radiatio thalamica intermedius; *Rad.thal.sup.*, radiatio thalamica superior; *St.med.*, stria medullaris; *St.term.*, stria terminalis; *Tr.cort.-thal.(to n.lat.)*, tractus cortico-thalamicus (to nucleus lateralis thalami); *Tr.op.*, tractus opticus; *Vent.*, ventriculus.

missuralis interanteromedialis (*Gurdjian*, '27), which is accompanied by fiber bundles. The nucleus anteromedialis or anterior medialis has the greatest caudal extent of any of the three anterior nuclear groups in the rat. There is rather general agreement that mammillo-thalamic fibers supply this nucleus in rodents.

c. Insectivores. In certain insectivores (the hedgehog, the elephant shrew, the pen-tailed shrew, and the lesser tree shrew) the anterior nuclei may be divided into a dorsal part, termed by *Le Gros Clark* ('29a), who has studied this form, the nucleus anterodorsalis and so designated in his figures, and a principal part, the medioventral extension of which becomes separated caudally to form the nucleus anteroventralis.   The relations in the forms studied by *Le Gros Clark*, with the exception of the hedgehog, Erinaceus, are essentially similar to those described for rodents, the anterodorsal and the anteromedial nuclei being interconnected by a gray commissure as in the rat, the rabbit, and the mouse.   In Erinaceus the nuclear pattern does not appear to have been so distinct as in the other insectivores studied.   *Le Gros Clark* was unable to identify a clearly defined nucleus anteromedialis, although by comparison with the other forms he was able to assign the name somewhat tentatively to an appropriate region of the thalamus. The cells of the anterodorsal nucleus, although deeply stained, are not larger than those of the anteroventral nucleus in Tupaia minor, while in the tree shrew (Ptilocercus) they are slightly larger and in Macroscelides they are very large.

   d. Carnivores.   The literature contains quite a number of descriptions of the anterior nuclear group in carnivores (*von Monakow*, '95 and '05, for the cat and the dog; *Winkler* and *Potter*, '14, for the cat; *Rioch*, '29, for the dog; *Ingram, Hannett*, and *Ranson*, '32, for the cat, and others).   Three anterior nuclei have been identified: (1) medialer Nebenkern des Tuberculum anterius (*von Monakow;* nucleus anterior *b, Winkler* and *Potter;* nucleus anterodorsalis, *Rioch* and *Ingram, Hannett*, and *Ranson*); (2) Hauptkern des Tuberculum anterius (*von Monakow;* nucleus anterior *a, Winkler* and *Potter;* nucleus anteroventralis, *Rioch* and *Ingram, Hannett*, and *Ranson*); (3) ventraler Nebenkern des Tuberculum anterius (*von Monakow;* nucleus anterior *c, Winkler* and *Potter;* nucleus anteromedialis, *Rioch* and *Ingram, Hannett*, and *Ranson*).   The following account is based primarily on the work of *Rioch*, with which *Huber* and *Crosby* are more directly familiar, and on available preparations.

   The nucleus anterodorsalis in the dog (*Rioch*, '29; also fig. 514) forms a cap over the dorsal and cephalic portions of the nucleus anteroventralis and the nucleus anteromedialis, from which it is separated by fibers.   Behind these latter nuclei, the nucleus centralis lateralis and the nucleus lateralis pars anterior form its ventromedial and ventrolateral boundaries, respectively.   The caudal boundary is formed by the nucleus lateralis pars anterior.   The nucleus anterior ventralis extends medialward near its cephalic end to interconnect with its fellow of the opposite side through a nucleus commissuralis interanterodorsalis, similar to that previously described for rodents.   Near the rostral end of the nucleus medialis dorsalis this medial prolongation of the nucleus disappears and the nucleus parataenialis forms its medial boundary.   The cells of the nucleus anterior dorsalis are large (*Winkler* and *Potter*) and have a roughly granular cytoplasm.

   The nucleus anteroventralis of the dog (fig. 514) lies lateral and ventrolateral to the nucleus anterior dorsalis and dorsal and then dorsomedial to the nucleus anteromedialis.   After the disappearance farther caudalward of this latter, the nucleus centralis lateralis constitutes the caudoventral and caudal boundaries.   Laterally lies the nucleus reticularis.   After their appearance, the nucleus ventralis and the nucleus lateralis pars anterior constitute the ventrolateral and laterocaudal boundaries, respectively.   The above account is based on available preparations and figures and descriptions of *Rioch* ('29) for the dog. With some slight differences in form relations, the account appears to be applicable to carnivores in general. A large-celled portion and a small-celled portion

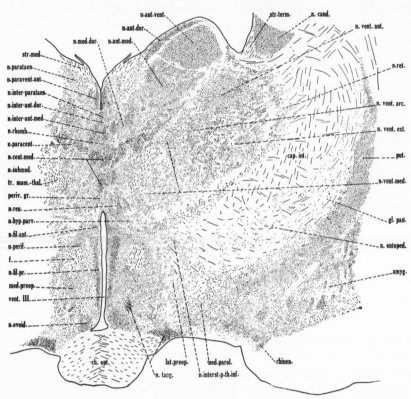

FIG. 514. Transverse section through the level of the rostral pole of the nucleus medialis dorsalis. Adult dog. Toluidin-blue preparation. *Rioch.*

amyg., amygdala; *cap.int.*, capsula interna; *ch.opt.*, chiasma opticum; *f.*, fornix; *gl.pall.*, globus pallidus; *lat.preop.*, lateral preoptic area; *med.preop.*, medial preoptic area; *n.ant.dor.*, nucleus anterodorsalis; *n.ant.med.*, nucleus anteromedialis; *n.ant. vent.*, nucleus anteroventralis; *n.caud.*, nucleus caudatus; *n.cent.med.*, nucleus centralis medialis; *n.entoped.*, nucleus entopeduncularis; *n.fil.ant.*, nucleus filiformis anterior; *n.fil.pr.*, nucleus filiformis principalis; *n.hyp.parv.*, nucleus hypothalamicus parvocellularis; *n.inter-ant.dor.*, nucleus commissuralis interanterodorsalis; *n.inter-ant.med.*, nucleus commissuralis interanteromedialis; *n.inter-parataen.*, nucleus commissuralis interparataenialis; *n.interst.p.th.inf.*, nucleus interstitialis pedunculi thalami inferioris; *n.med.dor.*, nucleus medialis dorsalis; *n.ovoid.*, nucleus ovoideus; *n.paracent.*, nucleus paracentralis; *n.parataen.*, nucleus parataenialis; *n.paravent.ant.*, nucleus paraventricularis anterior; *n.perif.*, nucleus perifornicalis; *n.ret.*, nucleus reticularis; *n.reu.*, nucleus reuniens; *n.rhomb.*, nucleus rhomboidalis; *n.submed.*, nucleus submedius; *n.tang.*, nucleus tangentialis; *n.vent.ant.*, nucleus ventralis, pars anterior; *n.vent.arc.*, nucleus ventralis, pars arcuata; *n.vent.ext.*, nucleus ventralis pars externa; *n.vent.med.*, nucleus ventralis, pars medialis; *periv.gr.*, periventricular gray; *put.*, putamen; *rhinen.*, rhinencephalon; *str.med.*, stria medullaris; *str.term.*, stria terminalis; *tr.mam.thal.*, tractus mamillo-thalamicus; *vent.III*, ventriculus tertius.

of the nucleus with intercalated fiber bundles have been described by *Rioch.* According to this latter observer the large cells of this nucleus in the dog are approximately of the same size or only slightly smaller than those in the nucleus anterodorsalis; the small cells may be only half the size of the larger.   In general the cytoplasm is less deeply stained and less granular than in the cells of the previously described nuclear group.   In the cat *Winkler* and *Potter* found cells of medium size and distinctly granular.   *Ingram, Hannett,* and *Ranson* ('32) called attention to the fact that this nucleus is really misnamed for the cat, since it has the most dorsal position of any of the three parts of the nuclear complex in this carnivore.   They retained the name of nucleus anteroventralis for convenience in comparison.

The nucleus anteromedialis (fig. 514), ventral and medial to the nucleus anteroventralis, is joined in the dog (*Rioch,* '29), and also in the cat (*Ingram, Hannett,* and *Ranson,* '32), as in various rodents (*d'Hollander,* '13; *Gurdjian,* '27), with its fellow of the opposite side by a gray commissure, the nucleus commissuralis interanteromedialis, the combined nuclei assuming a typical V-shape.   As in rodents and insectivores, rostrally the nucleus anteromedialis of the dog is in intimate association with the nucleus anteroventralis but becomes more distinct farther caudally.   At the caudal pole the nucleus passes over without sharp demarcation into the nucleus paracentralis and the nucleus centralis lateralis, which replace it.   The external medullary lamina separates the nucleus anteromedialis from the nucleus reticularis; the internal medullary lamina intervenes farther caudally between it and the nucleus ventralis.   The nucleus parataenialis and the lower part of the nucleus anterodorsalis lie dorsomedial to it.   On the whole, the neurons (*Winkler* and *Potter,* '14; *Rioch,* '29) resemble those of the nucleus anteroventralis.   *Rioch* recognized a dorsomedial large-celled and a ventromedial small-celled portion.   *Ingram, Hannett,* and *Ranson* ('32) found fusiform and polygonal cells containing large, oval nuclei in this cell mass.

e. Primates.   There has been a tendency among students of the primate diencephalon to divide the anterior nuclear group into two nuclei, an accessory anterior nucleus (*Vogt,* '09, noyau anterieur accessoire; *Friedemann,* '12, and *Pines,* '27, vorderer akcessorische Kern) and a principal anterior nucleus (noyau anterieur principal, *Vogt;* vorderer Hauptkern, *Pines;* vorderer Thalamuskern, *Friedemann*).   This latter nucleus has been subdivided secondarily into dorsolateral and ventromedial parts.   *Le Gros Clark* ('30) found a caplike anterodorsal nucleus in Tarsius, comparable to the nucleus of that name in carnivores, and a principal anterior nucleus, which this observer suggested may possibly represent the anteromedial, anteroventral, and submedius nuclei of carnivores.   In Microcebus *Le Gros Clark* ('31) identified all three nuclear groups forming the anterior nuclear complex, but found the anteroventral and anteromedial nuclei only occasionally separated from each other by the superior thalamic radiations. He regarded the anteromedial nucleus as including, in its caudal medial portion, the nucleus submedius, which he had stated earlier ('29) was represented probably in the ventromedial nucleus of lower forms.   The accessory anterior nucleus, as described and figured by *Friedemann* ('12) for Cercopithecus, is the homologue of the anterodorsal nucleus of Tupaia and other mammals, and consists of a relatively small band of deeply staining cells near the dorsal surface of the diencephalon, lateral to the stria medullaris and dorsal to the principal part of the anterior nucleus. Farther caudally this nucleus is dorsal to the chief medial nucleus and medial to the lateral thalamic nucleus. The principal portion of the anterior group lies ventral to the anterior accessory nucleus, ventrolateral to the nucleus parataenialis, and dorsal and dorsomedial to the lateral nucleus. Its dorsolateral and ventromedial portions are suggestive respectively of the anterior ventral and anterior medial nuclei of rodents. In essentials, the results of *Vogt* ('09) and *Pines* ('27) are in agreement with the account of *Friedemann* in so far as the nuclear pattern of the anterior group is concerned.

Particularly in man the nucleus anterodorsalis is frequently designated as the nuclei dorsales disseminati (*Marburg*, '04; *Sachs*, '09a; *Ingvar*, '23), for it is smaller in man and consists of scattered cell groups near the surface of the diencephalon. The principal anterior nucleus is termed the nucleus dorsalis magnus (*Sachs*, '09a; *Marburg*, '04), or simply the nucleus anterior (*Ingvar*, '23 and others; figs. 519 and 520). *Von Monakow* ('05) used the same names for the human anterior nuclear group that he had employed for their carnivore homologues. The accessory anterior (or anterior dorsal nucleus or nuclei dorsales disseminati) is included by *Malone* ('10) under his nucleus reuniens, while the other two anterior nuclei are represented by his pars dorsalis and his nucleus communis thalami. The work of *Malone* on the diencephalon has as its basis a study of cell character rather than nuclear configuration; as a consequence his results are not directly comparable with those of other workers. However, when the knowledge of the connections and functions of the human diencephalon are understood more thoroughly, it will be possible to correlate more completely the study of cell character with nuclear grouping, and such correlation in turn will throw much light on the relations and functions of the various parts. In certain cases both nuclear groups appear to be included under the name of the nucleus anterior. *Foix* and *Nicolesco* ('25) recognized in man only a single nucleus anterior which is probably comparable to the chief nucleus or Hauptkern of *Friedemann*. They described this as composed of multipolar cells, polygonal in outline. The majority of observers have had at their disposal only Weigert material of the human diencephalon and consequently no adequate account of this region in man is available.

The Fiber Connections of the Anterior Nuclear Group (Thalamic) in Various Mammals

The more important fiber connections of the anterior nuclear group, as they have been demonstrated in various mammals, are briefly summarized in the following paragraphs and are shown in figure 512.

The nucleus anterior dorsalis or anterodorsalis is connected with its fellow of the opposite side by means of commissural fibers (the commissura interanterodorsalis) in rodents (*Gurdjian*, '27) and probably in other mammals where midline nuclei are highly developed. It is connected with the telencephalon in the rat (*Le Gros Clark*, '32a, cingulate gyrus), in the rabbit (*Münzer* and *Wiener*, '02; *Ramón y Cajal*, '11), in insectivores (*Le Gros Clark*, '29a), in carnivores (*von Monakow*, '95, in the region of gyrus suprasylvius and gyrus fornicatus;

Le Gros Clark and *Boggon,* '33, gyrus cinguli), and in man (*Déjérine,* '01; *von Monakow,* '05, to the medial part of F_1 and gyrus fornicatus; *Forel,* '07).   Internuclear fibers connect this nucleus with the adjoining nuclear groups.   Such connections have been described particularly by *Gurdjian* (with the anterior group) and by *d'Hollander* (with the lateral nucleus).   *Ramón y Cajal* carried mammillo-thalamic fibers to this nucleus, the noyau angulaire; this connection has been questioned by various observers, but recent experimental work appears to indicate that it is present in the dog (*Glorieux,* '29) and also in the rat (*Le Gros Clark,* '32a).   This latter observer believed he was able to trace mammillo-thalamic fibers to the anterodorsal nucleus in normal preparations of Macroscelides, in which this cell group is particularly well developed.   *Le Gros Clark* thought that in the rat thalamo-mammillary fibers accompanied the mammillo-thalamic path, a view held by certain earlier observers but not supported by the results of the majority of later investigators.

The nucleus anteroventralis or anterior ventralis receives mammillo-thalamic fibers in various mammals, as shown by *Ramón y Cajal* ('11).   They have been described in the rat by *Gurdjian* ('27) and *Le Gros Clark* ('32a); in insectivores by *Le Gros Clark* ('29a); in carnivores by *Papez* ('29) and *Rioch* ('31), and in man by *von Kölliker* ('96) and by *Déjérine* ('01).   Connections with the telencephalon are regarded as probably present in the oppossum by *Chu* ('32a), and have been demonstrated for the rabbit by *Münzer* and *Wiener* ('02), for the mouse and other mammals by *Ramón y Cajal* ('11), for the rat by *Villaverde* ('23), *Gurdjian* ('27) and *Le Gros Clark* ('32a), for insectivores by *Le Gros Clark* ('29a), for the cat and the dog by *von Monakow* ('95) and *Papez* ('29), and for man by *Sachs* ('09a). *Déjérine* ('01), *Forel* ('07), and *Foix* and *Nicolesco* ('25) did not subdivide the anterior nucleus, but to their general group they carried fibers from the internal capsule.   *Winkler* ('21) believed that it was possible to obtain complete atrophy of the anterior nuclear group by destruction of cortical areas in the rabbit.   *Von Monakow* ('95) and *Tilney* and *Riley* ('21) regarded the anterior nuclei as connected with the frontal regions of the human cortex.   *Villaverde* ('23), a student of *Ramón y Cajal*, believed that destruction of the motor cortex in the rabbit led to degeneration of cortico-thalamic bundles to the anteroventral nucleus.   *Riese* ('24b), who according to his statement made an entirely similar lesion, obtained no degenerated fibers to the nucleus anterior thalami.   *Le Gros Clark* ('32a) destroyed the cingulate cortex in a rat and obtained results comparable to those described by *Villaverde*, and suggested that the results obtained by *Villaverde* were due to the depth of the lesion employed, which destroyed the path from the cingulate region to the thalamus.   Internuclear fibers associate the nucleus anteroventralis with other nuclei of the anterior group, and commissural fibers relate it with its fellow of the opposite side (*Gurdjian,* '27, and *Le Gros Clark,* '32).

The nucleus anteromedialis or anterior medialis also receives mammillo-thalamic fibers in rodents (*Ramón y Cajal,* '11; *d'Hollander,* '13; *Gurdjian,* '27; *Rioch,* '31, and *Le Gros Clark,* '32a).   Similar mammillo-thalamic connections have been described for insectivores by *Le Gros Clark* ('29a).   In most higher mammals this nuclear group is associated so intimately with the nucleus anteroventralis that no separate fiber connections can be demonstrated. Commissural fibers and internuclear fibers are present and *Münzer* and *Wiener* ('02) and *d'Hollander* ('13) have shown connections with the telencephalon in rabbits. The evidence for such a connection has not received general corroboration. *Rioch* ('31) stated that the nucleus receives fibers from the anterior thalamic radiations and the inferior thalamic peduncle in carnivores (conceivably such fibers may be either striatal or cortical) but *Le Gros Clark* ('32a) found no evidence that the anteromedial nucleus is connected with the cortex in the rat.

Résumé of Structure and Connections of the Anterior Nuclear Group of the Dorsal Thalamus

By way of summary of the anterior nuclear group, it may be stated that in the majority of mammals it is divisible into more or less distinct nuclear masses, and that of these masses the anteroventral and the anterodorsal have the evident connection with the cingulate region of the telencephalon but less probably are connected with the striatum. It appears that the anteromedial group also has a telencephalic path; the evidence at hand suggests that the connection is with the gyrus cinguli rather than with the striatum. Experimental evidence suggests that all of the three nuclear groups receive mammillo-thalamic fibers, but that the nucleus anterodorsalis receives relatively less of this system than do the other nuclei except in forms in which it is definitely enlarged. The anterior nuclear group is related by short internuclear fibers with the surrounding gray, and probably with the hypothalamus through the periventricular system, being a center of correlation for visceral, predominantly olfactory, impulses with somatic impulses and a region of discharge of such correlated impulses to higher centers. In man it may form, together with the medial nuclear group, a part of the discharge pathway for feeling tone through intracortical connections of the cingulate and frontal cortical areas (*Tilney* and *Riley*, '21; *Huber* and *Crosby*, '29).

The Nuclear Pattern of the Medial Nuclear Group of the Dorsal Thalamus

The medial nuclear group of the diencephalon includes the nucleus parataenialis, the nucleus medialis dorsalis, the nucleus parafascicularis, the nuclei of the habenulo-peduncular tract, the nucleus paracentralis, and the nucleus centralis lateralis. Not all of these have been demonstrated in all of the mammalian types. With these undoubted members of the medial division of the thalamus two other nuclear groups must be mentioned, nuclear groups which by certain observers are placed with the medial division of the thalamus and by other observers with the lateral division. The centers to which reference is here made are the noyau centré median Luysii, or the centromedian nucleus, and the nucleus medialis ventralis. With regard to the centromedian nucleus, *Huber* and *Crosby* ('29) wish to reiterate a statement previously made: "In its position and general relations in certain mammals, the centromedian nucleus appears to belong to the medial group; in its fiber connections and consequent functional significance, at least in higher mammals, it is more directly related to the ventral group of thalamic nuclei." The centromedian nucleus is here placed with the medial group very largely for ease of description. The nucleus medialis ventralis or nucleus submedius is placed sometimes with the medial group and sometimes with the lateral group of thalamic nuclei. By reason of the fact that it is difficult to separate it from the more medial extension of the ventral nucleus in many mammals, it is more easily discussed with the lateral division of the thalamus in the present account, but with full recognition of the fact that more must be known concerning the specific connections and homologies of this group before its correct place can be determined (see page 1113).

a. *Monotremes and Marsupials.* *Hines* ('29) identified a nucleus medialis in Ornithorhynchus. This nucleus is spherical in outline at its cephalic end, and she regarded this portion, on the basis of its fiber connections and appearance, as homologous with the nucleus rotundus of reptiles. Farther caudalward the nucleus becomes ellipsoidal in shape, showing a marked lateral expansion. *Hines* subdivided the nucleus into dorsolateral, mediolateral, and ventrolateral portions. This observer regarded the dorsolateral and ventrolateral nuclei formed in this manner as "but slight differentiation within the cellular area which is homologous to the nucleus lateralis thalami," while she believed that the rostral part of the ventrolateral nucleus, since it receives the trigeminal lemniscus, may be homologous to the centromedian nucleus, while the caudal part, which is the termination of the medial lemniscus, may be compared to the nucleus ventralis thalami. Evidently the nuclear complex termed the medial nucleus in Ornithorhynchus contains other centers than the similarly designated nucleus of other mammals.

The medial nuclear group has been described recently for the opossum by *Chu* ('32). He identified a nucleus parataenialis, similar to that found in rodents, which is situated at the rostral end of the diencephalon, between the nucleus medialis dorsalis and the anterior paraventricular gray, and dorsal to the nucleus anterodorsalis. The nerve cells constituting this nucleus are arranged in a relatively scattered manner. Laterocaudal to the nucleus parataenialis, *Chu* found the nucleus medialis dorsalis (nucleus medialis pars dorsalis of *Chu*), and medial and ventral to this latter nucleus, a nucleus medialis medialis (or pars medialis). This medial portion of the nucleus medialis *Chu* found to have smaller cells than the dorsal part of the nuclear mass and to be interconnected with its fellow of the opposite side through the nucleus rhomboidalis. Ventrolateral to the nucleus medialis pars medialis is the smallest celled portion of the nucleus medialis, the nucleus medialis ventralis. Medial to this nucleus lies the nucleus paracentralis, which consists of small neurons, oval in outline and closely arranged. The paracentral nucleus of the opossum was regarded by *Chu* as "chiefly for association between the lateral and medial groups of thalamic nuclei." The nucleus parafascicularis is said to lie ventral to the posterior commissure in the opossum in typical relation to the habenulo-peduncular tract.

b. *Edentates and Rodents.* In an edentate, the armadillo, *Papez* ('32) found a parataenial nucleus in its typical position in relation to the stria medullaris but not clearly separable from the rostral part of the nucleus medialis.   He carried it ventralward in front of the nucleus rhomboidalis into relation with his nucleus submedius.   The relatively distinct nucleus medialis, as modeled by *Papez* (fig. 523), apparently is the homologue of both pars dorsalis and pars medialis of the nucleus medialis of *Chu*, the dorsal and ventral portions presumably corresponding to dorsal and medial parts respectively, and is probably represented by the nucleus medialis dorsalis of rodents and carnivores, as described by *Gurdjian* ('27) and *Rioch* ('29), respectively.   A paracentral nucleus embedded in the internal medullary lamina, joining caudally the ventral part of the parafascicular nucleus (which *Papez* thought, with others, see page 1117, may be homologous to the centromedian nucleus) and a central lateral nucleus, situated between the medial and lateral thalamic regions, have been described in the armadillo.

The medial nuclear group has been studied most carefully in a number of rodents and insectivores.   Nucleus parataenialis in the rat (*Gurdjian*, '27; see also fig. 513) appears at the frontal end of the diencephalon, and extends backward to a plane caudal to the anterior end of the medial habenular nucleus, where it is replaced gradually by the nucleus medialis dorsalis.   At first it is medial and then ventral to the stria medullaris, to which it always lies in close proximity. An homologous nucleus was described for the rabbit by *Nissl* ('13) and by *d'Hollander* ('13).   Nucleus medialis dorsalis of rodents (fig. 515), which makes its appearance at a level near the caudal pole of the nucleus anterior dorsalis, lies lateral to the nucleus parataenialis cephalically, but farther caudally is almost continuous with the latter nucleus (*d'Hollander*, '13, rabbit) and gradually replaces it.   The nucleus medialis dorsalis in these rodents is more or less round or oval in outline and is large, consequently it forms a more or less conspicuous nuclear element from the level of its appearance to the caudal part of the diencephalon.   Associated with the caudal end of the nucleus medialis dorsalis is the nucleus parafascicularis (*Nissl*, hinterer ventralis Kern, '13; *d'Hollander*, '13; *Gurdjian*, '27), which is regarded as a differentiated portion of the latter nucleus formed by the passage of bundles of the habenulo-peduncular tract. The nucleus medialis dorsalis as thus described is the nucleus medialis *b* of *Winkler* and *Potter* ('11), which has been divided by these observers into a chief nucleus, the nucleus medialis *b*, and the nucleus medialis *bI*, consisting of smaller cells.   The two portions presumably correspond to the nucleus medialis dorsalis and the nucleus medialis medialis as recognized by *Chu* in the opossum (see p. 1113).   The nucleus medialis dorsalis of *Gurdjian* ('27) appears to correspond to the noyau antéro- ou supero-interne laterally, and the noyau supérior du raphe medially, as figured by *Ramón y Cajal* ('11) for the guinea pig, to the mediale hintere Kerngruppe of *Nissl* ('13), and to the noyau médial of *d'Hollander* ('13).   Nucleus paracentralis is the continuation lateralward of the nucleus centralis.   It is composed of cells scattered along the course of the internal medullary lamina.   Among rodents it has been described for the guinea pig and the mouse (*Ramón y Cajal*, '11, noyau falciforme), for the rabbit (*Nissl*, '13; *d'Hollander*, '13), and for the rat (*Gurdjian*, '27).   In the lateral part of the internal medullary lamina there is the homologue of the nucleus centralis lateralis of certain mammals: apparently this nucleus is not present in the mouse nor in the rat.

c. Insectivores.   The medial nuclear group has been described for the insectivore (Tupaia minor) by *Le Gros Clark* ('29).   In the parataenial nucleus he iden-

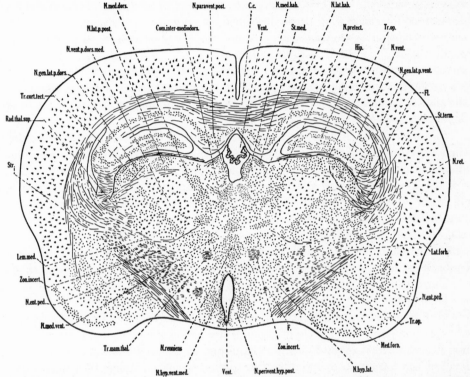

FIG. 515.   Cross section of the brain of the albino rat.   Note in particular the nucleus ventralis thalami.   The linearly arranged group of cells stands out plainly in all of the series.   Toluidin-blue preparation.   *Gurdjian*.   (Redrawn.)

C.c., corpus callosum; *Com.inter-mediodors.,* nucleus commissurae intermedialis dorsalis; *F.,* fornix; *Fl.,* fimbria fornicis; *Hip.,* hippocampus; *Lat.forb.,* lateral forebrain bundle (pedunculus cerebri); *Lem.med.,* lemniscus medialis; *Med.forb.,* medial forebrain bundle; *N.ent.ped.,* nucleus entopeduncularis; *N.gen.lat.p.dors.,* nucleus geniculatus lateralis pars dorsalis; *N.gen.lat.p.vent.,* nucleus geniculatus lateralis pars ventralis; *N.hyp.lat.,* nucleus hypothalamicus lateralis; *N.hyp. vent.med.,* nucleus hypothalamicus ventromedialis; *N.lat.hab.,* nucleus lateralis habenulae; *N.lat.p. post.,* nucleus lateralis pars posterior; *N.med.dors.,* nucleus medialis dorsalis; *N.med.hab.,* nucleus medialis habenulae; *N.med.vent.,* nucleus medialis ventralis; *N.paravent.post.,* nucleus paraventricularis posterior; *N.perivent.hyp.post.,* nucleus periventricularis hypothalamicus posterior; *N.pretect.,* nucleus pretectalis; *N.ret.,* nucleus reticularis thalami; *N.reuniens,* nucleus reuniens; *N.vent.,* nucleus ventralis thalami; *N.vent.p.dors.med.,* nucleus ventralis pars dorsomedialis; *Rad.thal.sup.,* radiatio thalamica superior; *St.med.,* stria medullaris; *Str.,* striatum; *St.term.,* stria terminalis; *Tr.cort.tect.,* tractus cortico-tectalis; *Tr.mam.thal.,* tractus mamillo-thalamicus; *Tr.op.,* tractus opticus; *Vent.,* ventriculus; *Zon.incert.,* zona incerta.

tified two regions, a large-celled lateral part and a small-celled medial part, which at no point are distinguishable from each other.   He regarded the small, irregular band of cells above the dorsomedial nucleus as the nuclei disseminati of other workers, but certainly the nucleus so labeled by *Ingvar* ('23) appears to be the nucleus anterodorsalis.   The nucleus medialis dorsalis (nucleus dorsomedialis,

Le Gros Clark), with its medial extension, the homologue of the rodent nucleus commissuralis intermediodorsalis, is present in insectivores. Lateral to this main nuclear mass are scattered cells which *Le Gros Clark* considered the homologue of the lateral small-celled portion of the medial nucleus as described for various primates. With this exception the general relations of the nucleus are directly comparable with those described for rodents by *Gurdjian* ('27) and further description is unnecessary. A nucleus parafascicularis is present in the usual relations to the habenulo-peduncular tract. *Le Gros Clark* ('29 and '30) recognized a centromedian nucleus (centré median de Luysii) in Tupaia in "the triangular mass of cells which appears as a differentiation of the caudal part of the paracentral nucleus in this insectivore." The nucleus paracentralis is well developed in insectivores.

d. *Carnivores.* A consideration of the medial group of thalamic nuclei in the carnivores indicates that the nucleus parataenialis (fig. 514) is a triangularly shaped nuclear mass bearing the usual positional relation to the stria medullaris. For the most part it lies at the dorsomedial angle of the diencephalon, but near its anterior end extends downward toward the nucleus commissuralis inter-parataenialis, through which it is fused with the nucleus of the other side (*Rioch*, '29, for the dog, and *Ingram, Hannett,* and *Ranson,* '32, for the cat). The caudal continuation of this nucleus over the nucleus medialis dorsalis, described by *Le Gros Clark* ('29) in insectivores, has been recognized by *Rioch* ('29) in the dog.

The nucleus medialis dorsalis (figs. 514, 516, 518) of carnivores is homologous to the nucleus of that name in other forms and lies in essentially the same relative position in all mammals, the differences being largely those of the establishment of exact boundaries and of no great importance for our present purposes. In the dog (*Rioch,* '29) it extends from a plane just in front of the optic chiasm to the level of the habenulo-peduncular tract, the associated nuclei of which tract lie in intimate relation with it and form the caudal part of its dorsal and its caudal boundaries. The cephalic part of the dorsal boundary is formed by the nucleus parataenialis. Except at its rostral pole, where it lies in relation laterally and ventrally with the nucleus anterior medialis, its lateral and ventral boundaries are formed by the internal medullary lamina. At its anterior pole the nucleus parataenialis lies medial to the nucleus medialis dorsalis, but behind this level the latter nucleus borders upon the midline group of nuclei and is connected with its fellow of the opposite side by a commissural nucleus. *Rioch* has divided the nucleus secondarily into a major portion, consisting of small and medium-sized cells, and a rostrolateral part composed of scattered, large cells. A large nucleus medialis dorsalis, with relations essentially similar to those described above, has been seen in the cat by *Winkler* and *Potter* ('14, who subdivided it into a nucleus medialis *b* and nucleus medialis *bI*) and by *Ingram, Hannett,* and *Ranson* ('32).

The nucleus parafascicularis (fig. 527) is a triangularly shaped nucleus pierced by the fibers of the habenulo-peduncular tract but apparently not in synaptic relation with them. This nucleus appears anteriorly at a plane just behind the caudal end of the nucleus paracentralis and extends caudalward to the level of the nuclei of the posterior commissure, being separated from them by a thin layer of fibers.   In association with the lateral border of this nucleus (fused with it caudomedially) is an area of scattered cells (fig. 527), among fibers of the internal medullary lamina.   This is believed to be the forerunner in carnivores of the centromedian nucleus or noyau centré median of *Luys* ('65) of higher mammals (*Rioch*, '31; *Ingram, Hannett,* and *Ranson*, '32).

The wedge-shaped nucleus tractus habenulo-peduncularis lateralis in the dog (*Rioch*, '29; fig. 516 of this text) is associated with the fibers forming the anterior three-fourths of the tract near their origin from the habenula and before their union with the posterior fourth.   The nucleus tractus habenulo-peduncularis medialis is a narrow band of cells associated with the medial portion of the habenulo-peduncular system.   For a detailed account of their form relations the work of *Rioch* ('29) on the dog should be consulted.   Presumably these nuclei are in synaptic relation with the associated fibers of the habenulo-peduncular tract. The lateral nucleus at least is the probable homologue of the nucleus tractus habenulo-peduncularis described for avian forms (*Huber* and *Crosby*, '29). Confirmation of the presence of these nuclear masses in the cat has been given by *Davenport* and *Ranson* ('30), and by *Ingram, Hannett,* and *Ranson* ('32) in their contributions on the cat diencephalon.

The nucleus paracentralis (figs. 514, 516, 518) in carnivores is similar to the nucleus of that name in other mammals, consisting of cells intercalated in the course of the internal medullary lamina and continuous medially with the nucleus centralis.   Lateral to the paracentral nucleus, and continuous with it ventro-medially, is the nucleus centralis lateralis, which lies in the dorsally directed portion of the internal medullary lamina.   The anterior, intermediate, and posterior portions of the lateral nucleus successively take part in forming the lateral boundary of the nucleus centralis lateralis; the nucleus medialis dorsalis lies in the angle formed by the nucleus paracentralis and the nucleus lateralis centralis.   For further details the original papers should be consulted (see *Winkler* and *Potter*, '14; *Rioch*, '29; *Ingram, Hannett,* and *Ranson*, '32).

e. Primates.   The components of the medial nuclear group have been studied in primates by a number of observers, including *Déjérine* ('01), *von Monakow* ('05), *Sachs* ('09, '09a), *Vogt* ('09), *Friedemann* ('12), *Ingvar* ('23), *Pines* ('27), and *Le Gros Clark* ('30).   A small parataenial nucleus was recognized in Tarsius by *Le Gros Clark* ('30).   In Cercopithecus, *Friedemann* ('12) divided the parataenial nucleus of his nomenclature into a subependymal and a parataenial portion (the nucleus parataenialis pars subependymarius and the nucleus parataenialis pars parastriata).   The former is the homologue of the anterior and posterior paraventricular nuclei described for rodents and carnivores, and as such is really a part of the midline group; the latter is the representative of the nucleus parataenialis of these lower mammals.   Similar nuclei have been described by *Vogt* ('09, noyau medial subependymarius and noyau medial parataenial) and *Pines* ('27) has recognized a medial and a lateral parataenial nucleus in the primates studied by him.   For man these nuclei have been less clearly defined; usually they have been included in the neighboring gray.   Thus the medial portion is the nucleus paramedianus of *Malone* ('10) and falls within the zentrales Höhlengrau of *von Monakow* ('95, '05) and *Forel* ('07) and the substance gris centrale of *Déjérine* ('01). The lateral part is included within the nucleus

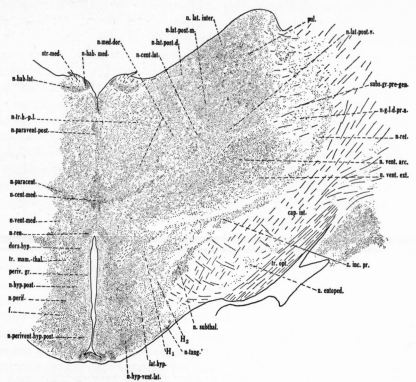

Fig. 516. Cross section through the level of the rostral pole of the habenular complex. Adult dog. Toluidin-blue preparation. *Rioch.*

cap.int., capsula interna; *dors.hyp.*, dorsal hypothalamic area; *f.*, fornix; H_1, field H_1 of *Forel*; H_2, field H_2 of *Forel*; *lat.hyp.*, lateral hypothalamic area; *n.cent.lat.*, nucleus centralis lateralis; *n.cent.med.*, nucleus centralis medialis; *n.entoped.*, nucleus entopeduncularis; *n.g.l.d.pr.a.*, nucleus geniculatus lateralis dorsalis, lamina principalis anterior; *n.hab.lat.*, nucleus habenularis lateralis; *n.hab.med.*, nucleus habenularis medialis; *n.hyp.post.*, nucleus hypothalamicus posterior; *n.hyp.vent.lat.*, nucleus hypothalamicus ventrolateralis; *n.lat.inter.*, nucleus lateralis intermedius; *n.lat.post.d.*, nucleus lateralis pars posterior, portio dorsalis; *n.lat.post.m.*, nucleus lateralis pars posterior, portio medialis; *n.lat.post.v.*, nucleus lateralis pars posterior, portio ventralis; *n.med.dor.*, nucleus medialis dorsalis; *n.paracent.*, nucleus paracentralis; *n.paravent.post.*, nucleus paraventricularis posterior; *n.perif.*, nucleus perifornicalis; *n.perivent.hyp.post.*, nucleus periventricularis hypothalamicus posterior; *n.reu.*, nucleus reuniens; *n.ret.*, nucleus reticularis; *n.subthal.*, nucleus subthalamicus; *n.tang.'*, nucleus tangentialis, scattered cells; *n.tr.h.-p.l.*, nucleus tractus habenulo-peduncularis lateralis; *n.vent.arc.*, nucleus ventralis, pars arcuata; *n.vent.ext.*, nucleus ventralis, pars externa; *n.vent.med.*, nucleus ventralis medialis; *periv.gr.*, periventricular gray; *pul.*, pulvinar; *str.med.*, stria medullaris; *subs.gr.pre-gen.*, substantia grisea pregeniculata; *tr.mam.-thal.*, tractus mamillo-thalamicus; *tr.opt.*, tractus opticus; *z.inc.pr.*, zona incerta proper.

reuniens of *Malone* ('10) and is frequently included within the nucleus medialis dorsalis (for example, *Sachs*, '09). Both portions of the parataenial nucleus lie within the dorsomedial part of the hyperchromatic ring surrounding the chief medial nucleus, as this has been described by *Foix* and *Nicolesco* ('25).

The chief medial nucleus (figs. 519 and 520), nucleus medialis dorsalis, or nucleus dorsomedialis of *Le Gros Clark* ('30), has been recognized so generally in primates including man, its general position resembles so closely that in carnivores, and the nucleus itself is so easily recognizable even in gross material, that a detailed account of its relationships is unnecessary. This nucleus is separated throughout much of its extent from the lateral division of the dorsal thalamus and from the nucleus medialis ventralis by the internal medullary lamina. Such remnants of the midline nuclei as remain in primates separate it from the ventricular wall, although the medial nuclei of the two sides at some levels closely approximate each other (*Friedemann*, '12). Cell-free zones separate it from the anterior group for the most part. The nucleus dorsomedialis in Tarsius (*Le Gros Clark*, homologous to the chief medial nucleus) has been divided into two portions (on the basis of cytoarchitectonic rather than myeloarchitectonic structure): (1) a principal part, composed of medium-sized cells and morphologically comparable to the main part of the nucleus as described for Cercopithecus by *Vogt* ('09) and *Friedemann* ('12), and (2) a lateral portion also homologous with the similarly designated portion in higher primates. This latter portion increases progressively from lower to higher primates.

The homologues of the nucleus paracentralis and the nucleus centralis lateralis have been identified by workers on primates below man and have been designated usually as the paralamellar portion (nucleus paracentralis) and the magnocellular portion (nucleus centralis lateralis or the nucleus of the internal medullary lamina — *Vogt*, '09; *Friedemann*, '12; *Pines*, '27; *Le Gros Clark*, '30). Material available indicates their presence in man, although no clear account of them is to be found in the literature concerned with this form. They are included in the nucleus reuniens of *Malone* ('10) and are probably a part of the hyperchromatic ring with which *Foix* and *Nicolesco* ('25) surrounded the medial nucleus.

A parafascicular nucleus has been demonstrated for primates (*Vogt*, '09; *Friedemann*, '12; *Pines*, '27; *Le Gros Clark*, '30). It is likewise present in man, and human material available indicates the presence of the nuclei tractus habenulo-peduncularis described by *Rioch* ('29). A centromedian nucleus (noyau centre médian, *Luys*) is a conspicuous element of the primate thalamus. It is included with the medial or, sometimes, with the lateral division, since it lies in intimate relation with the internal medullary lamina. *Woollard* ('25) and *Le Gros Clark* ('30) both recognized the presence of this nucleus in Tarsius, although the nuclear group thus designated may not be entirely the same in the two descriptions. A noyau centre médian was described by *Vogt* ('09) and *Friedemann* ('12) for Cercopithecus, by *Crouch* ('34a) for Macacus, and by *Déjérine* ('01), *Forel* ('07), *Sachs* ('09), *Foix* and *Nicolesco* ('25), and others for man.

The Fiber Connections of the Medial Nuclear Group (Thalamic) in Various Mammals

The fiber connections of the medial group of thalamic nuclei are rich and varied in character and appear to be most easily understood by considering them under the several mammalian orders and then summarizing the more pertinent results.

a. Marsupials. In the opossum (*Chu,* '32) the nucleus parataenialis, the nucleus medialis pars dorsalis, and the nucleus medialis pars ventralis are believed to be in relation with the intermediate and inferior thalamic radiations, while the nucleus medialis pars medialis is connected with the inferior thalamic radiations and possibly may receive fibers of the trigeminal lemniscus (*Chu,* '32a). The nucleus parafascicularis is said to be connected with the telencephalon by the inferior thalamic radiations.   *Chu* regarded the nucleus paracentralis as a correlation center between medial and lateral nuclear centers of the thalamus.

b. Edentates and Rodents. In the edentates *Papez* ('32) found rich connections between the nucleus medialis dorsalis (or the medial nucleus) of the thalamus and telencephalic centers, via thalamic radiations.   Of particular interest is his account of the extensive pericellular network by which the medial nucleus is joined to the ventral, medial, and lateral nuclei of the lateral division of the dorsal thalamus.   *Papez* found interconnections between the parafascicular nucleus and the nucleus medialis dorsalis (his medial nucleus).

A consideration of the fiber connections of the rodent medial group of thalamic nuclei indicates that the following connections have been established for the nucleus parataenialis of the rat (*Gurdjian,* '27): (1) thalamic radiations; (2) commissural connections with its fellow of the opposite side; and (3) connections with the nucleus medialis dorsalis.   To the rodent nucleus medialis dorsalis, *Ramón y Cajal* ('11) traced afferent fibers of unknown origin and found thalamo-cortical and probably cortico-thalamic bundles.   He traced commissural fibers into the medial portion of the nucleus (noyau superieur du raphé).   The nucleus is connected with the telencephalon in the rabbit (*Nissl,* '13) and the rat (*Gurdjian,* '26; *Le Gros Clark,* '32a, frontal regions; not found by *Waller,* '34, J. Comp. Neurol., vol. 60).   *D'Hollander* traced crossed and uncrossed fibers of the medial thalamic radiations to the internal medullary lamina, from which they probably entered the nucleus medialis dorsalis.   He suggested connections from the habenulo-peduncular tract and other habenular systems.   Internuclear fibers were traced from the nuclei centrales laterales of both sides in the rabbit (*d'Hollander,* '13) and from the nucleus parataenialis in the rat (*Gurdjian,* '27) to the nucleus medialis dorsalis.   In Marchi preparations of the rabbit, *Winkler* ('18) carried trigeminal lemnisci fibers into the edge of his nucleus medialis thalami (*c*), which apparently is gray in the region of the internal medullary lamina. *Allen* ('24) traced the superior cerebellar fibers in part to the medial nucleus in the guinea pig.   Earlier *Wallenberg* ('00) had described a trigeminal lemniscus to the nucleus medialis thalami, but it is probable that the area so designated by him is not that of later observers.   The nucleus parafascicularis is regarded as connected with the telencephalon by *Nissl* ('13) and by *Gurdjian* ('27) (by superior and intermediate thalamic radiations) and with the tectum by *Gurdjian.*

c. Carnivores. The observations of *von Monakow* ('95), of *Ramón y Cajal* ('11) (certain of which are based on carnivores), and of *Papez* ('29) indicate that the nucleus medialis dorsalis in carnivores, at least in the cat and the dog, is connected with the frontal part of the cortex. This cortical zone has been located by *von Monakow* ('95, '05) in the region in front of the gyrus sigmoideus. Ordinarily the path is termed the anterior thalamic peduncle and the direction of conduction is regarded as thalamo-cortical (*Ramón y Cajal*, '11, *Papez*, '29; *Glorieux*, '29, *Rioch*, '31; *Le Gros Clark* and *Boggon*, '33a) and perhaps as also cortico-thalamic (*Ramón y Cajal*, '11). *Von Monakow* ('95) suggested the possibility of ansa lenticularis connections. *Huber* and *Crosby* ('29, '30) and *Le Gros Clark* and *Boggon* ('33a) described periventricular fibers.

The nucleus paracentralis and the nucleus centralis lateralis are associated with commissural fibers and fibers of the internal medullary lamina in general, and the nuclei of the lateral and medial habenulo-peduncular tracts with the fibers of their respective tracts. The connections of the parafascicular nucleus in carnivores are said to be with the caudal part of the nucleus lateralis pars posterior, with the pretectal area, and with the periventricular system. It also sends fibers into the internal medullary lamina (*Rioch*, '32). The connections of the noyau centré median have not been demonstrated for these forms.

d. Primates. The connections of the nuclei of the medial group, in so far as they are known for primates, are much the same as for other mammals. The classical medial nucleus, the nucleus medialis dorsalis, has connections with the striatum (*Kodama*, '29, and many others; see pages 1444 and 1445 with bibliography; also figs. 521 and 632). Many observers have been unable to trace any lemnisci fibers to the nucleus (for example, *Le Gros Clark*, '32). In subprimates and primates certain workers (*Déjérine*, '01; *Winkler*, '18, rabbit; *Ariëns Kappers*, '21) described trigeminal lemnisci fibers and fibers from the superior cerebellar peduncle (*Winkler*, '18; *Ariëns Kappers*, '21; *Allen*, '24, guinea pig). *Bechterew* ('06) described connections of this nucleus with the tegmental region of the midbrain and the optic tectum. *Huber* and *Crosby* wish to take this opportunity of correcting a misstatement in an earlier paper ('29). *Probst* ('00) carried fibers to the medial division (not the medial nucleus) of the thalamus — to gray close to the internal medullary lamina. *Vogt* described the inferior thalamic peduncle as beginning in the fibrous portion of the medial nucleus (noyau medial fibreux) in Cercopithecus, and thought it probable that some of the bundles of this peduncle came into relation with the medial portion of his nucleus parataenialis. *Déjérine* ('01) considered that the cortical centers for this diencephalic area in man were to be found in the anterior and external parts of the frontal convolutions. He found it connected with the striatum through the ansa lenticularis and the lenticular fasciculus of *Forel*. *Von Monakow* ('05) designated the basal part of the convolutions F_1 and F_2 and the anterior island region, particularly that portion associated with his F_2, as the cortical zone of the human classical medial nucleus. *Sachs* ('09) carried efferent fibers from this nucleus to the caudate nucleus (see also *Papez*, '29), to the dorsal third of the lateral nucleus, and to the centré median nucleus of *Luys*. *Foix* and *Nicolesco* ('25) gave the following connections for the human nucleus medialis dorsalis (noyau interne): connections with the telencephalon by the anterior peduncle (cortical) and the inferior internal peduncle, and thalamo-striate and thalamo-olivary bundles. *Le Gros Clark* and *Boggon* ('35) found the chief medial nucleus (their nucleus dorsomedialis) connected with the area frontalis agranularis in Macacus. The medial nucleus of the primate thalamus has connections with the tuber cinereum region by way of periventricularly running fibers and rich internuclear connections with the surrounding thalamic gray (fig. 521).

With regard to the connections of the centromedian nucleus (noyau centré median) of the primates, opinions are not unanimous. According to *Déjérine* ('01), *Winkler* ('18), and *Foix* and *Nicolesco* ('25), who quoted a case studied by *Babinski* and *Nageotte*, this nucleus receives fibers of the lemnisci systems, probably largely of the trigeminal component, the number of such fibers being relatively small. *Déjérine* and *Foix* and *Nicolesco* have carried to it also fibers from the superior cerebellar peduncle and longitudinal fibers of the reticular formation. The importance of its relation with other thalamic nuclei has been emphasized by *Sachs* ('09), *Huber* and *Crosby* ('29), *Rioch* ('30), and *Le Gros Clark* ('30 and '32). *Sachs* found that it was particularly intimately related to the nuclei of the lateral division of the thalamus (see p. 1148). *Déjérine* ('01) found it connected with the superior portion of the parietal and precentral lobes. *Le Gros Clark* and *Boggon* ('35) were of the opinion that the centromedian nucleus has no thalamo-cortical connections, basing their conclusions on experimental work on Macacus. *Le Gros Clark* ('30 and '32) described rich tectal connections.

Résumé of Structure and Connections of the Medial Nuclear Group of the Dorsal Thalamus

The discussion of the functional significance of the medial division of the dorsal thalamus will be reserved until after the lateral and the metathalamic regions have been considered (pp. 1187 and 1188). However, it here appears desirable to summarize certain outstanding relations, applicable to mammals in general. The parataenial nucleus, where recognized, appears to be the recipient of fibers of the periventricular system, to be related to the inferior thalamic peduncle, to have internuclear relations with the nucleus anterodorsalis and the nucleus medialis dorsalis, and, in certain mammals such as rodents, to have commissural connections with the nuclei of the other side; connections with components of the stria medullaris appear to be indicated.

The nucleus medialis dorsalis (dorsomedial nucleus of *Le Gros Clark*, '32, and the medial nucleus of many neurologists) is known to have rich connections with the adjoining nuclei, particularly the ventral nucleus and the anterior group, and its connections with the striatum are admitted quite generally. There has been some question as to whether or not the nucleus medialis dorsalis has thalamo-cortical connections, but the balance of evidence appears distinctly in favor of such connections in higher mammals. There seems somewhat greater uncertainty as to the presence in all mammals of cortico-thalamic fibers, since their existence has been denied by certain observers, as for example *Glorieux* ('29), while recently their presence has been affirmed by *Le Gros Clark* ('32 and '32a). In figure 521 the connections are shown as passing in both directions between the medial nuclear group of the diencephalic region and the frontal region of the cortex.   The degree to which the nucleus may receive trigeminal (probably pain) impulses and fibers from the superior cerebellar peduncle (equilibratory impulses) appears still questionable or at least unsubstantiated by many observers.   Certainly such lemnisci connections do not appear to dominate the medial nucleus.

The nuclei tractus habenulo-peduncularis, where differentiated, are in synaptic relation with the appropriate fiber systems and apparently with the nucleus medialis dorsalis.   The nucleus parafascicularis has connections with the pretectal area, the caudal end of the posterior part of the lateral nucleus, and the internal medullary lamina.   In certain of the lower mammals it is not sharply separable from the centromedian nucleus.

The centromedian nucleus, which is scarcely more than a region of passage of fibers in lower mammals and has not been differentiated at all times in these forms, develops phylogenetically in close relation to the internal medullary lamina and probably receives its most important connections through this system in lower forms (as carnivores, *Rioch*, '31), although its internuclear relations are to be emphasized.   In higher forms it acquires more definite nuclear configuration and presumably with this increase in size and in differentiation are associated more specialized connections.   At least evidence has been presented suggesting that in the highest mammals this nucleus becomes a way station by which various ascending impulses (over the trigeminal lemniscus and the superior cerebellar peduncle) are relayed to the cortex.   This is contrary to the view of *Le Gros Clark* ('32) and *Le Gros Clark* and *Boggon* ('33a, '35) who regarded it as an intrathalamic correlation center, but who have studied its connections in the cat and the monkey.   Recently in two monkeys *Sager* ('33) found some slight cytologic changes in the centromedian nucleus following frontal lobe lesions, but the evidence which he presents is not as conclusive as might be desired.   The question as to possible lemnisci and cortical connections of the centromedian nucleus is as yet unsettled.   To *Huber* and *Crosby* it appears that certain of the results, which at face value seem directly opposed, actually are reconcilable.   It is quite within the realms of probability that the centromedian nucleus, which is differentiating through the mammalian phylum (for details of its phylogeny, see *Le Gros Clark*, '32), may acquire incoming lemnisci and outgoing cortical connections in the highest primates such as man, although such connections may be very small or lacking in lower primate and subprimate forms.   Certainly it should be stressed that the application of negative experimental evidence based on the study of certain forms must be applied with great care to other forms, when the regions involved are such as are undergoing marked differentiation and development and where considerable positive evidence to the contrary has been presented.

The Nuclear Pattern of the Midline Nuclear Group of the Dorsal Thalamus

In lower mammals the dorsal thalami of the two sides are fused together for the greater part of their extent and a series of nuclei appear in the region of fusion, to which the term of nuclei of the midline has been applied. In higher mammals the amount of fusion gradually decreases until in man, in a very considerable number of cases, the dorsal thalamic regions of the two sides are entirely separated in the midline. Naturally with the decrease in the area of fusion there is a corresponding decrease in the nuclear constituents of the midline group, until in primates these have disappeared entirely or mere vestiges of them remain. *Chu* ('32) published an account of the midline or central group of thalamic nuclei for the opossum, and *Papez* ('32) presented a similar account for the armadillo. The accounts follow closely the earlier work on rodents, insectivores, and carnivores. Since *Huber* and *Crosby* are more familiar with the work on rodents and carnivores, emphasis is laid on the details of arrangement of the midline group in these forms, while the conditions in other mammals are reviewed relatively briefly.

a. *Marsupials.* *Chu* ('32) described in the opossum a nucleus paraventricularis anterior which is found in the dorsal cephalic region of the dorsal thalamus, ventral to the medial habenular nucleus and medial to the parataenial nucleus. Continuous caudally with this nucleus paraventricularis anterior is the somewhat larger-celled nucleus paraventricularis posterior, which retains a periventricular position, but, according to *Chu*, enlarges somewhat at its caudal end into an angular group of cells. In the midline, immediately ventral to the nucleus paraventricularis anterior and medial to the nucleus medialis pars medialis of the opossum, lies the triangularly shaped nucleus rhomboidalis. *Chu* found the neurons forming this cell mass to be small or medium sized and regarded the group as commissural in character. Just ventral to the paraventricular nuclei, throughout the whole extent of the medial nuclei, scattered cells were found occupying a position in the midline and serving as a commissural nucleus (nucleus commissuralis) for the nuclei mediales partes mediales of the two sides. Obviously this represents the various commissural nuclei differentiated in this region in other forms such as rodents. Ventral to the commissural nucleus lies the nucleus centralis, which consists of medium-sized neurons with intermingled smaller cells and has the relations in the opossum typical for it in other mammals. The nucleus reuniens is relatively very large in the opossum, with larger, lighter staining neurons than the previously described nucleus, and extends from the cephalic pole to nearly the caudal pole of the diencephalon. It shows certain resemblances to the nucleus reuniens of forms below mammals.

b. *Edentates and Rodents.* In the armadillo, *Papez* ('32) described the same nuclear masses as those seen by *Chu* in the opossum, except that he identified a nucleus interventralis and did not recognize a distinct nucleus commissuralis. *Papez* found in this edentate the anterior paraventricular nuclei united by a "more distinctly commissural seam of cells." Cephalically the anterior paraventricular nucleus is bounded by the anterior nuclear group, the parataenial nucleus, the nucleus submedius, and the rhomboid nucleus, and caudally by the medial nucleus. According to *Papez* the intimate relation of the anterior paraventricular nuclei with the above mentioned nuclei suggests that "they probably represent undifferentiated residues of these bordering nuclei." The posterior paraventricular nucleus in the armadillo extends caudalward from the anterior paraventricular nucleus, reaching a position under the posterior commissure as in other forms.   The narrow band or "seam" of cells which *Papez* described ventral to it and between the two medial nuclei probably corresponds to the commissural nucleus described in the opossum by *Chu*.   The central nucleus has the usual relations.   The interventral nucleus, situated below the nucleus centralis, between the nuclei ventrales mediales in the armadillo, is probably the representative in this form of the nucleus commissuralis of certain rodents and carnivores. The nucleus reuniens of the armadillo has two triangular extensions, one on either side, which ultimately unite across the midline.   The extensions come into relation laterally with the nucleus submedius (or medialis medialis) and the nucleus ventralis medialis.

In the rodent the more dorsal of the midline cellular groups are the anterior and posterior paraventricular nuclei.   The anterior lies in the midline between the two parataenial nuclei (fig. 513).   At its cephalic end it is dorsal to the nucleus reuniens, but soon becomes separated from this latter nucleus by the intervention of other midline nuclei.   The anterior paraventricular nucleus is continuous cephalically with the periventricular gray and caudally with the posterior paraventricular nucleus on either side, this latter nuclear mass (fig. 515) being a paired structure extending from about the level of the anterior pole of the nucleus centralis to the posterior end of the diencephalon, to become continuous there with the mesencephalic periventricular gray.   In rabbits, apparently, the anterior and posterior paraventricular nuclei form a single nuclear mass (midline group, 1, *d'Hollander*, '13; nucleus paraependymalis, *Winkler* and *Potter*, '14). The posterior paraventricular nucleus is divisible secondarily into medial and lateral portions; of these the lateral is particularly associated with the medial habenulo-peduncular tract and may be comparable to the nucleus of that tract described in carnivores by *Rioch* ('29).

In a plane through the lateral habenular nucleus and in front of the anterior end of the lateral geniculate nucleus, certain of the midline group of nuclei are particularly well developed in the rat (*Gurdjian*, '27).   Reference to figure 513 shows the general relations of the greater number of the group.   Ventral to the nucleus paraventricularis anterior described above, from dorsal to ventral in the order named, are the nucleus commissuralis interanterodorsalis, the nucleus commissuralis interanteromedialis (noyau interdorsal, *Ramón y Cajal*, '11, not indicated in the figure), the nucleus rhomboidalis, and the nucleus reuniens.   The first two consist of cells intercalated in the course of commissural bundles connecting the anterodorsal and anteromedial nuclei respectively of the two sides. The use of the term nucleus rhomboidalis in the various mammals is somewhat misleading, since the limits of the cell mass or even the cell groups so designated do not appear in all cases to be the same.   In the mouse, the rabbit, and the guinea pig, *Ramón y Cajal* ('11) so designated a rhomboidal shaped mass situated in a plane passing through the habenular nuclei dorsally and the tuber cinereum ventrally.   It appears that the nucleus so described by *Ramón y Cajal* corresponds to both rhomboidal and central nuclei of certain observers.   Thus *Gurd-*

jian ('27) described nucleus rhomboidalis as formed of small cells which appear in planes through the rostral tip of the medial habenular nucleus, ventral to the nucleus commissuralis intermedialis and dorsal to the nucleus reuniens, and which extend caudalward to form a cap over the cephalic end of the nucleus centralis, this latter nucleus apparently occupying the position designated as nucleus rhomboidalis by *Ramón y Cajal* in more caudal sections. In most forms the nucleus rhomboidalis is carried farther caudalward, usually above the nucleus centralis (but not separated from it, as *Chu* has done, by commissural nuclei). The nucleus rhomboidalis of *Gurdjian* is probably number 2 of the *d'Hollander* midline group. The nucleus reuniens (figs. 513 and 515), as the name is used by *Gurdjian*, is the representative of (3) and (4) of the midline group of *d'Hollander* ('13). The nucleus reuniens extends from the rostral end of the diencephalon to a plane through the posterior pole of the habenular nuclei. At first it is just caudal to the nucleus paraventricularis anterior, but later it is separated from this cell group by the intervention of other nuclear masses, and ultimately reaches a position ventral to the nucleus rhomboidalis.

In planes behind the level of the nucleus rhomboidalis, a distinct change in the nuclear configuration of the midline group is to be noted. The paired posterior paraventricular nuclei replace the median anterior paraventricular cell mass. The nucleus commissuralis intermediodorsalis has appeared in approximately the position occupied by the commissural nuclei associating the anterior dorsal nuclear groups. Ventral to this nucleus and directly caudal to the nucleus rhomboidalis and to the nucleus commissuralis anterior dorsalis is the nucleus centralis, while beneath this latter nuclear group still lies the nucleus reuniens. Gradually this latter nucleus disappears but the nuclei paraventriculares posteriores (fig. 515) persist until posterior commissure levels are reached.

At the posterior end of the diencephalon a nucleus commissuralis interventralis is associated with fibers connecting the two ventral thalamic nuclei. Such a fiber bundle has been indicated by both *d'Hollander* ('13) and *Gurdjian* ('27). The nucleus centralis, which is always in close relation laterally with the paracentral nuclei (noyau falciformes, *Ramón y Cajal*, '11), is associated with decussating or commissural fibers which interconnect the nuclei mediales dorsales of the two sides, the two paracentral nuclei, and the two medial ventral nuclei. Possibly there are interconnections for the lateral nuclei also.

c. Insectivores. The midline group in insectivores has been described by *Le Gros Clark* ('29). He found the ventral part of his principal anterior nucleus, which corresponds to the nucleus anterior ventralis of rodents, connected with the homologous cell group of the other side by scattered cells and associated fiber bundles. Such cells are analogous, then, to the noyau interdorsal of *Ramón y Cajal* ('11) or the nucleus commissuralis interanteroventralis of *Gurdjian* ('27) and *Rioch* ('29). A similar cell band with associated fiber bundles unites the two anterodorsal or smaller dorsal nuclei of *Le Gros Clark* ('29), the homologue of the rodent nucleus commissuralis interanterodorsalis. A fusion of the dorsomedial nuclei of the two sides across the midline was recognized by this latter author, as was also a band of fibers connecting the medial portions of the ventral nuclei of the two sides. He found a nucleus reuniens and a nucleus centralis also in Tupaia, but it would appear that the nuclei do not correspond exactly to those described by *Gurdjian* ('27) for rodents, for the nucleus rhomboidalis of *Le Gros Clark* is homologous in part to the nucleus reuniens of *Gurdjian*, while the nucleus reuniens of the former includes the nucleus rhomboidalis of the latter. In the tree shrew (Tupaia minor) the nucleus centralis appears to be associated, as in the rat, with commissural fibers. The nucleus dorsalis of the raphé is probably the nucleus paraventricularis of *Gurdjian*.

d. Carnivores. The nucleus rhomboidalis of carnivores (fig. 514), according to *Rioch* ('29), appears immediately caudal to the cephalic end of the nucleus centralis or nucleus centralis medialis, dorsal to that nucleus and ventral to the nucleus commissuralis interanteromedialis and, farther caudalward, the periventricular gray. Its cephalic and caudal boundaries are formed by the nucleus commissuralis interanteromedialis and the periventricular system, with both of which it is continuous. The various cell groups termed the nucleus rhomboidalis have been discussed above. With the exception of differences in the nucleus rhomboidalis in rodents and carnivores, the absence in the dog of a commissural portion of the nucleus reuniens (although in the aevisa, Crossarchus obscurus, which is a small West African carnivore, and, in the cat, *Rioch*, '31 found a well-developed portion of the nucleus reuniens in the midline) and the presence in carnivores of an additional commissural nucleus, the nucleus interparataenialis, nuclear groups essentially comparable to those described for the rat by *Gurdjian* have been described by *Rioch* ('29) for carnivores (see figs. 514, 516, and 518). The differences, other than those mentioned, are minor ones — of importance only to those interested in the most detailed study of this region, and for such detail the original papers should be consulted.

Winkler and *Potter* ('14) described a nucleus reuniens in the cat, comparable to the nucleus rhomboidalis of *Rioch*, a nucleus centralis, and an unlabeled area, which (together with *Ma* of their figure *XA*) may represent the nucleus reuniens (see also *Rioch*, '29, p. 37). The major portion of the midline area, including the commissural nuclei, was termed by these observers the commissura media. *Papez* ('29, fig. 169) applied the name of massa intermedia to the commissural nuclei in carnivores. *Ingram, Hannett*, and *Ranson* ('32) described midline nuclei which agree in essentials with those described by *Rioch*.

e. Primates. Here the midline nuclei are poorly developed, due possibly to an increased unilateral independence of function (*Papez* and *Aronson*, '34). *Le Gros Clark* ('30) identified in Tarsius a poorly developed nucleus paraventricularis (fig. 517), a nucleus rhomboidalis, a relatively well-developed nucleus centralis medialis, and a nucleus reuniens. In Macac, *Crouch* ('34a) found interparataenial, interanteromedial, paraventricular, and medial central nuclei. *Vogt* ('09) distinguished no midline nuclei in Cercopithecus, but a relatively large commissura mollis, or massa intermedia, in the midline of which occurred the decussating fibers of the principal commissure, which could be followed to his noyau central. *Friedemann* ('12) described, in Cercopithecus, undifferentiated commissural gray down to the level of the nucleus reuniens in other forms, and then a differentiated nuclear mass, the nucleus ventralis commissurae mediae. The work of *Pines* ('27) indicates that there is a marked decrease in size and differentiation in the midline group in primates. In man the midline group is obviously very poorly developed. The nuclei are represented by central or

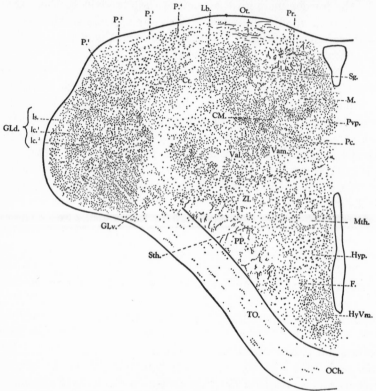

FIG. 517. Cross section through the optic chiasm of the brain of Tarsius, through the middle of the lateral geniculate body and immediately caudal to the upper end of the habenulo-peduncular tract. Toluidin-blue preparation. Redrawn from figure 7, of *Le Gros Clark*, '30.

CM., "centré median" nucleus; *Ct.*, cortico-tectal tract; *F.*, fornix; *GLd.ls.*, dorsal nucleus of lateral geniculate body, lamina superficialis; *GLd.lc.*[1] and *lc.*[2], dorsal nucleus of lateral geniculate body, lamina centralis; *GLv.*, ventral nucleus of lateral geniculate body; *Hyp.*, nucleus hypothalamicus posterior; *HyVm.*, nucleus hypothalamicus ventromedialis; *Lb.*, main part of lateral nucleus; *Mth.*, mammillo-thalamic tract; *OCh.*, optic chiasma; *P.*, pulvinar (pars posterior of lateral nucleus); *Pc.*, nucleus paracentralis; *Pr.*, nucleus pretectalis; *PP.*, pes pedunculi; *Pvp.*, nucleus paraventricularis posterior; *Sg.*, nucleus suprageniculatus; *Sth.*, nucleus subthalamicus; *TO.*, optic tract; *Val.*, nucleus ventralis anterolateralis; *Vam.*, nucleus ventralis anteromedialis; *ZI.*, zona incerta.

periventricular gray (substantia grise centrale of *Déjérine*, '01; zentrales Höhlengrau des dritten Ventrikles of *Edinger*, '08) and by the massa intermedia which appears in the position of the nucleus centralis of lower forms. In man it is little more than the partial fusion of the dorsal diencephalic walls, is often absent, and carries no commissural fibers. *Malone* ('10) included the greater number of these midline nuclei in his nucleus reuniens, which he found poorly developed in man.

The Fiber Connections of the Midline Nuclear Group (Thalamic) in Various Mammals

A consideration of the fiber connections of the midline group shows certain differences of opinion with regard to the specific connections.   In the opossum the nucleus rhomboidalis, the nucleus centralis, and the nucleus commissuralis of *Chu's* ('32a) account are said to receive fibers of the periventricular system, while the nucleus centralis also receives fascicles from the internal medullary lamina, and the nucleus reuniens is connected with the internal thalamic radiations.   In the armadillo, *Papez* ('32) found all of the midline nuclei lying in the course of periventricular fibers, but apparently specific connections only with the anterior paraventricular nucleus, which he regarded as connected with the dorsomedial hypothalamic and filiform nuclei.

The anterior and posterior paraventricular nuclei in the rat receive inferior thalamic radiations and are interconnected by internuclear fibers, while the latter nuclear mass is associated with the periventricular fiber system (*Gurdjian*, '27). The nucleus commissuralis interanterodorsalis and the nucleus commissuralis interanteromedialis are intercalated cells in the course of the commissure bundles connecting the anterior dorsal and anterior medial nuclei of the two sides.   The nucleus rhomboidalis of *Gurdjian's* terminology (p. 1126) receives fibers of the inferior thalamic radiations, while the fiber connections of the nucleus reuniens of this observer are the same as those of the nucleus paraventricularis posterior. The nucleus commissuralis interventralis carries fibers interconnecting the two ventral thalamic nuclei (*d'Hollander*, '13, and *Gurdjian*, '27).   *Waller* ('34, see p. 1120) found no cortical radiations from midline nuclei in the rat.

The medullated commissural fibers associated with the nuclei commissurales interanteromedialis, interanterodorsalis, and interparataenialis were found to be more pronounced in the aevisa than in the cat and the dog (*Rioch*, '31); the nucleus rhomboidalis, the nucleus reuniens, and the nucleus centralis medialis have connections with the periventricular system in carnivores (see fig. 518) and are connected by short, internuclear fibers with several adjoining nuclei.   *Rioch* ('31) traced fibers of the inferior thalamic peduncle to the nucleus reuniens and fascicles from the internal medullary lamina to the nucleus centralis.   *Le Gros Clark* and *Boggon* ('33a) carried periventricular fibers to midline nuclear groups of carnivores.

Little is known of the connections of the midline nuclear group in primates. It is believed that the groups probably receive, along with the nucleus medialis dorsalis, fibers from the tuber cinereum region by way of the diencephalic periventricular system, and that the midline gray joins with the nucleus medialis dorsalis in contributing fascicles to this fiber system (*Huber* and *Crosby*).

Résumé of Structure and Connections of the Midline Nuclear Group of the Dorsal Thalamus

In summarizing the thalamic midline nuclear group, certain general relations are to be emphasized and certain differences of terminology noted.   In forms below mammals, the midline area is differentiated into a series of nuclei which, while arranged according to the same general pattern, present considerable varia-

tions in the different forms.   The paraventricular nuclei are represented in practically all these forms, and they appear to be connected rather generally with
the periventricular fiber system and the surrounding gray, particularly the
nucleus medialis dorsalis.   One must assume that either the name nucleus rhomboidalis has been applied to several different nuclei near the midline portion of
the diencephalon or, what appears less probable, that the nucleus varies in the
different forms.   It would appear that the name nucleus rhomboidalis was
applied by *Ramón y Cajal* ('11) to the center known to later workers as the nucleus
centralis or nucleus centralis medialis.   The nucleus rhomboidalis of *Gurdjian*
('27), which fits like a cap over his nucleus centralis, probably represents the
cephalic part of the rhomboidal nucleus of *Ramón y Cajal*.   The nucleus
rhomboidalis of Tupaia (*Le Gros Clark*, '29), which lies ventral to the central
nucleus, probably represents gray situated just below (or the most ventral gray
of) the nucleus centralis, or the nucleus rhomboidalis of *Ramón y Cajal*, while
the rhomboidal nucleus of carnivores, as described by *Rioch*, and of Tarsius, as
seen by *Le Gros Clark* ('30), is dorsal to, and at certain levels almost inseparable
from, the nucleus centralis medialis.   The rhomboidal nucleus of *Chu* ('32) is
still another gray mass dorsal to the nucleus centralis medialis but separated
from it by his nucleus commissuralis.   Thus it is necessary to know, in comparing the accounts of the nucleus rhomboidalis in the several forms, which terminology is being followed; probably all of the several centers so designated
receive periventricular fibers.

    The commissural group is variously differentiated, depending on the form
considered, and the number of fibers associated with it is also variable.   However, in general this gray and its associated fiber bundles are concerned in the
interrelation of the two sides of the dorsal thalamus.

    The nucleus centralis medialis and the nucleus reuniens are evident in many
mammalian forms below primates, probably in all such forms, although the
latter nucleus does not always have a clearly differentiated midline portion.   The
nucleus centralis medialis and the nucleus reuniens are related to the periventricular system and the nucleus centralis medialis receives fibers via the internal
medullary lamina, while the nucleus reuniens in certain forms, perhaps in all, has
connections with the telencephalon.   It is evident that the group is better developed in mammals below primates than in primates, and that from lower to higher
primates there is somewhat of a decrease rather than an increase in the midline
centers.   Obviously, the midline group associates the dorsal thalami of the two
sides, but it is not clear why this associative function should decrease rather
than increase phylogenetically unless this is related to the progressive dominance
of the cortex in such higher forms and the gradual transference of higher asso-
ciations to cortical centers.

*The Lateral and Ventral Nuclear Groups of the Dorsal Thalamus Exclusive
of the Geniculate Nuclei*

    In the following account of the nuclei belonging to the lateral division of the
dorsal thalamus, it has been deemed advisable to discuss first the lateral group

proper, including the lateral nucleus with its various subdivisions, the pulvinar with the associated posterior nucleus and certain other smaller groups, such as the nucleus pretectalis and the large-celled optic nucleus, the ventral nuclear group with its various subdivisions, and certain associated groups, such as the nucleus submedius and the nucleus subparafascicularis. Later the medial and lateral geniculate nuclei will be discussed. The lateral and medial geniculates, the pretectal, and the large-celled optic nucleus are sometimes grouped together as the metathalamus; the last two may be mesencephalic.

a. Monotremes and Marsupials. One of the major constituents of the lateral division of the dorsal thalamus is the nucleus lateralis thalami. This nuclear mass has representatives in all mammalian forms, in so far as these have been studied, but its degree of differentiation varies with the position of the animal considered, there being a marked increase in the size and in the subdivisions of the nuclear group in proceeding from lower to higher forms.

As was noted previously (p. 1113), a part of what usually is considered the lateral division of the dorsal thalamus in Ornithorhynchus appears to be represented as subdivisions of the more caudal part of the medial nucleus, according to the interpretation of *Dr. Hines* ('29). Two other nuclear subdivisions, which possibly may belong to the lateral division, are this observer's nucleus mediolateralis, which is ventral to the nucleus dorsolateralis, dorsal and cephalic to the nucleus ventrolateralis, and medial to her pretectal nucleus, and her nucleus dorsolateralis, which she regarded as possibly a portion of the midbrain tegmentum. She recognized a nucleus pretectalis in these animals.

The nucleus lateralis thalami has been figured for the opossum by *Tsai* ('25, in figs. 7 and 8, pp. 183 and 184); it lies medial to the lateral geniculate nucleus and dorsolateral to the nucleus ventralis thalami. However, no account of the nucleus is to be found in the paper of *Tsai*, which is concerned primarily with optic centers. *Chu* ('32) recognized a nucleus lateralis and a nucleus lateralis pars posterior in the opossum. According to this observer, the former nucleus (comprising a cell mass of medium-sized, multipolar cells in the opossum) is situated between the nucleus medialis pars dorsalis medially and the lateral geniculate nucleus laterally and extends to the brain wall dorsally, while ventrally it approaches the ventral nucleus. From its cephalic pole, at a plane through the caudal, lateral end of the nucleus anteroventralis, it continues caudally, becoming somewhat enlarged and ultimately continuous with the pars posterior of the lateral nucleus. This pars posterior extends back to planes through the posterior commissure and into a position dorsomedial to the nucleus geniculatus medialis.

Ventromedial to the pars posterior of the lateral nucleus, *Tsai* ('25) and *Chu* ('32) identified a nucleus posterior comparable to that described for various rodents. *Chu* ('32) described a pretectal nucleus in the opossum comparable to that described by *Tsai* ('25), although he was not in agreement with the latter observer in regarding it as the forerunner of the pulvinar. In addition to the nuclei mentioned above, *Chu* identified a nucleus reticularis, situated at the line between the dorsal thalamus and the ventral thalamus, and a typical ventral nucleus situated in the ventral and ventromedial portion of the thalamus, between the internal medullary lamina with its associated cell groups on the one hand, and the reticular nucleus and external medullary lamina on the other hand. In the midline, he appears to have carried the nucleus into relation with the nucleus reuniens, suggesting that in the opossum a nucleus submedius has not been differentiated. The nucleus ventralis of the opossum has been subdivided by *Chu* into a pars lateralis and a pars medialis.

b. Edentates. In the armadillo, *Papez* ('32) found the lateral nucleus relatively poorly developed and only indistinctly separated on the basis of some slight differences in cell structure from the nucleus ventralis (pars) lateralis. The anterior portion of the lateral nucleus of the armadillo is shown in figure 523, from *Papez* ('32). The posterior portion of the lateral nucleus, or the pulvinar as *Papez* termed it, following the suggestion of *Gurdjian* ('27) and *Le Gros Clark* ('30), was found to be a "small but compact group of cells situated along the dorsal medial border of the lateral geniculate nucleus and its caudal extent running parallel to the pretectal nucleus." *Papez* regarded its relatively small size in the armadillo as associated with the relatively scanty development of the neopallial cortex and of the visual apparatus in this form.

In the armadillo, *Papez* ('32) identified a posterior nucleus, oval in outline and situated at the level of the posterior commissure and behind it, and believed it to be comparable to the posterior nucleus described under this name by *Winkler* and *Potter* ('11), *d'Hollander* ('13), *Gurdjian* ('27), and *Chu* ('32). This nuclear mass was termed the posterior nucleus by *Le Gros Clark* ('29) in Tupaia, and represented a major part, at least, of his pretectal nucleus in Tarsius (*Le Gros Clark*, '30). Dorsal to it is the pretectal area of *Papez*, consisting of scattered cells, which is combined with the posterior nucleus by certain observers. It seems probable that the posterior nucleus of *Papez* includes the nucleus of the posterior commissure as described by *Tsai* ('25). The pretectal nucleus of *Papez* "is an irregular crescentic group of cells situated obliquely along the anterior margin and beneath the lateral margin of the tectum." He separated from this nucleus the distinct lamina of cells which he termed the large-celled nucleus of the optic tract. Reference should be made here to figure 523.

According to this observer the nucleus ventralis lateralis marks the peak of nuclear development within the armadillo thalamus, being a large nuclear mass with conspicuous multipolar neurons, which is found through the caudal two-thirds of the diencephalon, lying in the usual position between the internal medullary lamina and paracentral and lateral central nuclei dorsomedially, and the external medullary lamina and the reticular nucleus ventrally and ventrolaterally. *Papez* emphasized particularly the close interrelation of the nucleus ventralis lateralis with the nuclei lateralis and suprageniculatus, and stated that this last mentioned nucleus, which is poorly developed or "rudimentary" in the armadillo, is represented by a group of cells which comes into relation dorsolaterally with the nucleus ventralis lateralis. The nucleus ventralis medialis, situated medial to the nucleus ventralis lateralis, is said to unite at appropriate levels with its fellow of the other side and so to form the under or ventral portion of the massa intermedia, which ventral portion is termed by *Papez* the nucleus inter-ventralis.   A nucleus reticularis, having the usual relations, was identified in the armadillo.   The submedius nucleus (nucleus medialis ventralis of many observers) lies medial to the nucleus ventralis medialis, with the ventral surface of which it is believed to be continuous in the armadillo.   Cephalically the nucleus submedius of the armadillo is continuous with the ventral tip of the parataenial nucleus, which it reaches by passing around the cephalic border of the nucleus anteromedialis.

b'. Rodents.   In the rodent a well-developed lateral thalamic nucleus (fig. 513) is to be found ventral and medial to the anterior dorsal and anterior ventral thalamic nuclei.   Caudal to the plane of the nucleus anterodorsalis the nucleus lateralis enlarges and occupies practically all of the dorsolateral part of the thalamic wall in the rat (*Gurdjian*, '27).   It lies dorsal to the nucleus ventralis, lateral to the nucleus medialis dorsalis, and medial to the reticular nucleus and its associated fiber bundle.   It is continuous caudalward above the nucleus ventralis pars dorsomedialis and medial to the nucleus geniculatus pars dorsalis as a special nuclear mass, the nucleus lateralis pars posterior (fig. 515).   In both the nucleus lateralis and its pars posterior the cell type is essentially the same, but the pars posterior, which is bordered dorsally and laterally by the optic tract, and is said to receive collaterals and possibly stem fibers from this fiber system, has a special connection with the cortex through the superior thalamic radiations.   As *Gurdjian* suggested, and as will be discussed later, this nucleus is probably the forerunner of the pulvinar of higher mammals.   A noyau laterale was described by *d'Hollander* ('13) in the rabbit and *Nissl* ('89) divided the nuclear mass into an anterior lateral nuclear group, a dorsal posterior nuclear group, and a ventral posterior nuclear group.

In the more caudal part of the rodent diencephalon, just medial to the nucleus lateralis pars posterior, the nucleus posterior of *Nissl*, *d'Hollander*, and *Gurdjian*, the noyau posterieur or bigeminum of *Ramón y Cajal*, and the nucleus pretectalis of *Le Gros Clark* ('32a) appears.   Followed caudalward the nucleus posterior increases in size and ultimately lies medial to the nucleus geniculatus medialis and the nucleus lateralis pars posterior, ventral to the tectum, and lateral to the commissura posterior.   At its caudal end it extends relatively far ventralward in the rat.   Dorsal and largely medial to the posterior nucleus is the pretectal area of *Gurdjian* which consists of "an undifferentiated mass of gray matter which is found rostral to the tectum and in front becomes continuous with the lateral nucleus."   This area of *Gurdjian* (N. pretect., fig. 515) includes the large-celled nucleus of the optic tract and the nucleus pretectalis of *Papez* ('32; together these constitute the large-celled nucleus of the optic tract of *Le Gros Clark*, '32a) and also the small area pretectalis of *Papez* (which probably falls within the nucleus pretectalis of *Le Gros Clark*).   The nucleus pretectalis of *Papez* is homologous with the similarly designated area of other forms.

Through its greatest extent the ventral thalamic nucleus of rodents is round or oval, and is surrounded laterally and ventrally by the external medullary lamina and the reticular nucleus.   Dorsal to it is the nucleus lateralis and medial to it the nucleus medialis and the nucleus medialis ventralis.   Its rostrocaudal extent is from a plane through the anterior third of the habenular complex to the cephalic border of the medial geniculate nucleus, with which it lies in close relation. Near its caudal end it is bounded on the lateral side by the lateral geniculate nucleus, on the medial side by the nucleus parafascicularis, ventrally by the zona incerta and dorsally by the posterior part of the nucleus lateralis. A dorsomedial portion is separable from the main mass. The above relations apply particularly to the nucleus in the rat (*Gurdjian*; also figs. 513 and 515). The nucleus has been recognized in many rodents, such as the mouse (*Ramón y Cajal*, '11) and the rabbit (*Winkler* and *Potter*, '11; *d'Hollander*, '13).

The nucleus reticularis belongs to the lateral division of the dorsal thalamus. Through a part of its extent it is in more intimate contact with the ventral nucleus and, through the rest of its extent, with the lateral nucleus. It consists in rodents of cells associated with the thalamic radiations. Its position is indicated in the figures. It extends from near the rostral end of the thalamus to a plane caudal to the habenular commissure. It may be subdivided into dorsal and ventral portions, but it appears to be essentially a nucleus intercalatus in the course of the internal capsule fibers. It has been described by various workers on rodents, including *Ramón y Cajal* ('11), *Winkler* and *Potter* ('11), *d'Hollander* ('13), and *Gurdjian* ('27). It is illustrated in figures 513 and 515.

The nucleus medialis ventralis in the rat appears cephalically behind the level of the rostral end of the nucleus medialis dorsalis, in a plane through the caudal pole of the nucleus anterior ventralis, and extends caudalward to the plane of the posterior commissure. It is lateral to the nucleus reuniens, ventral to the nucleus paracentralis and later to the nucleus commissuralis interventralis, and medial to the ventral nucleus. Anteriorly, on its ventral surface, lie the nucleus reticularis and the hypothalamic areas, and farther caudalward the zona incerta. The above account, based on rat material and agreeing with the descriptions and figures of *Gurdjian* ('27; see also fig. 515), is applicable, with relatively slight modifications, to other rodents such as the rabbit. The mammillo-thalamic tract lies in intimate relation with the nucleus throughout the greater part of the extent of that cell mass.

c. Insectivores. In insectivores a nucleus lateralis, homologous in general with the nucleus lateralis of rodents, has been identified by *Le Gros Clark* ('29). In Tupaia he was able to differentiate a more anterior portion, nucleus lateralis *A*, from a more caudal portion, nucleus lateralis *B*. Both of these divisions were included under the major portion of his lateral nucleus. In addition to these he recognized a nucleus lateralis pars posterior, homologous to the similarly named nucleus of *Gurdjian* ('27). He confirmed the fiber relations as given by the earlier observers and regarded favorably the homologizing of this portion with the pulvinar of higher forms.

The ventral nucleus in insectivores (*Le Gros Clark*, '29) corresponds in general to the ventral nucleus of other forms but appears to be somewhat differently subdivided than in rodents. In its general configuration, it resembles more closely the ventral nucleus of primates such as the lemur (*Pines*, '27), since within it may be recognized anterior and posterior groups, each of which may be further subdivided into lateral and medial nuclei.   The nucleus reticularis of insectivores does not differ essentially from that of rodents.

In Tupaia, *Le Gros Clark* described a pretectal nucleus and a nucleus posterior which he regarded as homologous to the similarly designated areas in the rat as described by *Gurdjian* ('27).   Later he suggested changing the name of the nucleus posterior to that of nucleus pretectalis and the area earlier designated by himself as the pretectal area to that of the large-celled nucleus of the optic tract.   The homologies of the nuclei so designated in the rat have been discussed on page 1133.   The matter will receive further consideration under the account of Tarsius (p. 1141), since this was the form in which the changes in nomenclature were made first.   The whole matter is reviewed briefly in the summary on page 1153.

d.   Carnivores.   The nuclei of the lateral division of the carnivore dorsal thalamus have been studied and described by various observers, among whom may be mentioned *Winkler* and *Potter* ('14), *Papez* ('29), *Rioch* ('29 and '31), and *Ingram, Hannett,* and *Ranson* ('32).   The nucleus lateralis in the dog was divided by *Rioch* ('29) into a pars anterior, a pars intermedialis, and a pars posterior.   Similar divisions were recognized in the cat by *Ingram, Hannett,* and *Ranson* ('32).   The nucleus lateralis pars anterior is situated in the latero-anterior portion of the dorsal thalamus, lateral and dorsolateral to the nucleus anterodorsalis and the nucleus anteroventralis and separated from them by the dorsal or internal medullary lamina.   It is somewhat pyramidal in shape, with its base toward the pars intermedialis of the lateral nucleus and its apex extending into a tuberculum on the dorsal surface of the thalamus.   The external medullary lamina separates it from the reticular nucleus.   The cells are polygonal or triangular in shape with deeply staining nuclei and "blotchy granulations" (*Rioch,* '29).   Caudal to the nucleus lateralis pars anterior and to the nucleus centralis lateralis, from which latter nucleus it is separated by a fiber bundle with intercalated cells, lies the nucleus lateralis pars intermedialis.   This nucleus has the shape of a thick convex lens.   It reaches the surface of the thalamus dorsally.   Medially it is bounded by the nucleus centralis lateralis except where the pars posterior of the lateral nucleus intervenes between these nuclear groups.   The external medullary lamina forms its lateral boundary.   The pulvinar joins it caudally and caudolaterally, and the pars posterior of the lateral nucleus joins it caudomedially.   The pars intermedialis (fig. 516), on the basis of cell arrangement and cell form, falls into three subdivisions, a dorsal, a lateral, and a medial.   For the details of the arrangement of these, the original papers should be consulted.   The nucleus lateralis pars posterior (figs. 516, 518, 527) is a region rather than a discrete nuclear mass, determined largely on the basis of intrinsic fiber bundles, and consequently arrangement of cells, rather than on differences in cytological characteristics of the region.   This nuclear mass may be somewhat incompletely divided into dorsal, medial, and ventral portions.   The rostral end of the nucleus extends forward ventral to pars intermedialis, while the caudal end reaches a plane through the caudal part of the habenular commissure and the nucleus of the posterior commissure, which forms its caudomedial boundary.

The remainder of the medial boundary, beginning in front of the caudal medial nucleus, is formed by the centromedial nucleus, then by the nucleus medialis

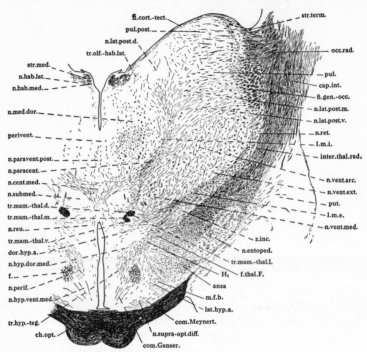

FIG. 518. A cross section through the diencephalon of the dog, showing certain medullated fiber tracts of the region.   *Rioch.*

ansa, ansa lenticularis; *cap.int.*, capsula interna; *ch.opt.*, chiasma opticum; *com.Ganser*, Ganser's supraoptic commissure; *com.Meynert*, Meynert's supra-optic commissure; *dor.hyp.a.*, dorsal hypothalamic area; *f.*, fornix; *f.thal.F.*, thalamic fasciculus of Forel; *fi.cort.-tect.*, fibrae cortico-tectales; *fi.gen.occ.* fibrae geniculo-occipitales; H_1, field H_1 of *Forel*; *inter.thal.rad.*, intermediate thalamic radiations; *l.m.e.*, lamina medullaris externa; *l.m.i.*, lamina medullaris interna; *lat.hyp.a.*, lateral hypothalamic area; *m.f.b.*, medial forebrain bundle; *n.cent.med.*, nucleus centralis medialis; *n.entoped.*, nucleus entopeduncularis; *n.hab.lat.*, nucleus habenularis lateralis; *n.hab.med.*, nucleus habenularis medialis; *n.hyp.dor.med.*, nucleus hypothalamicus dorsomedialis; *n.hyp.vent.med.*, nucleus hypothalamicus ventromedialis; *n.lat.post.m.*, nucleus lateralis, pars posterior, the middle portion; *n.lat.post.v.*, nucleus lateralis, pars posterior, the ventral portion; *n.med.dor.*, nucleus medialis dorsalis; *n.paracent.*, nucleus paracentralis; *n.paravent.post.*, nucleus paraventricularis posterior; *n.perif.*, nucleus perifornicalis; *n.ret.*, nucleus reticularis; *n.reun.*, nucleus reuniens; *n.submed.*, nucleus submedius; *n.supra-opt.diff.*, nucleus supraopticus diffusus; *n.vent.arc.*, nucleus ventralis, pars arcuata; *n.vent.ext.*, nucleus ventralis, pars externa; *n.vent.med.*, nucleus ventralis, pars medialis; *occ.rad.*, occipital-radiations; *perivent.*, periventricular system; *pul.*, pulvinar; *pul.post.*, pul-vinar, pars posterior; *put.*, putamen; *str.med.*, stria medullaris; *str.term.*, stria terminalis; *tr.hyp.-teg.*, tr ctus hypothalamicus tegmentalis; *tr.mam.-thal.d.*, tractus mamillo-thalamicus, dorsal bundle; *tr.mam.-thal.l.*, tractus mamillo-thalamicus, lateral bundle; *tr.mam.-thal.m.*, tractus mamillo-thalamicus, me-dial bundle; *tr.mam.-thal.v.*, tractus mamillo-thalamicus, ventral bundle; *z.inc.*, zona incerta.

dorsalis and the nucleus centralis lateralis. Ventrally the nucleus lateralis pars posterior extends to the nucleus ventralis, laterally to the pretectal area and the pulvinar, dorsally to the stratum zonale and caudally is continuous with the medial geniculate nucleus.   In this caudal region it is not possible to draw a line between the two areas and here two patches of cells have been identified in various mammals.   The more dorsal of these is a group of small, narrow cells intercalated in the course of the internal medullary lamina.   These constitute the nucleus limitans of *Friedemann* ('12) for Cercopithecus, of *Rioch* ('29) for the dog, and of *Ingram, Hannet*, and *Ranson* ('32) for the cat.   A more ventral group, which passes across the ventral part of the nucleus lateralis pars posterior from the cephalic pole of the medial geniculate nucleus, is the nucleus suprageniculatus of these observers.

The pulvinar (figs. 516, 518, and 527) in carnivores, as in insectivores and in certain primates, shows a division into several parts more or less indistinctly separated from each other.   The nucleus extends caudoventralward between the nucleus lateralis pars intermedialis and the nucleus posterior and is situated medial to the external medullary lamina, which separates it from the nucleus reticularis.   More caudally the pulvinar is medial to the capsular fibers of the lateral geniculate nucleus.   The nucleus lateralis pars posterior forms its medial and, more cephalically, its ventral boundary, while more caudally the nucleus posterior lies ventral to it.   With this nuclear mass *Rioch* ('31) included the nucleus pretectalis of his earlier account as the pulvinar pars posterior (fig. 518). *Ingram, Hannett*, and *Ranson* ('32) used this name for the area.   The area which *Rioch* ('31) regarded as homologous with the area pretectalis of lower forms is a mass of cells dorsal to the nucleus of the posterior commissure.   This has been identified recently in the cat by *Ingram, Hannett*, and *Ranson* ('32).   While the limits may not be quite the same, this nucleus corresponds in general to the pretectal nucleus described for marsupials and for rodents (pp. 1131 and 1133).

The nucleus posterior of *Rioch* ('29 and '31) and of *Ingram, Hannett*, and *Ranson* ('32) is a nuclear mass bounded by the large-celled nucleus of the optic tract, the pulvinar pars posterior, and the lateral and medial geniculate nuclei. Its rostral pole is continuous without sharp demarcation with the pulvinar and is regarded by certain observers as a part of this nuclear mass (the P_1 of *Le Gros Clark*, '30).   It is illustrated for the cat in figure 527.

The carnivore ventral nucleus as a whole extends throughout the greater part of the diencephalon in the ventrolateral portion of the dorsal thalamus. Throughout its extent it lies dorsal and dorsomedial to the external medullary lamina.   It begins far forward where this lamina constitutes its cephalic boundary and it extends caudalward to the medial geniculate nucleus.   *Rioch* ('29 and '31) has divided it into five subdivisions in carnivores, which correspond in general to those described in primates.   These divisions constitute the pars anterior, the pars medialis, the pars externa, the pars arcuata, and the pars commissuralis of the nucleus.   Similar divisions have been described for the cat by *Ingram, Hannett*, and *Ranson* ('32).   The following account is based more particularly on that given for the dog by *Rioch* and on preparations found in the Laboratory of Comparative Neurology, University of Michigan, the differences between the account for the dog and that for the cat not being significant for the present description.   In connection with the following account, figures 514, 516, and 518 should be consulted.

The pars anterior forms the anterior pole of the nucleus.   Its cephalic boundary is the external medullary lamina and its caudal boundary a fiber bundle extending up into the latter nucleus.   Ventrally lies the external medullary lamina until between it and the pars anterior intervenes the pars arcuata of the nucleus.   Dorsally the cephalic portion of the pars anterior is not sharply separable from the nucleus anteromedialis.   Behind this latter nucleus is the nucleus centralis lateralis and the caudal part of the dorsal boundary is formed by the pars intermedialis of the nucleus lateralis.   The cells of the pars anterior are irregularly arranged and are large and multipolar.

The nucleus ventralis pars medialis lies caudal to the pars anterior and forms throughout its extent the medial portion of the ventral nucleus.   Medially it lies in relation with the internal thalamic peduncle and then with the nuclei of the midline, and dorsomedially with the nucleus submedius, which latter cell mass it ultimately replaces.   The remainder of the dorsal boundary is formed by the internal medullary lamina.   It is replaced by the pars commissuralis.   Its cells are medium sized or smaller and vary somewhat in different parts.

The nucleus ventralis pars externa makes its appearance just ventral to the pars anterior and the pars medialis and dorsal to the nucleus reticularis.   Soon it becomes separated from the pars anterior by the intervention of the pars arcuata, for which it forms a blanket throughout most of its extent, disappearing in front of the caudal end of the pars arcuata, where its place is taken by the nucleus subparafascicularis and the medial part of the capsule of the medial geniculate. The cells of this nucleus are intercalated in the course of fiber bundles, and vary in size from small- or medium-sized cells to a patch, at the lateral border, of neurons as large as any found in the thalamus (*Rioch*, '29).

The pars arcuata, after its appearance, increases rapidly and takes on the characteristic shape from which it has received its name.   It is surrounded medially and ventrally, as indicated above, by the various other subdivisions of the ventral nucleus.   Behind the caudal pole of the pars anterior the nucleus centralis lateralis and then the lateral nucleus with associated fiber bundles form its dorsal boundary until the caudal pole is reached, where this boundary is established by the nucleus limitans and the internal medullary lamina dorsomedially, and the nucleus suprageniculatus dorsolaterally.   Behind the pars externa the pars arcuata extends to the external medullary lamina.   *Rioch* ('29) found cells similar to the pars anterior, intermingling with small- or medium-sized cells, in the anterior part of the nucleus.   Caudal to this a horizontal band of very large cells appears with interspersed medium-sized cells.   The neurons are scattered and somewhat smaller in the caudal pole of the nucleus.

The nucleus ventralis pars commissuralis is continuous with the nucleus ventralis pars medialis.   Its medial or central portion consists of cells in the course of commissural fibers.   Its lateral part, which ultimately fuses with the caudal end of the pars arcuata, is larger than the medial portion and has larger cells.

The nucleus submedius of the dog (*Rioch*, '29; figs. 514 and 518) is the nucleus medialis *a* (*Winkler* and *Potter*, '14) and the nucleus submedius (*Ingvar*, '23; *Ingram*, *Hannett*, and *Ranson*, '32) for the cat. It is probably the nucleus ventralis *b* of *von Monakow* ('95) for the cat and the dog. This nucleus forms a more or less conspicuous cell mass medial and ventromedial to the nucleus centralis and ventral to the nucleus paracentralis and the internal medullary lamina. The mammillo-thalamic tract separates it here, as in other mammals, from the medial portion of the ventral nucleus. Behind the tract a thin fiber band intervenes between the two nuclei, and later on they lie in close approximation and even intermingle. The nucleus reuniens lies medial to it cephalically but farther caudally periventricular fibers and cells form this boundary, which is frequently very thin, so that the nuclei of the two sides at certain levels lie very close together. The caudal boundary of the nucleus is formed by the nucleus ventralis medialis. The cells resemble those of the nucleus medialis dorsalis in staining qualities, although they may be slightly paler and smaller.

The nucleus subparafascicularis (*Rioch*, '29 and '21, for the dog; *Ingram*, *Hannett*, and *Ranson*, '32, for the cat) is usually included with the nucleus medialis ventralis within the medial group of nuclei. Because of their intimate relation with the ventral nucleus and their position outside of the internal medullary lamina, we are including them here, as *Le Gros Clark* has done, with the lateral group. The nucleus subparafascicularis (*Rioch*, '29 and '31) is situated in the external medullary lamina, caudal to the nucleus commissuralis interventralis. It consists of a group of small, intercalated neurons, the medial boundary of which, for a considerable distance, is formed by the habenulo-peduncular tract, and then by periventricular gray associated with the posterior commissure. It lies in immediate relation with the caudal end of the nucleus medialis pars externa, extending behind this level into relation with the medial part of the capsule of the medial geniculate nucleus (*Rioch*).

e. Primates. In primates a considerable number of studies involving the lateral nuclear groups have been carried out on various forms, including man. Among the workers interested in this particular field may be mentioned *van Gehuchten* ('97), *Déjérine* ('01), *von Monakow* ('05), *Sachs* ('09), *C. Vogt* ('09), *Ramón y Cajal* ('11), *Malone* ('10 and '12), *Friedemann* ('12), *Ingvar* ('23), *Pines* ('27), *Papez* ('29), *Le Gros Clark* ('30, '31), and *Crouch* ('34a). The account of the centers in these forms will be introduced by a brief review of the findings of *Le Gros Clark* ('30) in Tarsius.

In Tarsius a lateral nuclear complex (fig. 517), essentially in agreement with the pattern described for carnivores, has been found. It forms an eminence on the dorsal diencephalic wall, extending as far forward as the rostral end of the anteroventral nucleus, which is situated immediately ventromedial to it. Behind this latter nucleus the nucleus mediodorsalis (or nucleus dorsalis medialis) of *Le Gros Clark* ('30) lies medial to the nucleus lateralis, separated from it by the internal medullary lamina. Ventrally and laterally the external medullary lamina and the nucleus reticularis form its cephalic boundary, but farther caudally it extends down toward the ventral nuclear group. It is connected with the pars posterior of the lateral nucleus by a narrow band of cells in Tarsius which is comparable, according to *Le Gros Clark*, with the "Stelle des Pulvinar" of Cercopithecus (*Friedemann*, '12). The main mass of the lateral nucleus in lemurs (*Pines*, '27) and in Tarsius (*Le Gros Clark*) is divisible into two portions, a more dorsal part (usually designated as *La*) and a more ventral part (*Lb*), of which the latter appears to increase progressively from the lower to the higher primates.

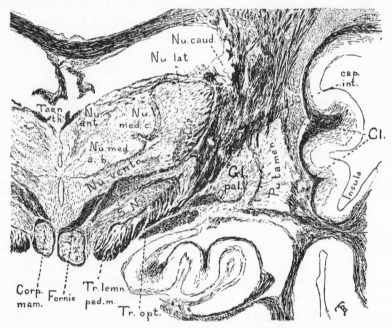

Fig. 519. A cross section through the region of the thalamo-striatal portion of the internal capsule. Note the position of the medial, ventral, and lateral thalamic nuclei and the transition of the peduncle into the internal capsule. *Ariëns Kappers.*

cap.int., capsula interna; Cl., claustrum; Corp.mam., corpus mamillare; Gl. pal., globus pallidus; Nu.ant., nucleus anterior thalami; Nu.caud., nucleus caudatus; Nu.lat., nucleus lateralis thalami; Nu.med.(a, b, c), nucleus medialis thalami; Nu.ventr., nucleus ventralis thalami; S.N., substantia nigra; Taen.th., taenia thalami; Tr.lemn.ped.m., tractus lemnisci medialis of the peduncle; Tr. opt., tractus opticus.

It is probable that *Le Gros Clark's* suggestion — that the pars anterior of the nucleus lateralis in carnivores is homologous with the anterior part of *La* in primates and that the pars intermedialis and the pars posterior are homologous to the caudal portion of the main lateral nucleus — is correct. The posterior part of the lateral nucleus in rodents and in insectivores is a region of passage of optic tract fibers, and this led *Gurdjian* ('27) and later *Le Gros Clark* ('29 and '30) to suggest that this region is to be regarded as the forerunner of the pulvinar of higher forms.

As equivalent to this posterior part of the latter nucleus, or at least as derived in part from it phylogenetically, *Le Gros Clark* ('30; fig. 517) identified a pulvinar in Tarsius. Cephalically this latter cell mass is separated from the remainder of the lateral nucleus by a sheet of cortico-tectal fibers, caudodorsally it reaches a position between the superior colliculus and the medial geniculate body, and caudoventrally between the upper portions of the medial and lateral geniculate nuclei.   The nucleus has been divided by this observer into a series of zones or laminae (P_1 to P_4) of which P_1 is the most ventral, lying directly dorsal to the lateral geniculate nucleus, and the zones following in order to P_4, which is situated near the tectum and just ventral to the optic tract.   *Le Gros Clark* stated with regard to the analysis of the carnivore diencephalon "that his (*Rioch's*) pulvinar, area pretectalis, and posterior nucleus together represent the pars posterior of the lateral nucleus in lower forms and the pulvinar of higher forms," obviously referring to the pars posterior described by *Gurdjian* ('27) and by himself ('29).   However, the carnivore nucleus posterior is a distinct entity with specific fiber connections, facts which do not necessarily vitiate its inclusion within the primate pulvinar.   A pretectal nucleus, homologous with the nucleus posterior of rodents, and a large-celled nucleus of the optic tract were described by *Le Gros Clark* ('30) for Tarsius (fig. 517) and for Microcebus ('31).   His pretectal nucleus includes the nucleus posterior (and adjacent gray) and presumably a dorsal nucleus of the posterior commissure.   A suprageniculate nucleus is present in Tarsius with relations similar to those given for carnivores.

In Microcebus, *Le Gros Clark* ('31) found the principal lateral nucleus of relatively the same size as that of Tarsius.   *Pines* ('27) found a lateral nucleus divisible into four parts in the lemur.   The lateral nuclear group, as described by *Vogt* ('09) and *Friedemann* ('12) for Cercopithecus, shows a very marked degree of differentiation.   It may be divided, according to these observers, into a nucleus lateralis dorsalis (lateraler Thalamuskern oberste Etage *La*) and a nucleus lateralis ventralis principalis.   This latter nuclear group in turn falls into oral and caudal portions.   The oral part consists of lateral and medial groups, and the caudal part consists of superior and inferior groups.   The nucleus lateralis dorsalis of Cercopithecus lies dorsolateral to the nucleus medialis dorsalis and forms an eminence on the dorsal surface of the diencephalon, in planes immediately caudal to the nucleus anterodorsalis (anterior *A* of *von Monakow*).   It extends caudalward, ventrolateral to the anterior thalamic nucleus of *von Monakow*.   In front of the cephalic pole of the nucleus lateralis dorsalis and dorsal to the ventral nuclear group is the cephalic portion of the nucleus lateralis ventralis principalis.   At this level it consists of a lateral (Lb_3) and a medial (Lb_4) nuclear group.   Traced caudalward, these groups disappear and their places are taken by two other subdivisions of the nucleus lateralis ventralis principalis, a caudal superior group (Lb_1), which lies ventrolateral to the nucleus lateralis dorsalis, ventral to the stria terminalis, and dorsolateral to the nucleus medialis dorsalis, and a caudal inferior group (Lb_2), which lies ventral and lateral to Lb_1 and approaches laterally the reticular nucleus or reticular zone. Lb_1 continues for a considerable distance caudalward, occupying essentially the same position. In addition to these major nuclear groups, *Vogt* ('09) recognized a nucleus lateralis ventralis accessorius, which he subdivided into dorsal and ventral portions. This accessory nucleus falls within the ventral part of the nucleus lateralis pars posterior of carnivores, and is the so-called transitional zone between the nucleus lateralis ventralis principalis and the caudal part of the ventral thalamic nucleus as described by *Friedemann* ('12).   The nuclei thus described for Cercopithecus are represented in man within the nucleus lateralis of *Ingvar* ('23), the nucleus lateralis dorsalis of *Marburg* ('04), the noyau externe of *Déjérine* ('01), and the nucleus communis thalami pars lateralis of *Malone* ('10).   *Foix* and *Nicolesco* ('25) recognized within their noyau externe an anterior portion, comparable with the nucleus lateralis dorsalis of *Vogt* ('09), and a dorsal portion which at least falls within the nucleus lateralis ventralis principalis of this latter observer. It is evident that further work needs to be done on the cytological differentiation (and fiber connections) of the human lateral thalamic nuclei.

In Macacus rhesus *Crouch* ('34a) found a well-developed pulvinar divisible into medial, lateral, and inferior portions.   Below the medial portion, between it and the medial geniculate, is his nucleus suprageniculatus.   *Crouch* described the narrow cell band, which had been termed earlier the nucleus limitans by *Friedemann* ('12) and *Pines* ('27) for primates, as "beginning at the posterior end of the nucleus parafascicularis and extending downward and lateralward toward the medial geniculate body."   In Cercopithecus the pulvinar is developed to a great extent and shows marked differentiation in both cytoarchitectonic and myeloarchitectonic preparations, as is indicated in the studies of *Vogt* ('09) and *Friedemann* ('12).   These observers divided the area into a number of regions of which only a brief summary can be given.   According to them the pulvinar falls into medial and lateral portions differentiable in cell preparations through the more or less irregular arrangement of the cells in the lateral region.   Beginning at the caudal end of the nucleus, the lateral portion is divisible into a dorsal part ($p\mu$) and a ventral part ($p\eta$).   The cells in $p\eta$ in general are somewhat smaller, although certain very large, deeply staining cells are present here.   In the same caudal planes the major portion of the medial nucleus is occupied by a single nuclear mass, $p\beta$.   A small enlargement in the dorsal region (pla) corresponds in position to that of the dorsal part of the lateral nucleus (la) farther forward, but is not differentiable cytologically from the surrounding regions.   The caudal, ventral part of the medial division of the pulvinar is $p\epsilon$ of *Vogt* ('09) or ($p\epsilon$) of *Friedemann* ('12). $p\eta$ and $p\mu$ were obtained by *Vogt* in myeloarchitectonic studies.   A further portion (lp), dorsal to $p\eta$, was obtained in fiber preparations but does not show cytoarchitectonically, but $p\epsilon$ is differentiable both myeloarchitectonically and cytoarchitectonically in proper planes.   In front of the planes just described, the mediodorsal part of the pulvinar consists of more or less scattered cells irregularly polyhedral in form and smaller and more intensely stained than those in $p\beta$.   In fiber preparations this region shows a fine fiber net. At this level the chief portion ($p\delta$) of the ventral pulvinar is occupied by a very dense arrangement of cells.   These are smaller on the whole than those in the more dorsal part of the pulvinar, with the exception of the region where they border on the lateral geniculate nucleus.   This region is the Hinterenkern of *von Monakow* ('05) and its oral portion falls within the area intergeniculata of *Malone* ('10).   The cephalic tip of the nucleus has been termed $p\mu\beta$ by *Friede-*

mann ('12), who regarded it as an intermingling of *pμ* and *pβ*.   *py₁* and *py₂* are parts of the nucleus limitans in the pulvinar.

A pulvinar has been generally recognized by students of the human diencephalon (fig. 520).   Thus it has been identified by *Déjérine* ('01), *von Monakow* ('05), *Forel* ('07), *Edinger* ('08), *Sachs* ('09), *Ingvar* ('23), *Foix* and *Nicolesco* ('25, under the name of noyau posterior), and others.   *Von Monakow* recognized a

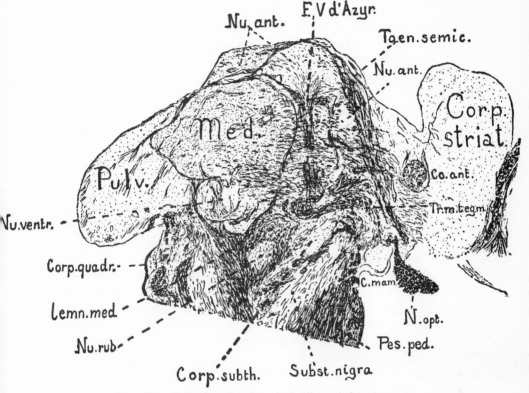

Fig. 520.   Sagittal section through the diencephalon of man.

pulvinar proper and a second group (hinterer Seehügelkern), which is the homologue of the nucleus posterior of lower forms as described by *d'Hollander* ('13), *Gurdjian* ('27), *Le Gros Clark* ('29), and others, but which was later included under the pulvinar complex by *Le Gros Clark* ('30), and represents *pη* as described by *Vogt* ('09) and by *Friedemann* ('12) ; here also falls the pretectal area of *Rioch* ('29) or his pulvinar pars posterior ('31) and possibly the cephalic end of the pretectal area (see, however, *Le Gros Clark*, '30).   Detailed studies of the cytological structure of the pulvinar in man are not available.   *Foix* and *Nicolesco* ('25) stated that it tends to be more or less compact in its central portion, with somewhat columnar disposition of its cells toward the external part where they are associated with fibers of the optic tract.   The pretectal nucleus may be drawn almost entirely within the superior colliculus in man (but this needs verification).   This nucleus is a mass of gray lateral to the deeper tectal areas and has been discussed on page 1073.   A large-celled nucleus of the optic tract is present.

The ventral nuclear group of primates has been described by numerous observers (*Vogt*, '09; *Friedemann*, '12; *Pines*, '27; *Le Gros Clark*, '32; *Crouch*, '34; and many others).   In Tarsius (*Le Gros Clark*) it is said to consist of anterior and posterior portions, each divisible in turn into medial and lateral parts.   For further details, the papers referred to above should be consulted.   *Crouch's* recent account of the ventral nuclei in Macacus rhesus may be regarded as typical of relations in these forms.   He divided the frontal end of the ventral nuclear group into a nucleus ventralis anteromedialis and a larger, more deeply stained nucleus ventralis anterolateralis, situated respectively medially and laterally as their names imply, but not sharply separable from each other.   The more medial (homologous to *vtm* of *Vogt*, *Friedemann*, and *Pines*) is secondarily divisible cytologically into ventromedial and dorsolateral portions, extends medially to the internal medullary lamina and the nucleus paracentralis, and, farther caudalward, to the mammillo-thalamic tract.   It is ventral to the nucleus lateralis anteromedialis.   The nucleus anterolateralis of *Crouch* (the nucleus *vtl* of *Friedemann*, *Pines*, and others), subdivided into dorsal and ventral parts, extends, from near the anterior pole of the thalamus, caudalward to the nucleus ventralis intermedius, being bounded laterally by the reticular nucleus and the external medullary lamina.   *Crouch* homologized the posteromedial and posterolateral portions of the ventral nucleus with the pars medialis and the pars anterior of the ventral nucleus of carnivores.

The nucleus ventralis intermedius of *Crouch* extends medially almost to the internal medullary lamina, spreads out dorsally between the anterior and posterior lateral nuclei, and caudally thins out into a smaller portion, which overlaps in part the nucleus posterolateralis.   Ventrolateral to it lie the reticular nucleus and the internal medullary lamina, and farther caudally, on the ventral side, the nucleus ventralis posteroinferioris.

The posterior part of the ventral nucleus was divided by *Crouch* into lateral, medial, and inferior portions.   The nucleus ventralis posterolateralis (included in the *va* of *Friedemann*, *Vogt*, and others) is ventral to the nucleus lateralis posterior and cephalad to the pulvinar and is characterized by its comparatively small-celled, dense appearance.   Probably with the nucleus posteroinferior, which lies ventrolateral to it, it forms the nucleus ventralis externus of *Rioch* (for carnivores) and of *Le Gros Clark* and *Boggon* ('35, for Macaca mulatta).   The nucleus ventralis posteromedialis of *Crouch*, which is ventral to the centromedian nucleus (noyau centré median), is termed the semilunar or arcuate nucleus by many students of the region.   It extends between the nucleus ventralis intermedius, cephalically, and the pulvinar caudally.

The Fiber Connections of the Lateral and Ventral Nuclear Groups of the Dorsal Thalamus Exclusive of the Geniculate Nuclei

The following connections have been described for the lateral, ventral, and pretectal regions of the lateral division of the dorsal thalamus in mammals.

a. Marsupials. In the opossum *Chu* ('32a) described superior thalamic radiations to the nucleus lateralis and the nucleus lateralis pars posterior, with optic fibers to the latter and possibly to the former nucleus. He found the chief connections of the posterior nucleus to be with the tectum and the posterior commissure (it is probable that his posterior nucleus also includes the dorsal nucleus of the posterior commissure of *Tsai*, '25). He believed that trigeminal and medial lemnisci fibers reach the ventral nucleus, and that both of its parts are connected to the forebrain through the inferior thalamic radiations. The nucleus pretectalis of *Tsai* and *Chu* receives fibers from the optic tract, inter-nuclear connections with other thalamic nuclei, and fiber fascicles associating it with the cortex and with the tegmentum.

b. Edentates and Rodents. *Papez* also traced thalamic radiations and optic fibers to the nucleus lateralis pars posterior or pulvinar of the armadillo. His nucleus ventralis lateralis was found to be in relation with the medial division of the medial lemniscus, with the telencephalon through thalamic radiations, and with the nucleus ventralis medialis through short internuclear fibers. Aside from its internuclear connections, the nucleus ventralis medialis in the armadillo receives commissural fibers from its fellow of the other side, and internuclear fibers from the dorsomedial hypothalamic area and the paracentral and, pre-sumably, the parafascicular nuclei, both of which latter nuclei receive the central tegmental tract. The posterior nucleus of the armadillo thalamus is said to receive optic tract fibers, the posterior commissure, and a bundle which proceeds from the nucleus to the tegmental region of the midbrain. The pretectal nucleus of *Papez* receives optic tract fibers, or at least their collaterals, and gives rise to pretecto-tegmental fibers. The large-celled nucleus of the optic tract (in the usage of *Papez*) is related to optic tract fibers.

The following connections have been described for the lateral nuclear group in rodents. Superior thalamic radiations (figs. 513 and 515) carrying possibly cortico-thalamic and thalamo-cortical fibers, internuclear connections with the dorsomedial portion of the nucleus ventralis, and possibly commissural connec-tions with the homologous nucleus lateralis of the other side have been described (*Gurdjian*, '27). Under the name of lateral thalamic radiations, *d'Hollander* ('13) described connections of this nucleus with the cortex in the rabbit, and he found internuclear connections with the nucleus anterodorsalis. *Münzer* and *Wiener* ('02) described connections in rodents between the lateral nucleus and the cortex and *Nissl* ('89) mentioned cortico-thalamic connections. *Le Gros Clark* ('32a) carried fibers from the parietal region of the rat cortex into the lateral nucleus in a single case. He found some evidence for thalamo-fugal fibers from the lateral nucleus to the parietal cortex. He was unable to trace ascending lemnisci fibers to this region. *Waller* ('34; see p. 1120) connected his nucleus lateralis anterior with the parietal cortex and his nucleus lateralis posterior with an area on the anterior margin of the lateral geniculate cortical area. Optic tract fibers pass through, possibly terminate within, the nucleus lateralis pars posterior and it is interconnected with the tectum and with the pars dorsalis of the lateral geniculate nucleus. All these connections indicate the probability that the pars posterior in rodents is the forerunner of the pulvinar. *Le Gros Clark* ('32a) was unable to establish terminations of optic fibers in this nucleus although many pass through it.

The nucleus posterior of rodents (according to the terminology of *Gurdjian*, '27, *Chu*, '32, and others or the nucleus pretectalis of *Le Gros Clark*, '30) has been shown to have connections with the cerebral cortex, but *Münzer* and *Wiener* ('02) and *Waller* ('34, see p. 1120) could not demonstrate any telencephalic connections to it.   The pretectal nucleus of *Le Gros Clark*, which, according to his statement with regard to Tupaia ('30, p. 196), is the posterior nucleus of *Gurdjian*, has corticofugal but apparently no corticopetal fibers.   *Papez* ('29) believed that the nucleus posterior (or pretectalis) has fibers passing to the cortex in the rat but he was not able to follow them throughout their entire course.   According to *Le Gros Clark*, nonretinal fibers of the optic tract reach this region, as well as lemnisci fibers, apparently of the spinal trigeminal and medial lemnisci systems. The number of optic fibers which pass to the large-celled nucleus of the optic tract is uncertain at present.   The connections of the pretectal nucleus of *Rioch* ('31), *Ingram, Hannett*, and *Ranson* ('32), and others have been discussed on p. 1148.

The ventral nucleus of rodents is connected with the cortex and with the tectum (*Gurdjian*, '27, and others).   *Probst* ('00) carried the medial lemniscus into the ventral nucleus (ventralis *a* of *von Monakow*, '05), trigeminal lemnisci fibers into the nuclei ventrales *a* and *b* of *von Monakow* and into the nuclei mediales *b* and *c* (which fall probably within the interlaminar nuclei — see *Rioch*, '29, and *Le Gros Clark*, '32a), and ascending secondary fibers from the cord (ventral spino-thalamic probably) to the ventral nucleus (nucleus ventralis). *Wallenberg* ('00) carried fibers from the fasciculus gracilis to ventromedial parts; those from the fasciculus cuneatus to middle and lateral parts, and the trigeminal fibers frontally "zur dorsalen Grenzschicht des ventralen Kernes."   In general, then, this represents a distribution from medial to lateral in the order in which they lie in the medial lemniscus, although of course there is some difference in cephalo-caudal plane.   It appears probable that the medial nucleus of *Wallenberg* is really the posterior nucleus of *Le Gros Clark* (pretectal nucleus of *Gurdjian*) or the prebigeminal nucleus of *Ramón y Cajal* ('11) as *Le Gros Clark* ('32a) has suggested.   In Marchi preparations, *Le Gros Clark* ('32a) has determined that the pattern of the thalamo-cortical connections in the rat is such that the fibers proceed by the shortest course to the cortex, those from the lateral and dorsal regions distributing to the dorsal portion of the parietal area while those remaining supply the more ventral part of this cortical area and the region of the insula.   *Wallenberg* ('00) in the rabbit and *Le Gros Clark* ('32a) in the rat found lemnisci connections not only with the ventral nucleus but also with the paracentral and lateral central nuclei.   *Woodburne* ('35) traced trigeminal lemnisci fibers (dorsal and ventral secondary ascending tracts of the trigeminal) to the ventral thalamic nucleus of the mouse.   *Le Gros Clark* ('32 and '32a) found the trigeminal lemnisci fibers distributed to the anteroventral extremity of the ventral nucleus. It is to be noted that this refers to those fibers arising from the chief sensory nucleus (the dorsal secondary ascending tract of the trigeminal), not to the fibers from the descending root of the trigeminal.   He found the medial lemniscus spreading out after entering the ventral, lateral border of the ventral nucleus.   A few fibers of this lemniscus swung forward into the region of the internal medullary lamina in the region of the nucleus centralis lateralis.   The reticular nucleus of the rat (*Gurdjian*, '27) carries fibers of passage between the dorsal thalamus and the telencephalon and probably receives collaterals of such fibers (figs. 513 and 515).

The nucleus medialis ventralis, *d'Hollander* ('13) and *Gurdjian* ('27), was believed by *Gurdjian* to receive forebrain fibers by way of thalamic radiations and to be connected with the contralateral nucleus through commissural fibers.   *Le Gros Clark* considered that its main connections in the rat were provided by short internuclear fibers which relate it to the ventral nucleus and the nucleus anteromedialis. It has connections with the globus pallidus, according to *Le Gros Clark*.

c. Carnivores.   In carnivores, numerous internuclear connections associate the various portions of the lateral nucleus with each other and with the surrounding gray.   All the parts of the lateral nucleus appear to be connected by thalamic radiations with the cortex (*von Monakow*, '95, and *Rioch*, '31).   In the dog and the cat, *von Monakow* ('95) found the caudal portion of the nucleus lateralis, his nucleus lateralis B, connected with the cortico-optic centers.   The remainder of his lateral nucleus receives radial fibers from the internal capsule, and in the cat and dog is especially related with the gyri suprasylvius, ectolateralis, and suprasplenius, and with the parietal cortex.   The nucleus posterior of *Glorieux* ('29; which includes the lateral nucleus, the pulvinar, and the suprageniculate nucleus of *Rioch*, '29 also '31) is said by this observer to give off the thalamo-cortical fibers to various regions of the cortex.   *Papez* ('29) and *Rioch* ('31) regarded the lateral nucleus as receiving lemnisci fibers; according to *Papez* this constitutes a spino-thalamic component (which would accord well with the interpretation of *von Monakow*, '05, and *Minkowski*, '23–'24).   *Glorieux* ('29) found unmyelinated optic fibers distributing to the pulvinar in the dog and showed the connection of this nucleus with the occipital regions of the cortex.   *Rioch* regarded the pulvinar as distinguished by the presence of fibers from the nucleus geniculatus lateralis, including fibers passing from the lamina principalis anterior of this nucleus (which does not supply the pulvinar, pars posterior) and by the presence of fibers of the occipital radiations which, according to this observer, terminate to a considerable extent in this nucleus.   The pulvinar pars posterior has similar connections, with the exceptions noted above, and also connections with the superior colliculus.   The nucleus posterior of the dog has connections with the lateral geniculate nucleus and it is entered at least by fibers from the medial geniculate nucleus; it receives thalamic radiations, according to *Rioch* ('31), and it is connected with the superior colliculus.   Fibers of the medial lemniscus were traced into it, although their termination was not seen.   A scattering of medial lemniscus fibers in the nucleus suprageniculatus was noted by this observer, although he was unable to verify their termination.   Connections of the nucleus suprageniculatus with the neighboring gray, the nucleus geniculatus medialis, the caudal part of the lateral nucleus and the nucleus parafascicularis, and fascicles to the internal medullary lamina and the tectum were described by *Rioch* for the dog, the cat, and the aevisa. To his pretectal area, *Rioch* ('31) traced fibers from the medial lemniscus, and established connections with the tectum and with the surrounding gray.

The ventral nucleus of carnivores receives fibers of the lemnisci systems and fascicles from the capsule of the red nucleus, including dento-rubro-thalamic bundles, and has connections with the cortex (*von Monakow*, '95). The nucleus submedius is closely connected with the ventral nucleus and receives fibers, according to *Rioch* ('31), from the nucleus reuniens, the contralateral nucleus centralis medialis (in the cat), and the periventricular system. The nucleus subparafascicularis has connections with the medial part of the ventral nucleus and with the periventricular system (*Rioch*). As in other mammals, the nucleus reticularis is a region of passage for internal capsule fibers, from which it probably receives impulses. The ventral division of the reticular nucleus, as made by *Glorieux* ('29), is believed by him to represent an hypothalamic nucleus. He traced what appears to be a part of the supraoptic system from this region to the nucleus geniculatus lateralis pars dorsalis, but was uncertain that this component arose in the reticular nucleus.

d. Primates. For the primates, cortical connections of the lateral thalamic nuclei have been quite generally conceded (*Déjérine*, '01 ; *von Monakow*, '05 ; *Sachs*, '09, and *Pines*, '27). *Sachs* carried to this nucleus fibers from precentral and postcentral gyri (in Macacus) and found thalamo-cortical fibers to the lower limb area of the cortex from the upper part of the nucleus and to the lower limb, upper limb, and face areas of the cortex from the middle part. He found more thalamo-cortical fibers to the precentral than to the postcentral gyrus and distinct internuclear connections with the centromedian nucleus (noyau centré médian) and the arcuate nucleus. *Von Monakow* ('05) found the nucleus distributing fibers in front of and behind the central gyri, including all areas except the extreme frontal, temporal, and occipital poles of the hemispheres. *Déjérine* ('01) likewise found cortical connections, both afferent and efferent, between the frontal, precentral, postcentral, and parietal gyri and the lateral nuclei of the thalamus. *Le Gros Clark* and *Boggon* ('35) described connections of the caudal half of the lateral nucleus (*Lb*) with the postsensory areas of the parietal lobe in Macacus, and of "the medial and dorsal part of the rostral end of the lateral nucleus (element *Lb*)" with the area frontalis agranularis. Certain observers, as *von Monakow*, appear to have regarded the lateral thalamic nucleus as the thalamic region concerned with lower limb centers to be projected on precentral and postcentral convolutions (*von Monakow*, '05 ; *Sachs*, '09 ; *Minkowski*, '23–'24). This would imply a distribution to this area of the lateral spino-thalamic tract (*Papez*, '29). The connection of the lateral nucleus with the cortex indicates beyond question that it develops hand in hand with the development of the cortical centers, increasing phylogenetically with the increase in size and differentiation. Its connection, not only with projection but also with non-projection areas of the cerebral cortex, is indicated by the work of various observers, and its reception of cortico-thalamic as well as its transmission of thalamo-cortical fibers indicates in our opinion (*Huber* and *Crosby*, '29) that it develops not only with the development of projection areas but also in conjunction with the development of association areas.   There has been no intention on our part, here or elsewhere, to state that this nuclear group develops independently of the projection areas (this requires further demonstration), but only to insist that factors other than those concerned with projection centers were of fundamental importance in determining its progressive differentiation.   An essentially similar interpretation was given by *Le Gros Clark* ('32).   By many observers the ventral nucleus is regarded in various mammals as the main receptive center for ascending systems to the thalamus (as for example, *Tschermak*, '98; *Wallenberg*, '00; *Déjérine*, '01; *Probst*, '02; *Lewandowsky*, '04; *Vogt*, '09; *Ramón y Cajal*, '11; *Winkler*, '18; and *Le Gros Clark*, '30).   The pulvinar is regarded as the recipient of optic tract fibers by the majority of observers, among whom may be mentioned *von Kölliker* ('99), *Déjérine* ('01), *Forel* ('97), and *Minkowski* ('20). *Brouwer* and *Zeeman* ('25 and '26, working on apes) and *Brouwer* ('27) questioned such a termination on the basis of experimental observation, regarding the optic tract as composed largely of fibers of passage to the tectum.   Possibly the statement of *Lorento de No* ('29, quoted by *Ariëns Kappers*, '29; see also *Rioch*, '31), that only unmedullated fibers of the optic tract terminate in the region, may explain some of the differences with regard to this matter.   The pulvinar is related to the lateral geniculate nucleus and to the tectum by means of geniculo-pulvinar fibers and by the brachium of the superior colliculus.   Such connections have been recognized by numerous observers.   In addition to these fiber fascicles there are connections with the cortex which, according to *Déjérine* ('01) and *Ramón y Cajal* ('11), are cortico-pulvinar in character from the visual area, but which, according to *von Monakow* ('05), *Edinger* ('08), *Foix* and *Nicolesco* ('25), and *Papez* ('29), are thalamo-cortical in character.   These connections are mentioned again on page 1463.

The pretectal nucleus has connections with the optic tract (p. 1073), the tectum, and possibly with other fibers in the region.   It gives rise to a descending pretecto-tegmental tract.   The large-celled nucleus of the optic tract has connections with the optic tract, although possibly such optic connections are not very numerous, and with the tectum.

The nucleus ventralis thalami is regarded as one of the major centers of termination for the ascending lemnisci systems in primates as in other mammals. *Déjérine* ('01) found his noyau externe portión ventral interconnected with the central gyri and the neighboring frontal and parietal regions.   In addition to these connections, this observer described bundles of the lemniscus medialis and fibers from the tegmental region and from the lenticular fasciculus of *Forel*. *Von Monakow* ('05) believed the oral part of his ventral nucleus (nucleus ventralis anterior) was connected with the anterior central convolution in the region bounding the precentral sulcus.   *Von Monakow* ('05) connected his nucleus ventralis (*a, b, c*, which includes the arcuate nucleus of *Flechsig*, '76, or the semilunar of *Friedemann*) in man with the opercular region of the cortex, the two central convolutions, and the gyrus supramarginalis.   In general he found the field for the nucleus ventralis *a* to be the more anterior, that for ventralis *b* the more posterior, and that for ventralis *c* farther basal, extending into the region of the sylvian fossa and perhaps the temporal pole. *Edinger* ('08) traced the medial lemniscus, trigeminal lemniscus, and spino-thalamic fibers to this ventral nuclear group. He believed this nucleus to be connected with the parietal cortex. *Vogt* ('09) traced lenticular radiations to the oral portion of this nucleus and prelemniscus fibers (dento-rubro-thalamic) to the intermediate part, and regarded the inferior (internal) thalamic peduncle as an afferent bundle of the region. The medial part of his lemniscus medialis and lemniscus medianus he carried to the semilunar nucleus, and other fascicles of the lemniscus medialis to the caudal part of the ventral nucleus. *Sachs* ('09) followed bundles of the medial lemniscus to the nucleus lateralis ventralis externus (comparable to part of the nucleus ventralis pars externus of carnivores), and thought such bundles possibly extended forward to the more oral part of the ventral nuclear group. He traced thalamo-cortical fibers to the first nucleus mentioned above, connections being made with the opercular region and facial areas of the postcentral gyrus. In Macacus he found the oral part of the ventral group connected with the pre- and postcentral gyri. To its pars anterior (noyau semilunaire anterieur) *Ramón y Cajal* ('11) traced the ascending trigeminal fibers, fibers of the superior cerebellar peduncle, connections from the reticular substance of the midbrain, and fibers associated with the medial longitudinal fasciculus. Internal capsule fibers pass from it to the cerebral cortex. *Ramón y Cajal* believed that ascending trigeminal fibers and cortico-thalamic and thalamo-cortical fibers are characteristic connections of the semilunar nucleus. *Foix* and *Nicolesco* ('25) described as connections of the oral part of the ventral nucleus, the thalamic fasciculus of Forel and thalamo-cortical fibers through the parietal stalk to the semilunar nucleus (and the associated noyau externe segment posteromedial), the dento-rubro-thalamic tract, and connections with the cortex through the parietal stalk. To the remaining caudal part of the nucleus, they carried fibers of the lemniscus medialis and found this area also contributed, with other parts of the ventral nucleus, to the parietal stalk. *Le Gros Clark* ('30) traced the medial lemniscus into the ventral nucleus. In Tarsius he found that, while there is not evident a distinct separation into two parts, there are, in general, two regions of distribution of this bundle, one fiber group terminating particularly in the anterolateral portion, the other in the posteromedial part of the nuclear area. The pars arcuata, pars anterolateralis, and the dorsal and medial part of the rostral end of the pars externa were regarded as connected with the precentral gyrus by *Le Gros Clark* and *Boggon*, the pars arcuata being related to the arm and leg areas. According to these observers, the postcentral area is supplied from the pars externa of the ventral nucleus. The antero-medial parts of the ventral nucleus are said to be projected in part on the area frontalis agranularis. In this connection, perhaps *Sager's* results should be noted, although they are less clear cut and at least subject to question. This last mentioned observer regarded the pars arcuata as projected chiefly on the face area of the cortex. Recently *Walker* has stressed the fact that there is a definite projection of the thalamic portions of the ventral

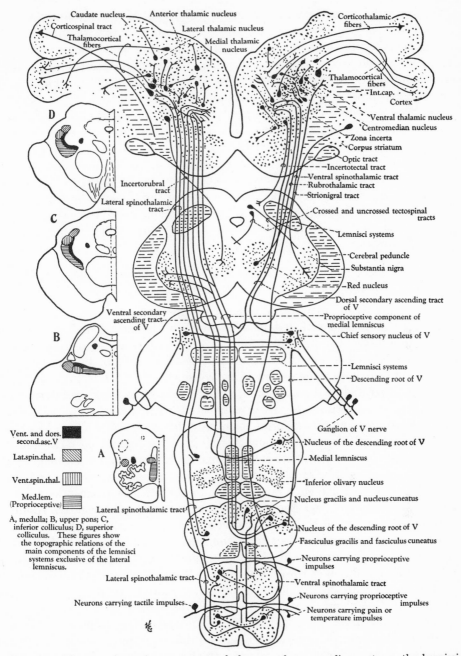

Caudate nucleus
Anterior thalamic nucleus
Corticospinal tract
Lateral thalamic nucleus
Thalamocortical fibers
Medial thalamic nucleus
Corticothalamic fibers
Thalamocortical fibers
Int.cap.
Cortex

D

Ventral thalamic nucleus
Centromedian nucleus
Zona incerta
Corpus striatum
Optic tract
Incertotectal tract
Ventral spinothalamic tract
Rubrothalamic tract
Strionigral tract

C

Incertorubral tract
Lateral spinothalamic tract
Crossed and uncrossed tectospinal tracts
Lemnisci systems
Cerebral peduncle
Substantia nigra
Red nucleus
Dorsal secondary ascending tract of V
Ventral secondary ascending tract of V
Proprioceptive component of medial lemniscus
Chief sensory nucleus of V

B

Lemnisci systems
Descending root of V

Ganglion of V nerve
Nucleus of the descending root of V
Medial lemniscus

Vent. and dors. second.asc.V

Lat.spin.thal.

Vent.spin.thal.

A

Inferior olivary nucleus
Nucleus gracilis and nucleus cuneatus

Med.lem. (Proprioceptive)

Lateral spinothalamic tract

A, medulla; B, upper pons; C, inferior colliculus; D, superior colliculus. These figures show the topographic relations of the main components of the lemnisci systems exclusive of the lateral lemniscus.

Nucleus of the descending root of V
Fasciculus gracilis and fasciculus cuneatus
Neurons carrying proprioceptive impulses

Lateral spinothalamic tract
Ventral spinothalamic tract
Neurons carrying proprioceptive impulses
Neurons carrying tactile impulses
Neurons carrying pain or temperature impulses

FIG. 521. Diagram of certain components of the secondary ascending systems, the lemnisci systems, exclusive of the lateral lemniscus. *Huber* and *Crosby*.

nucleus upon the areas bordering the central sulcus in Macacus, the most lateral portion being connected with the leg areas, the intermediate with the arm areas, and the medial with the face areas. A study of figure 521D shows that such a localization would accord very well with merely the normal spreading out of the components of the lemnisci systems as they approach the thalamus. The differentiation pattern within the thalamus is influenced, then, to a very great degree, if not predetermined, by the position of the component paths which make up the lemnisci systems (including spino-tectal, trigeminal and ascending proprioceptive, and possibly gustatory fibers) to this nucleus, as various observers have suggested (*Wallenberg*, '00; *Huber* and *Crosby*, '29; *Walker*, '34; *Le Gros Clark* and *Boggon*, '35; and others). The recent results obtained by *Brouwer* ('34) tend to show less definite localization within the thalamic ventral nucleus, but it is to be noted in this connection that his lesions were larger than those of *Walker*. A summary of the connections of the ventral nuclei is presented in fig. 521 (*Huber* and *Crosby*).

Résumé of Structure and Connections of the Lateral and Ventral Nuclear
Groups of the Dorsal Thalamus Exclusive of the Geniculate Nuclei

An attempt to summarize the nuclear groups and fiber connections of the lateral division of the dorsal thalamus (exclusive of the metathalamus) evidences the fact that there are still many points of dispute relative to these centers. The nucleus lateralis appears to be present in all mammals, but its degree of development varies with the orders under consideration. Thus, it is very small and poorly separated in the armadillo, while it is large and highly differentiated in carnivores and primates. It is connected with the cortex, particularly with the parietal regions, in forms such as rodents (*Le Gros Clark*, '32a), but apparently with other cortical regions as well in higher mammals. The question of its reception of lemnisci fibers is still a matter of dispute, *von Monakow* ('05), *Sachs* ('09), *Minkowski* ('23–'24), *Papez* ('29, spino-thalamic fibers), and *Rioch* ('31) being able to trace such connections to the nucleus while others (as for example, *Le Gros Clark* and *Boggon*, '35) have obtained only negative results in this respect. Certain of the observers who advocate such lemnisci connections believe that they carry impulses from the lower extremities. Whether or not such lemnisci connections are present, it is evident that the progressive development and differentiation of the lateral nucleus through mammals is associated to a marked degree with the development of the association centers, a point of view advocated by *Huber* and *Crosby* ('29) and *Le Gros Clark* ('32).

The pulvinar appears to be present in process of development in many, possibly in all, mammals, appearing first as a differentiated posterior portion of the lateral nucleus which lies in relation to the optic tract. Later this region increases greatly in size and presents within itself special differentiation. If it be considered exclusive of the posterior nucleus, which is often included in it in primates, it is found to be particularly a region of passage of optic fibers and its relation with such fibers, either directly or through collaterals, is still in question (see p. 1149). It has connections with the cortex; whether corticofugal, or both corticofugal and corticopetal, has not been determined satisfactorily.   There is evidence that corticopetal fibers do not pass to the visual projection centers but to the occipito-temporal cortex and the angular gyrus (*Minkowski*, '23–'24). *Le Gros Clark* and *Boggon* ('35) found connections between the region *pd* of the pulvinar and a portion of the parietal cortex, which in part is situated between the auditory and visual areas in Macacus.   In this form they were able to demonstrate no cortical connections from the parietal region to the chief part of the pulvinar (*pβ*).   The pulvinar is known to be in connection with the superior colliculus, and *Rioch* has indicated that this connection, in carnivores at least, is from the differentiated portion which he called pulvinar pars posterior.   The pulvinar has connections through the posterior commissure, not only with the contralateral tectum and pulvinar, but with the nuclei of the oculomotor nerve and the medial longitudinal fasciculus (*Foix* and *Nicolesco*, '25).   Hence, it is suggested that primarily the pulvinar does not represent a way station by means of which optic impulses are projected on to the cortex, as does the lateral geniculate nucleus, but rather develops, in part at least, hand in hand in relation to the visual association cortex, in the same manner as the lateral thalamic nucleus develops with the parietal and other cortical association areas.   That this region may contain an older portion related primarily to the superior colliculus and gray in the region of the commissure is probable.

With regard to the use of the terms pretectal nucleus and posterior nucleus, there exists unfortunate confusion.   The pretectal nucleus and the posterior nucleus of *Tsai* ('25), whose work was based on Weigert material of the opossum, have been studied by *Chu* ('32), and the nuclei there recognized appear to be homologous to the pretectal nucleus and the posterior nucleus of *Papez* ('32) for the armadillo and for the rat.   *Le Gros Clark* described a pretectal nucleus and a posterior nucleus in Tupaia corresponding, he believed, to the areas described by *Gurdjian* ('27) as pretectal area and posterior nucleus in the rat. Later *Le Gros Clark* ('30) decided to apply the name nucleus pretectalis to the nucleus posterior of his earlier account, and the name of large-celled nucleus of the optic tract (noyau de la voie optique, *Ramón y Cajal*, '11) to the nucleus he had described previously as the nucleus posterior in Tupaia.   That the nucleus so termed by him is precisely comparable to the nucleus pretectalis of *Tsai* ('25), *Rioch* ('31), *Ingram, Hannett,* and *Ranson* ('32) or *Papez* ('33) is possible, but of this *Huber* and *Crosby* are uncertain in view of the differences in form relations, since it appears to them that the nucleus so designated in Microcebus includes also the dorsal nucleus of the posterior commissure and associated gray, as described for carnivores, but in this interpretation they may be mistaken.   While giving bigeminal nucleus as an alternate name, *Ramón y Cajal* ('11) labeled his figure noyau posterieur.   In man a nuclear mass comparable to the pretectal nucleus of carnivores is closely related to the tectum (*Huber* and *Crosby*), making the general collicular region a light reflex center (see p. 1073), and has connections with the tectum, the optic tract, and other tectal systems, and has a descending path to the tegmental region including the Edinger-Westphal nucleus, part of this connection being by way of the posterior commissure.

The posterior nucleus of carnivores and primates (sometimes included in the pulvinar in these forms) has particularly interesting connections with the lemnisci systems and with the tectum, as well as with the cortex.   It serves functionally, then, as a way station to the cortex.

There is relatively general agreement that the ventral nucleus of mammals is a highly important way station for various types of ascending sensory impulses to the cortex;   that within this nucleus there exists localization of lemnisci terminations would appear evident, and also that the pattern of this localization may vary somewhat with the animal under consideration.   Thus *Wallenberg* ('00) believed that in the rabbit the more medial lemnisci fibers distributed to the more medial parts, the more lateral to the more lateral parts of the ventral nuclear group.   The distribution of the system as given by *Le Gros Clark* for the rat and *Walker* for Macacus have been referred to previously (page 1150). *Vogt* ('09) carried the more medial portions to the caudal part of the nucleus in Cercopithecus and the trigeminal lemniscus and the dento-rubro-thalamic fibers into the intermediate lateral parts, while the spino-thalamic passed to the lateral region.   All of these facts suggest a definite localization pattern based on the regional termination and position of the fibers in the ascending lemnisci systems (*Huber* and *Crosby*, '29).   From the ventral nucleus impulses are passed on to the postcentral and also to the precentral region of the cortex.   In this distribution the fibers in certain animals (rat, at least, *Le Gros Clark*, '30) follow the shortest possible course, with those from the more dorsal region reaching the upper part of the area and those from the more ventral regions the lower part of the area.   In this they follow the pattern of distribution of thalamo-cortical connections laid down by *Elliot Smith* in the Arris and Gale lectures in 1910.   The ventral thalamic nuclear group has short but important internuclear connections with the medial thalamic nucleus (*Papez*).   The nucleus submedius, which is comparable in part at least to the nucleus medialis ventralis of lower mammals, also receives fibers of the lemnisci systems, and this nucleus, together with the nucleus subparafascicularis, where present, is in intimate relation with the medial part of the ventral nucleus, with certain of the midline nuclei, and with the periventricular systems.

The Structure of the Lateral Geniculate Nucleus

The lateral geniculate nucleus is present throughout mammals.   In forms below primates it is generally recognized as consisting of two portions, a pars dorsalis and a pars ventralis (which belongs functionally and developmentally (*Gilbert*, '35, J. Comp. Neurol., vol. 62) to the ventral thalamus).

a. *Marsupials*.   In the opossum (*Tsai*, '25, and *Chu*, '32) the lateral geniculate nucleus forms almost all of the lateral wall of the diencephalon, its dorsal division being situated lateral to the lateral and anterior thalamic nuclei.   Immediately caudal to it is the medial geniculate nucleus and caudomedial the nucleus pretectalis.   *Tsai* identified both large and small cells within the nucleus, but his material was not favorable for a study of its cytologic structure.   The pars ventralis is situated ventral to the pars dorsalis and separated from it by a thick band of optic tract fibers.   In the nucleus geniculatus lateralis pars dorsalis, *Chu* found large, multipolar cells, while in the pars ventralis the neurons were small, medium sized, and elongated, but still multipolar.

b. *Edentates and Rodents*.   The lateral geniculate nucleus of the armadillo (*Papez,* '32; see also fig. 523) has the typical division into dorsal and ventral parts, the former portion consisting of large neurons, the latter of small neurons

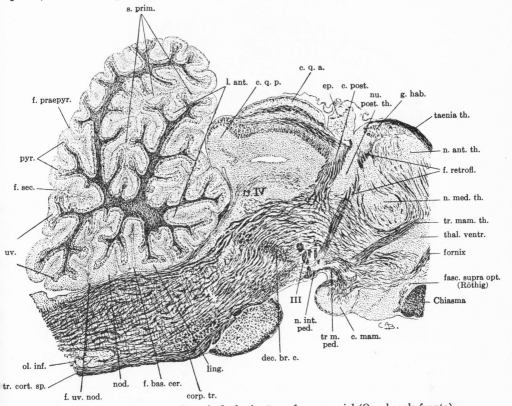

Fig. 522.   Sagittal section through the brain stem of a marsupial (Onychogale funata).

with intermingled medium-sized cells.   Lamination such as is found in higher mammals is lacking.

In rodents the lateral geniculate nucleus has been described by various observers (*Münzer* and *Wiener,* '02; *Winkler* and *Potter,* '11; *Brouwer,* '23; *Gurdjian,* '27, and others), a pars dorsalis and a pars ventralis being recognized easily.   The nucleus is bounded characteristically laterally and dorsally by the optic tract, ventrally by the pars ventralis of the lateral geniculate nucleus and the ventral thalamus, and medially by the pars posterior of the lateral nucleus.   In sections through its greater extent the pars dorsalis is round or oval in outline and has an irregularly striated appearance due to the presence within it of bands of cells intermingled with fibers of the optic tract.   It does not show a lamellar arrangement.   The nucleus geniculatus lateralis pars ventralis

of the rodent lies ventral to the pars dorsalis.   It has medium-sized and somewhat smaller cells and its relations in general are those characteristic of this area
in other forms.   The rodent lateral geniculate nucleus is seen in figure 515.

   c. Insectivores.   In insectivores *Woollard* ('26) and *Le Gros Clark* ('29) have
contributed the most to our present knowledge of the lateral geniculate complex.
Woollard showed that while both dorsal and ventral portions are present, the pars

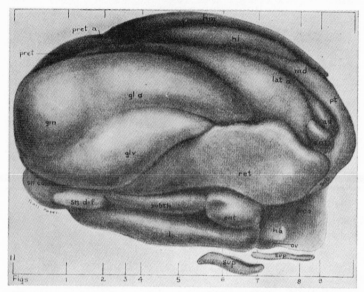

Fig. 523.   A lateral view of a wax model of the thalamic nuclei of the right
side in Armadillo.   *Papez.*

   ad, nucleus anterodorsalis; *ant,* nucleus anterior; *ent,* nucleus entopeduncularis; *gld,* nucleus geniculatus lateralis pars dorsalis; *glv,* nucleus
geniculatus lateralis pars ventralis; *gm,* nucleus geniculatus medialis; *ha,*
nucleus hypothalamicus anterior; *hl,* nucleus habenularis lateralis; *hm,*
nucleus habenularis medialis; *lat.a,* nucleus lateralis pars anterior; *md,*
nucleus medialis pars dorsalis; *ov,* nucleus ovoidalis; *pret.,* nucleus pretectalis;
pret.a, area pretectalis; *preo,* nucleus preopticus; *pt,* nucleus parataenialis;
ret, nucleus reticularis; *sn.comp,* substantia nigra pars compacta; *sn.dif,*
substantia nigra pars diffusa; *subthal,* nucleus subthalamicus; *sub,* nucleus
submedius; *sup,* nucleus supraopticus or tangentialis.

dorsalis is relatively small as compared with the pars ventralis.   He believed
this to be associated with the fact that vision in Tupaia is monocular and that
he was unable to find here retinal differentiation.   *Le Gros Clark* recognized
also dorsal and ventral portions in this nuclear mass and stated that "the size
and elaboration of this body form a remarkable feature of the thalamus of
Tupaia."   He found large, densely arranged and deeply staining cells in the
dorsal nucleus and was able to recognize a clear lamination except at its cephalic
end, in which region two distinctly separated laminae of large, polygonal cells
were recognizable in the medial part of the nucleus, and two less clearly separated
laminae were found in the lateral part.   These lateral and medial laminae
became continuous with each other at the upper pole of the nucleus.   The central

portion of the nucleus was found to be occupied by a rounded mass or core of cells which separated ventrally the medial and lateral laminae. The above laminae were recognized through the middle of the nucleus and gradually disappeared as they were followed either to the caudal or rostral extremity of the cell mass. Pars ventralis in Tupaia consists of smaller, less deeply staining and less closely packed cells. It is separable into medial and lateral portions, and *Le Gros Clark* himself suggested that the medial portion may be homologous to the pregeniculate area of higher forms.

d. Carnivores. The lateral geniculate nucleus in carnivores (figs. 509, 524, 527) has been described by a number of observers, most of whom had a preference for their own terminology. A detailed account of the cellular characteristics of the various parts of the nucleus can not be given here. *Ramón y Cajal* ('11) described in cat a lóbulo dorsal and a lóbulo redundo, which had been found by *Tello* ('04) to be parts of a single nuclear mass. This latter observer noted the characteristic S-shape of the dorsal part of the lateral geniculate nucleus and the presence of three medial laminae dividing the nuclear mass into a series of layers. He also recognized the presence of a small accessory or ventral nucleus. Most of his work was given to a study of the cells of the lateral geniculate nucleus as visible in Golgi preparations. Of such cells he gave excellent illustrations. *Minkowski* ('13) studied the cellular lamination in the lateral geniculate nucleus of the cat as this appeared in pathologic preparations following the enucleation of an eye. He found that in general after such an operation the alternate laminae degenerated. A detailed account of the cell laminae to be found in the lateral geniculate nucleus of carnivores may be obtained from the accounts of *Thuma* ('28) for the cat and *Rioch* ('29) for the dog. These accounts are in essential agreement with only such minor differences as might be expected from differences in the forms studied. Figure 524 is a schematic representation of a longitudinal section through the nucleus in the cat. It represents a reconstruction based on a transverse series. It shows clearly the S-shape of the pars dorsalis, the arrangement into laminae, and the general relations of the parts of the nuclear mass. From the reconstruction it is evident that the major portion of the mass is formed by the two laminae, A and A_1, which are continuous at the upper border of the nuclear mass. These laminae are composed of small, medium-sized, and large cells. The pars dorsalis B consists of spindle-shaped cells, most of which are small. The anterior and posterior parageniculate nuclei form a thin shell over the cephalic and caudal portions of the main nuclear mass as indicated in the figure, and are continuous respectively with the pars ventralis and with the pars dorsalis B.

e. Primates. In primates a large, well-organized lateral geniculate nucleus with dorsal and ventral portions has been seen in Tarsius (fig. 517) by both *Woollard* ('26) and *Le Gros Clark* ('30). The pars dorsalis is very highly differentiated. *Ziehen* ('03) recognized three medullary layers and three cell layers. These laminae fall into a single superficial or peripheral lamina and two central laminae. The peripheral lamina (*Le Gros Clark*) may be divided secondarily into two layers. The central laminae make up the middle portion of the nucleus.

The lateral and medial strata described by *Woollard* are the superficial lamina, and the central mass of *Woollard* forms the central laminae of *Le Gros Clark*. *Woollard's* study of the retina in Tarsius indicated that this animal has a primordium maculae lutae. He believed that the presence of this primordium is associated with the development of the central mass of the dorsal nucleus and that the macula is to be regarded as "represented diffusely in the medial and lateral geniculate body." In the marmoset, *Woollard* found a very marked differentiation and increase in size of this central mass, and regarded it as representing the localization of the macula in higher forms and as substantiating the findings of macular localization in human as presented by *Rönne* ('14).

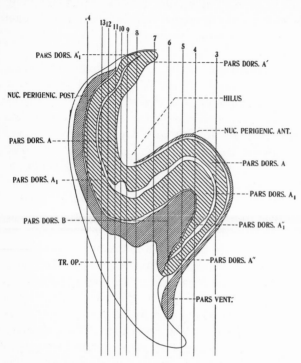

FIG. 524. Schematic representation of a longitudinal section through the lateral geniculate nucleus of the cat, reconstructed from the series of transverse sections. The plane of this diagram is not strictly dorsoventral, but is inclined toward the midline at an angle of 30° from the vertical. Since the nucleus inclines in this direction, a longitudinal section so taken gives a more accurate picture of the internal configuration of the nucleus than a section in the vertical plane. The vertical lines traversing the diagram locate the transverse sections drawn in figures 3 to 13 of the original contribution (*Thuma*, Jour. Comp. Neurol., Vol. 46, '28). *NUC.PERIGENIC.ANT.*, nucleus perigeniculatus anterior; *NUC.PERIGENIC.POST.*, nucleus perigeniculatus posterior; *PARS DORS. A, A', A'', A₁, B*, pars dorsalis A, A', A'', A₁, B; *PARS VENT.*, pars ventralis; *TR. OP.*, tractus opticus.

The pars ventralis of the lateral geniculate nucleus, while small in Tarsius as compared with that in lower forms, is still larger than that described for certain of the smaller lemurs such as Perodicticus (*Környey*, '27) and Chirogaleus (*Woollard* and *Beattie*, '27). *Woollard* stated that the pars ventralis is very greatly reduced in the marmoset. *Woollard's* idea that the development of the lateral geniculate nucleus phylogenetically is dependent upon two major factors, its connection with the cortex and its connection with the midbrain, seems to be borne out by the series of studies which have been made on this form. Phylogenetically the lateral geniculate nucleus grows up particularly as a nucleus intercalated in the course of fiber bundles between the retina and the midbrain region and as a part of a discharge path from the midbrain to the thalamus (tecto-thalamic connections; see *Huber* and *Crosby*, '26 and '33, bibliography for reptiles). These tecto-thalamic connections are of great importance in forms below mammals and in lower mammals, and in these forms the ventral part of the lateral geniculate nucleus is highly developed.   Passing from lower to higher mammals, the relative importance of the influence of the tectum over the thalamic centers appears to decrease, the amount of tecto-thalamic connections grows less and less, and other functions come to dominate the thalamic center.   This is the projection of optic impulses on the cortex, and presumably the differentiation of the pars dorsalis of the lateral geniculate nucleus goes hand in hand with the differentiation of visual centers within the cortex.

There is a high degree of differentiation in the primate lateral geniculate nucleus (fig. 525) as shown by work of *Vogt* ('09), *Friedemann* ('12), *Minkowski* ('20), *Környey* ('27), *Balado* and *Franke* ('29, '30, '31, '31a), *Le Gros Clark* ('32b), *Poliak* ('33), *Orlando* ('33), *Mackenzie* ('34), *Papez* and *Aronson* ('34), and others. The lamination is extraordinarily well marked, consisting of six bands of cells with intervening fiber layers.   A division into a small-celled portion comparable to the nucleus principalis of *Malone* ('10) and a large-celled portion comparable to nucleus magnocellularis is easily seen in the proper sections.   *Von Monakow* carried the divisions further by means of experimental studies (*von Monakow*, '88).   Those interested in the details of these further subdivisions are referred to the original papers.   A pars ventralis was not recognized in *Cercopithecus* (*Vogt*, '09; *Friedemann*, '12), nor has it been identified in man, but the lateral geniculate nucleus itself, of course, is generally recognized.   The figures of *Foix* and *Nicolesco* ('25) show that in man there is a very marked lamination of this nucleus.

The Fiber Connections of the Lateral Geniculate Nucleus

The pars dorsalis of the nucleus geniculatus lateralis has been recognized generally as one of the most important nuclei of termination for optic tract fibers and as an essential way station for these impulses to cortical optic centers and to reflex optic centers.   As afferent connections to the pars dorsalis may be mentioned : (1) the optic tract, (2) internuclear fibers from the pulvinar and adjoining nuclear masses, and (3) some few fascicles of the peduncle of the superior colliculus.   The efferent pathways are (1) the optic radiations, (2) the peduncle of the superior colliculus, and (3) internuclear connections with surrounding areas.

The pars ventralis of the nucleus geniculatus lateralis, as has been seen, is well developed only in lower mammals, where its major afferent connections are through (1) optic tract fibers, (2) the peduncle of the superior colliculus (geniculo-tectal connections; *Tsai*, '25; *Woollard*, '26; *Gurdjian*, '27), (3) fascicles of the dorsal supraoptic decussation (*Gurdjian*, '27), and (4) a geniculo-incertal tract (*Gurdjian*, '27 ; see also *Le Gros Clark*, '30).

The connections of these nuclei are understood best when considered in relation with the optic tract and the secondary and tertiary optic connections. The optic nerves, the optic tracts, and the pathways associated with optic impulses within the brain, according to *Langworthy* ('33) have "very little myelin at the time of birth but rapidly become medullated thereafter."   This observer stated that myelinization within this system seems to be hastened by stimuli from the eyes.   The following account of the system should be read in conjunction with figure 526 (see also *Huber* and *Crosby*, '29).   On pages 1073 to 1075, tectal and pretectal connections are given.   The first order neurons in the optic tract are found in the rods and cones of the retina.   Impulses pass from these cells, through the intermediation of bipolar neurons, to the inner or ganglion cell layer of the retina (*Ganser*, '82; *von Monakow*, '89; *Ramón y Cajal*, '11; also *Colucci*, '98; *Leonowa*, '96), processes of which form the optic nerve.   *Arey* and *Schaible* ('31) found no appreciable number of unmyelinated optic fibers in the dog, rabbit, or man.   Fibers to the retina by way of the optic nerve from the superficial layers of the superior colliculus have been described by a number of observers, among whom may be mentioned *Ramón y Cajal* ('89, for birds; also, '92, for mammals), *von Monakow* ('83a), and *Dogiel* ('95, for birds).   The nerves of the two sides undergo a complete decussation in lower mammals and a partial decussation in other mammals, including man.   Where partial decussation occurs, the nasal fibers cross in the optic chiasm and the temporal fibers proceed to the brain uncrossed.   *Henschen* ('90, '94, '00, '10) devoted much attention to the crossing of the optic nerve fibers and their relations in the chiasm region.   With other observers, such as *Wilbrand* and *Saenger* ('04), and *Rönne* ('11 and '14), he was able to recognize a compact papillo-macular bundle lying along the ventro-lateral part of the optic nerve, but gradually shifting toward its center and undergoing only a partial decussation in the chiasm so that the macula of each eye might be projected on both sides of the brain.   The number of crossed fibers shows a progressive increase in accordance with the development of binocular vision.   *Brouwer* and *Zeeman* ('25) and *Brouwer* ('27) obtained similar results.   They found that in the monkey the macular fibers shift from a lateral position to a central position when traced toward the chiasm, and that the lateral are the temporal and the medial the nasal fibers, with fibers of the inferior retinal quadrants situated below those from the superior quadrants.   *Von Kölliker* ('99) and *Ramón y Cajal* ('11) showed that in the rabbit and the cat certain of the optic fibers bifurcate in the chiasm region, one branch entering either tract.   *Henschen* ('10) and others have regarded this as indicating a two-sided projection of the macula of each eye, but the work of *Holmes* and *Lister* ('16), and *Brouwer* ('27) does not appear to indicate that the macula is completely represented on both sides of the brain.   *Baumgarten* ('81), *Ganser* ('82), *von Gudden* ('85), *Schlagenhaufer* ('97), *Henschen* ('10), and others felt that they were able to trace the bundles after decussation through the tract as discrete fiber masses, while still other observers have felt that recognition of the separate bundles is impossible.

On entrance to the brain the optic tract occupies the lateral surface of the diencephalon, passing directly dorsalward and caudalward toward the tectum. The major portion of the crossed fibers and certain of the uncrossed fibers pass to the dorsal part of the lateral geniculate.   Certain of the crossed fibers with a few of the uncrossed (in higher mammals such as cat, dog, ape, man, *Henschen*, '90; *Bernheimer*, '99; *Minkowski*, '13, for man) pass directly to the optic tectum, and still other optic tract fibers, both crossed and uncrossed (*Pavlov*, '00; *Probst*, '00b; *Winkler*, '11; *Minkowski*, '13) distribute to the pulvinar. *Brouwer* and *Zeeman* ('25; see also *Brouwer*, '27) felt that they were able to localize the various bundles in the optic tract in apes. They found the localization comparable to that in the optic nerve and optic chiasm, with the fibers from the superior retinal quadrants situated dorsally, those from the inferior retinal quadrants ventrally, with the macular fibers lying near the center of the bundle. Clinical evidence indicates that those optic tract fibers which distribute directly to the superior collicular region (including the pretectal nucleus) are more particularly concerned with light reflexes in man (and with certain simpler visual reflexes) since destruction of the lateral geniculate nucleus without involving the overlying optic tract destroys many visual reflexes and abolishes visual consciousness but does not destroy pupillary reflexes in man. The light reflex path has been discussed on page 1073 and need not receive further consideration here. In many mammals the optic tectum serves directly as an important visual reflex center, but in man, where but few of the uncrossed optic fibers reach the optic tectum directly, provision for projecting impulses carried by them is probably made through geniculo-tectal fibers with the lateral geniculate nucleus serving as a way station for at least certain visual reflexes (*Huber* and *Crosby*; see also fig. 526).

Bernheimer carried 70 per cent and *von Monakow* ('05) 80 per cent of all optic tract fibers to the lateral geniculate nucleus, but their ultimate distribution therein has been the subject of much discussion. *Minkowski* ('20; see also fig. 525) showed that the lamination in the lateral geniculate is associated with the distribution of the optic tract fibers, crossed and uncrossed fibers distributing to alternate laminae. For a long time there was no confirmation of this important observation of *Minkowski*, but it has received such confirmation recently in the studies of *Le Gros Clark* ('32) on Macacus and man and of *Orlando* ('33), *Hechst* ('33), and *Mackenzie* ('34) on man. The above results were based on studies of material prepared by Nissl methods following enucleation of the eye.

Using the Marchi method, *Brouwer* and his co-workers and students (*Oberbosch*, quoted from *Brouwer* and *Zeeman*, '26; *Brouwer* and *Zeeman*, '25, '26; *Brouwer*, '27) obtained another series of results. After small lesions of the rabbit's retina, *Oberbosch* traced optic tract fibers arising in the temporal portions of the homolateral retina to the medial portion and those from the nasal portions of the contralateral retina to the lateral portion of the dorsal part of the lateral geniculate nucleus, while he found the upper and lower quadrants projected ventrally and dorsally respectively. Taking into due account the differences in form of the lateral geniculate in the cat and the number of uncrossed fibers in this animal, the pattern of distribution of the optic tract fibers to the nucleus in this animal shows a general resemblance to that found in the rabbit (*Oberbosch*; *Brouwer* and *Zeeman*, '26). The medially situated center for binocular vision, which *Brouwer* and *Zeeman* ('25, '26; *Oberbosch*; *Brouwer*, '27) found to be small in the rabbit, is larger in the cat, according to these observers. In their study of the projection of the retina upon the lateral geniculate nucleus in the monkey, *Brouwer* and *Zeeman* ('25) found that the major portion of the dorsal nucleus of the lateral geniculate is associated with binocular vision, the portion serving monocular vision being a very small portion localized ventrally in the superficial cell layer.   These observers found a relatively sharp separation between the regions of the lateral geniculate concerned with macular and peripheral vision, except ventrally, where they found an overlap of the macular and peripheral fibers.   The macular fibers distributed to the central portion of the nucleus, reaching from the rostral to the caudal pole in the monkey, according to *Brouwer* and *Zeeman*, who stated further "that the dorsal half of the peripheral retina is projected medially in the external geniculate body, and the lower half laterally" and emphasized that their results did not support *Henschen's* theories (which implied that the dorsal part of the retina is projected dorsally, the ventral part ventrally) but were partly substantiated by a clinical case of right inferior quadratic hemianopsia described by *Winkler* ('12).   They do appear to have been in general agreement with the results obtained by a study of clinical cases by *Rönne* ('11, '14), who localized the center for macular vision in the central part of the lateral geniculate nucleus and the centers for peripheral vision laterally and medially.

Using, as their material, Nissl preparations of Macacus rhesus (Macaca mulatta) in which a small retinal lesion had been made some three months before killing the animals, *Le Gros Clark* and *Penman* ('34) found that the macular fibers (crossed nasal, uncrossed temporal) passed to all the laminae but were restricted to a "median sector" in the caudal two-thirds of the nucleus, the rostral one-third being concerned with peripheral vision, with the more rostral parts of the nucleus probably concerned with the reception of fibers from the retinal areas at a greater distance from the disk.   The macular area, as outlined by these last mentioned authors, is more circumscribed than that defined by *Brouwer* and *Zeeman* and they were able to relate their results to the nuclear lamination pattern described by *Minkowski* (fig. 525).

Henschen ('00, '26, etc.) accumulated evidence which he felt favored a very clean cut, point to point representation of the retina, including the macula, upon the lateral geniculate body and a correspondingly precise localization by projection over geniculo-cortical fibers within the striate area of the cortex.   While the experiments quoted in the preceding paragraph give convincing evidence of localization of retinal areas in specific parts of the dorsal part of the lateral geniculate nucleus, there is still need of further evidence for substantiating a finer localization in *Henschen's* sense.   However, the above quoted results, with others of similar type, indicate a greater degree of localization within the lateral geniculate than was supposed by *von Monakow*, who from an extensive series of studies on the optic system ('83a, '85, '88, '89, etc.; also '29, Chap. X), arrived at the conclusion that macular fibers reached most of the dorsal part of the lateral geniculate nucleus and distributed to the greater part of the optic cortical area.

Innumerable clinical and experimental cases and the evident existence of atrophy in the nucleus after cortical lesions (*von Monakow*, '83a, etc., *Brouwer*

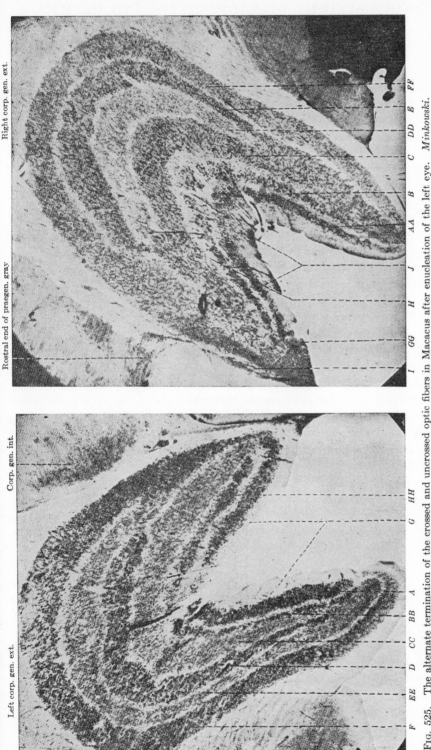

FIG. 525. The alternate termination of the crossed and uncrossed optic fibers in Macacus after enucleation of the left eye. *Minkowski.*

A, peripheral large-celled layer normal; AA, peripheral large-celled layer normal; BB, central large-celled layer atrophied; B, central large-celled layer normal; C, central middle-cell layer normal; CC, central middle-cell layer atrophied; DD, peripheral intermediate layer normal; D, peripheral intermediate layer atrophied; E, central intermediate layer normal; EE, central intermediate layer atrophied; F, peripheral middle-cell layer normal; FF, peripheral middle-cell layer atrophied; G, basal medullated region with small cells, normal; GG, same region as G, showing degeneration; H, medullary layer between the large-celled and middle-cell layers, normal; HH, same region as H, showing degeneration; I, ventromedial portion of the medullary capsule; J, small cells, atrophied.

1163

and *Zeeman*, '25; *Putnam*, '26; see also '26a and 26b; *Poliak*, '33) evidence the presence of geniculo-cortical fibers. These pass through the postlenticular portion of the internal capsule. *Flechsig* ('95 and '96), *Putnam*, and others believed them to be represented in the inferior longitudinal fasciculus; *von Monakow* regarded them as represented in palely staining, longitudinally running fibers adjacent to the ventricular gray. Decussating geniculo-cortical fibers through the corpus callosum were described by *Pfeifer* ('25) and denied by *van Valkenburg* ('12) and *Poliak* ('27, '32, '33). The localization within the visual cortex is discussed in Chapter X, pages 1650 to 1653, to which reference is made.

As is evident from the connections given by various observers, there is still some question whether visual consciousness may also enter the cerebral cortex by way of the pulvinar and pulvino-cortical connections. Optic fibers have been traced to the pulvinar by various observers (*von Kölliker*, '96; *Déjérine*, '01; *Forel*, '07; *Edinger*, '08; *Papez*, '29; *Le Gros Clark*, '30, and others). Recently *Brouwer* questioned the presence of terminations of optic fibers in this nucleus. He believed that, while optic fibers were present, they were to be regarded as fibers of passage, and that the pulvinar is concerned "with the movements of eye muscles and higher visual functions (stereoscopic vision, the recognition of the relative and absolute distance)" (*Brouwer*, '27, page 14). Probably also certain visual reflexes may be conditioned by way of impulses from cortical visual areas to the pulvinar and from the pulvinar to the tectal areas, providing thus a pathway for so-called cortical reflexes.

Visual reflexes are mediated by way of connections from the lateral geniculate nucleus to the superior colliculus. From this center connections with the eye muscle nuclei and with the nuclei of the motor centers of the brain stem and cord are made possible through tecto-oculomotor, tecto-tegmental, tecto-bulbar, lateral tecto-spinal, and perhaps medial tecto-spinal systems also.

In lower mammals, where the pars ventralis of the lateral geniculate nucleus is well developed, optic tract fibers appear to terminate in this gray mass (*Münzer* and *Wiener*, '02; *Gurdjian*, '27; *Le Gros Clark*, '29), although their distribution is small, but *Barris* and *Ingram* ('34) found no optic fibers to this nucleus in the cat. The pars ventralis (fig. 526) is essentially a dependency of the superior colliculus, as was stated before (p. 1158), and its major connections with that center are by the peduncle of the superior colliculus. It serves as a discharge center for the tectum through its connections with the efferent centers (the zona incerta) of the diencephalon. *Gurdjian* has described this latter connection, as well as the relation of the pars ventralis with its fellow of the opposite side and with the contralateral tectum through the dorsal supraoptic decussation. It is to be emphasized that the geniculo-incertal tract (or fasciculus geniculatus descendens), the geniculate bundles of the dorsal supraoptic decussation, and the tectal connections of the nucleus are all characteristic of the connections of the main nuclear mass of the lateral geniculate nucleus of reptiles (*Beccari*, '23; *Huber* and *Crosby*, '26; *Cairney*, '26, and others).

In addition to the main optic tract, the distribution of which has been described in the preceding paragraphs, two accessory optic tracts have been

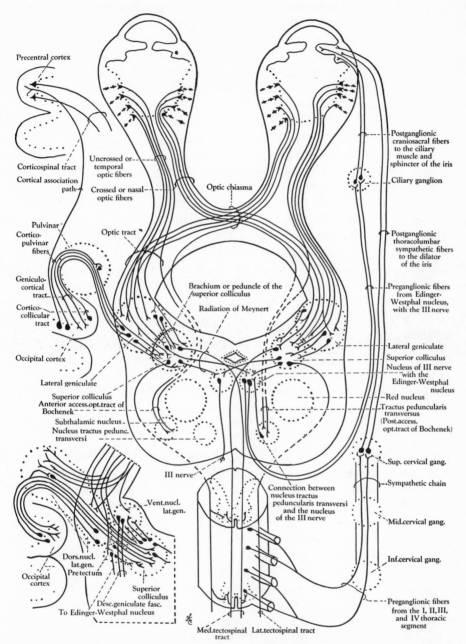

Precentral cortex

Corticospinal tract

Cortical association path

Uncrossed or temporal optic fibers

Crossed or nasal optic fibers

Optic chiasma

Postganglionic craniosacral fibers to the ciliary muscle and sphincter of the iris

Ciliary ganglion

Pulvinar
Cortico-pulvinar fibers

Optic tract

Geniculo-cortical tract

Cortico-collicular tract

Occipital cortex

Lateral geniculate

Superior colliculus
Anterior access.opt.tract of Bochenek

Subthalamic nucleus
Nucleus tractus pedunc. transversi

Brachium or peduncle of the superior colliculus

Radiation of Meynert

Postganglionic thoracolumbar sympathetic fibers to the dilator of the iris

Preganglionic fibers from Edinger-Westphal nucleus, with the III nerve

Lateral geniculate

Superior colliculus

Nucleus of III nerve with the Edinger-Westphal nucleus

Red nucleus

Tractus peduncularis transversus (Post.access. opt.tract of Bochenek)

Sup. cervical gang.

Sympathetic chain

III nerve

Vent.nucl. lat.gen.

Connection between nucleus tractus peduncularis transversi and the nucleus of the III nerve

Mid.cervical gang.

Inf.cervical gang.

Dors.nucl. lat.gen.
Pretectum

Occipital cortex

Superior colliculus
Desc.geniculate fasc.
To Edinger-Westphal nucleus

Med.tectospinal   Lat.tectospinal tract
                  tract

Preganglionic fibers from the I, II, III, and IV thoracic segment

FIG. 526. The optic connections as found in mammals, including visual conscious and visual reflex and light reflex paths. The small diagram at the lower left of the figure illustrates connections of pretectum, and of ventral and dorsal parts of lateral geniculate nucleus in forms in which the ventral part of the lateral geniculate nucleus is present. The superior colliculus of the large figure includes the pretectal nucleus together with the optic.tectum.

The larger generalized diagram shows also the anterior and posterior accessory optic tracts found in the opossum and rat and certain other mammals but said to be lacking in the cat (*Barris, Ingram,* and *Ranson,* '05, J. Comp. Neur., v. 62, p. 117). *Huber* and *Crosby.*

1165

recognized in certain mammals. They will be reviewed briefly in this connection, though not related structurally to the lateral geniculate nucleus.

The anterior accessory optic tract of *Bochenek* ('08) after reaching the brain separates from the remainder of the optic system and passes to the nucleus subthalamicus. The posterior accessory optic tract of *Bochenek* runs caudalward along the ventral surface of the brain, in relation to the cerebral peduncle, hence it is frequently termed the tractus peduncularis transversus (*Marburg*, '03 and '03a). This tract terminates in the nucleus tractus peduncularis transversi, and from this nucleus and also from the nucleus subthalamicus, connections with the oculomotor nuclei have been described. The functions of these accessory optic tracts are not agreed upon by all observers. It has been suggested that the posterior accessory optic tract may carry fibers to the retina. The posterior accessory optic tract or tractus peduncularis transversus has been described for certain mammals (*Marburg*, '03 and 03a; *Tsai*, '25; *Papez*, '29; *Le Gros Clark*, and others). Among those who have described the anterior accessory optic tract are *Bochenek* ('08), *Loepp* ('12), and *Tsai* ('25), but *von Monakow* ('05) did not find it in man. Both accessory tracts are well seen in rodents; *Barris, Ingram,* and *Ranson* found neither in the cat (fig. 526 and figure legend).

The Blood Supply of the Lateral Geniculate Nucleus

It is aside from the limits set for the present text to enter into an account of the blood supply of the various thalamic nuclei. However, opportunity is taken here to refer those interested in this phase of the subject to the recent account of *Abbie* ('34) of the blood supply of the lateral geniculate nucleus in certain submammals and mammals, including man.

Certain Theories of Binocular Vision

Ramón y Cajal ('11) explained in an ingenious way the relation of the partial decussation of the optic nerve in mammals to binocular vision by pointing out that in such animals the final image on the cortex forms a natural whole only if the projection from the nasal visual field of one eye coincides centrally with the temporal projection of the other eye. Such an attempt at explanation is obviously teleologic. It may be right from the standpoint of the survival of the fittest but it does not explain the means by which such an arrangement is perfected.[7] As hodogenetic questions demand a causal explanation, it seems perfectly proper that such an explanation should be made with regard to this partial decussation (*Ariëns Kappers;* also fig. 51). In this regard, one must remember the tendency of similarly stimulated nerve fibers to join each other, a fact for which many illustrations may be found in the nervous system and which may be explained in terms of the electrical charges. To understand the causal relations of this special question, one must start with an animal in which the directions of the eye axes when at rest are parallel, this being the case in various animals with passive binocular vision, which precedes active binocular vision. If

[7] This objection holds good for all teleologic explanations. The continuation of a useful arrangement is natural, but the question invariably is: How did this arrangement arise?

one supposes that a point which is situated in a lateral field of vision sends its rays to the eye, then it is evident that the nasal retinal fibers of one side and the temporal fibers of the other eye will be stimulated simultaneously, and that such fibers will tend to join each other in the optic tract.   Theoretically this junction could be perfected in two ways, since it might be as possible to change the direction of the nasal fibers, as that of the temporal fibers, into a homolateral course.   However, all nasal fibers, including those from the nasal part of the macula, keep their original course, and the new homolateral course is adopted only by the temporal fibers.   The question then arises, why the temporal fibers and those alone change their inherited course and so accomplish the fusing of the two groups.   The solution of this problem appears to be as follows (*Ariëns Kappers*, '20 and '29): In the eyes having parallel axes the light of an object at one side of the midline stimulates the nasal retina of one eye and, simultaneously, the temporal retina of the other eye.   A frontal object lying in the midline of the head is projected on both eyes on the temporal part of the retina when the eyes are not actively converging.   Thus, although in regard to laterally situated objects the temporal retinae correspond with the opposite nasal retinae, with mediofrontal objects the temporal fibers of each eye act together.   It is evident that the nasal fibers of both eyes cannot act together if the light comes from a single object.   The partial decussation then brings the temporal fibers of one eye into relation not only with the nasal fibers, but also with certain of the temporal fibers of the opposite eye.   This explains why the maximal number of uncrossed temporal fibers does not represent the sum total of all the temporal fibers but represents only a part of them.   The degree of temporal-nasal coöperation is regulated by a part of the crossing fibers.   The other portion makes possible bitemporal circummacular coöperation.   The macula belongs essentially to the temporal retina.   This is evident from its position in the lateral part of the eye, in man at a distance of about 3–4 mm. from the entrance of the optic nerve.

The Structure of the Medial Geniculate Nucleus

a. Lower Mammals.   The medial geniculate nucleus (fig. 501) was found in the opossum by *Tsai* ('25) and by *Chu* ('32).   *Hines* ('29) described it as a "small, olive-shaped body found toward the caudal end of the diencephalon in Ornithorhynchus."   It is well developed in edentates (fig. 505 ; see also *Papez*, '32).   *Münzer* and *Wiener* ('02), *Ramón y Cajal* ('11), *d'Hollander* ('13), *Gurdjian* ('27), and others have recognized this nucleus in rodents.   Both *Ramón y Cajal* and *Gurdjian* have divided it into several portions.   Thus *Gurdjian* recognized an oral and a caudal portion, the oral portion being divisible into a dorsomedial part and a lateral part.   *Ramón y Cajal* ('11) described an inferior lobe and a superior lobe.   According to *Le Gros Clark* ('33), "his superior lobe is really the caudal end of the pars posterior of the lateral nucleus" as is nucleus *b* of *Winkler* and *Potter* ('11).   As a whole in rodents the nucleus lies ventral to the lateral geniculate nucleus throughout its rostral third, but caudal to the posterior pole of the latter nucleus.   The medial geniculate body forms the most lateral portion of the diencephalon.   This nucleus consists of medium-sized and large cells.   In Tupaia (*Le Gros Clark*, '29), the nucleus was recognized.   Here its structure was found to be more or less homogeneous and to show, on the whole, less tendency to separate into various subdivisions than the homologous nucleus in lower forms.

In the medial geniculate nucleus in carnivores (figs. 509, 527; *Rioch*, '29, '31), a pars magnocellularis and a pars principalis have been recognized.   The pars magnocellularis corresponds to the dorsomedial portion of the oral division of the medial geniculate nucleus in rodents, and apparently to the pars orodorsalis of *Friedemann* ('12).   The pars principalis is comparable to the lateral portion of the oral part of the medial geniculate nucleus of rodents and possibly to the caudal part as well, and it corresponds to the pars lateralis of *Friedemann*.   Whether or not it includes the pars caudoventralis is uncertain.   This pars principalis in carnivores consists of medium-sized polygonal or triangular cells with relatively pale nuclei and deeply staining cytoplasm.   The cells are rather closely grouped together, lined up in the course of diagonally running fiber bundles.   At its cephalic end the pars principalis forms the ventral and lateral part of the nuclear mass, but followed caudalward it extends into the dorsomedial portion of the medial geniculate.   The pars magnocellularis consists of large cells with pale nuclei, intermingled with smaller cells.   It occupies the dorsomedial portion of the medial geniculate nucleus at first, but farther caudalward swings ventralward and medialward, forming the greater portion of the medial part of the nucleus throughout the anterior two-thirds of its extent.   Among those who have identified and studied this nucleus in carnivores may be mentioned *Winkler* and *Potter* ('14), *Rioch* ('29), and *Ingram, Hannett,* and *Ranson* ('32).

b. *Primates*.   In primates, however, there again is evidence of nuclear differentiation.   Here a central mass forms the major portion of the nucleus, surrounded dorsolaterally by a so-called pars lateralis, consisting of larger, more deeply staining, and more scattered cells, which are directly continuous into the nucleus suprageniculatus.   Caudoventrally a pars ventralis or noyau caudal gris of *Vogt* ('09) (the nucleus infrageniculatus of *Přecechtěl*, '25) is present.   The central group is comparable to the orodorsal part described by *Friedemann* for Cercopithecus, and the pars lateralis and pars ventralis correspond to the lateral and caudoventral portions in this latter animal.   In man (figs. 500 and 503) most observers have not subdivided the medial geniculate nucleus, but *Malone* ('10) recognized a nucleus ventralis and a nucleus dorsalis in the corpus geniculatum mediale of his account.

The Fiber Connections of the Medial Geniculate Nucleus

The major incoming connections of the medial geniculate are furnished by the lateral lemniscus, the peduncle or brachium of the inferior colliculus (figs. 503, 527, and 528), and the tecto-cerebellar tracts.   The chief efferent connection of the nucleus is the thalamo-cortical path, the auditory radiations, which in man runs sublenticularly to Heschl's convolution in the opercular portion of the superior temporal gyrus.   A tecto-cerebellar system of fibers is also present, which has been most thoroughly described by *Hines* ('29) for Ornithorhynchus, although it is recognized in higher forms, including man.   *Hines* described three such systems in Ornithorhynchus: a tractus tecto-cerebellaris dorsalis, a tractus tecto-

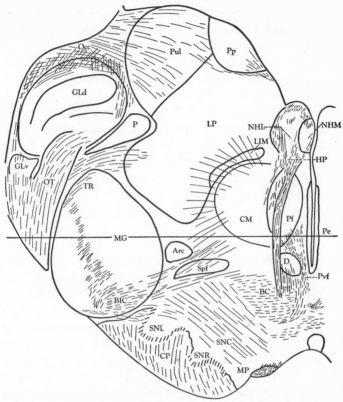

Fig. 527.   An outline drawing indicating the position of the nuclei near the caudal end of the diencephalon of the cat.   *Ingram, Hannett*, and *Ranson*.   (Redrawn from figure 21, Ingram, Hannett, and Ranson '32.) The horizontal line is used to indicate the exact or *O* horizontal plane which these observers established for use in further experimental work.

Arc, arcuate nucleus; *BC*, brachium conjunctivum; *BIC*, brachium of inferior colliculus; *CM*, centré median; *CP*, cerebral peduncle; *D*, nucleus of Darkschewitsch; *GLd*, nucleus geniculatus lateralis pars dorsalis; *GLv*, nucleus geniculatus lateralis pars ventralis; *HP*, tractus habenulo-peduncularis lateralis; *LIM*, *LP*, nucleus lateralis pars posterior; *MG*, nucleus geniculatus medialis; *MP*, mammillary peduncle; *NHL*, nucleus habenularis lateralis; *NHM*, nucleus habenularis medialis; *Occ*, occipital radiation; *OT*, optic tract; *P*, nucleus posterior; *Pe*, nucleus paraventricularis posterior; *Pf*, nucleus parafascicularis; *Pul*, pulvinar; *Pvf*, periventricular fibers; *SNC*, substantia nigra, pars compacta; *SNL*, substantia nigra, pars lateralis; *SNR*, substantia nigra, pars reticularis; *TR*, temporal radiation.

cerebellaris ventralis, and a tractus mesencephalicus quinto-cerebellaris, arising from cells of the mesencephalic nucleus of the trigeminal and probably comparable to the collaterals of the mesencephalic root traced by *Weinberg* ('28) to the cerebellum.   *Le Gros Clark* ('30) is of the opinion that the dorsolateral part of the nucleus is concerned with thalamo-cortical fibers, as is also the central mass, while the caudoventral part has fiber connections with the zona incerta. Interconnecting the medial geniculate nuclei and establishing inferior collicular-geniculate connections is the ventral supraoptic decussation (*Gudden*).

It is evident, then, that the medial geniculate nucleus is the thalamic center for auditory impulses and a necessary way station for such impulses to the cortex. It is also a center for reflex auditory activities, with a discharge path through the zona incerta. Its phylogeny has aroused very much interest. *Joustra* ('18) suggested that the nucleus isthmi might be regarded as the forerunner of the medial geniculate nucleus, and various observers (*Ariëns Kappers*, '21; *Larsell*, '23; *Huber* and *Crosby*, '26) noted that it had similar connections in amphibians and reptiles (p. 982). To such an interpretation certain observers and notably *Wallenberg* (who, however, used the name nucleus isthmi for the optic portion of that nuclear mass) have been opposed. The magnocellular part of the nucleus isthmi of reptiles more probably is represented by a group of neurons occurring in mammals (*Ariëns Kappers*, '29) in the frontal pontine and caudal peduncular region, laterodorsal to the pons and peduncle itself, and lying laterally against the lateral lemniscus and the ventrolateral spino-thalamic tract, — these form the nucleus dorsalis lemnisci lateralis of *Winkler* and *Potter* ('11, '14) or the parabigeminal nucleus of *Papez* ('29). *Prěcechtěl* ('25) and *Ariëns Kappers* regarded the medial geniculate nucleus as contributed to from the remainder of the nucleus isthmi. *Le Gros Clark* ('33) considered that the major portion of the mammalian medial geniculate "is developed as a caudoventral extension of the main sensory nucleus of the thalamus." *Beccari* ('23) suggested and *Frey* ('33) asserted that a subtectal reptilian nucleus represents the mammalian medial geniculate (p. 990) and the latter observer ('33a) identified a similar center in birds (p. 1047). For the interpretations of *Papez* see pages 1007 and 1049.

The connections of the auditory paths with the diencephalon and the cortex may be summarized briefly as follows and are shown in figure 528. Impulses entering the dendritic branches of the neurons constituting the spiral ganglia are conveyed by way of the neuraxes of these ganglion cells to the dorsal and ventral cochlear nuclei. From the dorsal cochlear nucleus, fibers swing directly toward the midline below the floor of the ventricle (the von Monakow or dorsal acoustic decussation), turn ventralward and lateralward, and enter the lateral lemniscus. They are joined by fibers arising from the ventral cochlear nucleus of the opposite side, which cross the medulla oblongata as fibers of the trapezoid body, and by neurons of the trapezoid gray of the same and opposite sides. In between the dorsal and ventral or trapezoid decussations, there may be a smaller decussation of fibers from the tuberculum acusticum, the so-called intermediate decussation of Held. These fascicles constitute, then, the lateral lemniscus, which ascends through the upper part of the pons in a position immediately lateral to the superior olive and in close relation to the lateral spino-thalamic, spino-tectal, and ventral spino-cerebellar systems. Above the cephalic pole of the superior olive the medial lemniscus and its associated bundles swing lateralward to join the lateral lemniscus. As the lower end of the midbrain is approached the lateral lemniscus swings dorsofrontalward and distributes in part to the inferior colliculus, where its fibers enter at the periphery, surrounding the central nucleus like

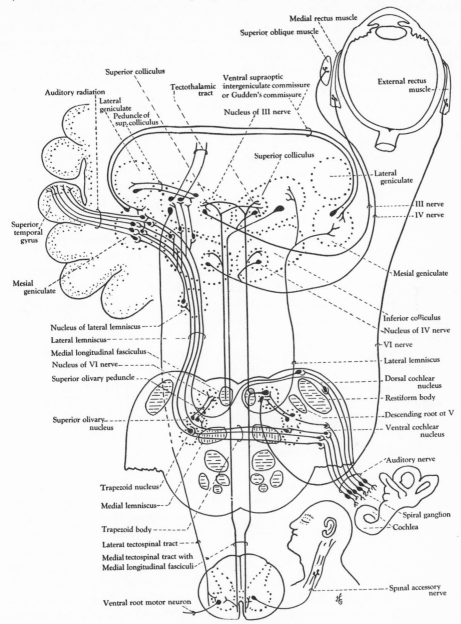

FIG. 528. Diagram showing auditory connections including auditory conscious and certain auditory reflex paths. *Huber* and *Crosby.*

the calyx of a flower, and then turn into the collicular gray. In part these fibers are terminal fibers. Some few of them may swing directly forward through the nucleus, and (in company with the acoustico-optic fibers) reach the superior colliculus.   However, the number of these latter is relatively very small in higher mammals.   The fibers of the lateral lemniscus reach the medial geniculate nucleus, where they terminate.   The peduncle of the inferior colliculus also carries forward auditory impulses from the inferior colliculus to the medial geniculate nucleus.   The medial geniculate nucleus in turn discharges auditory impulses to the transverse gyrus of the superior temporal convolution through the auditory radiations, which occupy the sublenticular portion of the internal capsule.   The inferior colliculus is to be regarded as a midbrain auditory reflex center.   The medial geniculate nucleus is a diencephalic auditory center concerned perhaps, to some extent, in thalamic auditory reflexes, but particularly important as a necessary way station in the path for auditory impulses to the cerebral cortex.   Figure 528, showing the relations here described, is taken from the 1929 paper of *Huber* and *Crosby* and from Piersol's Anatomy ('30).

The Ventral Thalamus or Subthalamus, Its Nuclei and Its Fiber Connections

Ventral to the sulcus medius and the dorsal thalamus and dorsal and dorsolateral to the hypothalamic areas lies that portion of the diencephalon termed either the ventral thalamus or the subthalamus.   It is characterized by certain major nuclear groups : (1) the entopeduncular nuclear group, including the nucleus decussationis supraopticae dorsalis, (2) the zona incerta with its associated fields of Forel, (3) the nucleus subthalamicus, (4) the red nucleus, and (5) the substantia nigra.   (6 and 7) Here also belong functionally the nucleus geniculatus lateralis pars ventralis, when present (p. 1154), and the nucleus geniculatus medialis pars ventralis (p. 1168).   The red nucleus (p. 1085) and the substantia nigra (p. 1092) belong primarily to the tegmental portion of the midbrain.

a. *The Entopeduncular Nuclear Group.*   The entopeduncular nuclear group (the noyau de la capsule interne) of *Ramón y Cajal* ('11) and *Morgan* ('27) includes both this latter nucleus and the entopeduncular nucleus of *Gurdjian* ('27; fig. 515), but consists of neurons resembling in cell type those constituting the globus pallidus, although sometimes slightly smaller.   These cells belong to the series of efferent neurons as judged by the criteria of *Malone*.   Often the nucleus is directly continuous with the globus pallidus, as in the cat (*Winkler* and *Potter*, '14, labeled *gl. p.*, plate 11 ; also *Rioch*, '29a), but it may be separated as in the rat (*Gurdjian*, '27) and the dog (*Rioch*, '29a).   The nucleus is intercalated in the course of the ansa lenticularis (*Morgan*, '27 ; *Rioch*, '29a; figs. 514, 516, 518) and is in synaptic relation with its fibers.   It is very old phylogenetically, being the homologue of the various entopeduncular groups described for reptiles and birds.   An especially differentiated nucleus, the nucleus decussationis supraopticae dorsalis (*Rioch*, '29a), is comparable to the nucleus of that name described earlier for reptiles and birds (*Huber* and *Crosby*, '26 and '29), and lies where the dorsolateral radiating fibers of the dorsal supraoptic decussation, with which its cells are in synaptic relation, cross the ansa lenticularis to form the connections described.   The synapses of the ansa fibers with the neurons of the nucleus entopeduncularis are said to be pericellular in character.   The ansa lenticularis is discussed in detail on pages 1446 to 1451.

b. Zona Incerta and Fields of Forel.   The zona incerta (figs. 511, 515 to 518, and 521) occupies the dorsal part of the subthalamic region, lying ventral to the external medullary lamina and the pars externa of the ventral nucleus of the dorsal thalamus and dorsal to the cerebral peduncle and the nucleus subthalamicus.   It is essentially a region of passage for fiber bundles.   It has been recognized by many students of the region, who have described it under a variety of names.   Thus it is the peripeduncular nucleus of *Malone* ('10), *Morgan* ('27), and *Papez* ('29).

In lower mammals, such as rodents (*Gurdjian*, '27, and others; fig. 515), the zona incerta usually has been considered as a single nuclear entity, but in higher mammals, such as carnivores and primates, it is divisible into two or more nuclear groups; (1) a more or less circumscribed, lens-shaped zona incerta proper (fig. 516), bounded dorsally by the external medullary lamina and in its caudal part by the zona incerta caudalis, the decussation of the cerebellar peduncle and the nucleus subthalamicus, and (2) a zona incerta caudalis, which is separated from the major portion of the region by bundles of the dorsal supraoptic decussation and associated fiber systems.   This region, as do other hypothalamic areas, receives fibers from the ansa lenticularis and is connected with the tectum by incerto-tectal fibers (*Gurdjian*, '27; figs. 511 and 521), and with the ventral part of the lateral geniculate nucleus by short connections and by collaterals of the descending fasciculus geniculatus descendens (comparable to that described by *Beccari*, '23, and *Huber* and *Crosby*, '26, for reptiles).   Bundles of the dorsal supraoptic decussation crossing this nuclear mass are related with striatal and perhaps subthalamic areas of the opposite side.   According to *Ramón y Cajal* ('11), the region receives collaterals of ascending lemnisci systems, and *Déjérine* ('01) traced to it fibers of the superior cerebellar peduncle and fibers from the red nucleus and the reticular formation.   It seems more probable that the connection is incerto-rubral in character (fig. 521).   Its medial portion is known to receive short internuclear fibers from the mammillary bodies (*von Kölliker*, '96; *Déjérine*, '01, and others).   Collaterals of internal capsule fibers were traced to the area in the rat (*Gurdjian*, '27) and *von Monakow* ('05) believed that in man there were cortical regions around the temporal pole, the operculum, and the island which were connected with the zona incerta. Various other connections have been cited for the area, but most of them require further verification.   In general one may say that the zona incerta is essentially a way station in the course of the ansa lenticularis and that it is very largely a region of passage for fiber systems from higher to lower centers.

The fields H_1 and H_2 of *Forel* ('72) may either be included with the zona incerta as an integral part of that cell mass, as *von Kölliker* ('96), *Foix* and *Nicolesco* ('25), *Gurdjian* ('27), and others have done, or they may be considered separately under the name of the reticular subthalamic nucleus, as *Papez* ('29) and *Rioch* ('29a) have done.

Medial to the zona incerta proper, fused with the medial tip of the zona incerta caudalis (at least in carnivores) and dorsolateral and caudal to the medial hypothalamic area, is a region of passage of fibers (H_1) containing the thalamic fasciculus of Forel (and here the associated dento-rubro-thalamic tract; figs. 516 and 518). Other fiber systems pass through the region. Elongated cells, in general of a type similar to those found in the zona incerta, are scattered among the fiber bundles. Ventral and lateral to field H_1, with which it is continuous, and dorsal to the nucleus subthalamicus is the field H_2 (fig. 518), also a region of passage of fiber bundles, particularly of the lenticular fasciculus of Forel. Associated with the field H_2, but extending up toward the region of junction·of the fields H_2 and H_1, are the rather large, scattered cells of the nucleus of the field of Forel. The above account is based primarily on carnivore material and follows the account of *Rioch*. Essentially similar conditions with some slight differences are to be found in other mammals. The field H_1 has been recognized by the great majority of students of the subthalamus since the time of *Forel* ('72 and '07; *Ramón y Cajal*, '11; *Foix* and *Nicolesco*, '25; *Morgan*, '27, and others). A considerable number of observers (for example, *von Kölliker*, '96, and *Foix* and *Nicolesco*, '25) have carried fibers from the region of the field of Forel through the commissure of Forel to the corresponding areas of the other side, thus providing for a cross connection of the ansa lenticularis to the regions in question. The connections and relations of the ansa lenticularis and the fields of Forel are discussed on pages 1446 and 1448 and illustrated in figure 632.

c. *Nucleus Subthalamicus.* The nucleus subthalamicus is an oval or biconvex mass of cells situated along the dorsal surface of the peduncle. Its position in marsupials and edentates is shown in figures 523 and 529, respectively; in carnivores in figure 516 and in man in figure 520. Its connections are diagrammed in part in figure 632. It is distinct dorsomedially in rodents and carnivores, and in these latter forms is cephalad to the substantia nigra, from which it is separated by a fiber bundle. In man the nucleus has shifted relatively somewhat farther lateralward and, with the greater growth forward of the substantia nigra, lies in part lateral to the cephalic tip of the latter cell mass. It has large, multipolar cells with coarse, rod-shaped granulations. This nucleus is frequently known, from its early discoverer, by the name of corpus Luysii. It has been termed the nucleus proprius peduncularis cerebri by *Winkler* and *Potter* (in the rabbit and cat, '11, '14), their nucleus subthalamicus falling within the zona incerta of most observers.

The major connections of the nucleus subthalamicus are with the striatum by way of the ansa lenticularis (figs. 511 and 632), and particularly through fibers entering its medial surface from the lenticular fasciculus (H_2) of Forel (*Déjérine*, '01; *von Monakow*, '95 and '05; *Ramón y Cajal*, '11; *Tsai*, '25; *Foix* and *Nicolesco*, '25; *Papez*, '29; *Rioch*, '29a, and others). Fibers arise in the nucleus and decussate in the commissure of Forel to reach the red nucleus of the other side (*von Kölliker*, '96) or to reach the contralateral subthalamic nucleus (*Foix* and *Nicolesco*, '25; *Gurdjian*, '27). Fibers of the dorsal supraoptic decussation have been traced in the opossum (*Tsai*, '25) and in the rat (*Gurdjian*, '27) to this nucleus. Similar connections have been described by *von Kölliker* ('96), *Déjérine* ('01), *Rioch* ('29a), and others. These constitute, probably, a crossed connection from the striatal region and belong essentially, then, to the ansa lenticularis sys-

tem.   Differences of opinion appear to exist with regard to possible cortical connections of the nucleus subthalamicus, such fibers having been described by *Foix*
and *Nicolesco* ('25) and denied by *von Monakow*.   *Déjérine* found a few cortical
fibers to the region.   Bundles arising in the nucleus subthalamicus accompany the
lenticular fasciculus of Forel to the substantia nigra, constituting a subthalamo-
nigral path (*Rioch*, '29a).   Internuclear fibers put it into close relation with the
surrounding regions, including the red nucleus.   In addition to the connections
thus far mentioned, all of which indicate that the nucleus subthalamicus is a
center intercalated primarily in the course of homolateral and contralateral
fibers from the hemisphere, there is another type of connection, the significance
of which is not fully understood as yet.   This is the connection of the optic tract
system with the nucleus subthalamicus through the tractus opticus accessorius
anterior, described first by *Bochenek* ('08) and verified by *Loepp* ('12) and later
by *Tsai* ('25).   Many observers have been unable to follow this path, and questions as to its direction of conduction and its significance have been raised frequently.   According to *Bochenek*, the bundle runs caudalward from the optic
chiasm through the depths of the subthalamus and terminates in the nucleus
subthalamicus.   This tract requires further verification.   It is illustrated in the
diagram, figure 526.   A center for the dilation of the pupil has been described in
the more frontal and medial portions of the nucleus subthalamicus (*Karplus* and
Kreidl, '09;   see also *Spiegel*, '28, and *Greving*, '28).   *Ingram, Ranson*, and
Hannett ('31) obtained such dilation from various other portions of the brain
stem as well as from the nucleus subthalamicus, which observations warrant
questioning the specificity of this nucleus as the pupil dilator center.

The Hypothalamus — Its Nuclear Masses and Fiber Connections

The hypothalamus consists in mammals of : (1) a non-olfactory commissural
portion, the pars optica hypothalami, which contains the optic chiasm and the
supraoptic commissure ; (2) a glandular portion, the hypophysis, and (3) certain
olfacto-visceral correlation centers which may be termed collectively either the
hypothalamic nuclei or the tuber cinereum and the mammillary bodies.

a. Pars Optica Hypothalami.   The optic chiasm is merely a region of passage
of optic fibers and has no significant relation with the hypothalamus.   It is considered under the fiber connections of the lateral geniculate nucleus of the thalamus (p. 1160).   The supraoptic system likewise consists of decussating fibers
connecting, for the most part, different regions of the midbrain and diencephalon.   It consists essentially of three commissural systems : (1) the dorsal supraoptic decussation ; (2) the ventral supraoptic decussation, and (3) Ganser's commissure.   The dorsal supraoptic decussation, sometimes Meynert's commissure
(figs. 511, 518, and 529), is relatively less well developed in mammals than in
reptiles and birds, and the origin and termination of its components are not as yet
thoroughly understood.   Three systems are recognized : (1) tectal fibers, which
connect the superior colliculus of one side with that of the other side and with
the contralateral ventral thalamic regions and which are frequently not demonstrable ; (2) intergeniculate fibers, which pass from the ventral part of the lateral

geniculate nucleus in lower mammals through the commissure to the homologous region of the other side (this connection is absent in higher mammals), and (3) decussating fibers of the ansa lenticularis, which connect the lenticular nucleus of one side with the subthalamic regions of the opposite side.   To these components various others have been added by different observers.

The ventral supraoptic decussation, or Gudden's commissure, interconnects the medial geniculate nuclei and the inferior colliculi of the two sides (fig. 528). The third commissure, or Ganser's commissure (fig. 518), is a system of crossed

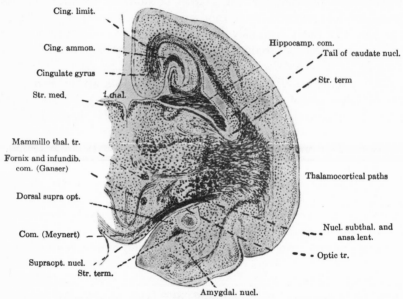

Cing. limit.

Cing. ammon.

Cingulate gyrus

Str. med.   t. chal.

Hippocamp. com.

Tail of caudate nucl.

Str. term

Mammillo thal. tr.

Fornix and infundib. com. (Ganser)

Dorsal supra opt.

Com. (Meynert)

Supraopt. nucl.

Str. term.

Amygdal. nucl.

Thalamocortical paths

Nucl. subthal. and ansa lent.

Optic tr.

Fig. 529.   Cross section of diencephalon and forebrain of a marsupial (Hypsiprymnus rufescens).

fibers which contains in part the fibrae ansulatae of lower forms.   These fibrae ansulatae have their origin in the ventral nucleus of the medial longitudinal fasciculus, decussate as Ganser's commissure in the caudal part of the posterior optic or supraoptic complex, and swing dorsalward in order to enter the medial longitudinal fasciculus.   With these fibrae ansulatae in Ganser's commissure are short fibers which interconnect hypothalamic regions near the ventricular wall. Thus *Wallenberg* regarded it as carrying decussating lemnisci fibers.   *Tsai* ('25) emphasized its connections with the nucleus subthalamicus (which *Déjérine* denied), and *Foix* and *Nicolesco* ('25) carried through the system crossed fibers from the substantia innominata of Reichert.   It is evident that there is necessity of further investigations in mammals before the relations of this system can be established beyond question.

b. The Hypophysis and the Diencephalic Secretory Ependyma.   The hypophysis is a rounded mass attached to the brain wall in front of the mammillary bodies by means of a stalk known as the infundibulum, into which is a greater or less continuation of the third ventricle.   In primates this ventricular space does not extend into the gland, but in certain carnivores such as the cat, there is a marked ventricular space within the neural lobe, and in Tamandua the wall may be greatly folded.   The gland arises from double anlagen as in lower forms, one portion representing the downfolding of the neural tube, by means of which the neural lobe is formed, and the other an upward folding of the dorsal wall of the oral cavity, known as Rathke's pouch (*Rathke*, '38), which gives rise to the anterior or oral lobe of the hypophysis.   The oral lobe is ultimately cut off entirely from the oral cavity.   Its anterior wall thickens through a multiplication of its cells, forming the pars distalis or pars oralis or the anterior lobe proper, and the space inside it is reduced to a narrow slit known as the residual lumen or the residual cleft.   The caudal wall of the anterior lobe becomes the pars intermedialis of the hypophysis.   Growing up from the pars oralis and spreading out along the wall of the tuber cinereum region in front of the attachment of the infundibulum is the pars tuberalis of the anterior lobe (*Tilney*, '11, and *Atwell*, '26).   Thus, in the fully formed hypophysis, may be found a pars oralis with a pars tuberalis, a pars intermedialis, and a pars neuralis.   The pars oralis and the anterior lobe, or pars principalis, consist, in higher mammals, of irregularly anastomosing trabeculae of cells, between which are wide open capillaries and certain smaller arteries.   Studies of the blood supply indicate that it is very rich in the pars oralis and relatively less rich in the pars tuberalis.   In the cords of cells are a variety of cell types, some with clear protoplasm which takes an acid stain, others with oxyphilic or basophilic granulations.   Several cell types have been described (*Addison*, '17, and *Bremer*, '27), for an account of which the various modern texts on histology should be consulted.   It is not known with certainty whether the differences in cells represent different stages in the production of secretion or different types of secretion.   The pars tuberalis and the pars intermedia resemble the anterior lobe in structure but show some differences in the proportion of the various types of cells and in the distinctness and size of the cords.   In certain places follicular-like spaces are formed, containing colloid substance.   The posterior or neural lobe contains ependyma and neuroglia cells and some nerve fibers.   Its function is uncertain.   By some it is regarded as having a specific secretion.   By others it is thought to be merely a region of passage by which the secretion of other portions of the hypophysis may reach the third ventricle. The pars oralis belongs to the series of glands which affect the growth of the body, and disturbances of its secretion produce the condition known as acromegaly.   The pars intermedia is sometimes said to be concerned in sugar metabolism.   After castration *Addison* ('17) saw changes in the hypophysis.

There exists an interrelation of the hypophysis with nuclear groups within the hypothalamus.   Thus fibers have been traced into the infundibular stalk in several mammals, including man, from the nucleus supraopticus (*Pines*, '25 ; *Greving*, '25 ; *Foix* and *Nicolesco*, '25 ; *Stengel*, '26 ; *Cushing*, '30), from the filiform nucleus (*Greving*, his paraventricular nucleus), and from nuclei of the tuber cinereum (*Nicolesco* and *Nicolesco*, '29).   The demonstration of a portal system in close relation to both the tuber cinereum and the hypophysis denotes the intimate functional relation of these centers (*Popa* and *Fielding*, '30).

Before entering upon a discussion of the hypothalamic gray, attention should be called to the modified ependyma along the ventricular wall, comparable to that found in lower forms (*Charlton; Ariëns Kappers*, '29), in which it has been thought to be secretory. How general the distribution of this modified ependymal area in mammals may be, is not known. Recently it has been described by *Papez* ('32) in the armadillo.

c. *The Olfacto-visceral Correlation Centers.* The hypothalamic nuclear gray (or tuber cinereum) in mammals, as in forms below mammalian types, is very intimately related to the preoptic region, and any line drawn between these regions in adult material is more or less arbitrary. The region has been studied by numerous observers and various terminologies have resulted which are difficult to codify, particularly since the work has been done on various groups of mammals and since the form relations vary somewhat in different vertebrate classes.

In the analysis of the mammalian hypothalamic region, essentially two general methods are used at the present time. According to one of these methods, major emphasis is laid on the cell types; according to the other method major emphasis is placed on nuclear grouping and on fiber connections. Neither of these interpretations is necessarily incorrect or necessarily opposed one to the other. They merely represent different modes of attacking the same problem. There is no question of the truth of the statement made by *Malone* ('14) that a study, even by experimental methods, of the various connections of the nuclei of any given region with other parts of the nervous system "without taking into consideration differences of cell character, fails to distinguish between differences of connections dependent merely upon spatial differences and those differences of connections which depend upon differences in cell activity, such cell activity being indicated not only in the nervous system but in all portions of the entire organism, by definite types of cell character." In a region where the topographic pattern and the cell type are reasonably closely correlated, the use of cell type in establishing nuclear boundaries is ideal, but where the neurons are scattered through an area in which are found cells of other types, experimental ablation of all the cells of a given type, without destroying many other areas, is attended with difficulty both as to performance and as to interpretation. The best evidence for functional analysis of such a region is to be found in a study of clinical cases of selective degeneration such as those reported by *Morgan* ('27, '28, '28a, and '30) and *Morgan* and *Gregory* ('30). Moreover, similarity in type of function does not signify precisely the same function. The dorsal efferent nucleus of the vagus, as studied by *Malone*, shows two cell types, larger neurons for preganglionic fibers which synapse with the cardiac ganglia through the vagus, and smaller neurons which supply preganglionic fibers through the vagus and bulbar accessory to synapse with sympathetic neurons in sympathetic ganglia on or near viscera from the neck to the descending colon. Such fibers are alike in general type of impulse carried, but their distribution gives them their specific significance. The same may be true of the hypothalamic centers. The topographic method is intended to provide the anatomical background for an analysis of the region, a means by which small, definable areas with their associated and intervening fiber bundles may be studied.   The fact that a fairly constant topographic arrangement of cells and fibers has been demonstrated in many mammals indicates that the pattern is no mere chance arrangement.   It appears certain that the results based on these two methods of approach will ultimately relate themselves satisfactorily.   Presumably those nuclear groups containing cells of like character will be found to be concerned with similar functions.

The subdivisions of the hypothalamic area on the basis of the topographic relations of the nuclear groups as this has been carried out by *Ramón y Cajal* ('11), *Friedemann* ('12), *Winkler* and *Potter* ('11 and '14), *Gurdjian* ('27), *Rioch* ('29), *Warner* ('29), *Grünthal* ('29, '30), *Krieg* ('32), *Chu* ('32), *Papez* ('32), *Crouch* ('34), and others will receive primary consideration.   A comparison of the various nuclear groupings described by the above listed observers evidences sufficient uniformity to indicate that much more than chance considerations of cell form and grouping are determining the pattern.   A brief statement of the hypothalamic centers, based particularly on the report of *Gurdjian* ('27) for the rat, is here given.   This furnishes a fairly typical picture of the hypothalamic area in mammals below primates, as ascertained through an analysis of topographic subdivisions of its gray.   In the rodent brain, beginning immediately behind the medial preoptic area, is found a larger, though not very sharply defined, nuclear mass, the nucleus hypothalamicus anterior of *Gurdjian* ('27; fig. 513) with which *Krieg* ('32) included the nucleus supraopticus diffusus. This nucleus is present in the opossum (*Chu*, '32) and the armadillo (*Papez*, '32; *Howe*, '33; fig. 523).   This region is capable of secondary subdivisions and in carnivores (*Rioch*, '29; *Ingram, Hannett*, and *Ranson*, '32) these subdivisions are sufficiently clear to justify separation of the area into a nucleus hypothalamicus anterior and a dorsal hypothalamic area, and they probably constitute part of the anterior nucleus of the tuber of *Friedemann* ('12).   To this general region come fibers of the preoptic and supracommissural components of the stria terminalis and collaterals of the medial cortico-hypothalamic tract.   Immediately ventral to the anterior hypothalamic area in the rodent is a small nucleus, which from its oval outline has been termed the nucleus ovoidus (*Gurdjian*, '27; fig. 513).   This falls within the noyau anterieur or principale of *Ramón y Cajal* and the ventral nucleus of the tuber cinereum of *Friedemann* ('12), and is the nucleus suprachiasmaticus of *Spiegel* and *Zweig* ('17), *Grünthal* ('30), and *Krieg* ('32) and the nucleus ovoideus of *Rioch* ('29; fig. 514) and *Ingram, Hannett*, and *Ranson* ('32). It receives fibers of the supracommissural component of the stria terminalis.   It also receives preoptic fibers of the stria and fascicles from the dorsal supraoptic decussation.   Lateral to the anterior hypothalamic nucleus, and not easily separated from the lateral preoptic area, is a nucleus hypothalamicus lateralis (fig. 515). This is intercalated in the course of the medial forebrain bundle.   It receives internuclear connections from surrounding hypothalamic nuclei and, according to *Gurdjian* ('27), constitutes one of the major contributors to the diencephalic periventricular system.   The nucleus hypothalamicus lateralis (*Gurdjian*, '27; *Rioch*, '29; *Krieg*, '32; *Chu*, '32; *Papez*, '32; *Ingram, Hannett*, and *Ranson*, '32;

Howe, '33) reaches throughout practically the entire extent of the hypothalamus, retaining its lateral position and its relation to the medial forebrain bundle.   As the optic tract fibers swing lateralward from the midline, the so-called nucleus supraopticus diffusus (*Gurdjian,* '27; *Chu,* '32; *Rioch,* '29, '31; also fig. 518) makes its appearance in the course of the ventral supraoptic decussation and dorsal to the nucleus ovoideus.   Separating the nucleus hypothalamicus anterior from the ventral wall is a nucleus periventricularis hypothalamicus anterior (*Gurdjian,* '27; *Papez,* '32; *Chu,* '32; fig. 513).   In the rat this is bordered dorsally by the principal portion, the pars principalis, of the nucleus filiformis (the nucleus filiformis of *Nissl, Gurdjian,* and *Krieg,* '32; nucleus paraventricularis 11 of *Greving,* '30).   This latter nucleus is clearly distinguishable through its triangular outline.   It lies immediately caudal to the anterior hypothalamic nucleus and medial to the lateral thalamic nucleus in planes passing through the pars dorsomedialis of the nucleus ventralis and the habenula.   It has been termed the pars principalis of the filiform nucleus by *Rioch* ('29).   It is part of the filiform nucleus of *Winkler* and *Potter* ('14), corresponds to the nucleus paraventricularis of *Malone* ('10 and '14), *Morgan* ('30a), and others (see page 1184), and is the nucleus hypothalamicus magnocellularis of *Warner* ('29) and *Papez* ('32).   The hypothalamic gray differentiates, then, in the rat (*Gurdjian; Krieg*), into a nucleus hypothalamicus ventromedialis, a nucleus hypothalamicus dorsomedialis, and a nucleus hypothalamicus posterior.   Comparable nuclei have been described by *Chu* ('32) for the opossum, by *Papez* ('32) for the armadillo, and by *Rioch* ('29) and *Ingram, Hannett,* and *Ranson* ('32) for the carnivores. In front of this level the nucleus paraventricularis hypothalamicus anterior has been replaced by a nucleus paraventricularis hypothalamicus posterior (16 of *Greving,* '30; nucleus arcuatus of *Krieg,* '32), which later on differentiates into a dorsal and a ventral portion.   The nucleus hypothalamicus ventromedialis lies, as its name indicates, in the ventral part of the hypothalamic area ventral to the nucleus hypothalamicus dorsomedialis, and medial and ventromedial to the nucleus hypothalamicus lateralis and to the fornix.   When well developed this mass is round in outline and is composed of medium-sized and small cells.   For part of its length it has a dorsomedial extension of cells which ultimately fuse again with the ventrolateral portion to form once more an oval mass.   This nucleus is one of the more evident groups of the hypothalamus, occupying the greater portion of the ventral part of the region in the midline.   It receives the supracommissural component of the stria terminalis and terminal fibers of the medial forebrain bundle and the medial cortico-hypothalamic tract.   The nucleus hypothalamicus dorsomedialis (see fig. 518 for the dog) begins well behind the cephalic pole of the nucleus hypothalamicus ventromedialis, to which it lies immediately dorsal.   Throughout much of its extent the mammillo-thalamic tract lies near its dorsal surface and the fornix system near its ventrolateral border.   Through its greatest extent it is oval in outline and a conspicuous nuclear component of the hypothalamus.   In addition to fibers of the medial forebrain bundle and the stria terminalis, the nucleus hypothalamicus dorsomedialis contributes fibers to the periventricular diencephalic system.   The nucleus hypothalamicus posterior (figs. 516 and 517) lies dorsal to the nucleus hypothalamicus dorsomedialis, and, according to *Gurdjian*, is continuous dorsally with the periventricular gray of the tegmentum.   Lateral to it is a mammillo-hypothalamic tract and then the lateral hypothalamic nucleus.   It contributes fibers to the diencephalic periventricular system and receives, as do the other hypothalamic nuclei, collaterals of the medial forebrain bundle.   The hypothalamic nuclei just discussed disappear in front of the mammillary region and their places are taken by the ventral and dorsal premammillary nuclei of the rodent, of which the former is in relation with the lateral hypothalamic nucleus and the latter in general with the medial hypothalamic area.   To this carnivore nucleus, comparable to the dorsal premammillary nucleus, *Rioch* ('29) applied the name of supramammillary nucleus and *Papez* ('32) and *Chu* ('32) have used this terminology.   The mammillary bodies are highly developed in many mammals (figs. 519, 520, 530) and fall usually into a lateral and medial or an external and internal mammillary nucleus.   *Gurdjian* ('27) recognized in the latter nucleus in the rat a pars medialis, a pars medianus, a pars lateralis, a pars commissurae dorsalis, and a pars commissurae ventralis; *Krieg* ('32) described a pars medialis, a pars lateralis, and a pars posterior (see original papers and figures).   The small rostral end of the nucleus mamillaris lateralis (nucleus premamillaris lateralis of *Krieg*, '32) is small and consists of linearly arranged cells along the ventrolateral border of the hypothalamus.   The nucleus increases in size when followed caudalward, its cells becoming larger and more granular, and then decreases again in its caudal third.   The mammillary bodies receive the terminal fibers of the fornix system.   According to certain observers (*Ramón y Cajal*, '11, and others) such fibers terminate in both the medial and lateral nuclei. According to other workers only the medial nucleus receives such fibers.   In the elephant *Přecechtěl* ('25) could trace fornix fibers farther caudalward to his nucleus ellipticus, just in front of the oculomotor nucleus.   From the medial mammillary nucleus arise the mammillo-thalamic and mammillo-tegmental systems to the anterior nuclei of the thalamus and the dorsal tegmental region of the midbrain respectively.   Ascending fibers of the mammillary peduncle have been traced by *Wallenberg* ('99, '04), *Ramón y Cajal* ('11), and *Papez* ('32) to the mammillary body. Short connections from the mammillary nuclei to the interpeduncular nuclei and to the surrounding hypothalamic and peduncular regions have been described.

The hypothalamic region in primates also falls into the same major subdivisions, as is indicated by the work of *Friedemann*. *Ramón y Cajal's* account, although somewhat less detailed, shows a general correspondence in pattern, so that it is reasonably certain that the hypothalamic region throughout mammals has a nuclear differentiation which follows a common pattern and which is expressive not only of cellular differentiation but of differences in fiber connections.   The diagram in figure 530, modified from the *Huber* and *Crosby* paper ('29), represents an attempt to summarize certain of these connections.   However, it does not show the connections with the hypophyseal region (see page 1183).   From this diagram it will be seen that stria terminalis fibers, arising from the amygdaloid regions of the hemisphere, distribute to all of the major hypothalamic areas as far caudal as the premammillary nuclei, except the nucleus ovoideus, the nucleus filiformis, the nucleus tangentialis, the nucleus supraopticus, and the periventricular gray. It will be seen also that medial forebrain fibers distribute to the lateral hypothalamic area and, either directly or through the collaterals, reach much of the medial hypothalamic area throughout its extent. The periventricular hypothalamic system arises from the dorsomedial and ventromedial hypo-

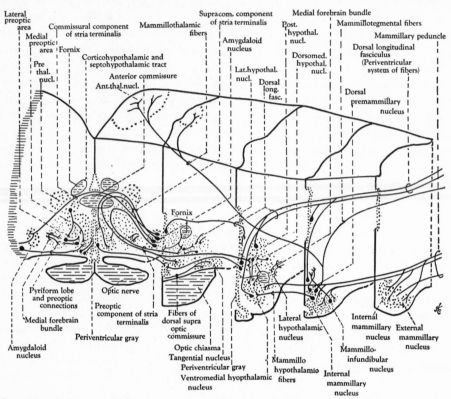

FIG. 530. A diagram which presents certain of the fiber connections of the preoptic area and the hypothalamic gray in mammals. *Huber* and *Crosby*.

thalamic nuclei, from the posterior hypothalamic nucleus, and from the diencephalic periventricular gray. This system discharges caudally to the dorsal tegmental nucleus and, after synapse there, reaches the preganglionic centers and other efferent centers of the brain stem. It serves as one of the discharge paths for the hypothalamic regions to the centers giving rise to preganglionic fibers. This hypothalamic periventricular system is a part of the dorsal longitudinal fasciculus of Schütz. Other components of it reach the tectum through its periventricular layer (*Huber* and *Crosby*, to be published; see also *Ramón y Cajal*, '11). Still other fibers distribute to the medial division of the dorsal thalamus (*Huber* and *Crosby*, '29, and others). Certain discharge paths may be by way of descending fibers to the tegmental gray and then, after synapse, by the central tegmental bundle and reticulo-spinal paths to lower centers.

Having discussed the analysis of the hypothalamic regions, as these have been studied in various mammals according to topographic methods, now certain investigations may be presented, which have their basis more particularly in the study of the architecture of the hypothalamic region as shown by the cytologic character of its constituents.   Only such fiber tracts will be mentioned here as have not been discussed previously.

Among the observers who have contributed to this field may be mentioned *Malone* ('10 and '14), *Greving* ('25 and '28), *Gagel* ('28), *Spiegel* and *Zweig* ('17), *Morgan* ('28, '28a, '30, '30a, and '30b), and *Morgan* and *Gregory* ('30).   It will be noted that several of the above mentioned investigators have studied human material; exceptions being the work of *Malone* ('14) on Macacus, lemurs, and cat, the studies of *Spiegel* and *Zweig* on rabbit, carnivores, and primates, and the work of *Morgan* on the dog.   The main subdivisions of the tuber cinereum, according to this terminology, are the substantia grisea, the supraoptic nucleus (ganglion opticum basale), the nucleus paraventricularis, and the nucleus tuberis lateralis (*Malone*, '10 and '14; *Greving*, '25 and '28, and *Morgan*, '30a).   The name substantia grisea (or zentrale Höhlengrau) is applied to the small neurons which lie along the ventricle and extend lateralward among the neurons constituting the other nuclei.   *Spiegel* and *Zweig* ('17) have subdivided this region to some extent.   They recognized particularly a nuclear mass dorsal to the chiasma in rabbits, carnivores, and primates, which they named the nucleus suprachiasmaticus (p. 1179).   The majority of the exponents of this particular method of analysis regard such subdivisions as representing merely cell condensation (*Greving*, '28; *Morgan*, '30a).   The substantia grisea gives rise to short fibers which distribute along the mesencephalic periventricular gray.   These fibers were termed the tractus substantiae griseae by *Greving* ('28), and probably are comparable to the periventricular system of fibers described by various observers.   A tractus hypothalamo-reticularis is said to arise from this general region, particularly from the nucleus reticularis hypothalami.

Capping the optic tract at its lateral border is the nucleus supraopticus (optic ganglion of *Malone*, '14, and *Morgan*, '30a).   This nucleus supraopticus is the homologue of the nucleus supraopticus diffusus in rodents (*Gurdjian*, '27) and other mammals (see p. 1180).   *Greving* ('28) applied the name of nucleus supraopticus pars dorsolateralis to the main nuclear mass, designating two smaller groups composed of the same type of neurons, but lying dorsomedial and ventromedial to the main group, as the pars dorsomedialis and the pars ventromedialis respectively.   Dorsal to the nucleus supraopticus pars dorsolateralis, at the middle level of the tuber cinereum, is a small cell group called the nucleus pallido-infundibularis by *Greving* ('22a and '28).   The fiber connections of the nucleus supraopticus, according to *Greving*, are provided in part by the tractus supraopticus inferior and the tractus supraopticus superior.   The tractus supraopticus inferior passes along the medial side of the optic tract to the central gray and to the nucleus of the tuber, but continues through this latter nucleus and enters the hypophysis to distribute to its posterior lobe, thus forming a supraoptico-hypophyseal path (*Greving*, '25 and '28).   Among other observers who have identified a hypothalamo-hypophyseal path, *Pines* ('25), *Stengel* ('26), *Nicolesco* and *Nicolesco* ('29), and *Cushing* ('30) are to be mentioned. According to *Lewy* ('24) and *Kary* ('24), impulses may pass from the hypophysis to the hypothalamus, notably the nucleus supraopticus. A second tract, the tractus supraopticus superior of *Greving* ('28), was not traced to its termination; according to this worker fronto-supraoptic fibers may be present.

Another nucleus recognized at the level of the nucleus supraopticus is the nucleus paraventricularis. This is comparable to the nucleus filiformis pars principalis of *Rioch* ('29) and others and to the nucleus hypothalamicus magnocellularis of *Röthig* ('09), *Warner* ('29), and *Papez* ('32). From this nucleus *Greving* ('28) traced a bundle of fibers which he termed the tractus paraventricularis cinereus and which he believed accompanied the tractus supraopticus-hypophyseus to the hypophysis. Recently *Scharrer* ('33) emphasized the fact, called attention to earlier by *Spiegel* and *Zweig* ('19), that the supraoptic and periventricular nuclei are phylogenetically old, being represented in forms below mammals, and stated that their customary histological appearance is not due to pathologic changes but is due to the special function of their neurons.

At these middle levels of the human tuber and extending caudalward are the two nuclei identified first by *Malone* ('14), the nucleus mamillo-infundibularis or tubero-mamillaris and the nucleus tuberis lateralis. The nucleus mamillo-infundibularis has cells of a type comparable to those of the nucleus supraopticus and the nucleus paraventricularis, and in the dog, according to *Morgan* ('30), is not easily differentiable at its cephalic end from the nucleus supraopticus. Behind the level of the chiasma the nucleus enlarges. The main mass of its cells lies at the ventrolateral periphery, but groups of neurons extend up around the fornix and certain scattered neurons of this nuclear mass reach the region dorsal and medial to this fiber bundle. The arrangement appears to be somewhat more compact in man, but in man, not only is there a well-developed lateral portion of the nucleus which cephalically reaches the ventral surface of the diencephalon, but there is also noted a medial portion found internal to the fornix column. *Morgan* ('30) studied the cytology of the neurons composing this nuclear mass and found them to have large cell bodies of an oval or rounded outline, and with cytoplasm containing "large, irregular shaped, darkly staining masses of Nissl substance." The nucleus mamillo-infundibularis, with other nuclear masses, contributes fibers to the tractus hypothalamo-reticularis of *Greving*, which may pass caudalward to the mesencephalon and perhaps to even more caudal centers.

The nucleus tuberis lateralis (*Malone*, '10 and '14; *Morgan*, '30) is composed, in the dog, of scattered neurons intermingled in part with the neurons of the nucleus mamillo-infundibularis. *Greving* ('28) described the nuclei tuberis as the chief nuclear masses of the region. The lateral nucleus is the larger and the medial nucleus is the smaller nuclear mass. Probably both of these groups are represented in the nucleus tuberis lateralis as described above for the dog. At the caudal end of the tuber, near the mammillary body, *Greving* recognized a nucleus interfornicatus in relation to the fornix column. The nucleus tuberis lateralis is said to give rise to the tractus tuberis and, toward the tegmental regions and together with the central gray and the nucleus supraopticus, is believed to have connections with the contralateral thalamus through the tractus thalamo-infundibularis. *Greving* ('25) described a fronto-tuberal path from telencephalic regions. According to *Spiegel* and *Zweig*, the nuclei tuberis, phylogenetically considered, are young structures.

The mammillary body has been described by *Greving* ('22 and '28), in accordance with the remainder of his terminology, as consisting of a nucleus magnocellularis, a nucleus parvocellularis, and a nucleus mamillaris cinereus. The scattered gray at the side of the nucleus he termed the substantia reticularis hypothalamica; another cell mass between the fornix and the optic chiasma he termed the nucleus intercalatus. The nucleus reticularis hypothalamica is believed to contribute to the tractus hypothalamicus reticularis of *Greving* ('28). The connections of the mammillary bodies have been discussed.

It is beyond the scope of the present summary to attempt any detailed account of the functions of the hypothalamic regions as these have been indicated in experimental and clinical work. There is a fair agreement that this portion of the brain is in some way related to visceral functions; that through its connections with lower, and presumably preganglionic, centers it maintains a regulatory effect over certain visceral functions. To what extent this is mediated by relations to centers supplying the organs directly and to what extent these hypothalamic functions are carried out by relations with preganglionic centers supplying the organs directly and to what extent by relations with glands of internal secretion which in turn affect the organs, is uncertain, although the suggestions that its functions are made possible through the endocrines are interesting and stimulating (see *Karplus* and *Kreidl*, '18; *Morgan*, '28 and '30a, and others). Certain of the statements with regard to the functions of the hypothalamus may be listed with reference to certain observers whose work discusses the matter in question. It would lead beyond the limits set to attempt a complete list, either as regards possible functions or as regards the students of the problem; however, it is felt that certain references listed may provide an introduction to the literature on this subject.

The following centers have been said to be present in the hypothalamus:

1. Centers affecting glands of internal secretion (*Karplus* and *Kreidl*, '18; *Morgan*, '28 and '30a; *Greving*, '28, and others). *Morgan* believed that "the nuclei of the tuber cinereum are probably secretory centers for certain internally secreting glands (especially the thyroids and suprarenals)." He thought that such centers might affect "metabolism, body temperature, blood pressure, heart rate, vasomotor function, motor activity of the intestinal canal, pupillary control, states of consciousness, and other vegetative functions." He regarded the nucleus tubero-mamillaris as being a center affecting the thyroid gland and the substantia grisea as probably related to the functional activity of the suprarenals.

2. Vasomotor centers, located somewhere near the nucleus subthalamicus (*Gerstmann*, '13; *Schrottenbach*, '16; *Karplus* and *Kreidl*, '18).

3. Temperature regulating center. This center was said by *Greving* ('28) to be located probably in the nucleus tuberis. Various observers have studied this possible function of the hypothalamus, among whom may be mentioned *Reichardt* ('13), *Walbaum* ('14), *Greving* ('28), and others.

4. Centers concerned with the regulation of the water and salt content of the body. *Aschner* ('12) and *Camus* and *Roussy* ('13; see also '20) obtained glycosuria and polyuria following injury to the hypothalamus. Polyuria followed hypothalamic injuries according to the results of *Cushing* ('12), *Bailey* and *Bremer* ('21), *Smith* ('27), and many others. *Camus, Gournay,* and *Le Grand* ('25) recognized the paraventricular nucleus as the center in the rabbit, the injury of which produced glycosuria. *Greving* ('28) regarded the nucleus supraopticus rather than the nuclei tuberis as functional in that respect. Adiposo-genital dystrophy results from an injury to the hypothalamus (*Cushing,* '12; *Smith,* '27), but may result from hypophyseal injury.

5. Centers, either hypothalamic or subthalamic or both, concerned with the regulation of smooth muscle and hence for regulating the size of the pupil of the eye (*Karplus* and *Kreidl,* '13), for contraction of the bladder (*Greving,* '22a and '28; *Karplus* and *Kreidl,* '18, and others), for acting on the intestinal muscle (*Greving,* '28, and others), and for the regulation of sweat and lachrymal glands (*Karplus* and *Kreidl,* '18; *Leschke,* '19, and others). These centers appear to lie in the neighborhood, at least, of the nucleus subthalamicus.

6. Centers concerned with the objective manifestations of various emotional states such as the so-called sham rage of the diencephalic or decorticate cat (*Bard,* '28; see also '29). These have been allocated to the more caudal and ventral part of the diencephalon.

RÉSUMÉ OF THE MAMMALIAN DIENCEPHALON

(See also résumé for each nuclear group.)

It is evident, after study of the material in this chapter on the mesencephalon and the diencephalon, as presented for the several vertebrate classes, that these segments of the brain stem constitute very highly specialized regions for Mammalia. In previous pages a summary of the data relating to the mesencephalon has been given. It is deemed consistent to emphasize here certain relationships of the mammalian diencephalon which are documented by the relatively detailed consideration presented in the foregoing pages of the diencephalon of various forms.

It is possible to demonstrate readily in mammals the four classical subdivisions of the diencephalon: the epithalamus, the dorsal thalamus, the ventral thalamus or subthalamus, and the hypothalamus.

The nervous portion of the epithalamus is constituted largely of the habenular nuclei and their associated fiber paths, the complex forming olfacto-somatic correlation centers, which vary directly in size with the relative development of the olfactory system, though influenced in development by their somatic connections. Of all of the parts of the mammalian diencephalon, the epithalamus is most directly comparable to the corresponding diencephalic region of lower vertebrates.

The dorsal thalamus may be divided arbitrarily by the internal medullary lamina into medial and lateral divisions. With the lateral division may be grouped the pretectal nucleus of lower mammals and the medial and lateral geniculates, which frequently are termed metathalamus. It must be emphasized in the beginning that this separation into medial and lateral divisions does not imply a phylogenetic separation into paleothalamus and neothalamus (*Huber* and *Crosby*, '29; *Le Gros Clark*, '32), since phylogenetically old and phylogenetically new gray masses are found in each.

Three major nuclear groups may be allocated to the medial division of the dorsal thalamus: the anterior nuclear group, the medial nuclear group, and the midline nuclear group. The anterior nuclear group, considered as a whole, is phylogenetically old, since representatives are present in reptilian and avian forms; however, its fullest nuclear differentiation is found in mammals (see also *Le Gros Clark*, '29). Considered as a whole, the anterior nuclear group constitutes an olfactory correlation center, receiving olfactory and olfacto-visceral impulses by way of the mammillo-thalamic tract and probably by way of the periventricular system. The extent to which these impulses are modified by connections with the surrounding gray is problematic, but it is postulated that such modification occurs. The discharge of the anterior nuclear group to the cortex provides an outlet by which these impulses may reach efferent paths, as well as consciousness. The discharge is to the cingulate region of the cortex.

The medial nuclear group, dominated by the classical medial thalamic nucleus, in all mammals probably is phylogenetically younger as a discrete nucleus than is the anterior nuclear group, although the anlage of the caudal end of this nucleus, which lies in relationship to the gray associated with the habenulo-peduncular tract, makes its appearance in submammalian forms. This viewpoint is not in accord with that of various observers (*Ariëns Kappers*, '20; *Hines*, '29; *Rioch*, '31), who regarded the nucleus rotundus as the forerunner of a part of the medial thalamic nucleus. The classical medial nucleus probably receives few if any direct lemnisci fibers in higher mammals, although trigeminal lemnisci fibers to it have been described by some observers in certain forms. Its most characteristic afferent connections are provided for by short internuclear fibers from the surrounding gray of the dorsal thalamus, and particularly from its ventral nucleus and midline nuclear gray, and by periventricular fibers from the hypothalamus, thus serving to correlate a variety of impulses — proprioceptive, exteroceptive, and interoceptive — the dominating impulse varying with each particular situation. After correlation in the medial nuclear group they are discharged, through the anterior thalamic radiations of the internal capsule (p. 1460), to the association centers of the frontal cortex. *Huber* and *Crosby* are in agreement with *Tilney* and *Riley* ('21) that these connections with the medial nuclear group and their projection on the frontal cortex provide the anatomic basis for feeling tone and the pleasure and pain complex, and probably, as the latter writers have supposed, constitute in part the anatomic basis for personality.

The centromedian nucleus probably is a relatively late mammalian acquisition as a specialized nucleus, which reaches its greatest development in the highest mammals. It has rich internuclear connections with the surrounding thalamic nuclei. As to whether it receives lemnisci fibers of certain types and projects impulses from them on the cortex in the highest primates, such as man, is still uncertain, although experimental evidence at present indicates that such connections are not present in lower primates or subprimates. The work of *Le Gros Clark* ('30, '32, and *Rioch*, '31) indicates that this nucleus has representation in lower mammals and may possibly be present in all mammals; however, it is much less clearly differentiated in these lower forms. It is quite probable that phylogenetically this nucleus differentiates in relation to the internal medullary lamina, as *Rioch* ('31) has suggested, but it appears to *Huber* and *Crosby* that it is highly improbable that the nucleus rotundus is its forerunner as *Rioch* ('31) appears to have believed.

The midline nuclear group, well developed in lower mammals, is poorly developed in primates and represented by mere vestiges in man. Where present it serves to relate the dorsal thalami of the two sides and lies in the course of and in interrelation with the periventricular system.

Only certain nuclei of the lateral division of the dorsal thalamus deserve special mention in this final summary. The lateral nucleus of this division is small in lower mammals and increases progressively, reaching its greatest size and differentiation in primates. It cannot be definitely stated at present as to whether it receives lemnisci fibers, since the results of studies on normal tissue as well as experimental observations are conflicting. However, it appears reasonably certain that whether or not it receives such lemnisci fibers, the progressive increase in its size and its differentiation are closely and directly correlated with the progressive increase in the association centers in the cortex, beginning with the parietal region, but in higher forms including both parietal and frontal association areas (*Huber* and *Crosby*, '29, and *Le Gros Clark*, '32). The pulvinar, which begins in part as a differentiation of the caudal end of the lateral nucleus, but which in higher forms is a composite of several nuclear groups of different phylogenetic ages, apparently bears somewhat the same relations to the visual association cortex as does the lateral nucleus to the parietal and frontal association areas.

The ventral nucleus of the thalamus, with its closely associated gray, constitutes the main nucleus of termination for ascending proprioceptive and exteroceptive impulses by way of the ascending secondary systems of the lemnisci type and the dento-rubro-thalamic path. From this nucleus such impulses are projected upon the precentral and postcentral gyri of the cerebral cortex, those reaching the precentral gyrus probably being proprioceptive in character. The localization pattern within the ventral nucleus has been plotted for various mammals, but as yet no uniform or constant pattern has been ascertained.

Associated functionally with the ventral nucleus are the medial and lateral geniculate nuclei, which project auditory and visual impulses, respectively, on the appropriate regions of the cortex. Both of these nuclei show increased differentiation in higher mammals, their size and differentiation being related in many mammals to the development of the senses of hearing and sight.   In lower mammals both a dorsal and a ventral part of the lateral geniculate nucleus are present, the ventral part being phylogenetically very old, having representation in the optic thalamic center of many lower vertebrates.   It is intimately related to the tectum, for which it serves in part as a discharge center, and with the decrease in the relative importance of the tectum, the ventral part of the lateral geniculate decreases in size.   The ventral part of the lateral geniculate nucleus is not definitely present in the highest mammals, including man.   The dorsal part of the lateral geniculate nucleus is represented in reptiles and progressively increases from lower to higher mammals (*Cairney*, '26, see bibliography for reptiles; *Huber* and *Crosby*, '29; *Herrick*, '33, see bibliography for amphibians; *Abbie*, '34).   This increased development is indicated particularly by the appearance of a complex pattern of lamination in the higher mammals.   Reference has been made to the fact that the quadrants of the retina find topographic representation within the dorsal part of the lateral geniculate.

The pretectal nucleus, which is phylogenetically old, being found in lower vertebrate forms, and the posterior nucleus, often included in the pulvinar, are recipients of lemnisci fibers and are related to the posterior commissure.   The pretectal nucleus also has connection with the lateral geniculate nucleus and with the tectum.   Both of these nuclei belong to the transition zone between the dorsal thalamus and the mesencephalon in lower mammals.   Gradually the pretectal nucleus becomes included within the superior collicular region until it is entirely mesencephalic in the highest mammals.

Before closing this summary relating to the dorsal thalamus, it should be stated that there exists considerable difference of opinion with regard to the cortico-thalamic fibers which pass to this region.   In certain of the lower mammals it is believed that all of the major nuclei receive such fibers, while in higher mammals certain observers have thought that such fibers were greatly reduced, particularly to the ventral nucleus.   Those workers who favor the presence of such cortico-thalamic fibers regard them as serving a regulatory function over the activities of the thalamus (*Head*, '20; *Stopford*, '30).   Another point worthy of comment in this connection is that emphasized by *Elliot Smith* ('10), who affirmed that the thalamo-cortical fibers proceed by the shortest possible path from their thalamic center to their cortical destination.   Thus the caudally situated lateral geniculate nucleus is connected with the caudal parts of the cortex, the medial geniculate nucleus with the temporal cortex, the ventral with the postcentral (and adjacent) cortex, and the medial nucleus with the frontal cortex.   While this pattern is most obvious in lower mammals, where the relations are less complicated, the pattern is present in higher mammals as well.

The ventral thalamus or subthalamus in reality constitutes the forward continuation of the tegmentum of the midbrain.   Into it extend the red nucleus and the substantia nigra, the functions of which have been summarized.   We limit ourselves here to the statement, that most of the major ventral thalamic nuclei, whatever else they may be, are way stations for discharge paths from the striatum by way of the ansa lenticularis, and that the specific character respectively of such discharges is determined by their nonstriatal connections.

The hypothalamus, aside from the portion allocated to internal secretion and certain commissural systems, which are largely fibers of passage, serves partly as an olfacto-visceral correlation center and partly, and perhaps more importantly, as a visceral region concerned in the regulation of certain visceral functions, probably through its discharge to preganglionic centers.

REVIEW OF THE PHYLOGENETIC DEVELOPMENT OF THE MESENCEPHALON AND DIENCEPHALON

INTRODUCTION

In the foregoing pages the mesencephalon and the diencephalon have been considered together, since both of them have developed as centers of secondary sensory systems and since they are, in part at least, in synaptic connection with the same paths. This interrelation is so great that it shows in the gradual shifting of certain of the mesencephalic connections to diencephalic centers and the coördinate development of the two areas in the course of phylogeny. Of the two the midbrain shows a greater interrelation to the medulla oblongata than does the diencephalon, so that throughout later development the former center remains as a "vital" correlation center while the diencephalon, through its projection on the telencephalon, is particularly, though not exclusively, the end station for epicritic paths. The sulcus limitans, which forms the boundary between basal and alar plates in embryonic development, is for the most part still relatively clearly distinguishable in the midbrain, and its basal portion contains there, as in the medulla oblongata, the motor nerve centers. In the diencephalon, on the contrary, primary motor centers are lacking and the basal plate has only a coördinative significance and is relatively less developed. This plate extends forward beneath the sulcus limitans, which bends in a ventral direction so that a continuation of this sulcus can be followed into the recessus preopticus, directly in front of the optic chiasm. The dorsal sensory correlative portion of the diencephalon extends forward and into relation with the portion of the brain in front of the preoptic recess, that is, with the telencephalon medium and the hemispheres. This extension of the alar plate forward and ventralward in the region of the diencephalon and telencephalon explains the relatively ventral place of entrance of the nervus terminalis, which carries sensory and preganglionic fibers. A frontal branch of the sulcus limitans, the sulcus medius thalami, in craniotes divides the diencephalon into a dorsal thalamus and a ventral thalamus. The dorsal thalamus is relatively very small in lower animals but gradually becomes larger, so that it is the largest portion of the diencephalon in higher mammalian types, including man. In this region exteroceptive and proprioceptive impulses passing to the telencephalon must synapse, and it serves, then, as a way station to the higher centers. Above the dorsal thalamus lies the epithalamic region, the major nuclear mass of which is constituted by the habenula. In front of the habenula lies the thin-walled parencephalon; behind it the pineal organs (including the anlagen for the parietal eye and the epiphysis).   Below the ventral thalamus, and usually somewhat medial to it, lies the hypothalamus.   The hypothalamic centers in general are coördination centers for olfactory and visceral and, in some cases, olfactory and gustatory impulses.   The hypophysis (or its forerunner in lower forms) and the pars optica hypothalami belong to the hypothalamus.

AMPHIOXUS

In Amphioxus it is difficult to speak of a mesencephalon, although the caudal portion of the diencephalic base probably is recognizable there through the presence of an infundibular organ.   The difficulty is increased through the lack of centers for optic and eye muscle nerves in these animals, since such centers usually are used to identify the mesencephalic areas.   It is possible that the epithelially roofed ventricular space, which lies almost directly caudal to the infundibular organ, corresponds in part at least to the midbrain ventricle in the craniotes (in Petromyzon also the tectum is partly choroidal).   The cells of Joseph, in the dorsal part of this region, are structures peculiar to this animal and of unknown function.   The diencephalon of Amphioxus cannot be separated from the prosencephalon.

CYCLOSTOMES

In cyclostomes, the craniote eyes first make their appearance as outbulgings of the ventrolateral portions of the diencephalic wall.   In Petromyzon all of the associated nervous structures of the eye are completely developed, and as a result the midbrain has the chief characteristics which are found in higher vertebrates.   The basal portion shows, in addition to very clearly developed oculomotor nuclei, numerous large, reticular cells and a nucleus interpeduncularis, which is the characteristic nucleus of termination of the fasciculus retroflexus. In the basal portion of the brain occur the terminations of the tractus octavomotorius anterior, which is accompanied, perhaps, by fibers of cerebellar origin. Most of the cells maintain a periventricular position.   Only a few have followed out along their peripherally branching dendrites and taken up a somewhat more lateral place.   Among such migratory cells are certain cells of origin for the commissura posterior.   The caudodorsal portions of the midbrain are connected with corresponding centers from the other side through the commissura transversa, the level of crossing of which is particularly noteworthy since it is in front of the position of the optic chiasm.   The supralimitary tegmental region, an end station of secondary sensory bulbar and perhaps also spinal paths, passes directly into the deep layers of the optic tectum, in which these sensory paths also terminate.   In part the tectum is ependymal.   The major portion of the optic tract appears to end in the tectum.   The lateral geniculate nucleus is small and may receive only collaterals and not stem fibers.   The impulses are correlated in the tectum and discharged to the medulla oblongata by way of the tectobulbar systems.

The habenular nuclei are very obvious in cyclostomes as a result of the excellent development of the olfactory functions in these animals. The greater size of the right habenular nucleus than of the left has not been explained in a satisfactory manner. It is stated frequently that this greater size is to be ascribed to differences in development of the epiphyseal region, for the fibers of the well-developed pineal organ pass to the right nucleus while those from the smaller parapineal body enter the left nucleus. The right nucleus receives, on the whole, more olfactory impulses from almost all portions of the telencephalon than does the left nucleus and the fasciculus retroflexus or habenulo-peduncular tract, arising from it, is larger than that from the left nucleus. The telencephalic commissural system, the commissura telencephali, crosses in relation to the habenulae.

A contrast of the dorsal and ventral divisions of the thalamus in these forms indicates that, of the two parts, the ventral portion is the larger. Still larger is the hypothalamus, which, like the ventral thalamus, serves particularly as an end station for telencephalic fibers and receives bulbar fibers. Efferent fibers of the diencephalon arise in the hypothalamus and, after correlation, impulses are discharged to visceral motor centers of the medulla oblongata by way of the mammillo-peduncular tract. The visceral correlative functions of the hypothalamus appear to rather overshadow the other types of correlation in these animals. The midbrain here appears to be concerned with somatic sensory correlations of the protopathic or vital type. The saccus vasculosus and infundibular organ are not present in these animals. The neural portion of the hypophysis, the pars intermedius, and the lateral lobe are present. The vestibule of the hypophysis is not yet formed, but persists as a nasal sulcus and stands in relation to the medial olfactory placode.

PLAGIOSTOMES

In plagiostomes the midbrain is better developed than in cyclostomes as a result of the more marked development of the optic nerve and the increase in the secondary projection paths of the medulla oblongata and the spinal cord. The tectum is fairly well differentiated and has no ependymal portion, and the basal portion of the midbrain is relatively more massive than in lower forms. In this basal region are terminal fibers of the fasciculus retroflexus and a considerable number of tracts which have their origin in the cerebellum and swing forward to the region of the hypothalamus. Secondary acoustico-lateral and trigeminal fibers terminate partly around the large-celled, half-moon-shaped nucleus situated at the entrance of the trochlear nerve, to which the name of nucleus isthmi has been applied. In still greater numbers they terminate in the medial and lateral tegmental nuclei and in the borders of the tectum.

The secondary trigeminal fibers extend forward to pretectal areas. Also secondary fibers of the acoustic nerve extend almost to the anterior part of the hypothalamus, up to the region of the optic chiasm (the tractus octavo-thalamicus et hypothalamicus). This topographic relation of the terminal fibers of the secondary acoustic and trigeminal paths with optic centers is an expression of the fact that the gravistatic and photostatic impulses are here very strongly correlated and that they are in relation with the primitive vital sensibility of the body and particularly of the head (muscle sense through the nucleus of the mesencephalic root of the trigeminal). The caudal tegmental region of one side is connected with that of the other side at the level of the chiasm through crossed fibers of the commissura transversa.

The tectum itself is better developed than the corresponding area in the cyclostomes. The optic fibers, which distribute to its upper third, pass on the light impulses to various intercalated neurons which lie near to the superficial surface of the tectum, and particularly to the ascending dendrites of more deeply situated cells (which by means of their axons distribute to the tractus tecto-bulbaris rectus et cruciatus) where these impulses correlate with those entering through the secondary acoustic and trigeminal paths. From the pretectal areas, and apparently also from the tegmental areas, fibers pass to the cerebellum by the tractus mesencephalo-cerebellaris and to the medulla oblongata by the tractus pretecto-bulbaris, which latter is strengthened by fibers of the posterior commissure. In this way the great influence of the midbrain upon body position is made effective.

The diencephalon is obviously more complicated than that in cyclostomes; the thin roof in front of the habenular nuclei (the parencephalon) passes over into a distinct velum transversum, which is regarded as the boundary between the telencephalon and the diencephalon. Pineal and parapineal organs of a glandular type are found, which show, in addition to bipolar ganglion cells, also rudiments of sense cells. The axis cylinders given off by the ganglion cells of the epiphysis pass into both habenular nuclei and into the commissura posterior and the territory immediately surrounding it. It is very interesting that the asymmetry of the habenular nuclei reverses the conditions seen in Petromyzon, since in the sharks and the rays the left nuclear mass is the larger and the left habenulo-peduncular tract is larger and more heavily medullated than the right. The connections of the habenular nuclei in the plagiostomes are in general the same as those described for the cyclostomes, and the habenular commissure is traversed here, as in the cyclostomes, by telencephalic fibers, the commissura superior telencephali. The dorsal part of the thalamus in the strict sense is differentiable from that of Petromyzon through the clearly developed nucleus geniculatus laterale, which receives collaterals from the optic tract, but still the dorsal thalamus in plagiostomes is relatively small. Evidence for the connection of the dorsal thalamus with the telencephalon is not available, and its caudal end receives only scattered bundles of the ascending trigeminal and acoustico-lateral paths from the medulla oblongata. The ventral thalamus and the hypothalamus have, in addition to descending pathways (a tractus strio-thalamicus et hypo-thalamicus), an ascending connection with the telencephalon. A tractus pallii is present which arises at the line between the hypothalamus and the midbrain and terminates in the telencephalon. The greater development of the ventral thalamus and the hypothalamus in plagiostomes is dependent upon the greater development of olfactory functions in these animals and upon the appearance of an infundibular organ in the form of a saccus vasculosus. Connections from the cerebellum and the medulla oblongata also increase its importance.   The gray substance is not so well differentiated.   In the caudal portion of the hypothalamus (in the tuber posterius) there is a poorly circumscribed ganglion sacci vasculosi, the first end station of the infundibular sense organ.   Other secondary fibers arising from the nucleus are lost partly in the dorsal thalamus and partly caudalward.   The capillaries of the saccus and of the hypophysis receive also fibers from the neighborhood of the recessus preopticus, which indicates that here a visceral center exists.   The descending fiber systems of the diencephalon arise partly from the gray of the hypothalamus (the inferior lobes) and assemble lateralward and above the nucleus interpeduncularis, passing through the base of the midbrain caudalward into the cerebellum (tractus lobocerebellaris) and especially into the medulla oblongata (tractus lobo-bulbaris), with the motor nuclei of which they are in synaptic relation.

GANOIDS AND TELEOSTS

On the whole, the brain of ganoids and teleosts shows a much sharper differentiation than does that of plagiostomes.   Its fiber bundles and centers are much more clearly circumscribed.   In the teleostean midbrain, the tectum and the tegmental regions are clearly differentiable from each other, and the tori semicirculares bulge out as separate eminences into the optic ventricle.   Somewhat farther caudalward the nuclei isthmi form likewise distinct structures.   The differentiation of the various midbrain regions varies considerably with the peripheral development of the sensory nerves, for in certain groups the vestibular and lateral-line sense organs are particularly highly developed (Mormyrus and siluroids), and in others the eyes have especially great functional significance (Gadidae and Pleuronectidae).   The octavo-mesencephalic fibers distribute to the tori semicirculares and the pretectal regions bordering on them frontally, but the trigeminal and spino-mesencephalic paths not only contribute fibers to the tegmental regions of the midbrain and to the tori semicirculares, but also terminate to a considerable extent, in teleosts, in the tectum itself, so that the midbrain roof remains a correlative center for optic and non-optic exteroceptive impulses which have to do, for the most part, with determining the relations of the body to surrounding objects.   In agreement with this is the experimentally determined influence of the midbrain on the position of the body, and the strong development of the connections both of the tectum and the tegmentum with the cerebellum by the tractus tecto-cerebellaris and the tractus mesencephalo-cerebellaris posterior, which unite in certain of these animals and in others enter the cerebellum separately.   The latter tract affects considerably the development of the valvula cerebelli.   The great influence which the vital correlation centers of the tectum and the tegmentum exert over the movements of these animals leads to the special development of the efferent tecto-bulbar paths, the ventral component of which is especially large.   This tract affects the position of the eye muscle nuclei, for the oculomotor nucleus extends in part, and the abducens nucleus as a whole, into a very marked ventral position in these forms.   To the medulla oblongata pass also pretectal or metathalamo-bulbar fibers which, arising from the more anterior tectal or pretectal areas, extend caudalward with the fasciculus longitudinalis medialis. The nucleus isthmi appears to play a great rôle as a correlation center between the photostatic and gravistatic centers, for it receives fibers of the acoustico-lateral lemniscus and perhaps also those from the ascending trigeminal path and is intimately interrelated with the tectum. Numerous commissural systems connect the two halves of the mid-brain. The commissura transversa, which interconnects the tori semicirculares and is related also to the nucleus isthmi, is present in cyclostomes and plagio-stomes. The commissura minor, recognized up to the present only in bony fishes, probably arises and ends in the tectum (*Ariëns Kappers*), and associated with this commissure is the commissura horizontalis (known only in these forms) which connects the nucleus rotundus (corpus glomerulosum) with the pretectal area and perhaps with the anterior tectal areas. The crossing of these com-missural systems occurs in the ventral part of the diencephalon.

The epithalamus in these animals is differentiable grossly from that in cyclo-stomes and plagiostomes through the lack of asymmetry in the habenular nuclei, although such asymmetry occasionally appears in certain bony fishes, in some the right, and in others the left nucleus being the larger. A commissura superior telencephali is present here, as in certain other forms, in association with other components of the habenular commissure. The parapineal organ has disap-peared. The pineal gland contains a rudiment of sense cells and bipolar gan-glion cells, the neuraxes of which terminate in the tectum and in the nucleus of origin of the medial longitudinal fasciculus.

The dorsal thalamus, more or less clearly separated through the sulcus medius from the ventral thalamus, is, on the whole, not so large. It is in relation with the habenular nuclei and sends fibers to the tectum. The lateral geniculate nucleus is often very well developed, occasionally it is even laminated. It receives fibers, and particularly collaterals, from the optic nerve and is connected with the tectum. The corpus glomerulosum pars anterior, lying in its vicinity, is intimately related to the corpus glomerulosum pars rotunda of Brickner.

The ventral thalamus and the hypothalamus form a prominent coördination region between the descending paths from telencephalic centers and ascending bul-bar systems, which include gustatory impulses from the superior secondary gustatory nucleus. In this hypothalamic region also terminate the neuraxes from the sense cells of the saccus vasculosus, the capillaries of which receive fibers from the nucleus magnocellularis preopticus (tractus thalamo-sacculosus et hypophyseos). (The glandular cells of the hypophysis also receive such fibers.) These connections indicate that preoptic and hypothalamic areas have a regulatory effect over the autonomic centers. This is a matter of particular interest because in the preoptic region end sensory fibers of the nervus terminalis, which are accompanied occasionally by preganglionic fibers to the capillaries of the frontal part of the head. The hypothalamus in this animal shows various commissural connections. Efferent paths of the hypothalamus send coördinat-ing impulses to the motor nuclei of the medulla oblongata and particularly to the nuclei of the trigeminal and facial nerves and the reticular elements lying in their vicinity by means of which the impulses are transferred to the spinal cord centers.

The amphibians, especially the tailless amphibians, in certain respects evidence the beginning of that higher development which comes to expression in reptiles and lower mammals. However, in many respects they still have a primitive structure. The base of the midbrain is characterized by an entirely primitive arrangement of its cells. In addition to the reticular elements which characterize this region in all mammals, an interpeduncular nucleus, which is relatively long and extends behind the midbrain in tailed amphibians, can be seen. In the caudal part of the tegmentum, at the level of exit of the trochlear roots, is the nucleus isthmi. It also is relatively sharply circumscribed and falls into two portions, a small-celled and a large-celled part. These are connected with secondary paths of the acoustic or acoustico-lateral and trigeminal systems as in fishes. The tectal connections of this nucleus are well developed and, in addition, fibers of the commissura transversa arise and end here. The tori semicirculares (or corpora posteriora) show their relation to the deep layers of the tectum, but exhibit a higher stage of development in that they are fused in the midline and only frontally are separated by a space. Through the growth of these centers the aqueduct of Sylvius is formed, which goes over into the ventricle of the optic tectum farther forward. The tori semicirculares are entirely covered over by the optic tectum. The connections with the secondary acoustico-lateral or acoustic and trigeminal fibers and the spino-mesencephalic fibers are comparable to those in fishes. A part of these fibers ascends into the optic tectum itself as in plagiostomes, but the portion so distributing is much larger in the tailed than in the tailless amphibians. It is evident from this that the tectum receives, even in blind urodeles, a considerable number of afferent fibers. In general it can be stated that the midbrain is to be regarded not only as an optic center but also as a correlation center for various vital impulses which play a rôle in primary muscle sense (the nucleus of the mesencephalic root of the trigeminal functions in this way). Also a tecto-cerebellar path is present, but from the corpus posterius. The optic tectum itself shows a more primitive structure in the urodeles than in the anura. It receives, in addition to the ascending secondary sensory fibers of proprioceptive and exteroceptive character, the optic nerves and fibers from the lateral geniculate nucleus. In general, the efferent paths are the same as those in fishes, but the connections with the cerebellum, if present at all, are small. The ventral tecto-bulbar paths are not nearly so large as in bony fishes, and this system does not exert so great an influence on the position of the eye muscle nuclei. Apparently fibers from the tectum to the retina are present. The commissura posterior is large but shows nothing of particular significance in its connections.

The diencephalon presents certain marked differences from that of higher fishes and these differences are indicated by both increases and decreases in differentiation. The parencephalon is small. The choroid plexus of the third ventricle passes over into the velum transversum.   The symmetrically developed epithalamus is not very large and the greater number of fibers crossing in the habenular commissure belong to the commissura superior telencephali.   The pineal organ is glandular in type but shows rudiments of sense cells and bipolar ganglion cells, the neuraxes of which pass into the posterior commissure.   The dorsal thalamus is greatly increased, and medial to the lateral geniculate nucleus is a mass of cells which may be regarded as representing the beginning of another differentiated portion of the dorsal thalamus.   This receives fibers from lower centers, perhaps ascending secondary trigeminal fibers.   Its gray sends fibers to the dorsolateral wall of the telencephalon.   This represents the earliest recognized projection from the dorsal thalamus to the telencephalon and the diencephalic centers concerned in it are sometimes spoken of as the neothalamus.

The dorsal thalamus shows an advance, then, from the condition in fishes, but the ventral thalamus is smaller and the hypothalamus is not nearly so well developed.   The secondary and tertiary olfactory paths from the telencephalon are large, as is to be expected from the strong development of olfaction in these animals.   Fibers carrying such impulses (the medial forebrain bundle and other bundles from the medial hemisphere wall and the stria terminalis) distribute in part to the ventral thalamus, in part to the preoptic region, and in still greater number to the hypothalamic areas.   The somatic portions of the telencephalon send fibers to the entopeduncular nucleus and to other regions of the ventral thalamus.   Certain of the somatic impulses pass still farther caudalward to the tegmental portions of the midbrain.   The very limited development of the hypothalamus, which scarcely shows lateral lobes, does not depend upon a limited development of the sense of smell, but is due to the failure of a saccus vasculosus to develop as well as to the reduction of other connections as a result of the limited development of gustatory impulses which in fishes are carried to the hypothalamic regions, and the small size of the cerebellum with the consequent decrease in size of the superior cerebellar peduncle.   In correspondence with this atrophy of the hypothalamus there are only a limited number of hypothalamobulbar connections, which are much less well developed in amphibians than in fishes.   This decrease in size and in number of paths in the amphibian as compared to the fish suggests that the hypothalamic areas as developed in the fishes owe their particular significance to the conditions of life in aquatic animals.   In studying the spinal cord of amphibians it was evident that the aboral reflexes pass out in large part from cranial nerves, and particularly from the trigeminus, so that skin sensibility in these animals has begun to prevail over the chemical sensibility of olfactory and gustatory types.

REPTILES

The midbrain and diencephalon of reptiles show many structures which suggest the differentiation of these regions in lower mammals.   The great reticular cells at the base of the midbrain, which are present in all vertebrates, appear in the reptile group, and organize themselves into a nuclear mass which may be compared with the large-celled portion of the nucleus ruber.   In the neighborhood of this nuclear mass the larger portion of the fibers of the superior cerebellar peduncle break up.   A relatively large cell group, a representative of the entopeduncular gray of reptiles, since it serves as a terminal station for a well-developed component of the ventral peduncle of the lateral forebrain bundle, may be regarded as a forerunner of the substantia nigra.   Dorsolateral to this nucleus, at the level of the decussation of the trochlear nerve, a nucleus isthmi is present, which in certain members of this class may reach a very great (crocodile) or even an enormous size (chameleon), and in others remains rather small.   The connections of the nucleus isthmi are the same as in lower animals.   Its relation to the lateral lemniscus is very evident in these forms, as are also its isthmo-tectal and tecto-isthmal fibers, the connections with the tectum being more marked than those with the tori semicirculares or inferior colliculi.   In certain reptiles, such as the alligator, the tori semicirculares occupy a position under the tectum and extending out into the ventricle.   They increase in other reptiles, and in the snake and lizard become so large that they form an eminence on the surface so that a condition approaching that of the corpora quadrigemina may be seen in these forms.   This greater development of the tori semicirculares in reptiles is associated with the more marked development of the cochlear system, which system is epicritic in its character.   In addition to fibers of the lateral lemniscus, the connections of the tori semicirculares are much the same as those described for teleosts, for they receive secondary fibers from the spinal nucleus of the trigeminal.   Certain fascicles from these secondary paths of the trigeminal and from the spinal mesencephalic fibers, carrying impulses from the exteroceptive centers of the spinal cord, also pass to the tectum and to the pretectal regions.

A comparison of corresponding regions in the amphibian and reptilian diencephalon shows an even more marked differentiation in the diencephalon than in the midbrain in the latter forms, but this development does not affect the epithalamic region to any great extent.   The epithalamic regions are symmetrical and have the usual connections with the telencephalon and the tectum.   A commissura superior telencephali is present.   A peculiarity of this region is the presence in certain reptiles (Sphenodon and certain lizards) of a parietal eye. In all reptiles, with the exception of crocodiles, a glandular epiphysis is present. The dorsal thalamus shows a great development of nuclei which are in intimate connection with telencephalic centers.   Prominent among these nuclei are the nucleus rotundus, the nucleus dorsolateralis anterior, the nucleus medialis anterior, the nucleus medialis posterior, and other adjoining areas.   Fibers from these centers are connected by way of the dorsal peduncle of the lateral forebrain bundle with the striatal and, probably indirectly, with the pallial regions of the hemisphere.   The impulses are ascending and probably, to some extent, descending.   To these nuclei are carried impulses from trigeminal and spinal centers, largely through connections with the tectal areas, perhaps in part by direct terminations of the secondary ascending tracts, but the present evidence for this latter connection is not wholly satisfactory.

The old connection of the telencephalon with the ventral thalamus and the hypothalamus is represented in the ventral peduncle of the lateral forebrain bundle of reptiles.   It is relatively well developed in reptiles and distributes to preoptic, and, to some extent, to hypothalamic areas.   It reaches the nucleus entopeduncularis, which is one of the reptilian representatives of the ventral thalamus of higher forms.   The medial forebrain bundle and various components of the fornix system connect the medial hemisphere walls with the hypothalamus.   A supraoptic commissure system is well developed in reptiles, where it is essentially a connection between the midbrain roof and the tori semicirculares of one side, and the ventral thalamus and midbrain areas of the other side.   It carries also crossed fibers for the medial longitudinal fasciculus and connects the nucleus isthmi of one side with its fellow of the opposite side and perhaps with contralateral tectal areas.

The hypothalamus is not so well developed in reptiles as in certain other forms but it does show a better nuclear differentiation than that found in amphibians.   The saccus vasculosus is lacking.   Tertiary gustatory paths to the hypothalamic regions have not been demonstrated.   The efferent connections for the hypothalamus and ventral thalamus are not well understood as yet.   Thalamo-bulbar and hypothalamo-peduncular tracts have been described.   A more detailed survey of the specific homologies of the various reptilian nuclear groups of the thalamus is to be found on page 1058.

BIRDS

The avian mesencephalon and diencephalon show a marked resemblance to the corresponding regions in certain reptilian forms, and comparisons between avian and mammalian diencephalons can be established with certainty only by tracing the structures back through reptiles.   Under the influence of the optic tract, and perhaps due to the pressure of the highly developed striatal region of the telencephalon, the dorsal part of the midbrain has been pushed lateralward and ventralward so that it lies in most birds lateral to the diencephalon, rather than caudal and dorsal to it as is the case in most other animals.   This shifting in position of the midbrain roof has led to a corresponding difference in the nuclei and tracts of the diencephalic regions.   Since the degree of shifting varies in different avian forms, there is a corresponding difference in the positions of homologous nuclei.   The tectum itself, while not different in principle from that in reptiles, is still more highly developed, showing an even greater differentiation into layers, although it retains the same strata.   In relation with it, as is the case with other vertebrate forms, near the floor of the ventricle are to be found the cells of the mesencephalic root of the trigeminal, and it receives fibers from the optic tract and ascending fibers from the spinal nucleus of the trigeminal, and from the spinal cord.   Obviously it is a correlation center in which optic impulses are related to other impulses of exteroceptive and proprioceptive character.   Its efferent paths are the same as in other forms, namely, tecto-bulbar, tecto-oculomotor, and possibly tecto-spinal fibers in certain birds. The dorsal tecto-bulbar system is particularly well developed in most avian forms.   The posterior commissure is highly developed and is concerned primarily in interconnecting the tectal and pretectal areas.   It carries also crossed fibers from the medial longitudinal fasciculus. The gray mass, comparable to the reptilian torus semicircularis, is entirely buried beneath the tectum, and forms an eminence on the under side of the ventricle. It is usually termed the nucleus mesencephalicus lateralis pars dorsalis and is connected with the nucleus isthmi and receives terminal fibers of the lateral lemniscus. The nucleus isthmi, as was seen in the preceding description, is very highly developed in avian forms and has certain components which have never been recognized in other animals. Thus it has a more dorsally situated portion which receives fibers from the optic tract and is connected with the oculomotor nuclei. This is the nucleus isthmi as it was first described. The other part of the nucleus isthmi, again divisible into several subsidiary groups, is a dependency of the lateral lemniscus system. It is this portion which is comparable to the nucleus isthmi as described in reptiles and amphibians. An interpeduncular nucleus and a nucleus ruber are both demonstrable in the tegmental portions of the midbrain in birds.

The pretectal and subpretectal areas are extremely well developed in avian forms; better developed probably than elsewhere in vertebrates. Conspicuous among these nuclear masses are the nucleus spiriformis, with its two portions, a lateral or ventrolateral and a medial or dorsomedial portion. The nucleus pretectalis is dorsal to and in front of the nucleus spiriformis pars lateralis, is probably comparable, together with the nucleus subpretectalis, to the pretectal complex of reptiles, although the latter nucleus occupies a characteristic position. These nuclei taken together serve as way stations to and from the tectum, but the more dorsally situated pretectal nucleus also has important connections with the posterior commissure, with the optic tract, and with the tectum, and probably has fibers from the telencephalon. The functions of these nuclei, other than as intermediaries between diencephalic and tectal centers, are somewhat uncertain. The spiriform nucleus is known to receive fibers from striatal areas, and it is possible that through its connection with lower centers it may serve as a way station for efferent impulses of the striatum. The lateral part of the spiriform nucleus has connections with the telencephalon through the ventral peduncle of the lateral forebrain bundle (strio-mesencephalic tract) and crossed connections in the posterior commissure. The medial division also has posterior commissure connections. To what extent the spiriform nucleus is connected with the nucleus of the medial longitudinal fasciculus is uncertain. The tegmentum certainly receives many fibers from the lateral forebrain bundle and from the occipito-mesencephalic tract. It is altogether probable that it, together with the entopeduncular groups of the thalamus, provides a pathway for the discharge of the striatum and so furnishes a means by which this latter center may exert its influence over body movements. The tectum and the tegmental centers, too, are in intimate connection with the cerebellum, and this applies not only to the nucleus ruber but also to the surrounding regions. In general, one might say that the midbrain in these animals consists of a wide variety of correlation centers concerned with gravistatic and photostatic functions as these affect vital head and body movements, and that it exerts an influence, modified undoubtedly through its connections with the telencephalon, on the motor centers which are indirectly concerned with these movements.

The epithalamic portions of the diencephalon in most birds are relatively poorly developed, particularly the habenular nuclei. This is to be expected in forms in which, for the most part, there is a relatively poor development of the olfactory system. In general the connections of epithalamic and hypothalamic centers are comparable to those found in such reptiles as the alligator, but relatively reduced in number.

All the major nuclear masses demonstrable in the reptilian dorsal thalamus are demonstrable in birds, but in addition there is an increase in the number of such nuclear masses and in the fiber systems associated with them. The positions of the specific nuclei also differ from those of homologous nuclei in reptiles, largely because of the ventral shifting of the tectal regions and the corresponding changes in position of the large tecto-thalamic bundles. It is possible, then, to compare these nuclear groups only by understanding their fiber connections. Many of the nuclei of the dorsal thalamus are related to telencephalic centers. They are the recipients of the dorsal peduncle of the lateral forebrain bundle. Among such nuclear masses may be mentioned the nucleus dorsolateralis anterior, the nucleus rotundus, the nucleus ovoidalis, and the nucleus intercalatus. These are only a few of the more conspicuous of the nuclear elements, the pattern being complex. Many of these nuclei discharge impulses forward to the striatum, and its development goes hand in hand with the development of that segment of the telencephalon. Some of the connections probably pass in the other direction and are strio-thalamic in character. Optic, tactile, temperature, and pain impulses reach the dorsal thalamus by way of the tectum and of the tecto-thalamic bundles, which are numerous and highly developed in avian forms. *Wallenberg* was able to trace ascending trigeminal fibers to the nucleus rotundus and the nucleus intercalatus, but such fibers are relatively few in number and it is probable that the dorsal thalamus in avian forms is largely dependent on tectal connections for its increase.

The ventral thalamus is represented by several nuclear groups in these forms, among which may be mentioned the nucleus ventralis anterior and the various entopeduncular groups. These entopeduncular groups are in synaptic relation with the ventral peduncle of the lateral forebrain bundle and they represent differentiated elements of a subthalamic area such as is to be found in mammalian forms. Through their connections with the tegmentum of the midbrain and perhaps even with lower centers, the influence of the striatum on associated movements is made possible. The supraoptic decussations are well developed, particularly that portion of the dorsal supraoptic bundle which connects the striatal areas of the two sides.

The hypothalamic regions, while showing considerable nuclear differentiation, are relatively small. They are in connection with the stria terminalis and the medial forebrain systems and with the fornix system. In other words they are dependencies of the olfactory portions of the telencephalon. Evidence for visual connections to these areas from lower centers is not as yet forthcoming, although experimental evidence indicates that such connections must be present.

In mammals the tectal portions of the midbrain are formed by the superior and inferior colliculi, of which the superior colliculi are comparable to the optic tectum of lower forms. The inferior colliculi are auditory reflex centers, and they are functionally, if not precisely morphologically, comparable to the tori semicirculares of lower forms. In lower mammals the superior colliculi serve for visual and other types of reflexes. In higher mammals the optic fibers reaching them are probably more particularly, although not exclusively, for light reflexes. Secondary optic impulses through the lateral geniculate nucleus place them also in the visual reflex path. It should be emphasized again that the action of light over the path for an increase in size of the pupils is an inhibitory action. Both the inferior and superior colliculi are interconnected and thus impulses passing through one of these centers exert an influence on impulses passing simultaneously through the other center. The descending paths of the superior colliculi have been enumerated elsewhere. It may be said here that they are typical of those described for lower forms. The superior colliculus is particularly connected with the diencephalic centers, the pulvinar, and the lateral geniculate nucleus. The inferior colliculus is similarly related with the medial geniculate nucleus. The nucleus of the mesencephalic root of the trigeminal has a position near the ventral wall in the roof of the midbrain comparable to its position in lower forms. The oculomotor and trochlear nuclei maintain their positions near the floor of the ventricle in relation to the medial longitudinal fasciculus, which is well developed in mammals, including man. In the tegmental portions of the midbrain (aside from certain commissural systems, among which may be mentioned the dorsal and ventral tegmental decussations, the decussation of the superior cerebellar peduncle, and the commissure of Forel) the most conspicuous element is the red nucleus. This forms a prominent mass in all mammalian brains. It is usually differentiable into two nuclear portions, of which the large-celled is the more primitive. In lower mammals it is confined to the midbrain region, but in primates it extends forward to the caudal end of the ventral thalamus. This, together with the commissural system and various other nuclear masses, such as the nucleus interstitialis and the nucleus of Darkschewitsch, lies within the tegmental portion of the midbrain. Here also is the interpeduncular nucleus with its highly developed habenulo-peduncular tract and its efferent connections with the dorsal tegmental nucleus through the pedunculo-tegmental system. The peduncular part of the midbrain increases progressively from higher to lower mammals with the increase in cortico-pontine, cortico-bulbar, and cortico-spinal paths, since these form its most ventral portion, the basis pedunculi. Their development goes hand in hand with the development of the projection and association areas of the hemisphere. The substantia nigra also increases in size and nuclear differentiation as higher mammals are reached.

The diencephalon in mammals has the customary epithalamic, thalamic, and hypothalamic divisions. Compared with lower forms the epithalamic portions are not highly developed, but they vary to some extent in the various mammals, depending largely, although not entirely, on the development of the olfactory system. The connections of the habenular nuclei are typical of those found in lower forms and need no further discussion. The pineal gland, as an organ of internal secretion, is present in all mammals except in some edentates and Sirenia (*Ariëns Kappers*). The posterior commissure, which lies between the midbrain and the diencephalon, is relatively poorly developed in certain lower mammals.

The dorsal thalamus reaches the peak of its development in the mammals and is progressively better and better developed in passing from lower mammals to higher mammals and ultimately to man. As the essential way station to the cerebral cortex, its development is a relatively accurate measure of the development of cortical areas. It falls into medial and lateral divisions, the medial containing anterior, medial, and midline groups, with the midline group poorly developed in higher mammals and almost absent in man. The anterior group is primarily an olfacto-visceral and olfacto-somatic correlation center, receiving olfactory visceral impulses from the hypothalamus and certain somatic impulses from the surrounding nuclei. Its discharge is probably to the gyrus cinguli of the cortex. The medial nuclear division (and presumably the midline group as well) is primarily concerned with interdiencephalic correlations, while the connection of certain members of the medial group with ascending secondary systems (lemnisci) has been granted by some observers and denied by others. Certainly such lemnisci fibers do not constitute major connections. On the whole the medial division of the dorsal thalamus is concerned in the correlation of exteroceptive and proprioceptive impulses reaching it by way of the ventral division of the dorsal thalamus, with olfacto-visceral impulses from the hypothalamic areas, by way of the periventricular system, and olfacto-somatic impulses from the habenula by way of the habenulo-thalamic tract. Such correlated material is discharged either to the ventral thalamus or subthalamus for thalamic reflexes, or more particularly to the frontal regions of the cortex or to the striatum. This connection of the medial nuclear group with the frontal cortex provides the anatomic basis for feeling tone and the pleasure pain complex. The centromedian nucleus is essentially a correlation nucleus interconnected on the one hand with the medial and on the other hand with the lateral division of the thalamus. It has been said to receive terminal fibers of the trigeminal lemniscus, connections from other of the lemnisci systems have been carried to it by certain observers, and it has been said to be connected with the cortex. Recent experimental work has failed to confirm the connections of this nucleus with the cortex and with the lemnisci systems. Whether such connections are present or absent in man remains to be proved.

The lateral division of the thalamus contains within it those centers which serve primarily as way stations to the cerebral cortex. Thus it has the various parts of the ventral thalamic nuclei which receive the major portion of the lemnisci fibers (medial, spinal, trigeminal) and the rubro-thalamic tract, and it is connected with the postcentral and, probably, with the precentral cortical gyri.   It provides the pathways into consciousness for pain, temperature, tactile, proprioceptive, and vestibular impulses.   Within the lateral division is situated also the pulvinar, which receives fibers from the occipital region of the cortex and possibly sends fibers to this region.   Here also lie the posterior nucleus and pretectal areas in lower mammals, which are usually grouped with the pulvinar complex of higher forms.   The lateral thalamic nucleus forms a conspicuous portion of the lateral division of the dorsal thalamus.   It is said to receive some few lemnisci fibers.   In man it is said to be connected with the cortex from the frontal pole to almost the occipital region (in lower mammals largely with the parietal region) and it seems rather certain that its development is dependent not only on its connection with projection but also on its connection with association areas of the hemisphere.   Essentially belonging to the lateral division of the dorsal thalamus are the two metathalamic nuclei, the medial and lateral geniculates.   The medial geniculate is a way station for auditory impulses passing to Heschl's convolution in the auditory cortical center.   The dorsal part of the lateral geniculate is a similar way station for visual impulses to the calcarine or visual cortex area.   It likewise is an important center for visual reflexes which find their outlet either through the superior colliculus or by connections of the nucleus with the ventral thalamus.

Of the dorsal thalamus, then, it may be said that it is essentially on the afferent side of the arc and that it has three major regions of discharge : to the cortex, to the striatum, and to the ventral thalamus.   A division of the dorsal thalamus into neothalamic and paleothalamic portions cannot be based on this separation into medial and lateral divisions, for both medial and lateral divisions have centers which have developed late in phylogenetic history, and both have centers which phylogenetically are very old (*Huber* and *Crosby*, '29 ; *Le Gros Clark*, '32).

The ventral or subthalamic regions in mammals, including man, are highly developed and clinically of great importance.   Functionally they belong with the tegmental and peduncular regions of the midbrain, as represented in the red nucleus and the substantia nigra.   These ventral thalamic centers (the entopeduncular nucleus, the zona incerta, and the nucleus subthalamicus), together with the red nucleus and the substantia nigra, afford the main path of discharge for the striatum, thus providing the way in which its action on associated movements may take effect.   The various theories regarding the functions of these nuclei have been discussed in detail.   To the ventral thalamus belong also the ventral portions of the lateral and medial geniculates.

The hypothalamus retains its primitive connection to the olfactory areas of the hemisphere and it receives connections from lower centers, perhaps by a series of chain neurons which bring forward visceral impulses of various types, including gustatory impulses.   It is, then, essentially an olfactory visceral correlation center.   Within it are also various efferent centers connecting with the preganglionic areas of the brain stem (through periventricular fibers and the dorsal longitudinal fasciculus).   Experimental work has shown that injuries or stimulation by various experimental procedures produce changes in blood pressure, pupillary changes, disturbances of heat regulation, and various impulses dependent upon the sympathetic system.   In some fashion the region is interlocked with the action of certain endocrine glands, but much remains to be done before a clear localization combining both the functional and structural patterns can be made.

BIBLIOGRAPHY

Mesencephalon and Diencephalon

For the literature on Amphioxus see Chapter II.

CYCLOSTOMES

AHLBORN, F. 1883. Untersuchungen über das Gehirn der Petromyzonten. Zeitschr. f. wissensch. Zool., Bd. 39, S. 191.

ARIËNS KAPPERS, C. U. 1920–21. Vergleichende Anatomie des Nervensystems. (German edition of present text.) E. F. Bohn, Haarlem.

CONEL, J. LeR. 1929. The development of the brain of Bdellostoma stouti. I. External growth changes. J. Comp. Neurol., vol. 47, p. 343.

DAMMERMAN, K. W. 1910. Der Saccus vasculosus der Fische, ein Tiefeorgan. Zeitschr. f. wissensch. Zool., Bd. 96, S. 654.

DENDY, A. 1906. The pineal sense organs and associated structures in Geotria and Sphenodon. Rep. Brit. A. Adv. Sc., York, p. 604.

——. 1907. On the parietal sense-organs and associated structures in the New Zealand lamprey (Geotria australis). Quart. J. Micr. Sc., vol. 51, p. 1.

EDINGER, L. 1906. Ueber das Gehirn von Myxine glutinosa. Abhandl. d. kön. preuss. Akad. d. Wissensch., Berlin.

HERRICK, C. J. 1910. The morphology of the forebrain in Amphibia and Reptilia. J. Comp. Neurol., vol. 20, p. 413.

——. 1921. A sketch of the origin of the cerebral hemispheres. J. Comp. Neurol., vol. 32, p. 429.

——. 1922. Functional factors in the morphology of the forebrain of fishes. Libro en honor de S. Ramón y Cajal, Madrid, vol. 1, p. 143.

——. 1924. Neurological foundations of animal behavior. H. Holt and Co., New York.

HERRICK, C. J., AND OBENCHAIN, J. B. 1913. Notes on the anatomy of a cyclostome brain: Ichthyomyzon concolor. J. Comp. Neurol., vol. 23, p. 635.

HOLM, J. F. 1901. The finer anatomy of the nervous system of Myxine glutinosa. Morphol. Jahrb., Bd. 29, S. 364.

HOLMGREN, N. 1919. Zur Anatomie des Gehirns von Myxine. Kungl. Svenska Vetenskaps akademiens Handlingar, Bd. 60, no. 7.

HUBER, G. CARL, AND CROSBY, E. C. 1934. The influences of afferent paths on the cytoarchitectonic structure of the submammalian optic tectum. Psychiatr. en Neurol. Bladen, Nos. 3 and 4, p. 459.

JANSEN, J. 1930. The brain of Myxine glutinosa. J. Comp. Neurol., vol. 49, p. 359.

JOHNSTON, J. B. 1902. The brain of Petromyzon. J. Comp. Neurol., vol. 12, p. 1.

——. 1910. A comment upon recent contributions on the brain of petromyzonts. Anat. Anz., Bd. 37, S. 153 u. 182.

——. 1912. The telencephalon in cyclostomes. J. Comp. Neurol., vol. 22, p. 341.

KOLZOFF. 1902. Entwicklungsgeschichte des Kopfes von Petromyzon planeri. Bull. Soc. impér. d. Nat. de Moscou, Nouvelle Serie, vol. 15.

RETZIUS, G. 1891. Zur Kenntnis des centralen Nervensystems von Myxine glutinosa. Biol. Untersuch., N. F., Bd. 2, S. 47.
——. 1893. Das Gehirn von Myxine glutinosa. Biol. Untersuch., N. F., Bd. 5, S. 55.
RÖTHIG, P., AND ARIËNS KAPPERS, C. U. 1914. Further contributions to our knowledge of the brain of Myxine glutinosa. Kön. Akad. v. Wetensch. te Amsterdam, vol. 17, p. 2.
SANDERS, A. 1894. Researches on the nervous system of Myxine glutinosa. Williams and Norgate, London.
SCHILLING, K. 1907. Ueber das Gehirn von Petromyzon fluviatilis. Abhandl. d. Senckenb. nat. Gesellsch., Frankfurt am Main, Bd. 30.
SCOTT, W. B. 1887. Notes on the development of Petromyzon. J. Morphol., vol. 1, p. 253.
STENDELL, W. 1914. Die Hypophysis cerebri. In A. Oppel's Lehrbuch der vergleichende mikroskopischen Anatomie der Wirbeltiere, Bd. 8. G. Fischer, Jena, 1896-1914.
STERZI, G. 1905. Sulla regio parietalis dei ciclostomi, dei selacii e degli olocefali. Anat. Anz., Bd. 27, S. 346 u. 412.
——. 1909. Il sistema nervoso centrale dei vertebrati. Vol. 1, Ciclostomi. A. Draghi, Padova.
STUDNIČKA, F. K. 1900. Untersuchungen über den Bau des Ependyms der nervösen Centralorgane. Anat. Hefte, Bd. 15, S. 301.
——. 1905. Die Parietalorgane. In A. Oppel's Lehrbuch der vergleichende mikroskopischen Anatomie der Wirbeltiere, Bd. 5. G. Fischer, Jena, 1896-1914.
TRETJAKOFF, D. 1909. Nervus mesencephalicus bei Ammocoetes. Anat. Anz., Bd. 34, S. 151.
——. 1909. Das Nervensystem von Ammocoetes. II. Gehirn. Arch. f. mikr. Anat., Bd. 74, S. 636.
——. 1915. Die Parietalorgane von Petromyzon fluviatilis. Zeitschr. f. wissensch. Zool., Bd. 113, S. 1.
WOERDEMAN, M. W. 1914. Vergleichende Ontogenie der Hypophysis. Arch. f. mikr. Anat., Bd. 86, S. 198.

PLAGIOSTOMES

ARIËNS KAPPERS. 1920-21. Vergleichende Anatomie des Nervensystems. (German edition of present text.) E. F. Bohn, Haarlem.
——. 1906. The structure of the teleostean and selachian brain. J. Comp. Neurol., vol. 16, p. 1.
ARIËNS KAPPERS, AND THEUNISSEN, W. F. 1908. Die Phylogenese des Rhinencephalons, des Corpus striatum und der Vorderhirn-Kommissuren. Folia Neurobiol., Bd. 1, S. 173.
BURCKHARDT, R. 1894. Die Homologieen des Zwischenhirndaches und ihre Bedeutung für die Morphologie des Hirns bei niederen Vertebraten. Anat. Anz., Bd. 9, S. 152.
——. 1895. Der Bauplan des Wirbelthiergehirns. Morphol. Arb. (Schwalbe), Bd. 4, S. 131.
——. 1907. Das Zentral-Nervensystem der Selachier als Grundelage für eine Phylogenie des Vertebratenhirns. I. Teil: Einleitung und Scymnus lichia. Nov. Act. Acad. Leopoldino-Carolinae nat. curios., Bd. 73.
——. 1911. Idem, II. Teil: Die übrigen Palaeoselachier. Nov. Act. Acad. Leopoldino-Carolinae nat. curios., Bd. 94, S. 1.
CATOIS, E. M. 1901. Recherches sur l'histologie et l'anatomie microscopique de l'encephale chez les poissons. Bull. scient. de la France et de la Belgique, vol. 36, p. 1.

CATTIE, J. T. 1882. Recherches sur la glande pineale (Epiphysis cerebri) des Plagiostomes, des Ganoides et des Téléostéens. Arch. de biol., vol. 3, p. 101.

DAMMERMAN, K. W. 1910. Der Saccus vasculosus der Fische, ein Tiefeorgan. Zeitschr. f. wissensch. Zool., Bd. 96, S. 654.

EDINGER, L. 1888. Untersuchungen über die vergleichende Anatomie des Gehirnes. I. Das Vorderhirn. Abhandl. d. Senckenb. nat. Gesellsch., Frankfurt am Main, Bd. 15.

——. 1893. Idem. Teil II. Das Zwischenhirn der Selachier und Amphibien. Abhandl. d. Senckenb. nat. Gesellsch., Frankfurt am Main, Bd. 18.

——. 1908. Vorlesungen über den Bau der nervösen Centralorgane des Menschen und der Thiere. 7te Aufl., F. C. W. Vogel, Leipzig.

GENTES, L. 1908. Développement comparé de la glande infundibulaire et des plexus choroïdes dorsaux chez la Torpille. Compt. rend. Soc. de biol., vol. 64, p. 687.

HERRICK, C. J. 1921. A sketch of the origin of the cerebral hemispheres. J. Comp. Neurol., vol. 32, p. 429.

——. 1922. Functional factors in the morphology of the forebrain of fishes. Libro en honor de S. Ramón y Cajal, Madrid, vol. 1, p. 143.

——. 1924. Neurological foundations of animal behavior. H. Holt and Co., New York.

HOLMGREN, N. 1918. Zum Bau der Epiphyse von Squalus acanthias. Arkiv för Zoologi, Bd. 11, no. 23, S. 1.

HOUSER, G. L. 1901. The neurones and supporting elements in the brain of a selachian. J. Comp. Neurol., vol. 11, p. 65.

HUBER, G. CARL, AND CROSBY, E. C. 1934. The influences of afferent paths on the cytoarchitectonic structure of the submammalian optic tectum. Psychiatr. en Neurol. Bladen, Nos. 3 and 4, p. 459.

JOHNSTON, J. B. 1905. The radix mesencephalica trigemini. The ganglion isthmi. Anat. Anz., Bd. 27, S. 364.

——. 1906. The nervous system of vertebrates. P. Blakiston's Son and Co., Philadelphia.

——. 1911. The telencephalon of selachians. J. Comp. Neurol., vol. 21, p. 1.

STERZI, G. 1905. Sulla regio parietalis dei ciclostomi, dei selachii e degli olocefali. Anat. Anz., Bd. 27, S. 346 u. S. 412.

——. 1909. Il sistema nervoso centrale dei vertebrati. Vol. 2, Pesci, Libro I. Selaci. A. Draghi, Padova.

STUDNIČKA, F. K. 1900. Untersuchungen über den Bau der Ependyms der nervösen Centralorgane. Anat. Hefte, Bd. 15, S. 301.

——. 1905. Die Parietalorgane. In A. Oppel's Lehrbuch der vergleichende mikroskopischen Anatomie der Wirbeltiere, Bd. 5. G. Fischer, Jena, 1896–1914.

TILNEY, F., AND WARREN, W. F. 1919. The morphology and evolutional significance of the pineal body. Am. Anat. Mem., No. 9, p. 5.

WALLENBERG, A. 1907. Beiträge zur Kenntnis des Gehirns der Teleostier und Selachier. Anat. Anz., Bd. 31, S. 369.

WOERDEMAN, M. W. 1914. Vergleichende Ontogenie der Hypophysis. Arch. f. mikr. Anat., Bd. 86, S. 198.

GANOIDS AND TELEOSTS

AREY, L. B. 1916. The function of the efferent fibers of the optic nerve of fishes. J. Comp. Neurol., vol. 26, p. 213.

ARIËNS KAPPERS, C. U. 1906. The structure of the teleostean and selachian brain. J. Comp. Neurol., vol. 16, p. 1.

——. 1907. Untersuchungen über das Gehirn der Knochenganoiden, Amia calva und Lepidosteus osseus. Abhandl. d. Senckenb. nat. Gesellsch., Frankfurt am Main. Bd. 30, S. 449.

Ariëns Kappers, C. U. 1920–21. Vergleichende Anatomie des Nervensystems. (German edition of present text.) E. F. Bohn, Haarlem.

Barnard, J. W. 1935. A phylogenetic study of the visceral afferent areas associated with the facial, glossopharyngeal, and vagus nerves and their fiber connections. The efferent facial nucleus. Dissertation.

Bellonci, J. 1888. Ueber die centrale Endigung des Nervus opticus bei den Vertebraten. Zeitschr. f. wissensch. Zool., Bd. 47, S. 1.

Boeke, J. 1901. Die Bedeutung des Infundibulums in der Entwickelung der Knochenfische. Anat. Anz., Bd. 20, S. 17.

Brickner, R. M. 1929. A description and interpretation of certain parts of the teleostean midbrain and thalamus. J. Comp. Neurol., vol. 47, p. 225.

Brookover, C. 1910. The olfactory nerve, the nervus terminalis and the pre-optic sympathetic system in Amia calva. J. Comp. Neurol., vol. 20, p. 49.

Burr, H. S. 1928. The central nervous system of Orthagoriscus mola. J. Comp. Neurol., vol. 45, p. 33.

Catois, E. M. 1901. Recherches sur l'histologie et l'anatomie microscopique de l'encephale chez les poissons. Bull. scient. de la France et de la Belgique, vol. 36, p. 1.

Cattie, J. T. 1882. Recherches sur la glande pineale (Epiphysis cerebri) des Plagiostomes, des Ganoides et des Téléostéens. Arch. de biol., vol. 3, p. 101.

Charlton, H. H. 1928. A gland-like ependymal structure in the brain. Kon. Akad. v. Wetensch. te Amsterdam, Proc. sect. sc., vol. 31, p. 1.

——. 1932. Comparative studies on the nucleus preopticus pars magnocellularis and the nucleus lateralis tuberis in fishes. J. Comp. Neurol., vol. 54, p. 237.

——. 1933. The optic tectum and the related fiber tracts in blind fishes. A. Troglichthys rosae and Typhlichthys eigenmanni. J. Comp. Neurol., vol. 57, p. 285.

Craigie, E. H., and Brickner, R. M. 1927. Structural parallelism in the midbrain and 'tweenbrain of teleosts and of birds. Kon. Akad. v. Wetensch. te Amsterdam, Proc. sect. sc., vol. 30, p. 695.

Dammerman, K. W. 1910. Der Saccus vasculosus der Fische, ein Tieforgan. Zeitschr. f. wissensch. Zool., Bd. 96, S. 654.

Edinger, L. 1908. Vorlesungen über den Bau der nervösen Centralorgane des Menschen und der Thiere. 7te Aufl., F. C. W. Vogel, Leipzig.

Elliot Smith, G. 1908. The cerebral cortex in Lepidosiren, with comparative notes on the interpretation of certain features of the forebrain in other vertebrates. Anat. Anz., Bd. 33.

Franz, V. 1911. Das Mormyridenhirn. Zool. Jahrb., Abt. f. Anat., Bd. 32, S. 465.

——. 1912. Beiträge zur Kenntnis des Mittelhirns und Zwischenhirns der Knochenfische. Folia neuro-biol., Bd. 6, S. 402.

von Fritsch, G. 1878. Untersuchungen über den feineren Bau des Fischgehirns. Mit besonderer Berüchtsichtigung der Homologien bei anderen Wirbeltierklassen. Berlin.

——. 1912. Ueber das Parietalorgan der Fische als funktionierendes Organ. Sitzungsb. d. Gesellsch. f. Morphol. u. Physiol., München, Bd. 27.

Fusari, R. 1887. Untersuchungen über die feinere Anatomie des Gehirnes der Teleostier. Internat. Monatschr. f. Anat. u. Physiol., Bd. 4, S. 275.

Gage, S. P. 1893. The brain of Diemyctylus viridescens from larval to adult life and comparisons with the brain of Amia and Petromyzon. The Wilder Quarter-Century Book, Ithaca, New York, p. 259.

van Gehuchten, A. 1894. Contribution à l'étude du système nerveux des téléostéens. La Cellule, vol. 10, p. 255.

Gentes, L. 1907. Lobe nerveux de l'hypophyse et du sac vasculaire. Compt. rend. Soc. de biol., vol. 62, p. 499.

GENTES, L. 1907. La glande infundibulaire des Vertébrés. Compt. rend. Soc. de biol., vol. 63, p. 122.

GIERSE. 1904. Das Gehirn und die Kopfnerven von Cyclothone acclinidens. Inaugural Dissertation. Leipzig.

GOLDSTEIN, K. 1905. Untersuchungen über das Vorderhirn und Zwischenhirn einiger Knochenfische (nebst einigen Beiträgen über Mittelhirn und Kleinhirn derselben.) Arch. f. mikr. Anat., Bd. 66, S. 135.

HALLER, B. 1898. Von Bau des Wirbelthiergehirns. I. Theil. Salmo und Scyllium. Morphol. Jahrb., Bd. 26, S. 345.

HERRICK, C. J. 1905. The central gustatory paths in the brains of bony fishes. J. Comp. Neurol., vol. 15, p. 375.

——. 1921. A sketch of the origin of the cerebral hemispheres. J. Comp. Neurol., vol. 32, p. 429.

——. 1922. Functional factors in the morphology of the forebrain of fishes. Libro en honor de S. Ramón y Cajal, Madrid, vol. 1, p. 143.

HERRICK, C. L. 1891. The commissures and histology of the teleost's brain. Anat. Anz., Bd. 6, S. 676.

HOCKE HOOGENBOOM, K. J. 1929. Das Gehirn von Polyodon folium Lacép. Jahrb. f. Morphol. u. mikr. Anat.; Abt. 2, Zeitschr. f. mikr.-anat. Forschung, Bd. 18, S. 311.

HOLMGREN, N. 1918. Zur Frage der Epiphysen-Innervation bei Teleostiern. Folia neuro-biol., Bd. 11, S. 1.

——. 1918a. Zur Kenntnis des Nervus terminalis bei Teleostiern. Folia neuro-biol., Bd. 11, S. 16.

——. 1918b. Ueber die Epiphysennerven von Clupea sprattus und Harengus. Arkiv för Zoologi, Bd. 11, no. 25, S. 1.

——. 1920. Zur Anatomie und Histologie des Vorder- und Zwischenhirns der Knochenfische. Acta Zool., Bd. 1, S. 137.

——. 1922. Points of view concerning forebrain morphology in lower vertebrates. J. Comp. Neurol., vol. 34, p. 391.

HOLMGREN, N., AND VAN DER HORST, C. J. 1925. Contribution to the morphology of the brain of Ceratodus. Acta Zool., Bd. 6, S. 59.

VAN DER HORST, C. J. 1917. The forebrain of Synbranchidae. Kon. Akad. v. Wetensch. te Amsterdam, Proc. sect. sc., vol. 20, p. 217.

HUBER, G. CARL, AND CROSBY, E. C. 1934. The influences of afferent paths on the cytoarchitectonic structure of the submammalian optic tectum. Psychiatr. en Neurol. Bladen, Nos. 3 and 4, p. 459.

JANSEN, JAN. 1929. A note on the optic tract in teleosts. Proc. Kon. Akad. Wetensch. te Amsterdam, vol. 32, p. 1104.

JEENER, R. 1930. Evolution des centres diencéphaliques périventriculaires des Téléostomes. Kon. Akad. v. Wetensch. te Amsterdam, Proc. sect. sc., vol. 33, no. 7, p. 755.

JOHNSTON, J. B. 1901. The brain of Acipenser. A contribution to the morphology of the vertebrate brain. Zool. Jahrb., Abt. f. Anat., Bd. 15, S. 59.

——. 1911. The telencephalon of ganoids and teleosts. J. Comp. Neurol., vol. 21, p. 489.

——. 1912. On the teleostean forebrain. Anat. Rec., vol. 6, p. 423.

KINGSBURY, B. F. 1897. The encephalic evaginations in ganoids. J. Comp. Neurol., vol. 7, p. 37.

KRAUSE, K. 1898. Experimentelle Untersuchungen über die Sehbahnen des Goldkarpfens (Cyprinus auratus). Arch. f. mikr. Anat., Bd. 51, S. 820.

KUDO, K. 1923. Contribution to the knowledge of the brain of bony fishes. Kon. Akad. v. Wetensch. te Amsterdam, Proc. sect. sc., vol. 26, p. 65.

DE LANGE, S. J.   1910.   The descending tracts of the corpora quadrigemina.   Folia neuro-biol., Bd. 3, S. 633.

LUNDBORG, H.   1894.   Die Entwicklung der Hypophysis und des Saccus vasculosus bei Knochenfischen und Amphibien.   Zool. Jahrb., Abt. f. Anat., Bd. 7, S. 667.

MALME, G.   1891.   Studien über das Gehirn von Knochenfische.   Kungl. Svenska Vet. Akad. Handlingar, Bd. 17, Afd. 4, no. 3.

MAYSER, P.   1881.   Vergleichend anatomische Studien über das Gehirn der Knochenfische mit besonderer Berücksichtigung der Cyprinoiden.   Zeitschr. f. wissensch. Zool., Bd. 36, S. 259.

MEADER, R. G.   1934.   The optic system of the teleost, Holocentrus.   I.   The primary optic pathways and the corpus geniculatum complex.   J. Comp. Neurol., vol. 60.

MIRTO, D.   1895.   Sulla fina anatomia del tetto ottico dei pesci teleostei e sull'origine reale del nervo ottico.   Riv. sper. di freniat., vol. 21, p. 136.

NEUMAYER, L.   1895.   Histologische Untersuchungen über den feineren Bau des Centralnervensystems von Esox lucius mit Berücksichtigung vergleichend-anatomischer und physiologischer Verhältnisse.   Arch. f. mikr. Anat., Bd. 44, S. 345.

PEARSON, A. A.   1933.   The acustico-lateral centers and the cerebellum, with connections, of fishes.   Dissertation.

RADL, E.   1915.   Zur Morphologie der Sehzentren der Knochenfische.   Morphol. Jahrb., Bd. 49, S. 509.

RAMÓN, P.   1890.   Investigaciones de histologia comparada en los centros de la visión de diferentes Vertebrados.   Zaragoza.

RAMÓN Y CAJAL, S.   1899.   Die Struktur des Chiasma opticum.   J. A. Barth, Leipzig.

——.   1909–11.   Histologie du système nerveux de l'homme et des vertébrés.   A. Maloine, Paris.

RAMSAY, E. E.   1901.   The optic lobes and optic tracts of Amblyopsis spelaeus De Kay.   J. Comp. Neurol., vol. 11, p. 40.

REISINGER, L.   1915.   Die zentrale Lokalisation des Gleichgewichtssinnes der Fische.   Biol. Centralbl., Bd. 35, S. 472.

RÖTHIG, P.   1911.   Beiträge zum Studium des Zentralnervensystems der Wirbeltiere.   3. Zur Phylogenese des Hypothalamus.   Folia neuro-biol., Bd. 5, no. 9, S. 913.

SHANKLIN, W. M.   1935.   On diencephalic and mesencephalic nuclei and fibre paths in the brains of three deep sea fish.   Phil. Tr. Roy. Soc. Lon., ser. B, no. 516, vol. 224, pp. 361–419.

SHELDON, R. E.   1912.   The olfactory tracts and centers in teleosts.   J. Comp. Neurol., vol. 22, p. 177.

STENDELL, W.   1914.   Die Faseranatomie des Mormyridengehirns.   Abhandl. d. Senckenb. nat. Gesellsch., Frankfurt am Main, Bd. 36.

STIEDA, L.   1868.   Studien über das zentrale Nervensystem der Knochenfische.   Zeitschr. f. wissensch. Zool., Bd. 18.

——.   1873.   Ueber die Deutung der einzelnen Teile des Fischgehirns.   Zeitschr. f. wissensch. Zool., Bd. 23.

STUDNIČKA, F. K.   1905.   Die Parietalorgane.   In A. Oppel's Lehrbuch der vergleichende mikroskopischen Anatomie der Wirbeltiere, Bd. 5.   G. Fischer, Jena, 1896–1914.

TILNEY, F., AND WARREN, W. F.   1919.   The morphology and evolutional significance of the pineal body.   Am. Anat. Mem., No. 9, p. 5.

TROJAN, E.   1906.   Ein Beitrag zur Morphologie des Tiefseefischgehirnes.   Mem. Mus. Comp. Zool., Harvard, vol. 30, p. 215.

WALLENBERG, A.   1907.   Beiträge zur Kenntnis des Gehirns der Teleostier und Selachier.   Anat. Anz., Bd. 31, S. 369.

——.   1913.   Beitrag zur Kenntnis der Sehbahnen der Knochenfische.   Le Névraxe, vol. 14, p. 251.

AMPHIBIANS

ARIËNS KAPPERS, C. U. 1920–21. Vergleichende Anatomie des Nervensystems. (German edition of present text.) E. F. Bohn, Haarlem.

ARIËNS KAPPERS, C. U., AND HAMMER, E. 1918. Das Zentralnervensystem des Ochsenfrosches (Rana catesbyana). Psychiat. en neurol. Bl., Amsterdam, vol. 22, p. 368.

BELLONCI, J. 1888. Ueber die centrale Endigung des Nervus opticus bei den Vertebraten. Zeitschr. f. wissensch. Zool., Bd. 47, S. 1.

BENEDETTI, E. 1927. Il telencefalo dei tritoni. Atti R. Accad. Naz. Lincei Rend. Cl. Sci. Fis. Mat. e Nat., vol. 5, p. 52.

———. 1928. Monit. Zool. ital., vol. 39, p. 52.

BENZON, A. 1926. Die markhaltigen Faserzüge im Vorderhirn von Cryptobranchus japonicus. Zeits. mikr.-anat. Forschung, Bd. 5, S. 285.

BERGQUIST, HARRY. 1932. Zur Morphologie des Zwischenhirns bei neideren Wirbeltiere. Acta Zool., Bd. 13, S. 57.

BOCHENEK, A. 1902. Neue Beiträge zum Bau der Hypophysis cerebri bei Amphibien. Bull. internat. Acad. d. sc. de Cracovie, p. 91.

BRAEM, F. 1898. Epiphysis und Hypophysis von Rana. Zeitschr. f. wissensch. Zool., Bd. 63, S. 433.

CAMERON, J. 1902-3. On the origin of the pineal body as an amesial structure, deduced from the study of its development in Amphibia. Proc. Roy. Soc., Edinburgh, vol. 24, p. 572.

DENDY, A., AND NICHOLLS, G. E. 1910. On the occurrence of a mesocoelic recess in the human brain and its relation to the sub-commissural organ of lower vertebrates; with special reference to the distribution of Reissner's fibre in the vertebrate series and its possible function. Proc. Roy. Soc., London, Ser. B, vol. 82, p. 515.

GAUPP, E. 1889. Anatomie des Frosches. Braunschweig.

VAN GEHUCHTEN, A. 1897. Le ganglion basal et la commissura habenulaire dans l'encephale de la Salamandre. Bull. Acad. roy. de Belgique, vol. 24.

DE GRAAF, H. W. 1886. Zur Anatomie und Entwicklung der Epiphyse bei Amphibien und Reptilien. Zool. Anz., Bd. 9, S. 191.

HERRICK, C. J. 1910. The morphology of the forebrain in Amphibia and Reptilia. J. Comp. Neurol., vol. 20, p. 413.

———. 1914. The medulla oblongata of larval Amblystoma. J. Comp. Neurol., vol. 24, p. 343.

———. 1917. The internal structure of the midbrain and thalamus of Necturus. J. Comp. Neurol., vol. 28, p. 215.

———. 1925. The amphibian forebrain. III. The optic tracts and centers of Amblystoma and the frog. J. Comp. Neurol., vol. 39, p. 433.

———. 1930. The medulla oblongata of Necturus. J. Comp. Neurol., vol. 50, p. 1.

———. 1933. The amphibian forebrain. VI. Necturus. J. Comp. Neur., vol. 58, p. 1.

———. 1933a. The amphibian forebrain. VII. The architectural plan of the brain. J. Comp. Neur., vol. 58, p. 481.

———. 1933b. VIII. Cerebral hemispheres and pallial primordia. J. Comp. Neur., vol. 58, p. 737.

———. 1934. IX. Neuropil and other interstitial nervous tissue. J. Comp. Neur., vol. 59, p. 93.

HOLMGREN, N. 1918. Zur Kenntnis der Parietalorgane von Rana temporaria. Arkiv för Zoologi, Bd. 11, no. 24, S. 1.

HUBER, G. CARL, AND CROSBY, E. C. 1933. The reptilian optic tectum. J. Comp. Neurol., vol. 57, p. 57.

HUBER, G. CARL, AND CROSBY, E. C. 1933a. A phylogenetic consideration of the optic tectum. Proc. Nat. Acad. Sc., vol. 19, p. 15.

——. 1934. The influences of afferent paths on the cytoarchitectonic structure of the submammalian optic tectum. Psychiat. en Neurol. Bl., Nos. 3 and 4, p. 459.

JOHNSTON, J. B. 1909. The morphology of the forebrain vesicle in vertebrates. J. Comp. Neurol., vol. 19, p. 457.

——. 1923. See bibliography for mammals.

KINGSBURY, B. F. 1895. On the brain of Necturus maculatus. J. Comp. Neurol., vol. 5, p. 139.

KÖPPEN, M. 1888. Zur Anatomie des Froschgehirns. Arch. f. Anat. u. Physiol., Anat. Abt., S. 1.

KREHT, H. 1930. Ueber die Faserzüge im Zentralnervensystem von Salamander maculosa. Zeits. mikr.-anat. Forschung, Bd. 23, S. 239.

——. 1931. Ueber die Faserzüge im Zentralnervensystem von Proteus anguineus. Ibid., Bd. 25, p. 376.

LARSELL, O. 1923. The cerebellum of the frog. J. Comp. Neurol., vol. 36, p. 104.

——. 1931. The cerebellum of Triturus torosus. J. Comp. Neurol., vol. 53, p. 1.

McKIBBEN, P. S. 1911. The nervus terminalis in urodele Amphibia. J. Comp. Neurol., vol. 21, p. 261.

MYERS, B. D. 1901. The chiasma of the toad (Bufo lentiginosus) and of some other vertebrates. Zeitschr. f. Morphol. u. Anthropol., Bd. 3, S. 183.

RAMÓN, P. 1896. l'Encephale des amphibiens. Bibliog. anat., vol. 4.

RÖTHIG, P. 1911. Beiträge zum Studium des Zentralnervensystems der Wirbeltiere. 1. Ein Faserzug am Boden des Recessus praeopticus (Tractus praeopticus) bei den Amphibien. Arch. f. mikr. Anat., Bd. 77, S. 48.

——. 1923. Idem. 8. Ueber das Zwischenhirn der Amphibien. Arch. f. mikr. Anat., Bd. 98, Heft 3 u. 4.

——. 1924. Idem. 9. Ueber die Faserzüge im Zwischenhirn der Urodelen. Jahrb. f. Morphol. u. mikr. Anat.; Abt. 2, Zeitschr. f. mikr.-anat. Forschung, Bd. 1, Heft 1.

——. 1926. Idem. 10. Ueber die Faserzüge im Vorder- und Zwischenhirn der Anuren. Jahrb. f. Morphol. u. mikr. Anat.; Abt. 2, Zeitschr. f. mikr.-anat. Forschung, Bd. 5, S. 23.

——. 1927. Idem. 11. Ueber die Faserzüge im Mittelhirn, Kleinhirn und der Medulla oblongata der Urodelen und Anuren. Jahrb. f. Morphol. u. mikr. Anat.; Abt. 2, Zeitschr. f. mikr.-anat. Forschung, Bd. 10, S. 381.

——. 1931. Einige Erfahrungen mit technischen Methoden zur Untersuchung kleinerer Gehirne. Jahrb. f. Morphol. u. mikr. Anat.; Abt. 2, Zeitschr. f. mikr.-anat. Forschung, Bd. 24, S. 399.

RUBASCHKIN, W. 1903. Zur Morphologie des Gehirns der Amphibien. Arch. f. mikr. Anat., Bd. 62, S. 207.

SNESSAREW, P. 1908. Ueber die Nervenfasern des Rhinencephalons beim Frosche. J. f. Psychol. u. Neurol., Bd. 13, S. 97.

STENDELL, W. 1914. Die Faseranatomie des Mormyridengehirns. Abhandl. d. Senckenb. nat. Gesellsch., Frankfurt am Main, Bd. 36.

STIEDA, L. 1875. Ueber den Bau des centralen Nervensystems der Amphibien und Reptilien. W. Engelmann, Leipzig.

STUDNIČKA, F. K. 1905. Die Parietalorgane. In A. Oppel's Lehrbuch der vergleichende mikroskopischen Anatomie des Wirbeltiere, Bd. 5. G. Fischer, Jena, 1896–1914.

TILNEY, F., AND WARREN, W. F. 1919. The morphology and evolutional significance of the pineal body. Am. Anat. Mem., No. 9, p. 5.

WLASSAK, R. 1893. Die optischen Leitungsbahnen des Frosches. Arch. f. Anat. u. Physiol., Physiol. Abt., Suppl.-Bd. S. 1.

REPTILES

ARIËNS KAPPERS, C. U.   1908.   Weitere Mitteilungen über die Phylogenese des Corpus striatum und des Thalamus.   Anat. Anz., Bd. 33, S. 321.
——.   1920–21.   Vergleichende Anatomie des Nervensystems.   (German edition of present text.)   E. F. Bohn, Haarlem.
——.   1929.   The evolution of the nervous system.   E. F. Bohn, Haarlem.
ARIËNS KAPPERS, C. U., AND THEUNISSEN, W. F.   1908.   Die Phylogenese des Rhinencephalons, des Corpus striatum und der Vorderhirnkommissuren.   Folia neurobiol., Bd. 1, S. 173.
BECCARI, N.   1923.   Il centro tegmentale o interstiziale ed altre formazioni poco note nel mesencefalo e nel diencefalo di un rettile.   Arch. ital. di anat. e di embriol., vol. 20, p. 560.
BELLONCI, J.   1888.   Ueber die centrale Endigung des Nervus opticus bei den Vertebraten.   Zeitschr. f. wissensch. Zool., Bd. 47, S. 1.
BÉRANECK, E.   1892.   Sur le nerf pariétal et la morphologie du troisième œil des vertébrés.   Anat. Anz., Bd. 7, S. 674.
BURCKHARDT, R.   1894.   Die Homologien des Zwischenhirndaches bei Reptilien und Vögeln.   Anat. Anz., Bd. 9, S. 320.
CAIRNEY, J.   1926.   A general survey of the forebrain of Sphenodon punctatum.   J. Comp. Neurol., vol. 42, p. 255.
CHRISTENSEN, K.   1927.   The morphology of the brain of Sphenodon.   Univ. of Iowa Studies in Nat. Hist., vol. 12, no. 1.   Iowa City, Iowa.
CROSBY, E. C.   1917.   The forebrain of Alligator mississippiensis.   J. Comp. Neurol., vol. 27, p. 325.
DENDY, A.   1899.   Outlines of the development of Tuatara, Sphenodon (Hatteria) punctatus.   Quart. J. Micr. Sc., vol. 42, p. 1.
——.   1910.   On the structure, development, and morphological interpretation of the pineal organs and adjacent parts of the brain in the tuatara (Sphenodon punctatus).   Proc. Roy. Soc., London, Ser. B, vol. 82, p. 629.
DURWARD, A.   1930.   The cell masses in the forebrain of Sphenodon punctatum.   J. Anat., vol. 65, p. 8.
EDINGER, L.   1888.   Untersuchungen über die vergleichende Anatomie des Gehirns.   I. Das Vorderhirn.   Abhandl. d. Senckenb. nat. Gesellsch., Frankfurt am Main, Bd. 15.
——.   1896.   Neue Studien über das Vorderhirn der Reptilien.   Abhandl. d. Senckenb. nat. Gesellsch., Frankfurt am Main, Bd. 19.
——.   1899.   Untersuchungen über die vergleichende Anatomie des Gehirns.   IV. Studien über das Zwischenhirn der Reptilien.   Abhandl. d. Senckenb. nat. Gesellsch., Frankfurt am Main, Bd. 20, S. 1.
——.   1908.   Vorlesungen über den Bau der nervösen Centralorgane des Menschen und der Thiere.   7te Aufl., Bd. 2.   F. C. W. Vogel, Leipzig.
ELLIOT SMITH, G.   1903.   On the morphology of the cerebral commissures in the Vertebrata with special reference to an aberrant commissure found in the forebrain of certain reptiles.   Tr. Linnean Soc., London, Zool. Ser., vol. 8, pt. 12.
——.   1910.   Some problems relating to the evolution of the brain.   Arris and Gale Lectures.   Lancet, vol. 1, pp. 1, 147, and 219.
FREDERIKSE, A.   1931.   The lizard's brain.   An investigation on the histological structure of the brain of Lacerta vivipara.   C. C. Callenbach, Baarn (Holland).
FREY, E.   1933.   Ueber die basale Opticuswurzel und die caudalen Verbindungen der Commissura transversa Gudden der Reptilien.   Kon. Akad. v. Wetensch. te Amsterdam, Proc. sect. sc., vol. 36, p. 217.

GAGE, S. P. 1895. Comparative morphology of the brain of the soft shelled turtle (Amyda mutica) and the English sparrow (Passer domesticus). Proc. Am. Micr. Soc., vol. 17, p. 185.

GISI, M. J. 1907. Das Gehirn von Hatteria punctata. Lippert and Co., Naumburg.

DE GRAAF, H. W. 1886. Zur Anatomie und Entwicklung der Epiphyse bei Amphibien und Reptilien. Zool. Anz., Bd. 9, S. 191.

GROSS, J. 1903. Ueber die Sehnervenkreuzung bei den Reptilien. Zool. Jahrb., Abt. f. Anat., Bd. 17, S. 763. Reviewed in Biol. Centralbl., Bd. 10, S. 869, 1903.

HALLER, B. 1900. Vom Bau des Wirbeltiergehirns. Morphol. Jahrb., Bd. 28, S. 347.

HERRICK, C. J. 1910. The morphology of the forebrain in Amphibia and Reptilia. J. Comp. Neurol., vol. 20, p. 413.

HERRICK, C. L. 1890. Notes upon the brain of the alligator. J. Cincinnati Soc. Nat. Hist., vol. 12, p. 129.

——. 1891. Contributions to the comparative morphology of the central nervous system. II. Topography and histology of the brain of certain reptiles. J. Comp. Neurol., vol. 1, p. 14.

——. 1893. Idem. III. Topography and histology of the brain of certain reptiles. J. Comp. Neurol., vol. 3, p. 77 and p. 119.

HINES, M. 1923. The development of the telencephalon in Sphenodon punctatum. J. Comp. Neurol., vol. 35, p. 483.

——. 1929. See bibliography for mammals.

VAN HOEVELL, J. J. L. D. 1911. Remarks on the reticular cells of the oblongata in different vertebrates. Kon. Akad. v. Wetensch. te Amsterdam, Proc. sect. sc., vol. 13, pt. 2, p. 1047.

HOFFMANN, C. K. 1890. Reptilia-Epiphyse und Parietalauge. In H. G. Bronn's Klassen und Ordnungen des Thier-Reichs, Bd. 6, Abt. 3. C. F. Winter, Leipzig u. Heidelberg.

HUBER, G. CARL, AND CROSBY, E. C. 1926. On thalamic and tectal nuclei and fiber paths in the brain of the American Alligator. J. Comp. Neurol., vol. 40, p. 97.

——. 1933. The reptilian optic tectum. J. Comp. Neurol., vol. 57, p. 57.

——. 1933a. A phylogenetic consideration of the optic tectum. Proc. Nat. Acad. Sc., vol. 19, p. 15.

——. 1934. The influences of afferent paths on the cytoarchitectonic structure of the submammalian optic tectum. Psychiat. en Neurol. Bl., Nos. 3 and 4, p. 459.

HUMPHREY, O. D. 1894. On the brain of the snapping turtle, Chelydra serpentina. J. Comp. Neurol., vol. 4, p. 73.

INGVAR, S. 1923. On thalamic evolution. Acta Med. Scandinavica, vol. 59, p. 696.

JOUSTRA, N. 1918. Over de homologie van het ganglion isthmi. Psychiat. en neurol. Bl., Amsterdam, vol. 22, p. 361.

KLINCKOWSTRÖM, A. 1893. Le premier développement de l'œil pinéal, l'epiphyse et le nerf pariétal chez Iguana tuberculata. Anat. Anz., Bd. 8, S. 289.

KÖPPEN, M. 1890. Beiträge zur vergleichenden Anatomie des Centralnervensystems der Wirbeltiere. Zur Anatomie des Eidechsengehirns. Morphol. Arb. (Schwalbe), Bd. 1, Heft. 3.

DE LANGE, S. J. 1910. The descending tracts of the corpora quadrigemina. Folia neuro-biol., Bd. 3, S. 633.

——. 1911. Das Vorderhirn der Reptilien. Folia neuro-biol., Bd. 5, S. 548.

——. 1912. The red nucleus in reptiles. Kon. Akad. v. Wetensch. te Amsterdam, Proc. sect. sc., vol. 14, pt. 2, p. 1082.

——. 1913. Das Zwischenhirn und das Mittelhirn der Reptilien. Folia neuro-biol., Bd. 7, S. 67.

LEYDIG, F. 1891. Das Parietalorgan der Amphibien und Reptilien. Abhandl. Senckenb. nat. Gesellsch., Frankfurt am Main, Bd. 16.

LEYDIG, F.   1896.   Zur Kenntnis der Zirbel und Parietalorgane.   **Abhandl.** Senckenb. nat. Gesellsch., Frankfurt am Main, Bd. 19.

MEYER, A.   1892.   Ueber das Vorderhirn einiger Reptilien.   **Zeitschr. f. wissensch.** Zool., Bd. 55, S. 63.

NOWIKOFF, M.   1907.   Ueber das Parietalauge von Lacerta agilis und Anguis fragilis. Biol. Centralbl., Bd. 27, S. 364 u. 405.

PALMGREN, A.   1921.   Embryological and morphological studies on the midbrain and cerebellum of vertebrates.   Acta Zool., Bd. 2, S. 1.

RABL-RÜCKHARD, H.   1878.   Das Centralnervensystem des Alligators.   Zeitschr. f. wissensch. Zool., Bd. 30, S. 336.

——.   1894.   Einiges über das Gehirn der Riesenschlange.   Zeitschr. f. wissensch. Zool., Bd. 58, S. 694.

RAMÓN, P.   1891.   El encéfalo de los reptiles.   Barcelona.

——.   1896.   Estructura del encéfalo del Cameleón.   Rev. trimest. micrograf., vol. 1, p. 46.

——.   1897.   El fasciculo longitudinal posterior en los reptiles.   Rev. trimest. micrograf., vol. 2, p. 153.

RAMÓN Y CAJAL, S.   1904.   Textura del sistema nervioso del hombre y de los vertebrados.   Vol. 2.   N. Moya, Madrid.

——.   1909–11.   Histologie du système nerveux de l'homme et des vertébrés. A. Maloine, Paris.

REESE, A. M.   1908.   The development of the American alligator.   Smithsonian Misc. Coll., no. 1791, vol. 51.   Published by the Smithsonian Institute, Washington.

——.   1910.   The development of the brain of the American alligator: the paraphysis and the hypophysis.   Smithsonian Misc. Coll., vol. 54, no. 1922.   Published by the Smithsonian Institution, Washington.

RÖTHIG, P.   1911.   Beiträge zum Studium des Zentralnervensystems der Wirbeltiere. 3. Zur Phylogenese der Hypothalamus.   Folia neuro-biol., Bd. 5, S. 913.

SHANKLIN, W. M.   1930.   The central nervous system of Chameleon vulgaris.   Acta Zool., Bd. 11, S. 425.

——.   1933.   The comparative neurology of the nucleus opticus tegmenti with special reference to Chameleon vulgaris.   Acta Zool., vol. 14, p. 163.

SMITH, G. ELLIOT.   1903.   On the morphology of the cerebral commissures in the Vertebrata with special reference to an aberrant commissure found in the forebrain of certain reptiles.   Tr. Linnean Soc., London, Zool. Ser., vol. 8, pt. 12.

——.   1910.   Some problems relating to the evolution of the brain.   Arris and Gale Lecture.   Lancet, vol. 1, pp. 1, 147, and 219.

SORENSEN, A. D.   1893.   The pineal and parietal organ in Phrynosoma coronata. J. Comp. Neurol., vol. 3, p. 48.

——.   1894.   Comparative study of the epiphysis and roof of the diencephalon. J. Comp. Neurol., vol. 4, pp. 72 and 153.

SPENCER, B.   1886.   Preliminary communication on the structure and presence in Sphenodon and other lizards of the median eye, described by von Graaf in Anguis fragilis.   Proc. Roy. Soc., London, vol. 40, p. 559.

SPENCER, W. B.   1887.   On the presence and structure of the pineal eye in Lacertilia. Quart. J. Micr. Sc., vol. 27, p. 165.

STENDELL, W.   1914.   Die Hypophysis cerebri.   In A. Oppel's "Lehrbuch der vergleichende mikroskopischen Anatomie der Wirbeltiere," Bd. 8.   G. Fischer, Jena, 1896–1914.

STIEDA, L.   1875.   Ueber den Bau des centralen Nervensystems der Amphibien und Reptilien.   Ueber den Bau des centralen Nervensystems der Schildkröte. W. Engelmann, Leipzig.   Later edition in 1893.

STUDNIČKA, F. K. 1905. Die Parietalorgane. In A. Oppel's "Lehrbuch der vergleichende mikroskopischen Anatomie der Wirbeltiere," Bd. 5. G. Fischer, Jena, 1896–1914.

TILNEY, F., AND WARREN, W. F. 1919. The morphology and evolutional significance of the pineal body. Am. Anat. Mem., No. 9, p. 5.

TUGE, H. 1932. Somatic motor mechanisms in the midbrain and medulla oblongata of Chrysemys elegans (Wied). J. Comp. Neurol., vol. 55, p. 185.

UNGER, L. 1911. Untersuchungen über die Morphologie und Faserung des Reptiliengehirns. II. Das Vorderhirn des Alligators. Sitzungsb. d. K. Akad. d. Wissensch. zu Wien, Math.-nat. Cl., Bd. 120, Abt. 3, S. 177.

VAN VALKENBURG, C. T. 1911. Zur vergleichenden Anatomie des mesencephalen Trigeminusanteils. Folia neuro-biol., Bd. 5, S. 360.

WALDSCHMIDT, J. 1887. Zur Anatomie des Nervensystems der Gymnophionen. Jenaische Zeitschr. f. Naturw., Bd. 20, S. 461.

WARNER, F. J. 1931. The cell masses in the telencephalon and diencephalon of the rattle snake, Crotalus atrox. Kon. Akad. v. Wetensch. te Amsterdam, Proc. sect. sc., vol. 34, no. 8, p. 1156.

WEINBERG, E. 1928. The mesencephalic root of the fifth nerve. A comparative anatomical study. J. Comp. Neurol., vol. 46, p. 249.

WESTON, J. K. 1933. The reptilian vestibular and cerebellar gray with fiber connections. (Dissertation.)

WYETH, F. J., AND ROW, R. W. H. 1923. The structure of the pituitary body in Sphenodon punctatum. Acta Zool., Bd. 4, S. 1.

BIRDS

ARIËNS KAPPERS, C. U. 1920–21. Vergleichende Anatomie des Nervensystems. (German edition of present text.) E. F. Bohn, Haarlem.

——. 1924. Tabulae anatomo-comparativae cerebri. Amsterdam.

BELLONCI, J. 1883. Les lobes optiques des oiseaux. Arch. ital. de biol., vol. 4, p. 21.

——. 1888. Ueber die centrale Endigung des Nervus opticus bei den Vertebraten. Zeitschr. f. wissensch. Zool., Bd. 47, S. 1.

BOK, S. T. 1915. Die Entwicklung der Hirnnerven und ihrer zentralen Bahnen. Die Stimulogene Fibrillation. Folia neuro-biol., Bd. 9, S. 475.

BOYCE, R., AND WARRINGTON, W. B. 1898, 1899. Observations on the anatomy, physiology, and degenerations of the nervous system of the bird. Proc. Roy. Soc., London, vol. 64, p. 176. See also Phil. Tr. Roy. Soc., London, Ser. B, vol. 191, p. 293.

BREMER, F., AND LEYS, R. 1927. Recherches sur la physiologie du cervelet chez le pigeon. Arch. internat. de physiol., vol. 28, p. 58.

BUMM, A. 1883. Das Grosshirn der Vögel. Zeitschr. f. wissensch. Zool., Bd. 38, S. 430.

BURCKHARDT, R. 1894. Die Homologien des Zwischenhirndaches bei Reptilien und Vögeln. Anat. Anz., Bd. 9, S. 320.

CAMERON, J. 1903–4. On the origin of the epiphysis cerebri as a bilateral structure in the chick. Proc. Roy. Soc., Edinburgh, vol. 25, pt. 1, p. 160.

CRAIGIE, E. H. 1928. Observations on the brain of the humming bird (Chrysolampis mosquitus Linn. and Chlorostilbon caribaeus Lawr.). J. Comp. Neurol., vol. 45, p. 377.

——. 1930. Studies on the brain of the kiwi (Apteryx australis). J. Comp. Neurol., vol. 49, p. 223.

——. 1931. The cell masses in the diencephalon of the humming bird. Kon. Akad. v. Wetensch. te Amsterdam, Proc. sect. sc., vol. 34, p. 1038.

CRAIGIE, E. H., AND BRICKNER, R. M. 1927. Structural parallelism in the midbrain and 'tweenbrain of teleosts and of birds. Kon. Akad. v. Wetensch. te Amsterdam. Proc. sect. sc., vol. 30, p. 695.

EDINGER, L. 1896. See bibliography for reptiles.

——. 1908. Vorlesungen über den Bau der nervösen Centralorgane des Menschen und der Thiere. 7ᵗᵉ Aufl., F. C. W. Vogel, Leipzig. See also 1896 and 1911 editions.

EDINGER, L., AND WALLENBERG, A. 1899. Untersuchungen über das Gehirn der Tauben. Anat. Anz., Bd. 15, S. 245.

EDINGER, L., WALLENBERG, A., AND HOLMES, G. 1903. Untersuchungen über die vergleichende Anatomie des Gehirns. 5. Das Vorderhirn der Vögel. Abhandl. d. Senckenb. nat. Gesellsch., Frankfurt am Main, Bd. 20, Heft 4, S. 343.

FOÀ, C. 1912. Hypertrophie des testicules et de la crete l'extirpation de la glande pinéale chez le coq. Arch. ital. de biol., vol. 57, p. 233.

FRENKEL, B. 1911. Ein Beitrag zur Kenntnis der im Tectum opticum der Vögel entstehenden Bahnen. Anat. Anz., Bd. 40, S. 199.

FREY, E. 1933. Ueber die basale Opticuswurzel and die caudalen Verbindungen der Commissura transversa Gudden der Vögel. Kon. Akad. v. Wetensch. te Amsterdam, Proc. sect. sc., vol. 36, p. 351.

GAGE, S. P. 1895. Comparative morphology of the brain of the soft shelled turtle (Amyda mutica) and the English sparrow (Passer domesticus). Proc. Am. Micr. Soc., vol. 17, p. 185.

VAN GEHUCHTEN, A. 1892. La structure des lobes optiques chez l'embryon de poulet. La Cellule, vol. 8, fasc. 1, p. 1.

GROEBBELS, F. 1922. Die Lage- und Bewegungsreflexe der Vögel. Mitteilung I und Mitteilung II. Zeitschr. f. Biol., Bd. 76 (N. F., Bd. 58), S. 83 u. 127.

——. 1924. Untersuchungen über den Thalamus und das Mittelhirn der Vögel. Anat. Anz., Bd. 57, S. 385.

——. 1926. Die Lage- und Bewegungsreflexe der Vögel. Mitteilung III. Der Effekt der operativen Entfernung der Bogengänge und Ampullen und die Lage und Bewegungsreflexe der Haustaube. Arch. f. d. ges. Physiol. (Pflüger's), Bd. 214, S. 721.

——. 1927. Idem. IV. Mitteilung. Der Effekt der galvanischen Reizung der Bogengänge und Ampullen auf die Lage- und Bewegungsreflexe der Haustaube. Zugleich ein Beitrag zur Strömungstheorie. Arch. f. d. ges. Physiol. (Pflüger's), Bd. 216, S. 507.

——. 1927. Idem. V. Mitteilung. Die physiologische Gruppierung der Lage- und Bewegungsreflexe der Haustaube und ihre weitere Analyse durch Labyrinthen-entfernung und galvanische Reizung nach Entfernung der Labyrinths und seiner Teile. Arch. f. d. ges. Physiol. (Pflüger's), Bd. 217, S. 631.

——. 1927. Idem. VI. Mitteilung. Degenerationsbefunde im Zentralnervensystem der Taube nach Entfernung des Labyrinths und seiner Teile. Arch. f. d. ges. Physiol. (Pflüger's), Bd. 218, S. 89.

——. 1927. Idem. VII. Mitteilung. Die Wirkung zweizeitiger Labyrinthopera-tionen auf die Lage- und Bewegungsreflexe der Haustaube. Arch. f. d. ges. Physiol. (Pflüger's), Bd. 218, S. 198.

——. 1927. Idem. VIII. Mitteilung. Die Wirkung zweiseitiger Labyrinthopera-tionen auf die Lage- und Bewegungsreflexe der Haustaube. Arch. f. d. ges. Physiol. (Pflüger's), Bd. 218, S. 408.

——. 1828. Idem. IX. Mitteilung. Die Wirkung von Kleinhirnläsionen und ihre anatomisch-physiologische Analyse. Arch. f. d. ges. Physiol. (Pflüger's), Bd. 221, S. 15.

——. 1928. Idem. X. Mitteilung. Die Analyse der Beziehungen zwischen Laby-rinth und Kleinhirn. Arch. f. d. ges. Physiol. (Pflüger's), Bd. 221, S. 41.

GROEBBELS, F.   1928.   Idem.   XI. Mitteilung.   Die Analyse der Stützreaktion (Mit Unterstützung der Notgemeinschaft der Deutschen Wissenschaft).   Arch. f. d. ges. Physiol. (Pflüger's), Bd. 221, S. 50.

HERMAN, W.   1925.   The relations of the corpus striatum and the pallium in Varanus and a discussion of their bearing on birds, mammals, and man.   Brain, vol. 48, p. 362.

HUBER, G. CARL, AND CROSBY, E. C.   1929.   The nuclei and fiber paths of the avian diencephalon, with consideration of telencephalic and certain mesencephalic centers and connections.   J. Comp. Neurol., vol. 48, p. 1.

———.   1933.   A phylogenetic consideration of the optic tectum.   Proc. Nat. Acad. Sc., vol. 19, p. 15.

———.   1934.   The influences of afferent paths on the cytoarchitectonic structure of the submammalian optic tectum.   Psychiat. en Neurol. Bl., Nos. 3 and 4, p. 459.

HUNTER, J. I.   1923.   The forebrain of Apteryx australis.   Kon. Akad. v. Wetensch. te Amsterdam, Proc. sect. sc., vol. 26, p. 807.

INGVAR, S.   1923.   On thalamic evolution.   Acta Med. Scandinavica, vol. 59, p. 696.

JELGERSMA, G.   1895.   Die sensiblen und sensorischen Nervenbahnen und Centren. Neurol. Centralbl., Bd. 14, S. 290.

———.   1896.   De verbindingen van de groote hersenen by de vogels met de oculomotori-uskern.   Feestbundel uitgegeven doorde Nederlandsche Vereeniging von Psychiatrie, p. 241.

———.   1897.   De oorsprong der motorische oogzenvwen bij de vogels.   Psychiat. en neurol. Bl., Amsterdam, vol. 1, p. 23.

KALISCHER, O.   1905.   Das Grosshirn der Papageien in anatomischer und physiologischer Beziehung.   Abhandl. d. kön. preuss. Akad. d. Wissensch., Berlin, Abh. 4, S. 1.

VON KÖLLIKER, A.   1896.   Handbuch der Gewebelehre der Menschen, Aufl. 6, Bd. 2. W. Engelmann, Leipzig.   (1889–1902.)

KOSAKA, K., AND HIRAIWA, K.   1915.   Zur Anatomie der Sehnervenbahnen und ihrer Zentren.   Folia neuro-biol., Bd. 9, S. 367.

LIVINI, F.   1906.   Intorno ad alcune formazioni accessorie della vôlta del procencefalo in embrioni di uccelli (Columba livia dom. e Gallus dom.).   Anat. Anz., Bd. 28, S. 241.

———.   1906.   Formazioni della vôlta del procencefalo in alcuni uccelli.   Arch. ital. di anat. e di embriol., vol. 5, p. 377.

MESDAG, T. M.   1909.   Bijdrage tot de ontwikkelingsgeschiedenis van de structuur der hersenen by het kipembryo.   Dissertation, Amsterdam.

MITCHELL, W.   1861.   Am. J. Med. Sc., pp. 323 and 326.   (Quoted from Muskens, '30.)

MÜNZER, E., AND WIENER, H.   1898.   Beiträge zur Anatomie und Physiologie des Centralnervensystems der Taube.   Monatschr. f. Psychiat. u. Neurol., Bd. 3, S. 379.

MUSKENS, L. J. J.   1914.   An anatomico-physiological study of the posterior longitudinal bundle in its relation to forced movement.   Brain, vol. 36, p. 352.

———.   1927.   Supravestibular connections.   Kon. Akad. v. Wetensch. te Amsterdam, vol. 31.

———.   1929.   The tracts and centers in the pigeon dominating the associated movements of the eyes (and other movable parts) in the sense of lateral deviation in the horizontal end of rotation in the frontal plane.   J. Comp. Neurol., vol. 48, p. 267.

———.   1930.   Zum Studium der Blicklähmungen, Blickkrämpfe und gewisser Nystagmusformen, insbesondere derjenigen in der vertikalen Richtung.   Deutsche Zeitschr. f. Nervenh., Bd. 115, S. 81.

———.   1930a.   On tracts and centers involved in the upward and downward associated movements of the eyes after experiments in birds.   J. Comp. Neurol., vol. 50, p. 289.

PALMGREN, A.   1921.   Embryological and morphological studies on the midbrain and cerebellum of vertebrates.   Acta Zool., Bd. 2, S. 1.

PAPEZ, J. W.   1929.   Comparative neurology.   Thomas Y. Crowell Co., New York.

PERLIA, DR.   1889.   Ueber ein neues Opticuscentrum beim Huhne.   Arch. f. Ophth. (von Graefe's), Bd. 35, S. 20.

RAMÓN, P.   1898.   Centros ópticos de las aves.   Rev. trimestr. micrograf., vol. 5.

RAMÓN Y CAJAL, S.   1891.   Sur la fine structure du lobe optique des oiseaux et sur l'origine réelle des nerfs optiques.   J. internat. d'anat. et physiol., vol. 8, p. 337.

——.   1908.   Les ganglions terminaux du nerf acustique des oiseaux.   Trab. d. lab. de invest. biol. Univ. de Madrid, vol. 6, p. 195.

——.   1909–11.   Histologie du système nerveux de l'homme et des vertébrés. A. Maloine, Paris.

RENDAHL, H.   1924.   Embryologische und morphologische Studien über das Zwischenhirn beim Huhn.   Acta Zool., Bd. 5, S. 241.

RIS, F.   1899.   Ueber den Bau des Lobus opticus der Vögel.   Arch. f. mikr. Anat., Bd. 53, S. 106.

ROGERS, F. T.   1919.   Experimental studies of the optic thalamus and the corpus striatum.   J. Nerv. and Ment. Dis., vol. 49, p. 1.

——.   1920.   Studies on the brain stem.   IV.   On the relation of the cerebral hemispheres and thalamus to arterial blood pressure.   Am. J. Physiol., vol. 54, p. 355.

——.   1921.   The relation of the cerebral hemispheres to the sympathetic nervous system.   Am. J. Physiol., vol. 55, p. 310.

——.   1921a.   The effects of pituitary extract on the body temperature of animals rendered poikilothermous by destruction of the optic thalamus.   Proc. Soc. Exper. Biol. and Med., vol. 19, p. 125.

——.   1922.   A note on the excitable areas of the cerebral hemispheres of the pigeon. J. Comp. Neurol., vol. 35, p. 61.

——.   1923.   The relation between lesions of the brain stem, water elimination and body temperature.   Am. J. Physiol., vol. 66, p. 284.

——.   1924.   On hyperthermias induced by cerebral lesions and pituitary extract. Am. J. Physiol., vol. 68, p. 139.

——.   1924a.   Studies on the brain stem.   VIII.   Diuresis and anhydremia following destruction of the thalamus.   Am. J. Physiol., vol. 68, p. 499.

——.   1924b.   Studies on the brain stem.   IX.   On the relation of cerebral puncture hyperthemia to an associated anhydremia.   Am. J. Physiol., vol. 68, p. 507.

ROGERS, F. T., AND LACKEY, R. W.   1923.   Studies on the brain stem.   VII.   The respiratory exchange and heat production after destruction of the body temperature-regulating centers of the thalamus.   Am. J. Physiol., vol. 66, p. 453.

ROGERS, F. T., AND WHEAT, S. D.   1921.   Studies on the brain stem.   V.   Carbon dioxide excretion after destruction of the optic thalamus and the reflex functions of the thalamus in body temperature regulation.   Am. J. Physiol., vol. 57, p. 218.

SALA.   1905.   Sulla fina struttura dei centre ottici degli uccelli.   Mem. d. R. Ist. Lombardo di sc. e lett., Cl. di sc., mat. e nat., vol. 20, fasc. 5.

——.   1906.   Idem.   Mem. d. R. Ist. Lombardo di sc. e lett., Cl. di sc., mat. e nat., vol. 20, fasc. 7.

——.   1907.   Sulla fina struttura dei centri ottici degli uccelli.   Lab. di pat. gen. ed istol. d. R. univ. di Pavia.

SANDERS, E. B.   1929.   A consideration of certain bulbar, midbrain, and cerebellar centers and fiber tracts in birds.   J. Comp. Neurol., vol. 49, p. 155.

SCHROEDER, K.   1911.   Der Faserverlauf im Vorderhirn des Huhnes.   Jour. f. Psychol. u. Neurol., Bd. 18, S. 115.

SINGER, J., AND MÜNZER, E. 1890. Beiträge zur Anatomie des Centralnervensystems, insbesondere des Rückenmarkes. Denkschr. d. K. Akad. d. Wissensch. zu Wien, Math.-nat. Cl., Bd. 57, S. 569.

STIEDA, L. 1869. Studien über das zentrale Nervensystem der Vögel und Säugetiere. Zeitschr. f. wissensch. Zool., Bd. 19, S. 1.

STILLING, J. 1882. Untersuchungen über den Bau der optischen Centralorgane. (Quoted from Perlia ('89. See S. 282 in von Graefe's Arch. f. Ophth., Bd. 35, Abt. 1.)

STUDNIČKA, F. K. 1905. Die Parietalorgane. In A. Oppel's Lehrbuch der vergleichende mikroskopischen Anatomie der Wirbeltiere, Bd. 5. G. Fischer, Jena, 1896–1914.

TEN CATE, J. 1926. Contribution à la physiologiè comparée du cervelet. I. Le cervelet du pigeon. Arch. néerl. de physiol., vol. 11, p. 1.

TILNEY, F., AND WARREN, W. F. 1919. The morphology and evolutional significance of the pineal body. Am. Anat. Mem., No. 9, p. 5.

TURNER, C. H. 1891. Morphology of the avian brain. J. Comp. Neurol., vol. 1, pp. 39 and 107.

WALLENBERG, A. 1898. Die secundäre Acusticusbahn der Taube. Anat. Anz., Bd. 14, S. 353.

——. 1898a. Das mediale Opticusbündel der Taube. Neurol. Centralbl., Bd. 17, S. 532.

——. 1898b. Eine Verbindung caudaler Hirnteile der Taube mit dem Striatum. Neurol. Centralbl., Bd. 17, S. 300.

——. 1900. Ueber zentrale Endstätten des Nervus octavus der Taube. Anat. Anz., Bd. 17, S. 102.

——. 1902. Eine zentrifugalleitende direkte Verbindung der frontalen Vorderhirnbasis mit der Oblongata (und Rückenmark) bei der Ente. Anat. Anz., Bd. 22, S. 289.

——. 1903. Der Ursprung des Tractus isthmo-striatus (oder bulbo-striatus) der Taube. Neurol. Centralbl., Bd. 22, S. 98.

——. 1904. Neue Untersuchungen über den Hirnstamm der Taube. Anat. Anz., Bd. 24, S. 142 u. S. 357.

——. 1906. Die basalen Aeste des Scheidewandbündels der Vögel. Anat. Anz., Bd. 28, S. 394.

——. 1928. Quoted from Craigie, '30.

——. 1934. Über Verbindungen des Tractus occipito-mesencephalo-bulbaris mit einem Vestibularis-Endkern bei der Saatkrahe (Corvus frugilegus L.). Anat. Anz., Bd. 78, S. 438.

WESTPHAL, K. 1898. Ueber Acusticus, Mittel- und Zwischenhirn der Vogel. Dissertation, Berlin.

MAMMALS

ABBIE, A. 1933. The blood supply of the lateral geniculate body. J. Anat., vol. 67, p. 491.

D'ABUNDO, G. 1910. La physiopathologie de la couche optique. Arch. ital. de biol., vol. 53, p. 321.

ACHÚCARRO, N. 1913. La estructura secretora de la glándula pineal humana. Communic. a la Soc. Española de Biol., 24 de Oct. y 21 de Nov. de 1913.

ADDISON, W. H. F. 1917. The cell-changes in the hypophysis of the albino rat, after castration. J. Comp. Neurol., vol. 28, p. 441.

ADDISON, W. H. F., AND FRAZER, D. A. 1932. Variability of pigmentation in the hypophysis and parathyroids of the gray rat (Mus norvegicus). J. Comp. Neurol., vol. 55, p. 513.

ALLEN, W. R. 1923. Origin and destination of the secondary visceral fibers in the guinea pig. J. Comp. Neurol., vol. 35, p. 275.

——. 1924. Distribution of the fibers originating from the different basal cerebellar nuclei. J. Comp. Neurol., vol. 36, p. 513.

ANTON, G., AND ZINGERLE, H. 1902. Bau, Leistung und Erkrankung des menschlichen Stirnhirnes. Graz.

AREY, L. B., AND SCHAIBLE, A. J. 1934. The nerve-fiber composition of the optic nerve. Proc. A. Am. Anatomists, Anat. Rec., vol. 58, p. 3.

ARIËNS KAPPERS, C. U. 1908. Weitere Mitteilungen über die Phylogenese des Corpus striatum und des Thalamus. Anat. Anz., Bd. 33, S. 321.

——. 1920–21. Vergleichende Anatomie des Nervensystems. (German edition of present text.) E. F. Bohn, Haarlem.

——. 1929. The evolution of the nervous system. E. F. Bohn, Haarlem.

ASCHNER, B. 1912. Ueber die Funktion der Hypophyse. Arch. f. d. ges. Physiol. (Pflüger's), Bd. 146, S. 1.

ATWELL, W. J. 1918. The development of the hypophysis cerebri of the rabbit (Lepus cuniculus L.). Am. J. Anat., vol. 24, p. 271.

——. 1926. The development of the hypophysis cerebri in man, with special reference to the pars tuberalis. Am. J. Anat., vol. 37, p. 159.

——. 1932. Functional relations of the hypophysis and the brain. Endocrinology, vol. 16, p. 242.

ATWELL, W. J., AND WOODWORTH, E. A. 1926. The relative volumes of the three epithelial parts of the hypophysis cerebri. Anat. Rec., vol. 33, p. 377.

BAILEY, F. R., STRONG, O., AND ELWYN, A. 1925. Textbook of histology. W. Wood and Co., New York.

BAILEY, P. 1916. Morphology of the roof plate of the forebrain and lateral choroid plexuses in the human embryo. J. Comp. Neurol., vol. 26, p. 79.

BAILEY, P., AND BREMER, F. 1921. Experimental diabetes insipidus. Arch. Neurol. and Psychiat., vol. 28, p. 773.

BALADO, M., AND FRANKE, E. 1929. Sobre el modo de penetracion de las fibras de la bandeleta optica en el cuerpo geniculado externo. Rev. de la Soc. Argent. de Biol., vol. 5, p. 707.

——. 1930. Degeneración alternada de las capas del cuerpo geniculado externo, del hombre, después de la extirpación del globo ocular derecho. Arch. Argent. de Neurol., vol. 6, p. 77.

——. 1931. Estudios sobre las vias ópticas. El cuerpo geniculado externo del hombre. I. Bol. del Inst. de Clin. Quirúrg., vol. 7, p. 5.

——. 1931a. Estudios sobre las vias ópticas. Geniculado externo del maimon — Pithecus nemestrinus, nemestrinus, Linneo. El Dia Medicó, vol. 3, p. 890.

BARD, P. 1928. A diencephalic mechanism for the expression of rage with special reference to the sympathetic nervous system. Am. J. Physiol., vol. 22, p. 490.

——. 1929. The central representation of the sympathetic system as indicated by certain physiologic observations. Arch. Neurol. and Psychiat., vol. 22, p. 230.

BARRIS, R. W., AND INGRAM, W. R. 1934. Optic connections of the midbrain and thalamus. Proc. A. Am. Anatomists, Anat. Rec., vol. 58, p. 3.

BAUER, J. 1909. Die Substantia nigra Soemmeringii. Eine vergleichendanatomische Studie nebst einem Beitrag zur Kenntnis des dunkeln Pigmentes des Nervenzellen. Arb. a. d. neurol. Inst. a. d. Wien. Univ. (Obersteiner's), Bd. 17, S. 435.

BAUER-JOKL, M. 1917. Ueber das sogenannte Subcommissuralorgan. Arb. a. d. neurol. Inst. a. d. Wien. Univ. (Obersteiner's), Bd. 22, S. 41.

BAUMGARTEN, P. 1881. Zur sogenannten Semidecussation der Opticusfasern. Med. Centralbl., No. 31, p. 501. See also Arch. f. Ophth. (von Graefe's), Bd. 27, S. 342.

1222 NERVOUS SYSTEMS OF VERTEBRATES AND OF MAN

BAZZETT, H. C., AND PENFIELD, W. G. 1922. A study of the Sherrington decerebrate animal in the chronic as well as the acute condition. Brain, vol. 45, p. 185.

BEATTIE, J., BROW, G. R., AND LONG, C. N. H. 1930. Physiological and anatomical evidence for the existence of nerve tracts connecting the hypothalamus with spinal sympathetic centers. Proc. Roy. Soc., London, Ser. B, vol. 106, p. 253.

VON BECHTEREW, W. 1884. Ueber die Verbindung der sogenannten peripheren Gleichgewichtsorgane mit dem Kleinhirn. Arch. f. d. ges. Physiol. (Pflüger's), Bd. 34, S. 362.

——. 1894. Die Leitungsbahnen im Gehirn und Rückenmark. Leipzig. 2ᵗᵉ Aufl. in 1899.

——. 1906. Ueber die absteigenden Verbindungen des Thalamus. Neurol. Centralbl., Bd. 25, S. 546.

——. 1908. Die Funktionen der Nervencentra. G. Fischer, Jena.

BERITOFF, J. S., AND MAGNUS, R. 1914. Zusatz bei der Korrektur. Arch. f. d. ges. Physiol. (Pflüger's), Bd. 159, S. 249.

BERL, V. 1902. Einiges über die Beziehungen der Sehbahnen zu dem vorderen Zwei-hügel der Kaninchen. Arb. a. d. neurol. Inst. a. d. Wien. Univ. (Obersteiner's), Bd. 8, S. 308.

BERNHEIMER, ST. 1899. Die Reflexbahn der Pupilarreaction. Arch. f. Ophth. (von Graefe's), Bd. 47, Abt. 1, S. 1.

——. 1907. Zur Kenntnis der Guddenschen Kommissur. Arch. f. Ophth. (von Graefe's), Bd. 67, S. 78.

BIANCHI, V. 1909. Anatomische Untersuchungen über die Entwicklungsgeschichte der Kerne des Thalamus opticus des Kaninchens. Monatschr. f. Psychiat. u. Neurol., Bd. 25, Ergänzungsheft, S. 425.

BIEMOND, A. 1930. Experimentell-anatomische Untersuchungen über die cortifugalen optischen Verbindungen bei Kaninchen und Affen. Zeitschr. f. d. ges. Neurol. u. Psychiat., Bd. 129, S. 65.

BIONDI, G. 1916. Studi sulla ghiandola pineale. Riv. ital. di neuropat., psichiat. ed elettrot., vol. 9, pp. 251 and 269.

BISCHOFF, E. 1900. Beitrag zur Anatomie des Igelgehirnes. Anat. Anz., Bd. 18, S. 348.

BOCHENEK, A. 1908. Ueber zentrale Endigung des Nervus opticus. Bull. internat. Acad. d. sc. de Cracovie, Cl. de sc., math. et Naturw., p. 91.

BOLK, L. 1910. The development of the hypophysis of primates, especially of Tarsius. Kon. Akad. v. Wetensch. te Amsterdam, Proc. sect. sc., vol. 13, pt. 2, p. 660.

BOUMAN, K. H. 1905. Experimenteele onderzoekingen over het cerebrale optische stelsel. Dissertatie, Amsterdam.

BOYCE, R. 1894. A contribution to the study of some of the decussating tracts of the mid- and inter-brain, and of the pyramidal system in the mesencephalon and bulb. Proc. Roy. Soc., London, vol. 56, p. 305.

BREMER, J. L. 1927. A textbook of histology arranged on an embryological basis. P. Blakiston's Son and Co., Philadelphia.

BROUWER, B. 1917. Ueber die Sehstrahlung des Menschen. Monatschr. f. Psychiat. u. Neurol., Bd. 41, S. 129 u. 203.

——. 1919. Examen anatomique du système nerveux central des deux chats décrits par J. G. Dusser de Barenne. Arch. néerl. de physiol., vol. 4, p. 124.

——. 1920. The significance of phylogenetic and ontogenetic studies for the neuro-pathologist. J. Nerv. and Ment. Dis., vol. 51, p. 113.

——. 1923. Experimentell-anatomische Untersuchungen über die Projection der Retina auf die primären Opticuszentren. Schweiz. Arch. f. Neurol. u. Psychiat., Bd. 13, S. 118.

BROUWER, B. 1927. Anatomical, phylogenetical, and clinical studies on the central nervous system. Herter Foundation Lectures, Johns Hopkins University, School of Medicine. Williams and Wilkins, Baltimore.

BROUWER, B., AND ZEEMAN, W. P. C. 1925. Experimental anatomical investigation concerning the projection of the retina on the primary optic centres in apes. J. Neurol. and Psychopath., vol. 6, p. 1.

———. 1926. The projection of the retina in the primary optic neuron in monkeys. Brain, vol. 49, p. 1.

BROWN, T. G. 1913. On postural and non-postural activities of the midbrain. Proc. Roy. Soc., London, Ser. B., vol. 87, p. 145.

———. 1915. On the activities of the central nervous system of the unborn foetus of the cat, with a discussion of the question whether progression is a "learnt" reflex. J. Physiol., vol. 49, p. 208.

BRUNNER, H., AND SPIEGEL, E. A. 1919. Vergleichend-anatomische Studien am Hapalidengehirn. Folia neuro-biol., Bd. 11, S. 171.

CAMUS, J., AND ROUSSY, G. 1913. Local anatomique des lésions de la base du cerveau qui provoquent la polyurie. Compt. rend. Soc. de biol., vol. 75, p. 628.

———. 1920. Experimental researches on the pituitary body. Endocrinology, vol. 4, p. 507.

CAMUS, J., GOURNAY, J. J., AND LE GRAND, A. 1925. Diabète suiré par lésion nerveuse. La presse méd., vol. 33, p. 249.

CASTALDI, L. 1923. Studi sulla struttura e sullo sviluppo del mesencefalo. I. Ricerche in Cavia cobaya. Arch. ital. di anat. e di embriol., vol. 20, p. 23.

———. 1924. Idem. II. Ricerche in Cavia cobaya. Arch. ital. di anat. e di embriol., vol. 21, p. 172.

———. 1926. Idem. III. Ricerche in Cavia cobaya. Arch. ital. di anat. e di embriol., vol. 23, p. 481.

CHU, H.–N. 1932. The cell masses of the diencephalon of the opossum, Didelphis virginiana. Monograph of the National Research Institute of Psychology, No. 2. Peiping, China. July, 1932.

———. 1932a. The fiber connections of the diencephalon of the opossum, Didelphis virginiana. Monograph of the National Research Institute of Psychology, No. 3. Peiping, China. October, 1932.

CLARK, W. E. LE GROS. See Le Gros Clark.

COBB, S., BAILEY, A. A., AND HOLTZ, P. R. 1917. On the genesis and inhibition of extensor rigidity. Am. J. Physiol., vol. 44, p. 239.

COLLIER, J., AND BUZZARD, F. 1901. Descending mesencephalic tracts in cat, monkey, and man; Monakow's bundle; the dorsal longitudinal bundle; the ventral longitudinal bundle; the ponto-spinal tracts, lateral and ventral; the vestibulo-spinal tract; the central tegmental tract (centrale Haubenbahn); descending fibers of the fillet. Brain, vol. 24, p. 177.

COLUCCI, C. 1898. Ricerche sull'anatomia e sulla fisiologia dei centri visioi cerebrali. Atti della R. Accademia medicochirurgica di Napoli.

CRAIGIE, E. H. 1925. An introduction to the finer anatomy of the central nervous system based upon that of the albino rat. Univ. of Toronto Press.

CREUTZFELDT, H. G. 1912. Ueber das Fehlen der Epiphysis cerebri bei einigen Säugern. Anat. Anz., Bd. 42, S. 517.

CROUCH, R. L. 1934. The nuclear configuration of the hypothalamus and the sub-thalamus of Macacus rhesus. J. Comp. Neurol., vol. 59, p. 431.

———. 1934a. The nuclear configuration of the thalamus of Macacus rhesus. J. Comp. Neurol., vol. 59, p. 451.

CUSHING, H. W. 1912. The pituitary body and its disorders. J. B. Lippincott Co., Philadelphia and London.

Cushing, H. W. 1930. Lister lecture. On neurohypophyseal mechanisms from a clinical standpoint. The Lancet, vol. 2, pp. 119 and 175.

Cutore, G. 1910. Il corpo pineale di alcuni mammiferi. Arch. ital. di Anat. e di Embriol., vol. 9, p. 402; also p. 599.

——. 1912. Alcune notizie sul corpo pineale del Macacus sinicus L. e del Cercopithecus griseus viridis L. Folia neuro-biol., Bd. 6, S. 267.

Darkschewitsch, L. 1886. Ueber die sogenannten primären Opticus-centren und ihre Beziehung zur Grosshirnrinde. Arch. f. Anat. u. Physiol., Anat. Abt., S. 249.

Davenport, H. A., and Ranson, S. W. 1930. The red nucleus and adjacent cell groups. Arch. Neurol. and Psychiat., vol. 24, p. 257.

Déjérine, M. et Mme. 1895. Sur les connexions du ruban de Reil avec la corticalite cerebrale. Compt. rend. Soc. de Biol., Dixième Série, vol. 2, p. 285.

Déjérine, J. 1895–1901. Anatomie des centres nerveux. J. Reuff, Paris.

——. 1914. Sémiologie des affections du système nerveux. Masson et Cie., Paris.

Dendy, A., and Nicholls, G. E. 1910. On the occurrence of a mesocoelic recess in the human brain, and its relation to the sub-commissural organ of lower vertebrates; with special reference to the distribution of Reissner's fibre in the vertebrate series and its possible function. Proc. Roy. Soc., London, Ser. B, vol. 82, p. 515.

Dexler, H. 1897. Untersuchungen über den Faserverlauf im Chiasma des Pferdes und über den binoculären Sehact dieses Thieres. Arb. a. d. neurol. Inst. a. d. Wien. Univ. (Obersteiner's), Bd. 5, S. 179.

Dogiel, A. S. 1895. Ein besonderer Typus von Nervenzellen in der mitteleren gangliösen Schieht der Vogel-Retina. Anat. Anz., Bd. 10, S. 750.

Droogleever Fortuyn, A. B. 1912. Die Ontogenie der Kerne des Zwischenhirns beim Kaninchen. Arch. f. Anat. u. Physiol., Anat. Abt., S. 303.

von Economo, C. J. 1902. Die centralen Bahnen des Kau- und Schluckactes. Arch. f. d. ges. Physiol. (Pflüger's), Bd. 91, S. 629.

——. 1911. Ueber dissoziierte Empfindungslähmung bei Ponstumoren und über die zentralen Bahnen des sensiblen Trigeminus. Jahrb. f. Psychiat. u. Neurol., Bd. 32, S. 107.

von Economo, C. J., and Karplus, J. P. 1909. Zur Physiologie und Anatomie des Mittelhirns. Arch. f. Psychiat., Bd. 46, S. 377.

Edinger, L. 1908. Vorlesungen über den Bau der nervösen Centralorgane des Menschen und der Thiere. F. C. W. Vogel, Leipzig. See also edition of 1911.

Edinger, L., and Wallenberg, A. 1901. Untersuchungen über den Fornix und das Corpus mamillare. Arch. f. Psychiat., Bd. 35, S. 1.

Elliot Smith, G. 1896. The brain of a foetal Ornithorhynchus. Part I. The forebrain. Quart. J. Micr. Sc., vol. 39, p. 181.

——. 1907. On the nature of the faisceau en écharpe of Féré. Rev. Neurol. and Psychiat., vol. 5, p. 360.

——. 1910. Some problems relating to the evolution of the brain. Arris and Gale Lectures. Lancet, vol. 1, pp. 1, 147, and 219.

Falta, W. 1913. Die Erkrankungen der Blütdrusen. J. Springer, Berlin.

Da Fano, D. 1909. Studien über die Veränderungen im Thalamus opticus bei Defektpsychosen. Monatschr. f. Psychiat. u. Neurol., Bd. 26, Ergänzungsheft, S. 4.

Favaro, G. 1904. Le fibre nervose prepineali e pineali nell'encefalo dei Mammiferi. Arch. ital. di anat. e di embriol., vol. 3, p. 750.

Feliciangeli, G. 1910. Experimenteller Beitrag zur Kenntnis der Funktion des Stirnlappens des Hundehirns. Folia neuro-biol., Bd. 4, S. 449.

Flechsig, P. 1876. Die Leitungsbahnen im Gehirn und Rückenmark des Menschen. W. Engelmann, Leipzig.

FLECHSIG, P. 1895. Weitere Mitteilungen über die Sinnes und Associationscentren der menschlichen Gehirns. Neurol. Centralbl., Bd. 14, S. 1118.

———. 1896. Weitere Mitteilungen über den Strabkranz der menschlichen Grosshirns. Neurol. Centralbl., Bd. 15, S. 2.

FOIX, C., AND NICOLESCO, J. 1925. Les noyaux gris centraux et la region mesencephalo-sous-optique. Masson et Cie, Paris.

FOREL, A. 1872. Beiträge zur Kenntnis des Thalamus opticus und der ihn umgebenden Gebilde bei den Säugethieren. Sitzungsb. d. K. Akad. d. Wissensch. zu Wien, Math.-nat. Cl., Bd. 66, Abt. 3, S. 25.

———. 1877. Untersuchungen über die Haubenregion und ihre oberen Verknüpfungen im Gehirne des Menschen und einiger Säugethiere, mit Beiträgen zu den Methoden der Gehirnuntersuchung. Arch. f. Psychiat., Bd. 7, S. 393.

———. 1877a. Untersuchungen über die Haubenregion und ihre Verknüpfungen im Gehirne des Menschen und einiger Säugethiere, mit Beiträgen zu den Methoden der Gehirnuntersuchung. Arch. f. Psychiat., Bd. 7, S. 393.

———. 1907. Gesammelte hirnanatomische Abhandlungen. Reinhardt, München.

FRANKL-HOCHWART, L. 1902. Zur Kenntnis der Anatomie des Gehirns der Blindmaus (Spalax typhlus). Arb. a. d. neurol. Inst. a. d. Wien. Univ. (Obersteiner's), Bd. 8, S. 190.

FRASER, E. H. 1902. An experimental research into the relations of the posterior longitudinal bundle and Deiters' nucleus. J. Physiol., vol. 27, p. 372.

FRETS, G. P. 1916. Zwei Fälle mit einer Commissura anterior secundaria mollis, ein Fall ohne Commissura anterior und die Variabilität der Massa intermedia. Folia neuro-biol., Bd. 10, S. 19.

FRIEDEMANN, M. 1912. Die Cytoarchitektonik des Zwischenhirns der Cercopitheken mit besonderer Berücksichtigung des Thalamus opticus. J. f. Psychol. u. Neurol., Bd. 18, Ergänzungsheft 2, S. 309.

FUSE, G. 1911. Striae acusticae v. Monakowi beim Menschen. Riv. di patol. nerv. e ment., vol. 30, p. 912.

———. 1912. Striae medullares acusticae (Piccolohomini). Riv. di patol. nerv. e ment., vol. 31, p. 463.

GAGEL, O. 1928. Zur Topik und feineren Histologie det vegetativen Kerne des Zwischenhirns. Zeitschr. f. d. ges. Anat.; Abt. 1, Zeitschr. f. Anat. u. Entwicklungsgesch., Bd. 87, S. 558.

GANSER, S. 1882. Vergleichend-anatomische Studien über das Gehirn des Maulwurfes. Morphol. Jahrb., Bd. 7, S. 501.

VAN GEHUCHTEN, A. 1900. Anatomie du systeme nerveux. Uystpruyst-Dieudonne, Louvain.

———. 1904. Connexions centrales du noyau de Deiters et des Masses grises voisines. Le Névraxe, vol. 6, p. 19.

GEMELLI, A. 1906. Ulteriori osservazioni sulla struttura dell'ipofisi. Anat. Anz., Bd. 28, S. 613.

GERSTMANN, J. 1913. Zur Frage der sympathischen Gehirnbahnen. Jahrb. f. Psychiat. u. Neurol., Bd. 34, S. 287.

———. 1916. Zur Kenntnis der Störungen des Körpergleichgewichtes nach Schipsverletzungen des Stirnhorns. Monatschr. f. Psychiat. u. Neurol., Bd. 40, S. 354.

GIERLICH, N. 1916. Zur vergleichenden Anatomie der aus dem Grosshirn stammenden Faserung. 1. Der Anteil des Pes pedunculi am Pedunculusquerschnitte bei verschiedenen Säugetieren. Anat. Anz., Bd. 49, S. 24.

GLORIEUX, P. 1929. Anatomie et connexions thalamiques chez le chien. J. de Neurol., vol. 29, p. 525.

GRAY, L. P. 1926. Some experimental evidence on the connections of the vestibular mechanism in the cat. J. Comp. Neurol., vol. 41, p. 319.

GREVING, R.   1922.   Die Pathogenese des Fiebers mit besonderer Berücksichtigung der neurologischen und physiologischen Grundlagen die Wärmeregulation.   Deutsche med. Wochenschr., Bd. 48, Nos. 50–51, S. 1673 u. 1996.

——.   1922a.   Zur Anatomie, Physiologie und Pathologie der vegetativen Zentren im Zwischenhirn.   Zeitschr. f. d. ges. Anat.; Abt. 3, Ergeb. d. Anat. u. Entwicklungsgesch., Bd. 24, S. 348.

——.   1925.   Beitrag zur Innervation der Hypophyse.   Klin. Wochenschr., Bd. 4, S. 2181.

——.   1928.   Die zentralen Anteile des vegetativen Nervensystems.   In G. von Möllendorf's Handbuch der mikroskopischen Anatomie des Menschen.   Bd. 4, Nervensystem.   J. Springer, Berlin.

GRIFFIN, A. M., AND WINDLE, W. F.   1931.   The relation of the level of transection of the brain stem to the occurrence of decerebrate rigidity in newborn rabbits.   Am. J. Physiol., vol. 97, p. 397.

GRÜNTHAL, E.   1929.   Der Zellaufbau des Hypothalamus beim Hunde.   Zeitschr. f. d. ges. Neurol. u. Psychiat., Bd. 120, S. 157.

——.   1930.   Vergleichend anatomische und entwicklungsgeschichtliche Untersuchungen über die Zentren des Hypothalamus der Säuger und des Menschen.   Arch. f. Psychiat., Bd. 90, S. 216.

VON GUDDEN, B.   1874.   Ueber die Kreuzung der Fasern im Chiasma nervorum opticorum.   Arch. f. Ophth. (von Graefe's), Bd. 20, Abt. 2, S. 249.

——.   1876, 1879.   Idem.   Arch. f. Ophth. (von Graefe's), Bd. 21, Abt. 3, S. 199; Bd. 25, Abt. 1, S. 1, u. Abt. 4, S. 237.

——.   1885.   Ueber die Sehnerven, die Sehtractus, das Verhältnis ihrer gekreuzten und die Centren der letzeren ungekreuzten Bündl ihre Seh- und Pupillarfasern.   Tagblatt der 58 Vers. deutsch Naturf- und Aerzte in Strassburg.   (Quoted from Minkowski '20.)

——.   1889.   Gesammelte und hinterlassene Abhandlungen herausgegeben von H. Grashey.   J. F. Bergmann, Wiesbaden.

GURDJIAN, E. S.   1925.   Olfactory connections of the albino rat, with special reference to stria medullaris and anterior commissure.   J. Comp. Neurol., vol. 38, p. 127.

——.   1926.   The hypothalamus in the rat.   Anat. Rec., vol. 32, p. 208.

——.   1927.   The diencephalon of the albino rat.   Studies on the brain of the rat. No. 2.   J. Comp. Neurol., vol. 43, p. 1.

HALBAN, H., AND INFELD, M.   1902.   Zur Pathologie der Hirnschenkelhaube mit besonderer Berücksichtigung der posthemiplegischen Bewegungserscheinungen.   Arb. a. d. neurol. Inst. a. d. Wien. Univ. (Obersteiner's), Bd. 9, S. 329.

HATSCHEK, R.   1903.   Zur Kenntnis des Pedunculus corporis mammillaris, des Ganglion tegmenti profundum und der dorso-ventralen Raphefaserung in der Haube.   Arb. a. d. neurol. Inst. a. d. Wien. Univ., Bd. 10, S. 81.

——.   1903a.   Sehnervenatrophie bei einem Delphin.   Arb. a. d. neurol. Inst. a. d. Wien. Univ. (Obersteiner's), Bd. 10, S. 223.

——.   1907.   Zur vergleichenden Anatomie des Nucleus ruber tegmenti.   Arb. a. d. neurol. Inst. a. d. Wien. Univ. (Obersteiner's), Bd. 15, S. 89.

HATSCHEK, R., AND SCHLEISINGER, H.   1902.   Der Hirnstamm des Delphins (Delphinus delphis).   Arb. a. d. neurol. Inst. a. d. Wien. Univ. (Obersteiner's), Bd. 9, S. 1.

HEAD, H.   1920.   Studies in neurology.   Vol. 2, Oxford University Press.

HECHST, B.   1933.   Uber das Verhalten der äusseren Kniehöcker und der Sehrinde bei einseitiger peripherer Blindheit.   Arch. f. Psychiat., vol. 100, p. 491.

HELD, H.   1893.   Die centrale Gehörleitung.   Arch. f. Anat. u. Physiol., Anat. Abt., S. 201.

HENSCHEN, S. E.   1890–1894.   Klinische und anatomische Beiträge zur Pathologie des Gehirns.   Bds. 1–4.   Almquist u. Wiksell, Upsala.

HENSCHEN, S. E.   1898.   Ueber Localisation innerhalb des äusseren Knieganglions. Neurol.   Centralbl., Bd. 17, S. 194.

——.   1900.   Révue critique de la doctrine sur le centre cortical de la vision.   Rapport du XIII Congrès international de Médicine, Paris.

——.   1910.   Zentrale Sehstörungen.   Lewandowsky's Handbuch der Neurologie, Bd. 1, Pt. 2, S. 891.   J. Springer, Berlin, 1910–9.

——.   1926.   Zur Anatomie der Sehbahn und des Sehzentrums.   Arch. f. Ophth. (von Graefe's), Bd. 118, S. 403.

HERRICK, C. J.   1921.   Brains of rats and men.   Chicago.

HERRING, P. T.   1927.   The pineal region of the mammalian brain: its morphology and histology in relation to function.   Quart. J. Exper. Physiol., vol. 17, p. 125.

HERZOG, F.   1906.   Ueber die Sehbahn, das Ganglion opticum basale und die Faser-systeme am Boden des dritten Hirnventrikels in einem Falle von Bulbusatrophie beider Augen.   Deutsche Zeitschr. f. Nervenh., Bd. 30, S. 223.

HIJMANS VAN DEN BERGH, A. A., AND VAN HASSELT, J. A.   1913.   Tumor glandulae pinealis, sive epiphysis cerebri.   Nederl. tijdschr. v. geneesk., vol. 57, pt. 1, p. 1271.

HINES, M.   1925.   The midbrain and thalamus of Ornithorhynchus paradoxus.   Proc. A. Am. Anatomists, Anat. Rec., vol. 29, p. 361.

——.   1929.   The brain of Ornithorhynchus Anatinus.   Phil. Tr. Roy. Soc., London, Ser. B, vol. 217, p. 155.

HINSEY, J. C., AND RANSON, S. W.   1928.   A note on the significance of the hypo-thalamus for locomotion.   J. Comp. Neurol., vol. 46, p. 461.

HINSEY, J. C., RANSON, S. W., AND DIXON, H. H.   1930.   Responses elicited by stimu-lation of the mesencephalic tegmentum in the cat.   Arch. Neurol. and Psychiat., vol. 24, p. 966.

HINSEY, J. C., RANSON, S. W., AND McNATTIN, R. F.   1930.   The rôle of the hypo-thalamus and mesencephalon in locomotion.   Arch. Neurol. and Psychiat., vol. 23, p. 1.

HIS, W.   1904.   Die Entwickelung des menschlichen Gehirns während der ersten Monate.   S. Hirzel, Leipzig.

HOCHSTETTER, F.   1919–1929.   Beiträge zur Entwicklungsgeschichte des menschlichen Gehirns.   F. Deuticke, Wien u. Leipzig.

D'HOLLANDER, F.   1913.   Recherches anatomiques sur les couches optiques.   Le Névraxe, vol. 14–15, p. 470.

HOLMES, G., AND LISTER, W. T.   1916.   Disturbances of vision from cerebral lesions, with special reference to the cortical representation of the macula.   Brain, vol. 39, p. 34.

HONEGGER, J.   1890.   Vergleichende anatomischen Untersuchungen über den Fornix.   Recueil. zool. suisse, vol. 5.

HOWE, H.   1933.   The basal diencephalon of the armadillo.   J. Comp. Neurol., vol. 58, p. 311.

HUBER, G. CARL, AND CROSBY, E. C.   1929.   The nuclei and fiber paths of the avian diencephalon, with consideration of telencephalic and certain mesencephalic centers and connections.   J. Comp. Neurol., vol. 48, p. 1.

——.   1933.   A phylogenetic consideration of the optic tectum.   Proc. Nat. Acad. Sc., vol. 19, p. 15.

HUET, W. G.   1911.   Zwischenhirn und Halssympathicus.   Arch. f. d. ges. Physiol. (Pflüger's), Bd. 137, S. 627.

INGRAM, W. R., HANNETT, F. L., AND RANSON, S. W.   1932.   Topography of the nuclei of the diencephalon of the cat.   J. Comp. Neurol., vol. 55, p. 333.

INGRAM, W. R., RANSON, S. W., AND HANNETT, F. L.   1931.   Pupillary dilatation pro-duced by direct stimulation of the tegmentum of the brain stem.   Am. J. Physiol., vol. 98, p. 687.

INGVAR, S. 1923. On thalamic evolution. Acta Med. Scandinavica, vol. 59, p. 696.

JACOBSON, L. 1909. Ueber die Kerne des menschlichen Hirnstammes. Aus dem Anhang zu den Abhandlungen der Berl. Akad. d. Wiss. (Quoted from Malone, '10.) See also Neurol. Centralbl., Bd. 28, S. 674.

JAKOB, A. 1923. Die extrapyramidalen Erkrankungen. J. Springer, Berlin.

——. 1925. The anatomy, clinical syndromes and physiology of the extrapyramidal system. Arch. Neurol. and Psychiat., vol. 13, p. 596.

JELLIFFE, S. E., AND WHITE, W. A. 1929. Diseases of the nervous system. 5th edition. Lea and Febiger, Philadelphia.

JOHNSTON, J. B. 1923. Further contributions to the study of the evolution of the forebrain. J. Comp. Neurol., vol. 35, p. 337.

JORDAN, H. E. 1911. The histogenesis of the pineal body of the sheep. Am. J. Anat., vol. 12, p. 249.

——. 1911a. The microscopic anatomy of the epiphysis of the opossum. Anat. Rec., vol. 5, p. 325.

——. 1912. Results of recent studies of the mammalian epiphysis cerebri. Proc. Am. Micr. Soc., vol. 31, p. 231.

JOUSTRA, N. 1918. Over de homologie van het ganglion isthmi, Psychiat. en Neurol., Bl., vol. 22, p. 361.

KARPLUS, J. P., AND VON ECONOMO, C. J. 1909. Zur Physiologie und Anatomie des Mittelhirns. Arch. f. Psychiat., Bd. 46, S. 275.

KARPLUS, J. P., AND KREIDL, A. 1913. Ueber die Bahn des Pupillar-reflexes (die reflektorische Pupillenstarre). Arch. f. d. ges. Physiol. (Pflüger's), Bd. 149, S. 115.

——. 1918. Gehirn und Sympatheticus. IV. Mitteilung. Arch. f. d. ges. Physiol. (Pflüger's), Bd. 171, S. 192. (See also Bd. 129, S. 138, 1909; Bd. 135, S. 401, 1910; Bd. 143, S. 109, 1912.)

KARY, C. 1924. Pathologisch-anatomische und experimentelle Untersuchungen zur Frage des Diabetes insipidus und der Beziehungen zwischen Tuber cinereum und Hypophyse. Virchow's Arch. f. path. Anat., Bd. 252, S. 734.

KIDD, P. 1910. Pineal experimentation. Brit. Med. J., p. 2002.

DE KLEIJN, A., AND MAGNUS, R. 1920. Ueber die Unabhängigkeit der Labyrinthreflexe vom Kleinhirn und über die Lage der Zentren für die Labyrinthreflexe im Hirnstamm. Arch. f. d. ges. Physiol. (Pflüger's), Bd. 178, S. 124.

KODAMA, S. 1928-9. Ueber die sogenannten Basalganglien. (Morphogenetische und pathologisch-anatomische Untersuchungen); pathologisch-anatomische Untersuchungen mit Bezug auf die sogenannten Basalganglien und ihre Adnexe. Ueber die Faserverbindungen zwischen den Basalganglien und ihren Adnexen, sowie den übrigen subkortikalen Kerngebieten beim Menschen, nebst einigen experimentellen Mitteilungen kritsche Betrachungen. Schweiz. Arch. f. Neurol. u. Psychiat., Bd. 23, S. 38, 1928 u. Bd. 23, S. 179, 1929.

KOHNSTAMM, O., AND QUENSEL, F. 1908. Ueber den Kern des hinteren Längsbundels, den roten Haubenkern und den Nucleus intratrigeminalis. Neurol. Centralbl., Bd. 27, S. 242.

VON KÖLLIKER, A. 1896. Handbuch der Gewebelehre des Menschen. Aufl. 6, Bd. 2. W. Engelmann, Leipzig. 1889-1902.

——. 1899. Chiasma opticum. (Quoted from Minkowski, '20.)

KÖRNYEY, S. 1927. Zur vergleichende Morphologie des lateralen Kniehöckers der Säugethiere. Arb. a. d. neurol. Inst. a. d. Wien. Univ. (Obersteiner's), Bd. 30.

——. 1927a. Experimentalstudien am Nervensystem von E. A. Spiegel. X. Mitt.: Tonusänderung, inbesondere der Rumpfmuskulatur bei Beizung des Mittelhirnquerschnittes. Arb. a. d. neurol. Inst. a. d. Wien. Univ. (Obersteiner's), Bd. 30, S. 120.

KOSAKA, K., AND HIRAIWA, K. 1915. Zur Anatomie der Sehnervenbahnen und ihrer Zentren. Folia neuro-biol., Bd. 9, S. 367.

KRABBE, K. H. 1911. Sur la gland pineale chez l'homme. Nouvelle iconographie de la salpetrière, vol. 24, p. 257.

——. 1915. Histologic studies of the pineal gland. Histologihi Anderiogelsis over corpus pineale. Biblio f. Laeges, Kibin 107, p. 175. (Quoted from Tilney and Warren '19.)

——. 1916. Histologische und embryologische Untersuchungen über die Zirbeldrüse des Menschen. Anat. Hefte, Bd. 54, S. 191.

KREIDL, A. 1914. Zur Frage der sekundären Hörbahnen. Monatschr. f. Ohrenh., Bd. 48, S. 1.

KRIEG, W. J. S. 1932. The hypothalamus of the albino rat. J. Comp. Neurol., vol. 55, p. 19.

DE LANGE, S. J. 1910. The descending tracts of the corpora quadrigemina. Folia neuro-biol., Bd. 3, S. 633.

LANGWORTHY, O. 1933. Development of behavior patterns and myelinization of the nervous system in the human fetus and infant. Publ. 443, Carnegie Institution of Washington.

LANGWORTHY, O. R. 1924. A physiological study of the reactions of young decerebrate animals. Am. J. Physiol., vol. 69, p. 254.

——. 1925. The development of progression and posture in young opossums. Am. J. Physiol., vol. 74, p. 1.

——. 1926. Relation of onset of decerebrate rigidity to the time of myelinization of tracts in the brain-stem and spinal cord of young animals. Contrib. Embryol. No. 89, Publ. Carnegie Inst., Washington, vol. 17, p. 125.

——. 1928. A correlated study of the development of reflex activity in the fetal and young kittens and the myelinization of tracts in the nervous system. Contrib. Embryol. No. 114, Publ. Carnegie Inst., Washington, vol. 20, p. 127.

——. 1928a. The behavior of pouch-young opossums correlated with myelinization of tracts in the nervous system. J. Comp. Neurol., vol. 46, p. 202.

——. 1929. A correlated study of the development of reflex activity in fetal and young kittens and the myelinization of tracts in the nervous system. Contrib. Embryol., Publ. Carnegie Inst., Washington, vol. 20, p. 127.

LAUGHTON, N. B. 1924. Studies on the nervous regulation of progression in mammals. Am. J. Physiol., vol. 70, p. 358.

——. 1926. Studies on young decerebrate mammals. Am. J. Physiol., vol. 75, p. 339.

——. 1928. Studies on the occurrence of extensor rigidity in mammals as a result of cortical injury. Am. J. Physiol., vol. 85, p. 78.

LE GROS CLARK, W. 1929. The thalamus of Tupaia minor. J. Anat., vol. 63, p. 177.

——. 1929a. Studies on the optic thalamus of the Insectivora. The anterior nuclei. Brain, vol. 52, p. 334.

——. 1930. The thalamus of Tarsius. J. Anat., vol. 64, p. 371.

——. 1931. The brain of Microcebus murinus. Proc. Zool. Soc., London, vol. 30, p. 463, pt. 2.

——. 1932. The structure and connections of the thalamus. Brain, vol. 55, p. 406.

——. 1932a. An experimental study of thalamic connections in the rat. Phil. Tr. Roy. Soc., London, Ser. B, vol. 222, p. 1.

——. 1932b. A morphological study of the lateral geniculate body. Brit. J. P. Opthom., May.

——. 1933. The medial geniculate body and the ganglion isthmi. J. Anat., vol. 67, p. 536.

LE GROS CLARK, W., AND BOGGON, R. H. 1933. On the connections of the anterior nucleus of the thalamus. Phil. Trans. Roy. Soc., vol. 222, p. 1.

——. 1933a. On the connections of the medial cell groups of the thalamus. Brain, vol. 56, p. 83.

LE GROS CLARK, W., AND PENMAN, G. 1934. The projection of the retina on the lateral geniculate body. Proc. Roy. Soc., vol. 114, p. 291.

LEONOWA, O. 1896. Beiträge zur Kenntnis der secundären Veränderungen der primaren optischen Centren und Bahnen in Fällen von congenitaler Anophthalmie und Bulbusatrophie bei neugeborenen Kindern. Arch. f. Psychiat., Bd. 28, S. 53.

LESCHKE, E. 1919. Beiträge zur klinischen Pathologie des Zwischenhirns. I. Mittheilung. Klinische und Experimentelle über Diabetes insipidus, seine Beziehungen zur Hypophyse und Zwischenhirns. Feitsch. f. Klin. Med., Bd. 87, S. 201.

LESCHKE, E., AND SCHNEIDER. 1920. Einfluss des Zwischenhirns auf den Stoffwechsel. Verhandl. I. Kongr. f. inn. Med.

LEWANDOWSKY, M. 1904. Untersuchungen über die Leitungsbahnen des Truncus cerebri und ihren Zusammenhang mit denen der Medulla spinalis und des Cortex cerebri. G. Fischer, Jena.

LEWY, F. H. 1924. Infundibuläre Veränderungen beim Diabetis insipidus und die Beziehungen zwischen Tuber cinereum und Hypophyse. Zentralbl. f. d. ges. Neurol. u. Psychiat., Bd. 37, S. 398.

LINDON MELLUS, E. 1907. Relations of the frontal lobe in the monkey. Am. J. Anat., vol. 7, p. 227.

LOEPP, W. H. 1912. Ueber die zentralen Opticusendigung beim Kaninchen. Anat. Anz., Bd. 40, S. 309.

LORENTE DE NO. 1929. (Quoted from Ariëns Kappers, '29.)

LOTHEISSEN, G. 1894. Ueber die Stria medullaris thalami optici ihre Verbindungen. Anat. Hefte, Bd. 4, S. 225.

LUYS, J. 1865. Recherches sur le système nerveux cérébro-spinal. J.-B. Baillière et Fils, Paris.

MACKENZIE, I. 1934. Degeneration of the Lateral Geniculate Bodies. Jour. Path., vol. 39, p. 113.

MAGNUS, R. 1916. Beiträge zum Problem der Körperstellung. Arch. f. d. ges. Physiol. (Pflüger's), Bd. 163, S. 405.

——. 1924. Körperstellung. J. Springer, Berlin.

——. 1925. Animal posture. Croonian Lecture. Proc. Roy. Soc., London, Ser. B, vol. 98, p. 339.

MAGNUS, R., AND DE KLEIJN, A. 1912. Die Abhängigkeit des Tonus der Extremitätenmuskeln von der Kopfstellung. Arch. f. d. ges. Physiol. (Pflüger's), Bd. 145, S. 455.

MALONE, E. F. 1910. Ueber die Kerne des Menschlichen Diencephalon. Abhandl. d. kon. preuss. Akad. d. Wissensch., Berlin, Phys.-math. Cl., Abh. 1, S. 1.

——. 1912. Observations concerning the comparative anatomy of the diencephalon. Anat. Rec., vol. 6, p. 281.

——. 1914. The nuclei tuberis laterales and the so-called ganglion opticum basale. Johns Hopkins Hospital Reports, Monographs. New Series No. 6. Johns Hopkins Press, Baltimore.

MANN, G. 1905. On the thalamus. Brit. Med. J., vol. 1, p. 289.

MARBURG, O. 1903. Basale Opticuswurzel und Tractus peduncularis transversus. Arb. a. d. neurol. Inst. a. d. Wien. Univ. (Obersteiner's), Bd. 10, S. 66.

——. 1903a. Idem. Centralbl. f. Physiol., Bd. 17, S. 30.

——. 1904, 1910. Mikroskopisch-topographischer Atlas des menschlichen Zentralnervensystems. F. Deuticke, Leipzig u. Wien. 2te Aufl. in 1910.

MARBURG, O.   1909.   Zur Kenntnis der normalen und pathologischen Histologie der Zirbeldrüse.   Die Adipositas cerebralis.   Arb. a. d. neurol. Inst. a. d. Wien. Univ. (Obersteiner's), Bd. 17, S. 217.

———.   1916.   Das Kleinhirn beim angeborenen Hydrocephalus.   Arb. a. d. neurol. Inst. a. d. Wien. Univ. (Obersteiner's), Bd. 21, S. 213.

———.   1920.   Neue Studien über die Zirbeldrüse.   Arb. a. d. neurol. Inst. a. d. Wien. Univ. (Obersteiner's), Bd. 23, S. 1.

MELLA, H.   1923.   The diencephalic centers controlling associated locomotor movements.   Arch. Neurol. and Psychiat., vol. 10, p. 141.

MIHALKOVICZ, V.   1874.   Entwicklung der Zirbeldrüse.   Centralbl. f. d. med. Wissensch., Bd. 12, S. 241.

MINGAZZINI, G.   1889.   Sur la fine structure de la substantia nigra Sömmeringii.   Arch. ital. de biol., vol. 12, p. 93.

———.   1913.   Experimentelle Untersuchungen über die Beziehungen der Grosshirn und der Netzhaut zu den primären Opticuszentren.   Arb. a. d. hirnanat. Inst. in Zürich, Bd. 7, S. 259.

———.   1919.   Ueber Verlauf, die Endigung und die zentrale Repräsentation von gekreuzten und ungekreutzen Sehnervenfasern bei einigen Säugetieren und beim Menschen.   Schweiz. Arch. f. Neurol. u. Psychiat., Bd. 7, S. 201.

———.   1928.   Medulla oblongata und Brücke.   In G. von Möllendorf's Handbuch der mikroskopische Anatomie des Menschen, Bd. 4, Nervensystem, S. 579.   J. Springer, Berlin.

MINKOWSKI, M.   1913.   Experimentelle Untersuchungen über die Beziehungen des Grosshirns und der Netzhaut zu den primären Opticuszentren.   Arb. a. d. hirnanat. Inst. zu Zürich., Bd. 7, S. 259.

———.   1920.   Ueber den Verlauf, die Endigung und die zentrale Repräsentation von gekreuzten und ungekreuzten Sehnervenfasern bei einigen Säugetieren und beim Menschen.   Schweiz. Arch. f. Neurol. u. Psychiat., Bd. 6, S. 201 ; Bd. 7, S. 268.

———.   1923–1924.   Étude sur les connexions anatomiques des circonvolutions rolandiques, pariétales et frontales.   Schweiz. Arch. f. Neurol. u. Psychiat., Bd. 12, S. 71 u. 227 ; Bd. 14, S. 255 ; Bd. 15, S. 97.

MIRTO, D.   1896.   Sulla fina anatomia delle regioni peduncolare e subtalamica nell'uomo.   Riv. di pat. nerv., vol. 1, p. 57.

———.   1896a.   Contributo alla fina anatomia della substantia nigra di Sömmering e del peduncolo cerebrale dell'uomo.   Riv. sper. di freniat., vol. 22, p. 197.

VON MONAKOW, C.   1882.   Ueber einige durch Exstirpation circumscripter Hirnrindenregionen bedingte Entwickelungshemmungen des Kaninchengehirns.   Arch. f. Psychiat., Bd. 12, S. 141.

———.   1883.   Experimentelle Untersuchungen über Hirnrindenatrophien.   Neurol. Centralbl., Bd. 2, S. 505.

———.   1883a.   Experimentelle und pathologisch-anatomische Untersuchungen über die Beziehungen der sogenannten Sehsphäre zu den infracorticalen Opticuscentren und zum N. opticus.   Arch. f. Psychiat., Bd. 14, S. 699.

———.   1885.   Einiges über die Ursprungscentren des N. opticus und über die Verbindungen derselben mit der Sehsphäre.   Verhandl. d. physiol. Gesellsch. zu Berlin.

———.   1885a.   Neue experimentelle Beiträge zur Anatomie der Schleife.   Neurol. Centralbl., Bd. 4, S. 265.

———.   1888.   Experimentelle und pathologisch-anatomische Beiträge zur Kenntnis der optischen Leitungsbahnen und Zentren.   Korrespondenzbl. f. Schweiz. Aerzte, Bd. 18.

———.   1889.   Experimentelle und pathologisch-anatomische Untersuchungen über die Beziehungen der sogenannten Sehsphäre zu den infracorticalen Optikuscentren und zum Nerv. opticus.   Arch. f. Psychiat., Bd. 20, S. 714.   See also Bd. 16, S. 151, 1885.

VON MONAKOW, C. 1895. Experimentelle und pathologisch-anatomische Untersuchungen über die Haubenregion, den Sehhügel und die Regio subthalamica nebst Beiträgen zur Kenntnis früh erworbener Gross- und Kleinhirndefecte. Arch. f. Psychiat., Bd. 27, S. 1 u. S. 386.

——. 1904. Ueber den gegenwärtigen Stand der Frage nach der Lokalisation im Grosshirn. Ergeb. d. Physiol., Bd. 3, Abt. 3, S. 100.

——. 1905. Gehirnpathologie. 2te Aufl., A. Hölder, Wien.

——. 1910. Der rote Kern, die Haube und die Regio subthalamica bei einigen Säugetieren und beim Menschen. Arb. a. d. hirnanat. Inst. in Zürich, Bd. 4, S. 103.

——. 1929. Zur Frage der "Brainkommission" (Internationale Hirnkommission) und einer international organisierten Hirnforschung. Schweiz. Arch. f. Neurol. u. Psychiat., vol. 24.

MORGAN, L. O. 1927. The corpus striatum. A study of secondary degeneration following lesions in man and symptoms and acute degenerations following experimental lesions in cats. Arch. Neurol. and Psychiat., vol. 18, p. 495.

——. 1928. Localized cell destruction and degenerative processes in the brain in idiopathic epilepsy. Proc. Soc. Exper. Biol. and Med., vol. 25, p. 444.

——. 1928a. Further observations on mamillo-infundibular region of diencephalon: relation to epilepsy, dementia, and the psychoses. Proc. Soc. Exper. Biol. and Med., vol. 25, p. 617.

——. 1930. The nuclei of the region of the tuber cinereum: degenerative changes in epilepsy, with a discussion of their significance. Arch. Neurol. and Psychiat., vol. 24, p. 267.

——. 1930a. Cell groups in the tuber cinereum of the dog, with a discussion of their function. J. Comp. Neurol., vol. 51, p. 271.

——. 1930b. The rôle of the tuber cinereum and the thyroid gland in experimental fever in the dog. Anat. Rec., vol. 45, p. 233.

MORGAN, L. O., AND GREGORY, H. S. 1930. Pathological changes in the region of the tuber cinereum in idiopathic epilepsy. Am. J. Psychiat., vol. 9, p. 805.

MORGAN, L. O., AND JOHNSON, C. A. 1928. Symptoms resembling epilepsy following experimental lesions in the brain of the dog. Proc. Soc. Exper. Biol. and Med., vol. 25, p. 442.

——. 1930. Experimental lesions in the tuber cinereum of the dog, followed by epileptiform convulsions and changes in blood chemistry. Arch. Neurol. and Psychiat., vol. 24, p. 696.

MOTT, F. W. 1907. Bilateral lesion of the auditory cortical center; complete deafness and aphasia. Brit. Med. J., vol. 2, p. 310.

MÜNZER, E., AND WIENER, H. 1902. Das Zwischen- und Mittelhirn des Kaninchens und die Beziehungen dieser Teile zum übrigen Centralnervensystem, mit besonderer Berücksichtigung der Pyramidenbahn und Schleife. Monatschr. f. Psychiat. u. Neurol., Bd. 12, S. 241.

MURIE, J. 1885. Further observations on the Manatee. Tr. Zool. Soc., London, vol. 11, p. 19.

MUSKENS, L. J. J. 1914. An anatomico-physiological study of the posterior longitudinal bundle in its relation to forced movement. Brain, vol. 36, p. 352.

——. 1922. The central connections of the vestibular nuclei with the corpus striatum and their significance for ocular movements and for locomotion. Brain, vol. 45, p. 454.

——. 1930. Anatomo-physiologische Correlation von dem Globus pallidus und dem hinteren Längsbündel. Schweiz. Arch. f. Neurol. u. Psychiat., Bd. 26, S. 27.

MUSSEN, A. T. 1927. Experimental investigations on the cerebellum. Brain, vol. 50, p. 313.

MYERS, B. D.   1902.   Beitrag zur Kenntnis des Chiasmas und der Commissuren am Boden des dritten Ventrikels.   Arch. f. Anat. u. Physiol., Anat. Abt., S. 347.

NEIDING, M.   1911.   Ueber die Kerne des Diencephalon bei einigen Säugetieren. Abhandl. d. kon. preuss. Akad. d. Wissensch., Berlin.

NICOLESCO, I., AND NICOLESCO, M.   1929.   Quelques données sur les centres végétatifs de la région infundibulo-tubérienne et de la frontière diencéphalo-télencéphalique. Rev. neurol., vol. 2, p. 289.

NISSL, F.   1889.   Die Kerne des Thalamus beim Kaninchen, Tageblatt der 62. Versamml. d. deutsch. Nat. u. Aerzte in Heidelberg.

——.   1911.   Zur Lehre der Lokalisation in der Grosshirnrinde des Kaninchens. Sitzungsb. d. Heidelberger Akad. d. Wissensch., Math.-naturw. Kl., Abh. 38.

——.   1913.   Die Grosshirnanteile des Kaninchens.   Arch. f. Psychiat., Bd. 52, S. 867.

OBERSTEINER, H.   1901, 1912.   Anleitung beim Studium des Baues der nervösen Zentralorgane im gesunden und kranken Zustände.   F. Deuticke, Leipzig, Wien.

ORLANDO, R.   1933.   Sobre atrofia alternada de las capas del cuerpo geniculado externo en el hombre.   Arch. Argent. Neurol., vol. 9, p. 122.

PALMGREN, A.   1921.   Embryological and morphological studies on the midbrain and cerebellum of vertebrates.   Acta Zool., Bd. 2, S. 1.

PAPEZ, J.   1923.   The thalamic end of the medial fillet.   Anat. Rec., vol. 25, p. 146.

——.   1926.   Reticulospinal tracts in the cat.   Marchi method.   J. Comp. Neurol., vol. 41, p. 365.

——.   1929.   Comparative neurology.   T. Y. Crowell Co., New York.

——.   1932.   The thalamic nuclei of the nine-banded armadillo (Tatusia novemcinata). J. Comp. Neurol., vol. 56, p. 49.

PAPEZ, J., AND ARONSON, L.   1934.   Arch. Neurol. and Psychiat., vol. 32, p. 1.

PAPEZ, J. W., AND FREEMAN, G. LaV.   1930.   Superior colliculi and their fiber connections in the rat.   J. Comp. Neurol., vol. 51, p. 409.

PARKER, K. M.   1917.   The development of the hypophysis cerebri, pre-oral gut, and related structures in Marsupialia.   J. Anat., vol. 51, p. 181.'

PAVLOW, M.   1900.   Les connexions centrales du nerf optique chez le lapin.   Le Névraxe, vol. 1, p. 235.

——.   1900a.   Quelques points concernant le role physiologique du tubercule quadrijuneau supérieur, du noyau rouge et de la substance réticulaire de la calotte.   Le Névraxe, vol. 1, p. 331.

——.   1900b.   Un faisceau descendant de la substance réticulaire du mésencéphale. Le Névraxe, vol. 1, p. 271.

——.   1900c.   Le faisceau de v. Monakow, faisceau mésencéphalospinal latéral ou faisceau rubro-spinal.   Le Névraxe, vol. 1, p. 151.

——.   1900d.   Les voies descendantes des tubercules quadrijumeaux supérieurs. I. Le faisceau longitudinal predorsal ou faisceau tecto-bulbaire.   Le Névraxe, vol. 1, p. 57.

——.   1900e.   Les voies descendantes des tubercules quadrijumeaux supérieurs. II. Le faisceau de Münzer ou faisceau tecto-protubérantiel et les voies courtes. Le Névraxe, vol. 1, p. 129.

PFEIFER, R. A.   1925.   Myelogenetisch-anatomische Untersuchungen über den centralen Abschnitt der Sehbahn.   Monogr. a. d. Ges. d. Neurol. u. Psychiat., Bd. 43, S. 146.

PIERSOL, G. A.   1930.   Human anatomy.   9th edition revised under the supervision of G. Carl Huber.   J. B. Lippincott Co., Philadelphia and London.

PINES, J. L.   1925.   Ueber die Innervation der Hypophysis cerebri. II. Mitteilung. Ueber die Innervation des Mittel- und Hinterlappens der Hypophyse.   Zeitschr. f. d. ges. Neurol. u. Psychiat., Bd. 100, S. 123.

——.   1927.   Zur Architektonik des Thalamus opticus beim Halbaffen (Lemur catta). J. f. Psychol. u. Neurol., Bd. 33, S. 31.

POLIAK, S. 1927. An experimental study of the associational, callosal, and projectional fibers of the cerebral cortex of the cat. J. Comp. Neurol., vol. 44, p. 197.

——. 1932. The main afferent fiber systems of the cerebral cortex in Primates. Univ. California Publ. in Anat., vol. 2. Univ. of California Press, Berkeley.

——. 1933. A contribution to the cerebral representation of the retina. J. Comp. Neurol., vol. 57, p. 541.

POLIMANTI, O. 1906–7. Sulla valenza motoria della pupilla. Arch. di ottal., Napoli, vol. 14, p. 85.

——. 1911. Contributi alla fisilogia del sistema nervoso centrale e del movimento deipesci. I. Selacoidei (Scyllium patalus Curier e Scyllium canicula L.). Zool. Jahrb., Zool. Abt. Bd. 30, S. 473.

POLVANI, F. 1913. Studio Anatomico della Glandola Pineale Umana. Folia neuro-biol., Bd. 7, S. 655.

POPA, G., AND FIELDING, U. 1930. A portal circulation from the pituitary to the hypothalamic region. J. Anat., vol. 65, p. 88.

POPPI, U. 1927. Ueber die Fasersysteme der Substantia nigra. Arb. a. d. neurol. Inst. a. d. Wien. Univ. (Obersteiner's), Bd. 29, S. 8.

——. 1928. Su alcuni sistema di fibri nel tegmento mesencefalico. Riv. di pat. nerv., vol. 33, p. 59.

PŘECECHTĚL, A. 1925. Some notes upon the finer anatomy of the brain stem and basal ganglia of Elephas indicus. Kon. Akad. v. Wetensch. te Amsterdam, Proc. sect. sc., vol. 28, p. 1.

PROBST, M. 1898. Experimentelle Untersuchungen über das Zwischenhirn und dessen Verbindungen, besonders die sogenannte Rindenschleife. Deutsche Zeitschr. f. Nervenh., Bd. 13, S. 384.

——. 1900. Physiologische, anatomische und pathologisch-anatomische Unter-suchungen des Sehhügels. Arch. f. Psychiat., Bd. 33, S. 721.

——. 1900a. Experimentelle Untersuchungen über die Schleifenendigung, die Hauben-bahnen, das dorsale Längsbündel und die hintere Commissur. Arch. f. Psychiat., Bd. 33, S. 1.

——. 1900b. Ueber den Verlauf der Sehnervenfasern und deren Endigung im Zwischen- und Mittelhirn. Monatschr. f. Psychiat. u. Neurol., Bd. 8, S. 165.

——. 1901. Zur Kenntnis der Bindearmes, der Haubenstrahlung, und der Regio sub-thalamica. Monatschr. f. Psychiat. u. Neurol., Bd. 10, S. 288.

——. 1901a. Ueber den Verlauf der centralen Sehfasern (Rinden-Sehhügelfasern) und deren Endigung im Zwischen- und Mittelhirne und über die Associations- und Commissurenfasern der Sehsphäre. Arch. f. Psychiat., Bd. 35, S. 22.

——. 1902. Zur Anatomie und Physiologie des Kleinhirns. Arch. f. Psychiat., Bd. 35, S. 692.

——. 1902a. Ueber centripetale Rückenmarksfasern zur Substantia reticularis. Monatschr. f. Psychiat. u. Neurol., Bd. 11, S. 3.

——. 1902b. Experimentelle Untersuchungen über die Anatomie und Physiologie der Leitungsbahnen des Gehirnstammes. Arch. f. Anat. u. Physiol., Anat. Abt. Suppl.-Bd., S. 147.

——. 1902c. Ueber die Bedeutung des Sehhügels. Wien klin. Wochenschr., S. 932.

——. 1903. Ueber die Leitungsbahnen des Gehirns mit besonderer Berücksichtigung der Anatomie und Physiologie des Sehhügels. Jahrb. f. Psychiat. u. Neurol., Bd. 23, S. 18.

——. 1903a. Ueber die anatomischen und physiologischen Folgen der Halbseiten-durchschneidung des Mittelhirns. Jahrb. f. Psychiat. u. Neurol., Bd. 24, S. 219.

——. 1905. Ueber die Kommissur von Gudden, Meynert und Ganser und über die Folgen der Bulbusatrophie auf die zentrale Sehbahn. Monatschr. f. Psychiat. u. Neurol., Bd. 17, S. 1.

PROBST, M.   1902c.   Ueber die Bedeutung des Sehhügels.   Wien. klin. Wochenschr., S. 932.

PRUS, J.   1899.   Ueber die bei elektrischer Reizung des Corpus striatum und des Thalamus opticus auftretenden Erscheinungen.   Wien. klin. Wochenschr., Bd. 12, S. 1199.

PUTNAM, T. J.   1926.   Studies on the central visual system.   II. A comparative study of the form of the geniculo-striate visual system of mammals.   Arch. Neurol. and Psychiat., vol. 16, p. 285.

——.   1926a.   Idem.   III. The general relationships between the external geniculate body, optic radiation and visual cortex in man : report of two cases.   Arch. Neurol. and Psychiat., vol. 16, p. 566.

——.   1926b.   Idem.   IV. The details of the organization of the geniculo-striate system in man.   Arch. Neurol. and Psychiat., vol. 16, p. 683.

PUTNAM, T. J., AND PUTNAM, I. K.   1926.   Studies on the central visual system. I. The anatomic projection of the retinal quadrants on the striate cortex of the rabbit.   Arch. Neurol. and Psychiat., vol. 16, p. 1.

RADEMAKER, G. G. J.   1926.   Die Bedeutung der roten Kerne und des übrigen Mittelhirns für Muskeltonus, Körperstellung und Labyrinthreflexe.   J. Springer, Berlin.

RAMÓN Y CAJAL, S.   1892.   La rétine des vertébrés.   La Cellule, vol. 9 (1893), p. 121.

——.   1899–1904.   Textura del sistema nervioso del hombre y de vertebrados. N. Moya, Madrid.

——.   1909–11.   Histologie du système nerveux de l'homme et des vertébrés. A. Maloine, Paris.

RANSON, S. W.   1931, 1932.   The anatomy of the nervous system.   4th edition.   W. B. Saunders Co., Philadelphia and London.

RANSON, S. W., AND HINSEY, J. C.   1929.   The crossed extensor reflex in deafferentiated muscle after transection of the brain stem at varying levels.   J. Comp. Neurol., vol. 48, p. 393.

RANSON, S. W., AND INGRAM, W. R.   1932.   The diencephalic course and termination of the medial lemniscus and the brachium conjunctivum.   J. Comp. Neurol., vol. 56, p. 257.

RANSON, S. W., AND MAGOUN, H. W.   1933.   The central path of the pupillo-constrictor reflex in response to light.   Arch. Neurol. and Psychiat., vol. 30, p. 1193.

——.   1933.   Respiratory and pupillary reactions induced by electrical stimulation of the hypothalamus.   Arch. Neurol. and Psychiat., vol. 29, p. 1179.

RASMUSSEN, A.   1932.   Secondary vestibular tracts in the cat.   J. Comp. Neurol., vol. 54, p. 143.

——.   1932a.   The principal nervous pathways.   The Macmillan Co., New York.

REDLICH, E.   1899.   Beiträge zur Anatomie und Physiologie der motorischen Bahnen bei der Katze.   Monatschr. f. Psychiat. u. Neurol., Bd. 5, S. 112.

REICHARDT, M.   1913.   Ueber die Störungen der Körper Temperatur und der vasomotorisch-tropischen Funktionen bei Hirnerkrankungen.   Zeitschr. f. d. ges. Neurol. u. Psychiat., Bd. 18, S. 417.

RETZIUS, G.   1898.   Zur Kenntnis der lateralen Fläche des Mesencephalons und ihrer Umgebung.   Biol. Untersuch., N. F., Bd. 8, S. 65.

RIESE, W.   1924.   Zur vergleichenden Anatomie der Striofugalen Faserung.   Zentralbl. f. d. ges. Neurol. u. Psychiat., Bd. 34, Heft 3, S. 153.   Anat. Anz., Bd. 57, S. 487.

——.   1924a.   Ueber faseranatomische Verbindungen im "striären System" der wasserlebenden Säuger.   Zeitschr. f. d. ges. Neurol. u. Psychiat., Bd. 90, S. 591.

——.   1924b.   Beiträge zur Faseranatomie der Stammganglien.   J. f. Psychol. u. Neurol., Bd. 31, S. 81.

RIOCH, D. McK. 1929. Studies on the diencephalon of Carnivora. Part I. The nuclear configuration of the thalamus, epithalamus, and hypothalamus of the dog and cat. J. Comp. Neurol., vol. 49, p. 1.

——. 1929a. Idem. Part II. Certain nuclear configurations and fiber connections of the subthalamus of the dog and cat. J. Comp. Neurol., vol. 49, p. 121.

——. 1931. Idem. Part III. Certain myelinated fiber connections of the diencephalon of the dog (Canis familaris), cat (Felis domestica), and aevisa (Crossarchus obscurus). J. Comp. Neurol., vol. 53, p. 319.

——. 1931a. A note on the centre median nucleus of Luys. J. Anat., vol. 65, p. 324.

ROGERS, F. T. 1924. An experimental study of the cerebral physiology of the virginian opossum. J. Comp. Neurol., vol. 37, p. 265.

RONGE, P. H. 1929. A propos des connexions pédonculo-tegmentaires. J. de neurol., vol. 29, p. 489.

RÖNNE, H. 1911. Ueber die Bedeutung des makularen Aussparung im hemianopischen Gesichtsfelde. Klin. Monatsbl. f. Augenh., Bd. 49, S. 289.

——. 1914. Die anatomische Projektion der Macula im Corpus geniculatum externum. Zeitschr. f. d. ges. Neurol. u. Psychiat., Bd. 22, S. 469.

RÖTHIG, P 1909. Reichbahnen, Septum und Thalamus bei Didelphis marsupialis. Abhandl. d. Senckenb. nat. Gesellsch., Frankfurt am Main, Bd. 31, S. 1.

——. 1911. Beiträge zum Studium des Zentralnervensystems der Wirbeltiere. 3. Zur Phylogenese der Hypothalamus. Folia neuro-biol., Bd. 5, S. 913. See also Arch. f. mikr. Anat., Bd. 77, S. 48.

ROUSSY, G. 1907. La couche optique. Thèse de Paris, p. 175. G. Steinheil, Paris.

RÜTISHÄUSER, F. 1899. Experimenteller Beitrag zur Stabkranzfaserung im Frontalhirn des Affen. Monatschr. f. Psychiat. u. Neurol., Bd. 5, S. 161.

SACHS, E. 1909. Eine vergleichende anatomische Studie des Thalamus opticus der Säugetiere. Arb. a. d. neurol. Inst. a. d. Wien. Univ. (Obersteiner's), Bd. 17, S. 280.

——. 1909a. On the structure and functional relations of the optic thalamus. Brain, vol. 32, p. 95.

SAGER, O. 1933. Recherches sur la somatopie sensitive dans le thalamus des singes, étudiées par la méthode de dégénerescence rétrograde. Amsterdam.

LA SALLE ARCHAMBAULT. 1914–5. Les connexions corticales du noyau rouge. Nouvelle iconographie de la salpetrière, vol. 27, p. 188.

SALZER, F. 1880. Ueber die Anzahl der Sehnervenfasern und der Retinazapfen im Auge des Menschen. Sitzungsb. d. K. Akad. d. Wissensch. zu Wien, Math.-nat. Cl., Bd. 81, Abt. 3, S. 7.

SANO, T. 1910. Beitrag zur vergleichenden Anatomie der Substantia nigra, des Corpus Luysii und der Zona incerta. Monatschr. f. Psychiat. u. Neurol., Bd. 27, S. 110, 274, 381 u. 476.

SCHARRER, E. 1933. Die Erklärung der scheinbar pathologischen Zellbilder im Nucleus supraopticus und Nucleus paraventricularis. Zeits. f. d. ges. Neurol. u. Psychiat., Bd. 145, S. 462.

SCHLAGENHAUFER, F. 1897. Anatomische Beiträge zum Faserverlauf in den Sehnervenbahnen und Beitrag zur tabischen Sehnervenatrophie. Arb. a. d. neurol. Inst. a. d. Wien. Univ. (Obersteiner's), Bd. 5, S. 1.

SCHNOPFHAGEN, F. 1877. Beiträge zur Anatomie des Sehhügels und dessen nächster Umgebung. Sitzungsbl. d. K. Akad. d. Wissensch. zu Wien, Math.-nat. Cl., Bd. 76, Abt. 3, S. 315.

SCHROTTENBACH, H. 1916. Beiträge zur Kenntnis der Uebertragung vasovegetativer Funktionen im Zwischenhirn. Zeitschr. f. d. ges. Neurol. u. Psychiat., Bd. 33, S. 229. Referate und Ergebnisse, Bd. 14, S. 371, 1917.

SHERRINGTON, C. S. 1896. A textbook of Physiology. Part 3. The Central nervous system. Macmillan and Co., New York.

SHERRINGTON, C. S.   1906.   The integrative action of the nervous system.   C. Scribner's Sons, New York.

SINGER, J., AND MÜNZER, E.   1889.   Beiträge zur Kenntnis der Sehnervenkreuzung. Denkschr. d. K. Akad. d. Wissensch. zu Wien, Math.-nat. Cl., Bd. 55, Abt. 2, S. 163.

SMITH, G. ELLIOT.   See Elliot Smith.

SMITH, P. E.   1927.   The disabilities caused by hypophysectomy and their repair. J. A. M. A., vol. 88, p. 158.

SPATZ, H.   1927.   Physiologie und Pathologie der Stammganglien.   Handb. norm. u. path. Physiol., Bd. 10, S. 318.   J. Springer, Berlin.

SPIEGEL, E. A.   1928.   Die Zentren des autonomen Nervensystems.   Monographien Neur. (Foerster u. Wilmanns).   Berlin.

———.   1932.   The centers of the vegetative nervous system.   Bull. Johns Hopkins Univ., vol. 50, p. 237.

SPIEGEL, E. A., AND ZWEIG, H.   1917.   Zur Cytoarchitektonik des Tuber cinereum. Arb. a. d. neurol. Inst. a. d. Wien. Univ. (Obersteiner's), Bd. 22, S. 278.

SPITZER, A., AND KARPLUS, J. P.   1907.   Ueber experimentelle Läsionen an der Gehirnbasis. (Anatomische Ergebnisse nebst einigen physiologischen Bemerkungen.) Arb. a. d. neurol. Inst. a. d. Wien. Univ. (Obersteiner's), Bd. 16, S. 348.

STENGEL, E.   1926.   Ueber den Ursprung der Nervenfasern der Neurohypophyse im Zwischenhirn.   Arb. a. d. neurol. Inst. a. d. Wien. Univ. (Obersteiner's), Bd. 28, S. 25.

STERZI, G.   1914–1915.   Anatomia del sistema nervoso centrale dell'uomo.   Vols. 1–2. A. Draghi, Padova.

STOPFORD, J. S. B.   1930.   Sensation and the sensory pathway.   London.

STUDNIČKA, F. K.   1905.   Die Parietalorgane.   A. Oppel's Lehrbuch der vergleichende mikroskopischen Anatomie der Wirbeltiere, Bd. 5.   G. Fischer, Jena, 1896–1914.

TARASEWITSCH, J.   1902.   Zum Studium der mit dem Thalamus opticus und Nucleus lenticularis in Zusammenhang stehenden Faserzüge.   Arb. a. d. neurol. Inst. a. d. Wien. Univ. (Obersteiner's), Bd. 9, S. 251.

TARTUFERI, F.   1885.   Sull'anatomia minuta dell'eminenze bigemine anteriori dell'-uomo.   Arch. ital. per le mal nerv., Milano, vol. 22, p. 3.

TELLO, F.   1904.   Disposición macroscópica y estructura del cuerpo geniculado externo. Trab. d. lab. de invest. biol. Univ. de Madrid, vol. 3, p. 39.

TESTUT, L.   1911–1921–23.   Traité d'anatomie humaine.   O. Doin et fils, Paris.

THIELE, F. H.   1905.   On the efferent relationship of the optic thalamus and Deiters' nucleus to the spinal cord, with special reference to the cerebellar influx of Dr. Hughlings Jackson and the genesis of the decerebrate rigidity of Ord and Sherrington. J. Physiol., vol. 32, p. 358.

THUMA, B. D.   1928.   Studies on the diencephalon of the cat.   I. The cytoarchitecture of the corpus geniculatum laterale.   J. Comp. Neurol., vol. 46, p. 173.

TILNEY, F.   1911.   Contribution to the study of the hypophysis cerebri with especial reference to its comparative histology.   Mem. Wistar Inst. Anat. and Biol., No. 2.

———.   1914.   An analysis of the juxta-neural-epithelial portion of the hypophysis cerebri, with an embryological and histological account of an hitherto undescribed part of the organ.   Internat. Monatschr. f. Anat. u. Physiol., Bd. 30, S. 258.

TILNEY, F., AND RILEY, H. A.   1921.   The form and functions of the central nervous system.   P. Hoeber, New York.

TILNEY, F., AND WARREN, W. F.   1919.   The morphology and evolutional significance of the pineal body.   Am. Anat. Mem., No. 9, p. 5.

TSAI, C.   1925.   The optic tracts and centers of the opossum, Didelphis virginiana. J. Comp. Neurol., vol. 39, p. 173.

———.   1925a.   The descending tracts of the thalamus and midbrain of the opossum, Didelphis virginiana.   J. Comp. Neurol., vol. 39, p. 217.

TSCHERMAK, A. 1898. Ueber den centralen Verlauf der aufsteigenden Hinterstrang-bahnen und deren Beziehungen zu den Bahnen im Vorderseidenstrang. Arch. f. Anat. u. Physiol., Anat. Abt., S. 291.

VAN VALKENBURG, C. T. 1912. Caudal connections of the corpus mammillare. Kon. Akad. v. Wetensch. te Amsterdam, Proc. sect. sc., vol. 14, pt. 2, p. 1118.

DA VILLAVERDE, J. 1923. Beitrag zur Kenntnis der kortikothalamischen Beziehungen in der motorischen Zone beim Kaninchen. Schweiz. Arch. f. Neurol. u. Psychiat., Bd. 13, S. 665.

VILLIGER, E. 1925. Brain and spinal cord. Edited by Addison. J. B. Lippincott Co., Philadelphia and London.

VOGT, C. 1909. La myéloarchitecture du thalamus du cercopithèque. J. f. Psychol. u. Neurol., Bd. 12, S. 275.

VOGT, C., AND VOGT, O. 1919. Zur Kenntnis der pathologischen Veränderungen des Striatum und des Pallidum und zur Pathophysiologie dabei auftretenden Krank-heitserscheinungen. Sitzungsb. d. Heidelberger Akad. d. Wissensch., Math.-naturw. Kl., Abt. 13, S. 14.

——. 1920. Zur Lehre der Erkrankungen des striärens Systems. J. f. Psychol. u. Neurol., Bd. 25, S. 631.

WALBAUM, H. 1914. Hirnbefunde an durch Hirnreizung hyperthermisch gemachten Kaninchen und ihre Beziehungen zur Hyperthermie. Arch. f. exper. Path. u. Pharmakol., Bd. 75, S. 423.

WALLENBERG, A. 1899. Notiz über einen Schleifenursprung des Pedunculus corporis mamillaris beim Kaninchen. Anat. Anz., Bd. 16, S. 156.

——. 1900. Sekundäre sensible Bahnen im Gehirnstamme des Kaninchens, ihre gegenseitige Lage und ihre Bedeutung für den Aufbau des Thalamus. Anat. Anz., Bd. 18, S. 81.

——. 1901. Giebt es centrifugale Bahnen aus dem Sehhügel zum Rückenmark? Neurol. Centralbl., Bd. 20, S. 50.

——. 1904. Neue Untersuchungen über den Hirnstamm der Taube. Anat. Anz., Bd. 24, S. 142.

——. 1905. Sekundäre Bahnen aus den frontalen sensiblen Trigeminuskerne des Kaninchens. Anat. Anz., Bd. 26, S. 145.

——. 1922. Beitrag zur Kenntnis der zentrifugalen Bahnen des Striatum and Pallidum bei Menschen. Jahresversammlung der Gesellschaft deutscher Nervenärzte und Psychiatre, Bd. 30.

——. 1925. Beiträge zur Kenntnis des Iltisgehirns. Zeitschr. f. d. ges. Anat.; Abt. 1, Zeitschr. f. Anat. u. Entwicklungsgesch., Bd. 79, S. 352.

WARNER, F. J. 1929. The hypothalamus of the opossum (Didelphis virginiana). J. Nerv. and Ment. Dis., vol. 70, p. 485.

WEED, L. H. 1914. Observations upon decerebrate rigidity. J. Physiol., vol. 48, p. 205.

——. 1917. The reactions of kittens after decerebration. Am. J. Physiol., vol. 43, p. 131.

WEED, L. H., AND LANGWORTHY, O. R. 1925. Decerebrate rigidity in the opossum. Am. J. Physiol., vol. 72, p. 25.

WEIGERT, C. 1895. Beitrag zur Kenntnis normalen menschlichen Neuroglia. Abhandl. d. Senckenb. nat. Gesellsch., Frankfurt am Main, Bd. 19.

WEINBERG, E. 1928. See bibliography, page 427.

WILBRAND, H., AND SAENGER, A. 1904. Die Neurologie des Auges. Bd. I–VII (par-ticularly Bd. III) and Bd. VII, 1917. Bergmann. (Quoted from Minkowski '20.)

WILSON, S. A. K. 1914. An experimental research into the anatomy and physiology of the corpus striatum. Brain, vol. 36, p. 427.

WINDLE, W. F. 1929. The relation of the level of transection of the brain-stem to the occurrence of decerebrate rigidity in young animals. J. Comp. Neurol., vol. 48, p. 227.

———. 1930. Normal behavioral reactions of kittens correlated with the postnatal development of nerve-fiber density in the spinal gray matter. J. Comp. Neurol., vol. 50, p. 479.

WINDLE, W. F., AND GRIFFIN, A. M. 1931. Observations on embryonic and fetal movements of the cat. J. Comp. Neurol., vol. 52, p. 149.

WINKLER, C. 1907. The central course of the nervus octavus and its influence on motility. Verhandl. d. kon. Akad. v. Wetensch. te Amsterdam, Tweede Sectie, Deel 14, No. 1.

———. 1911. A tumor in the pulvinar thalami optici. A contribution to the knowledge of the vision of forms. Kon. Akad. v. Wetensch. te Amsterdam, Proc. sect. sc., vol. 13, pt. 2, p. 928. Opera Omnis, vol. 5. Folio neuro-biol., Bd. 7

———. 1913. On localised atrophy in the lateral geniculate body causing quadrantic hemianopsia of both the right lower fields of vision. Kon. Akad. v. Wetensch. te Amsterdam, Proc. sect. sc., vol. 15, pt. 2, p. 840. Folia neuro-biol., Bd. 7.

———. 1918–1921. Anatomie du système nerveux. Bd. II, E. F. Bohn, Haarlem.

———. 1933. Kon. Akad. Wetensch., Proc. sect. sc., vol. 36, p. 13.

WINKLER, C., AND VAN LONDEN, D. M. 1908. About the function of the ventral group of nuclei in the thalamus opticus of man. Kon. Akad. v. Wetensch. te Amsterdam, Proc. sect. sc., vol. 11, pt. 1, p. 295.

WINKLER, C., AND POTTER, A. 1911. An anatomical guide to experimental researches on the rabbit's brain. W. Versluys, Amsterdam.

———. 1914. An anatomical guide to experimental researches on the cat's brain. W. Versluys, Amsterdam.

WOODBURNE, R. T. 1935. A phylogenetic consideration of the primary and secondary centers and connections of the trigeminal complex in a series of vertebrates. Dissertation.

WOOLLARD, H. H. 1925. The anatomy of Tarsius spectrum. Proc. Zool. Soc., London, vol. 70, p. 1071.

———. 1926. Notes on the retina and lateral geniculate bodies in Tupaia, Tarsius, Nycticebus, and Hapale. Brain, vol. 49, p. 1.

———. 1928. Epicritic and dyscritic systems in a primitive primate. J. Anat., vol. 62, p. 276.

WOOLLARD, H. H., AND BEATTIE, J. 1927. The comparative anatomy of the lateral geniculate body. J. Anat., vol. 61, p. 414.

YOSHIDA, I. 1924. Ueber den Ursprung der kortikopetalen Hörbahn beim Kaninchen. Folia anat. Japon., Bd. 2, S. 289.

ZEEMAN, W. P. C., AND TUMBELAKA, R. 1916. Das zentrale und periphere optische System bei einer kongenital blinden Katze. Arch. f. Ophth., Bd. 91, S. 242.

ZIEHEN, T. 1903. Einiges über den Faserverlauf im Mittel- und Zwischenhirn von Tarsus spectrum. Monatschr. f. Psychiat. u. Neurol., Bd. 14, S. 54.

———. 1903a. Ueber den Bau des Gehirns bei den Halbaffen und bei Galeopithecus. Anat. Anz., Bd. 22, S. 506.

———. 1908. Das Centralnervensystem der Monotremen und Marsupialier. II. Teil: Denkschr. d. med.-naturw. Gesellsch. zu Jena, Bd. 6, pt. 2, S. 789. (Bd. 3 of Semon's Zool. Forschungsreisen.)

———. 1908a. Die Commissura media. Neurol. Centralbl., Bd. 27, S. 651.

ZWANENBURG. 1915. Quantitatief onderzoek over den bouw van het netvlies. Dissertatie, Amsterdam.